THE ROUTLEDGE HANDBOOK OF PHILOSOPHY OF ANIMAL MINDS

While philosophers have been interested in animals since ancient times, in the last few decades the subject of animal minds has emerged as a major topic in philosophy. *The Routledge Handbook of Philosophy of Animal Minds* is an outstanding reference source to the key topics, problems and debates in this exciting subject and is the first collection of its kind. Comprising nearly fifty chapters by a team of international contributors, the *Handbook* is divided into eight parts:

- Mental representation
- Reasoning and metacognition
- Consciousness
- Mindreading
- Communication
- Social cognition and culture
- Association, simplicity, and modeling
- Ethics.

Within these sections, central issues, debates and problems are examined, including: whether and how animals represent and reason about the world; how animal cognition differs from human cognition; whether animals are conscious; whether animals represent their own mental states or those of others; how animals communicate; the extent to which animals have cultures; how to choose among competing models and explanations of animal behavior; and whether animals are moral agents and/or moral patients.

The Routledge Handbook of Philosophy of Animal Minds is essential reading for students and researchers in philosophy of mind, philosophy of psychology, ethics and related disciplines such as ethology, biology, psychology, linguistics and anthropology.

Kristin Andrews is York Research Chair in Animal Minds in the Department of Philosophy at York University in Toronto, Canada, and is the author of two books: *Do Apes Read Minds? Toward a New Folk Psychology* (2012) and *The Animal Mind* (Routledge 2015).

Jacob Beck is an Associate Professor of Philosophy and member of the Centre for Vision Research at York University in Toronto, Canada.

ROUTLEDGE HANDBOOKS IN PHILOSOPHY

Routledge Handbooks in Philosophy are state-of-the-art surveys of emerging, newly refreshed, and important fields in philosophy, providing accessible yet thorough assessments of key problems, themes, thinkers, and recent developments in research.

All chapters for each volume are specially commissioned, and written by leading scholars in the field. Carefully edited and organized, *Routledge Handbooks in Philosophy* provide indispensable reference tools for students and researchers seeking a comprehensive overview of new and exciting topics in philosophy. They are also valuable teaching resources as accompaniments to textbooks, anthologies, and research-orientated publications.

Recently published:

THE ROUTLEDGE HANDBOOK OF PHILOSOPHY OF ANIMAL MINDS

Edited by
Kristin Andrews and Jacob Beck

LONDON AND NEW YORK

First published 2018
by Routledge

2 Park Square, Milton Park, Abingdon, Oxfordshire OX14 4RN
52 Vanderbilt Avenue, New York, NY 10017

Routledge is an imprint of the Taylor & Francis Group, an informa business

First issued in paperback 2019

British Library Cataloguing-in-Publication Data
A catalogue record for this book is available from the British Library

Library of Congress Cataloging-in-Publication Data
Names: Andrews, Kristin, 1971– editor. | Beck, Jacob, editor.
Title: The Routledge handbook of philosophy of animal minds / edited by
    Kristin Andrews and Jacob Beck.
Description: 1 [edition]. | New York : Routledge, 2017. | Series: Routledge
    handbooks in philosophy | Includes bibliographical references and index.
Identifiers: LCCN 2017003315 | ISBN 9781138822887 (hardback : alk.
    paper) | ISBN 9781315742250 (e-book)
Subjects: LCSH: Animal psychology. | Animal psychology—Philosophy. |
    Animal intelligence.
Classification: LCC QL785 .R76 2017 | DDC 591.5—dc23
LC record available at https://lccn.loc.gov/2017003315

ISBN: 978-1-138-82288-7 (hbk)
ISBN: 978-0-367-87129-1 (pbk)

Typeset in Bembo
by Apex CoVantage, LLC

CONTENTS

Contents

Contents

NOTES ON CONTRIBUTORS

Colin Allen wrote his chapter while Provost Professor of Cognitive Science and of History & Philosophy of Science & Medicine in the College of Arts and Sciences at Indiana University, Bloomington, and a faculty member of Indiana University's Center for the Integrative Study of Animal Behavior and the Program in Neuroscience. From August 2017 he will be a member of the History and Philosophy of Science Department at the University of Pittsburgh.

Sean Allen-Hermanson is an Associate Professor of Philosophy at Florida International University in Miami specializing in the philosophy of mind and cognitive science. His work on animals includes articles on Morgan's Canon and consciousness in bees, monkeys and bats.

Kristin Andrews is York Research Chair in the Philosophy of Animal Minds at York University in Toronto, Canada, and is the author of two books: *Do Apes Read Minds? Toward a New Folk Psychology* (MIT Press 2012) and *The Animal Mind* (Routledge 2015).

Dorit Bar-On is Professor of Philosophy at the University of Connecticut. She has published widely on issues in mind, language and epistemology, and is the author of *Speaking My Mind: Expression and Self-Knowledge* (Oxford University Press 2004). She is Director of the Expression, Communication, and Origins of Meaning research group.

Jacob Beck is an Associate Professor of Philosophy and member of the Centre for Vision Research at York University in Toronto, Canada. His research centers on the nature of mental representations, including concepts, perceptions and analog representations.

José Luis Bermúdez is Professor of Philosophy at Texas A&M University. His books include *The Paradox of Self-Consciousness* (MIT Press 1998), *Thinking without Words* (Oxford University Press 2003), *Philosophy of Psychology: A Contemporary Introduction* (Routledge 2005), *Decision Theory and Rationality* (Oxford University Press 2009), *Cognitive Science: An Introduction to the Science of the Mind* (Cambridge University Press 2014, 2nd ed.) and *Understanding "I": Language and Thought* (Oxford University Press 2017).

Maria Botero is an Assistant Professor in the Psychology and Philosophy Department at Sam Houston State University. With the support of the Jane Goodall Institute, she has conducted inter-disciplinary studies in mother–infant interaction in chimpanzee (*Pan troglodytes schweinfurthii*) pairs from the Kasekela community at Gombe National Park, Tanzania. Her published work examines primate communication, anxiety-related behavior in orphans, the effects of the mother–infant interaction for the development for the primate mind, and methods used in Primatology.

Matthew Boyle is Professor of Philosophy at the University of Chicago. Until 2016, he was Professor at Harvard University. He writes primarily on the philosophy of mind and on figures in the history of philosophy, especially Kant.

Derek H. Brown is an Associate Professor with a Research Appointment in the Department of Philosophy at Brandon University, Canada. At the time of writing, he is a Visiting Fellow at Clare Hall College, University of Cambridge.

Rachael L. Brown is a lecturer in the School of Philosophy in the Research School of Social Sciences at The Australian National University in Canberra, Australia. She has also held positions at Macquarie University and the University of Western Ontario.

Cameron Buckner began studying artificial intelligence at Texas Tech University and com-pleted his PhD in Philosophy at Indiana University, Bloomington. After an Alexander von Humboldt Fellowship at Ruhr-University, Bochum, he became an Assistant Professor at the University of Houston.

Stephen A. Butterfill researches and teaches on joint action, mindreading and other philo-sophical issues in cognitive science at the University of Warwick (UK).

Elisabeth Camp is Associate Professor of Philosophy at Rutgers University, New Brunswick. Her research focuses on thoughts and utterances that don't fit standard propositional models, including animal cognition, maps, frames, metaphor, slurs and sarcasm. Her work has appeared in journals including *Mind*, *Nous*, *Philosophy and Phenomenological Research*, *Philosophical Quarterly* and *Philosophical Studies*.

Hayley Clatterbuck is Assistant Professor in Philosophy at the University of Rochester. Her research investigates questions of human cognitive uniqueness and the nature of explanation in evolutionary biology.

Alasdair Cochrane is Senior Lecturer in Political Theory at the University of Sheffield. He is an expert on the relationship between animal ethics and political theory, and has written many articles and book chapters on the topic as well as two books: *An Introduction to Animals and Political Theory* (Palgrave) and *Animal Rights without Liberation* (Columbia). He has also written papers on various issues within the areas of human rights, bioethics, philosophy of punishment and environmental ethics.

Mike Dacey is Assistant Professor of Philosophy at Bates College in Maine. His research focuses on inferences from behavioral observations to the nature of psychological processes, including the role of modeling and conceptions of simplicity.

Andrew Fenton is Assistant Professor in the Departments of Philosophy at Dalhousie University and California State University, Fresno. Much of his research focuses on animal ethics and the philosophy of autism, though he also works in epistemology, neuroethics and the philosophy of animal cognition. Currently, he is extending his work in animal ethics from laboratory research to animal agriculture.

Simon Fitzpatrick is Associate Professor of Philosophy at John Carroll University in Cleveland, Ohio. His research lies primarily in the philosophy of psychology and philosophy of science, focusing in particular on the philosophy of animal cognition, empirical moral psychology, and the role of considerations of simplicity/parsimony in scientific investigation. His work has appeared in journals such as *Mind and Language*, *Philosophy of Science*, *Erkenntnis* and *Journal of the History of Biology*.

Shaun Gallagher is the Lillian and Morrie Moss Professor of Excellence in Philosophy at the University of Memphis. His areas of research include phenomenology and the cognitive sciences, especially topics related to embodiment, self, agency and intersubjectivity, hermeneutics, and the philosophy of time. Gallagher has a secondary research appointment at the University of Wollongong, Australia. He holds the Humboldt Foundation's Anneliese Maier Research Award (2012–18). He is a founding editor and a co-editor-in-chief of the journal *Phenomenology and the Cognitive Sciences*. His publications include *How the Body Shapes the Mind* (Oxford University Press 2005); *The Phenomenological Mind* (with Dan Zahavi, Routledge 2008; 2nd ed. 2012); *Phenomenology* (Palgrave Macmillan 2011); and *Enactivist Interventions: Rethinking the Mind* (Oxford University Press in press).

Christopher Gauker is the Professor of Theoretical Philosophy at the University of Salzburg in Austria. His most recent book is *Words and Images: An Essay on the Origin of Ideas* (Oxford University Press 2011).

Rocco J. Gennaro is Professor of Philosophy at the University of Southern Indiana, USA. Two of his most recent books are *The Consciousness Paradox: Consciousness, Concepts, and Higher-Order Thoughts* (MIT Press 2012) and *Consciousness* (Routledge 2017).

Hans-Johann Glock is Professor of Philosophy at the University of Zurich, Visiting Professor at the University of Reading and an Alexander-von-Humboldt Research Prize Awardee. He is the author of *A Wittgenstein Dictionary* (Blackwell 1996), *Quine and Davidson* (Cambridge University Press 2003) and *What Is Analytic Philosophy?* (Cambridge University Press 2008).

Peter Godfrey-Smith is Distinguished Professor of Philosophy at the Graduate Center, City University of New York, and Professor of the History and Philosophy of Science at the University of Sydney. He is the author of five books, including *Darwinian Population and Natural Selection*, which won the 2010 Lakatos Award, and most recently *Other Minds: The Octopus, the Sea, and the Deep Origins of Consciousness*.

Grant Goodrich completed his PhD in History and Philosophy of Science at Indiana University, Bloomington. He teaches philosophy at The Citadel.

Mitchell S. Green is Professor of Philosophy at the University of Connecticut. His research interests include pragmatics, the evolution of communication, self-knowledge and self-deception, and aesthetics. His publications include *Self-Expression* (Oxford University Press), "Imagery, Expression, and Metaphor" (*Philosophical Studies*), "Assertion" (*Oxford Handbooks Online*), and

"Learning to Be Good (or Bad) in (or Through) Literature" (*Fictional Characters, Real Problems: The Search for Ethical Content in Literature*). Green is also founding director of Project High-Phi, which supports philosophical inquiry in American high schools.

Thibaud Gruber is a Scientific Collaborator at the Swiss Center for Affective Sciences at the University of Geneva, Switzerland, and a Postdoctoral Fellow of the Swiss National Science Foundation at the Department of Zoology, Oxford University, UK. He is interested in comparative cognition and evolutionary anthropology, with a specific focus on the evolution of culture and communication in great apes. His research is currently funded by the SNSF.

Lori Gruen is the William Griffin Professor of Philosophy at Wesleyan University, where she also is the coordinator of Wesleyan Animal Studies. She is the author and editor of nine books and dozens of articles and chapters. Gruen has documented the history of The First 100 chimpanzees in research in the US (http://first100chimps.wesleyan.edu) and has an evolving website that documents the journey to sanctuary of the remaining chimpanzees in research labs, The Last 1,000 (http://last1000chimps.com).

Marta Halina is University Lecturer in the Department of History and Philosophy of Science (HPS) at Cambridge University and a Fellow of Selwyn College, where she directs studies in HPS and the Psychological and Behavioural Sciences.

Christoph Hoerl is Professor of Philosophy at the University of Warwick. His research is mainly in the philosophy of mind, with a particular interest in philosophical questions about the nature of temporal experience, memory, and our ability to think about time.

Bryce Huebner is an Associate Professor in the Philosophy Department at Georgetown University. He is the author of *Macrocognition: A Theory of Distributed Minds and Collective Intentionality*. His research focuses on group cognition, moral psychology, and the philosophy of the social and cognitive sciences.

Dale Jamieson is Professor of Environmental Studies and Philosophy at New York University (NYU), and founding director of the Animal Studies Initiative. He co-edited the pioneering collections *Interpretation and Explanation in the Study of Animal Behavior* (Westview 1990) and *Readings in Animal Cognition* (MIT Press 1996) with Marc Bekoff. His most recent books are *Assessing Assessments: Historical and Philosophical Study of Scientific Assessments for Environmental Policy in the Late Twentieth Century* (forthcoming from Chicago University Press), co-authored with Michael Oppenheimer, Naomi Oreskes and others; *Environment and Society: A Reader* (NYU Press 2017), co-edited with Christopher Schlottmann and others; and *Love in the Anthropocene* (OR Books 2015), a collection of essays and short stories co-authored with Bonnie Nadzam.

David Michael Kaplan is a Senior Lecturer in the Department of Cognitive Science, an Associate Investigator in the ARC Centre of Excellence in Cognition and its Disorders, and an Associate Investigator in the Perception and Action Research Centre at Macquarie University, Australia.

Andrew Knoll is Lecturer in Philosophy at the University of Maryland, College Park. His work focuses on the role intentional content plays in empirical theories of perception, motor control and linguistics.

Robert Lurz is Professor of Philosophy at Brooklyn College, City University of New York. His research is on theory of mind, introspection, appearance-reality discrimination, and consciousness in animals. He has written *Mindreading Animals* (MIT Press 2011) and edited *The Philosophy of Animal Minds* (Cambridge University Press 2009).

Mohan Matthen is Canada Research Chair in Philosophy of Perception at the University of Toronto. He is the author of *Seeing, Doing, and Knowing* (Oxford University Press 2005) and editor of the *Oxford Handbook of the Philosophy of Perception* (Oxford University Press 2015).

Teresa McCormack is Professor of Cognitive Development at the School of Psychology, Queen's University Belfast. His research currently focuses on the development of temporal cognition and of regret. She has co-edited a number of interdisciplinary volumes with Christoph Hoerl.

Irina Mikhalevich is Assistant Professor of Philosophy at Rochester Institute of Technology, and a former McDonnell Postdoctoral Fellow in the Philosophy-Neuroscience-Psychology Program at Washington University in St. Louis. Her research examines conceptual and methodological problems in comparative cognition science and their implications for the treatment of nonhuman animals.

Richard Moore is a Postdoctoral Researcher at the Berlin School of Mind and Brain, Humboldt-Universität zu Berlin. He writes on the changes in communication and social learning that led to the phylogenetic emergence of uniquely human forms of cognition and culture, and conducts empirical studies of the communicative abilities of children and animals.

Jesse Prinz is a Distinguished Professor of Philosophy and Director of Interdisciplinary Science Studies at the City University of New York, Graduate Center. His books include *Furnishing the Mind, Gut Reactions, Beyond Human Nature* and *The Conscious Brain*.

Joëlle Proust works at Institut Jean-Nicod, Ecole Normale Supérieure (Paris, France), as a Director of Research for the Pierre-Gilles de Gennes Foundation. She has headed several interdisciplinary collaborative projects on animal metacognition and on the development and cross-cultural diversity of human metacognition.

Grant Ramsey is a BOFZAP Research Professor in the Institute of Philosophy at KU Leuven, Belgium. His work centers on the philosophical problems at the foundation of evolutionary biology. He has published widely in this area, as well as in the philosophy of animal behavior, human nature, and the moral emotions. He runs the Ramsey Lab (www.theramseylab.org), a highly collaborative research group focused on issues in the philosophy of the life sciences.

Michael Rescorla is Professor of Philosophy at the University of California, Los Angeles. He received his PhD from Harvard University in 2003. His research lies within the philosophies of mind, language and logic.

Georges Rey is Professor of Philosophy at the University of Maryland, College Park. He has published extensively in the philosophy of mind and cognitive science, particularly on the role of intentionality in not only animal navigation, but in early visual and linguistic processing.

Bernard E. Rollin is University Distinguished Professor of Philosophy and Professor of Bio-medical Sciences and Animal Sciences at Colorado State University. He is a pioneer in the study of animal ethics and animal consciousness. Rollin is a 2016 recipient of the Public Responsibility in Medicine and Research (PRIM&R) Lifetime Achievement Award for research ethics – the first time this has ever been awarded to an animal ethicist.

Mark Rowlands is Professor of Philosophy at the University of Miami. He is the author of eighteen books, including *Animals Like Us* (Verso 2002), *Can Animals be Moral?* (Oxford University Press 2012) and *The Philosopher and the Wolf* (Granta 2008).

Eric Saidel is an Assistant Professor in the Philosophy Department at George Washington University. His research on animal minds focuses on questions relating to the nature of evidence we can have for the presence of nonhuman animal psychology.

Laura Schlingloff is a PhD student in the Department of Cognitive Science at the Central European University in Budapest. She previously completed an MA in Mind and Brain at the Berlin School of Mind and Brain, Humboldt-Universität zu Berlin.

Adam Shriver is a Postdoctoral Research Fellow at the W. Maurice Young Centre for Applied Ethics at the University of British Columbia. Previously he was a Visiting Fellow at the Center for Neuroscience and Society at the University of Pennsylvania, and a Postdoc at the Rotman Institute of Philosophy and the Brain and Mind Institute at Western University. He received his PhD in Philosophy from Washington University in St. Louis.

Eli Shupe is a graduate student at Rutgers University, New Brunswick. Her research is in cognitive science and the philosophy of mind, with a focus on animal cognition. She has spent time as a visiting researcher at the Max Planck Institute for Evolutionary Anthropology and the Wolfgang Köhler Primate Research Centre. Her work has appeared in *Philosophical Studies*.

Christine Sievers is a PhD researcher at the Philosophy Seminar at the University of Basel and at the Comparative Cognition Department at the University of Neuchâtel. She is working theoretically and empirically on questions regarding communicative interactions and communicative signal use in human and nonhuman animals.

Ulrich Stegmann is a Senior Lecturer in Philosophy at the University of Aberdeen. He is the editor of *Animal Communication Theory: Information and Influence* (Cambridge University Press 2013).

Michael Trestman is an independent scholar residing in San Francisco, CA. His research focuses on animal consciousness and cognition.

Michael Tye encountered philosophy at Oxford and has taught at London University, Temple University and the University of St Andrews. He is currently the Dallas TACA Centennial Professor in Liberal Arts at the University of Texas at Austin.

Sarah Vincent is the Florida Blue Center for Ethics Post-Doctoral Fellow at the University of North Florida (Jacksonville, FL). Her areas of research are philosophy of psychology/cognitive science and applied ethics, most especially with respect to nonhuman animals. She was previously a Post-Doctoral Visitor at York University (Toronto), and she earned her doctorate at the University of Memphis (Memphis, TN) in 2015.

Markus Wild teaches philosophy at the University of Basel. He has worked on early modern philosophy, the philosophy of animal minds, and animal ethics. He is author of *Tierphilosophie* (2008) and *Fische: Kognition, Bewusstsein, Schmerz* (2012); co-editor of *Animal Minds and Animal Ethics* (2013); and co-author of "Exorcising Grice's ghost: an empirical approach to studying intentional communication in animals" (*Biological Review* 2016).

ACKNOWLEDGEMENTS

We would like to thank our colleagues and students at York University for many enlightening conversations about animal minds. We are also grateful to our editors at Routledge, Tony Bruce and Adam Johnson, for all of their help. Finally, we would like to express appreciation to our families for their support, patience, and animal spirits. Kristin thanks Brian Huss, Alexandra, and Mono. Jacob thanks Monika Jankowiak, Emil, Julian, and Lucas.

INTRODUCTION

Kristin Andrews and Jacob Beck

This volume collects forty-nine original essays that provide opinionated introductions to a variety of philosophical topics concerning (nonhuman) animal minds. The essays are written by established or emerging leaders in the field, and yet are accessible to newcomers who have some experience with philosophical writing. As the volume provides a broad snapshot of the state of the art in the philosophy of animal minds, our expectation is that it will also serve as a useful reference work for more seasoned scholars.

While philosophers have been interested in animal minds since ancient times, interest in the topic has reemerged over the past forty or fifty years. Especially over the past couple of decades, the field has truly begun to flourish, with philosophers taking a special interest in animal mental representation, rationality, consciousness, metacognition, mindreading, perception, learning, communication, ethics, social cognition, and culture. This flourishing has been abetted by an explosion of fascinating empirical research in comparative psychology, cognitive ethology, and related disciplines, along with an increased tendency among philosophers to engage with empirical research.

Enlarging the focus of philosophy of mind to include not just humans, but animals, has several advantages. First, insofar as philosophers of mind are concerned to provide nonchauvinistic analyses of minds and mind-related properties, it is useful to consult a diversity of examples beyond the human case. While imagination can help in this regard, it is often difficult to determine from the armchair whether a putatively imagined mind or mind-related property is genuinely possible.

Second, animal minds can shed light on human minds by serving as a foil for comparison. If we're interested in what makes humans special or unique, we can compare ourselves to other creatures that have minds and attend to the differences. Thinking about animal minds can thus enhance our understanding of our own natures.

Finally, animals are our neighbors. We share our planet — and sometimes even our homes — with animals. Many of us form relationships with animals. Even those of us who prefer human companions tend to find animals fascinating to observe. We all face ethical questions about whether to consume animals and how to treat them. We thus have strong reasons to try to understand animal minds on their own terms, independently of whether they shed light on the nature of minds in general or human minds in particular.

The essays in this volume have been separated into eight sections. While the essays within each section tend to have much in common, there are interesting points of contact across sections as well. In the remainder of this introduction, we'll provide a brief summary of each contribution and highlight some of the larger themes that emerge.

Mental representation

The ability to represent the world is often considered a mark of the mental. But when does mental representation arise? Do sunflower buds represent the sun since they follow it throughout the day? What about simple animals, such as insects? Andrew Knoll and Georges Rey shed light on these foundational questions by investigating the navigational abilities of ants and bees, and draw lessons about the minimal requirements for mental representation.

In part because analytic philosophy was dominated by the study of language throughout most of the twentieth century, philosophers have tended to view mental representation through a linguistic lens. But when we focus on animal cognition, the linguistic lens often seems to distort its target. Many philosophers have wanted to attribute nonlinguistic representations to animals. In their own ways, Christopher Gauker, Michael Rescorla, and Jacob Beck all investigate this option.

Gauker suggests that animal cognition could be subserved by *imagistic representations*. He reviews several studies of tool use in nonhuman primates, and argues that imagistic representations can explain their results. Rescorla examines a second type of representation that is commonly attributed to nonlinguistic animals – *cognitive maps*. He reviews the impressive navigational capacities of a range of animals, discusses when cognitive maps are appropriately attributed to explain those capacities, and investigates their representational properties. Beck summarizes research into *analog magnitude representations* of numerosity and duration, and argues that they are nonlinguistic. But since Beck is interested in whether animals have a language of thought, and evidence for the presence of nonlinguistic representations doesn't amount to evidence for the absence of linguistic representations, Beck also critically reviews a more direct line of evidence – research into the logical abilities of animals.

Christoph Hoerl and Teresa McCormack argue for a fundamental reorientation in the investigation of whether animals have *episodic memories* – conscious recollections of particular past events. Whereas most commentators take the main controversy to concern whether animals' representations of particular past events are *conscious*, Hoerl and McCormack argue that it isn't even clear that animals represent particular past events *qua* past events in the first place. Animals might have representations only of the present that they update in ways that are sensitive to the passing of time. Hoerl and McCormack close with two suggestions about how this issue can be empirically tested.

Mohan Matthen and Derek Brown focus on animal minds in order to illuminate the nature of color. Matthen argues that due to differences in their visual systems, humans and many animals perceive fundamentally different colors. As a result, there are many colors – indeed, many systems of colors – that humans never perceive. Brown accepts Matthen's conclusion and argues that it puts pressure on *color objectivism*, which holds that colors are mind-independent properties. Brown contends that color objectivism struggles to explain how manipulating the colors of objects (e.g., by painting a wall) systematically influences both human and animal color perception.

Reasoning and metacognition

What sorts of reasoning capacities do animals have and how does animal reasoning differ from human reasoning? These questions naturally bleed into two others. First, since the concept of reasoning is intimately tied to the concept of rationality, the question of whether animals can reason is closely connected to the question of whether animals are rational. Second, it is natural to suppose that "metacognition" – the capacity for higher-order cognition – is an especially important type of reasoning, and thus that the question of whether an organism is capable of metacognition is of fundamental significance. The chapters in this section address these questions about reasoning, rationality, and metacognition from a variety of perspectives.

Hans-Johann Glock notes that the question of whether animals have propositional attitudes such as beliefs is intimately connected to the questions of whether they exhibit rationality and engage in reasoning. He says yes to all three questions. Paying special attention to the well-known arguments of Donald Davidson, he contends that *a priori* arguments against animal belief, rationality, and reasoning are unsuccessful. He also presents two positive arguments designed to lend support to the affirmation of animal belief, rationality, and reasoning.

Elisabeth Camp and Eli Shupe, Matthew Boyle, José Luis Bermúdez, and Eric Saidel explore the issue of human uniqueness, but they focus on different properties that might ground this supposed uniqueness. Camp and Shupe concentrate on instrumental reasoning. For example, a high school student might decide to spend many hours studying calculus, not because she enjoys studying calculus or finds it valuable in itself, but because she wants to get into a good college and believes that doing well in her calculus class will help her achieve that end. Camp and Shupe argue that the ability to engage in instrumental reasoning marks an important type of cognitive flexibility, and so we should be interested in whether nonhumans can reason instrumentally. After clarifying what instrumental reasoning is, they review empirical evidence that some animals do, in fact, reason instrumentally.

Boyle develops and defends the Aristotelian idea that human minds differ not only in degree, but in kind, from animal minds because humans alone are *rational*. He interprets this to mean not that humans alone are intelligent, nor that humans alone are capable of instrumental reasoning, but that humans alone have the capacity to reflect on the reasons for their beliefs and actions, and to then revise their beliefs and actions in light of those reasons.

Bermúdez argues that humans are unique for a different reason. According to Bermúdez, an organism cannot think about a thought without linguistically representing that thought. Thus, the ability to think about one's own propositional attitudes (metacognition) or another's propositional attitudes (mindreading) requires a facility with language. Bermúdez concludes that nonlinguistic animals cannot think about thinking.

Saidel argues that many animals, including even chimpanzees, lack a concept of self. Like Boyle and Bermúdez, Saidel takes care to emphasize that he is not denying that animals have rich mental lives, including a variety of mental representations. But he argues that a careful examination of the extant empirical literature suggests that they do not have a self-concept.

Like Bermúdez and Saidel, Joëlle Proust asks if animals are capable of metacognition. She reviews experimental evidence suggesting that they are, but takes a deflationary interpretation of what metacognition is. According to Proust, metacognition in both animals and humans is grounded in *affordance sensings*, which are feeling-based evaluative attitudes. Thus, while metacognition isn't uniquely human, that's in part because – even in humans – it doesn't require the sophisticated ability to think about one's thoughts.

Consciousness

There is surely no greater philosophical puzzle than how to understand consciousness, or "what it's like" to have an experience. The phrase "what it's like" derives from Thomas Nagel's famous discussion of bat consciousness. Nagel assumed that bats are conscious – that there's "something it's like" to be a bat. But he questioned how much we can know about what it's like to be a bat, and in particular whether we can know what it's like for a bat to experience echolocation. In his contribution, Sean Allen-Hermanson challenges this orthodoxy. He argues that there's a fairly simple answer to what it's like for a bat to experience echolocation: it's like hearing. One consideration he takes to support this answer is that blind people who become expert echolocators report that their echolocatory phenomenology is auditory. Allen-Hermanson then considers why so many philosophers, from Nagel onwards, have overlooked the obviousness of this answer, and what that tells us about the fallibility of our judgments about phenomenology.

Whereas Allen-Hermanson is primarily concerned with the question of what animal consciousness is like, a related question is how we can tell if a given species is conscious at all. Like Nagel, Allen-Hermanson assumes that bats are conscious. But what justifies that assumption? How do we know which species are conscious? The remaining chapters on consciousness are primarily concerned with this question.

Since we know we are conscious, the natural way to evaluate whether other species are conscious is to compare them to us. Broadly speaking, there are two dimensions of possible comparison – behavioral and neural. Michael Tye's contribution focuses on the first. He proposes that we should attribute pain to animals when they behave similarly to humans in contexts where we know that humans feel pain, and there are no defeaters. (As an example of a defeater, Tye cites a case in which we find that a being's behavior is controlled by a silicon chip with a giant lookup table inscribed on it.) Tye then reviews evidence that teleost fish (i.e., fish with bony skeletons, such as trout) behave similarly to humans in contexts where humans feel pain, but that elasmobranchs (i.e., fish with cartilaginous skeletons, such as sharks) and insects do not. Tye concludes that teleost fish feel pain, but that elasmobranchs and insects do not.

Adam Shriver also takes up the question of whether animals feel pain, though he explicitly appeals to comparisons of neural mechanisms in addition to comparisons of behavior. Shriver reviews evidence that the *affective* dimension of pain – whether the subject finds it unpleasant – can be dissociated from the *sensing* of pain – roughly, its location, type, and intensity. For example, humans with damage to certain brain regions, or under the influence of certain drugs, report sensing pain, but not being bothered by it. Shriver then summarizes evidence for a similar dissociation in animals, and argues that for many purposes (especially ethical), it is the affective dimension that we should be interested in when we try to understand animal pain.

Jesse Prinz explicitly endorses comparing human and animal neural mechanisms to determine which species are conscious. He takes as his starting point the AIR theory of consciousness he has defended elsewhere, which holds that a representation is conscious just in case it's at what he calls an "intermediate" level of sensory processing and is placed into working memory by attention. He then considers what the empirical literature has to say about whether various taxa – ranging from mammals to insects – have analogous neural mechanisms to those that are associated with attended, intermediate representations in humans. Although Prinz stresses that the current evidence is too limited to draw firm conclusions in many cases, he tentatively suggests that consciousness is surprisingly widespread, extending even to insects—though not, perhaps, to amphibians or reptiles.

Like Prinz, Rocco Gennaro begins with a general theory of consciousness that he finds attractive and then applies it to animals. Gennaro endorses higher-order thought (HOT) theory, which maintains that a mental state of a subject (e.g., your desire for cake) is conscious just in case the subject has a thought representing the mental state (e.g., you think: *I want to eat cake*). Appealing to the empirical literature on metacognition, Gennaro argues that animals can be conscious according to HOT since they have metacognition. (There are obvious links here to the discussions of metacognition in the previous section – particularly those of Bermúdez, Saidel, and Proust. For a criticism of HOT theory, see Tye's chapter.)

Michael Trestman and Peter Godfrey-Smith take up the question of which species are conscious from an evolutionary perspective. Each is concerned to explain where in the evolutionary history of animals consciousness emerged. Trestman argues that phenomenological insights into the temporal dynamics of consciousness and considerations about the cognitive requirements for complex spatially situated behavior converge on the conclusion that consciousness emerged three times in animal evolution – in vertebrates, arthropods, and cephalopods. Godfrey-Smith's contribution is more tentative. He considers three broad possibilities for the origins of consciousness: increased information processing and integration; sensing and perceiving; and evaluative experiences, or feelings. Given each possibility, Godfrey-Smith speculates where in the tree of life consciousness might be expected to surface.

Mindreading

One of the most fecund areas of research for philosophers working on animal cognition is mindreading, or theory of mind. In particular, philosophers are interested in an empirical research program designed to investigate animal social cognition, especially whether animals understand that others have beliefs (mindreading belief) or that others have perceptions (mindreading perception). The chapters in this section largely focus on research that has been done with great apes and corvids.

The first three chapters examine a debate about how animals are able to predict behavior. There is a large body of evidence that animals are able to predict the behavior of conspecifics. The question that remains is how animals are able to do this. According to the behavior-reading hypothesis, animals predict what someone is going to do without understanding anything about the causal structure of the individual, but instead by associating observable cues with behaviors. In contrast, the mindreading hypothesis is that animals do indeed have the ability to infer the mental states of others, such as beliefs, desires, and sensory experiences such as perceptions. The behavior-reading hypothesis is non-mentalistic, in that it says a behavior-reader need not have any understanding of other minds, whereas the mindreading hypothesis is explicitly mentalistic.

Robert Lurz's chapter focuses on the methodological question of whether we can ever distinguish between these two hypotheses, given what has come to be known as the "logical problem." This problem is that the observable cues used in tests for mindreading are confounded with the mental states being investigated. Lurz argues that while none of the perceptual mindreading tests have avoided the logical problem, a slight modification of a recent experiment with corvids could decide the question.

Marta Halina's chapter is a direct response to Lurz's pessimism about the current state of research on perceptual mindreading. By engaging with the methodology of the experiments, and by considering work in philosophy of science on the nature of ascribing unobservable entities in explanation, Halina argues that the current state of the science should be taken as sufficient evidence that apes mindread perceptions.

Hayley Clatterbuck examines whether causal models will help decide between behavior-reading and mindreading hypotheses. In discussions of the relative simplicity of mindreading and behavior-reading hypotheses, it has been suggested that intervening mentalistic variables help to unify types of behaviors, and so examining relationships among different sorts of successes on tasks might decide between the two hypotheses. Clatterbuck argues that behavior-reading models can share this syntactic property with mindreading models. An appeal to the structure of causal models does not help solve the problem. Instead, we need to look at the semantic properties of the models in order to decide between them.

Three of the chapters (those by Kristin Andrews, Stephen Butterfill, and Sarah Vincent and Shaun Gallagher) move away from the debate between mindreading and behavior-reading by considering different cognitive mechanisms or practices that could be involved in both the human and nonhuman ability to predict and explain others' behaviors. All three of these approaches take as given that great apes are mentalists of a sort, but they deny that this means that apes understand that others have beliefs.

Andrews examines a recent experiment which suggests, for the first time, that great apes can pass a false belief task, but she questions what this finding means. She suggests that apes may not be solving this task by attributing false beliefs, as we would be warranted in drawing this conclusion only if particular theories about the nature of belief are true. She notes that there are alternative mentalist explanations for how chimpanzees and humans might pass false belief tasks, and suggests we need to look for larger patterns of behavior before concluding that apes understand false belief.

Butterfill's chapter introduces an alternative to behavior-reading and mindreading theories. His minimal mindreading theory states that understanding others involves tracking their mental states without representing those states as such, and he takes this option to be a viable explanation for the success of animals on "theory of mind" tasks. He defends this option against the behavior-reading alternative, in part by drawing a distinction between two forms of behavior-reading.

Vincent and Gallagher also introduce a different way of thinking about the question of whether apes have a theory of mind, by suggesting we should instead ask whether they are enactive perceivers of practical and social affordances. Vincent and Gallagher think that humans do not rely on a theory of mind either, but instead are able to perform the functions associated with mindreading beliefs, including predicting and explaining behavior, through a direct access to others' minds that we gain from interacting with them. They advocate for different kinds of experiments that involve interactions between conspecifics in order to determine whether chimpanzees have human-like social cognition.

Communication

The focus of the five chapters on animal communication is H. P. Grice's theory of meaning and whether it serves as a useful model for investigating intentional animal communication. Grice's theory is discussed, and rejected, by almost all of the authors in this section. Grice's theory takes communication to require that signalers and receivers understand the intentions of another. The cognitive requirements of this theory are related to the ability to mindread (attribute mental states to others). Because it is reasonable to doubt that animals and young children mindread, but perhaps not so reasonable to be skeptical of their ability to communicate, every chapter in this section offers an account of communication that does not require mindreading. The accounts discussed here are consistent with the view that animal communication is continuous with human language. Among animal cognition researchers, however, Gricean theories are quite popular. Theories that take intentionality to be required for communication, such as those of Michael Tomasello and Thom Scott-Philips, are also targets of criticism.

One of the puzzles that arise from Gricean theories has to do with how communication could have evolved given that intentionality is needed on both sides of the communicative interaction. In their chapter, Dorit Bar-On and Richard Moore work to dissolve this puzzle by examining the claim that there is an asymmetry in the pragmatics of animal communication. Animal calls do not appear to be sensitive to others' goals or mental states, yet animals still appear to interpret these signals. That is, while production may not be intentional, reception appears to be. Bar-On and Moore challenge the idea that animals are intentional receivers but not producers, arguing that by the logic of the asymmetry argument, receivers do not interpret signalers as intentional communicators in any sense. If the asymmetry argument is sound, then receivers understand only natural meaning, e.g., that a dark sky means that it will likely rain. Bar-On and Moore go on to consider reasons for accepting the continuity of human language and animal communication systems.

In her single-authored chapter, Bar-On offers an alternative to Grice's theory of meaning. According to her account, communication is a kind of social, intersubjective, world-directed, and open behavior that is biologically designed to express one's mental states to communicative partners, who in turn are able to predict the behavior of the communicator and who can then act in response to the communicator's expressed state. This theory of expressive communication is contrasted with views like Tomasello's that take human language to be different in kind from animal signaling systems, and she examines how corvids and chimpanzees might count as expressive communicators.

Mitchell Green also challenges Gricean accounts of meaning and communication by focusing on the semantic content of signals. Green argues that all Gricean accounts (which he refers to as Intention-Based Semantic (IBS) accounts) share two problems: they explain meaning in terms of intention without showing how intention can be more basic than meaning, and they require sophisticated cognitive capacities. He takes these problems to be fatal for IBS accounts, and provides his own alternative theory of semantic meaning. Green's Intention-Free Semantics (IFS) includes a category of meaning he calls organic meaning, which arises via a process of ritualization of signals. These signals acquire a predictable significance within a community. Green examines the signals of a number of taxa from the perspective of IFS to determine what kind of meaning might be present.

Ulrich Stegmann's chapter continues the investigation of the content of signals by surveying explicit and implicit accounts of signal content in animal cognition, biology, and ethology, and compares these to theories of intentional semantic content. While theories of animal communication rely on appeal to information signaling, Stegmann worries that these accounts do not share a clear view about the nature of information. After critically examining Fred Dretske and Ruth Millikan's non-inferential theories of meaning, Stegmann develops a related account, which he takes to be a promising way of understanding animal communication.

Christine Sievers, Markus Wild, and Thibaud Gruber point out that the popularity of Gricean theories has shaped the research focus, and that if we adopt different theories, we will need to seek different kinds of evidence. They advocate Millikan's theory of meaning, and examine what findings might serve as empirical evidence of communicative abilities according to that theory. Flexibility of behavior is of particular importance.

Social cognition and culture

While we might think of culture as something unique to humans, involving opera houses or temples or museums, among anthropologists and biologists culture is often understood in a broader sense (though they sometimes use the term "traditions" rather than "culture"). In the last fifteen years, animal cognition researchers have published reports arguing that there is culture in a number of different species, including nonhuman primates and cetaceans.

The very notion of culture is the topic of Grant Ramsey's chapter. He investigates various definitions of culture, and identifies what he takes to be the essential ingredients of culture with the aim of providing a fuller picture of what constitutes cultural practices. Ramsey's definition of culture takes it to consist of information transmitted between individuals or groups that creates a lasting change in behavioral practices.

Grant Goodrich endorses Ramsey's definition and examines kinds of culture and the different cognitive capacities that are required for them. Goodrich argues that culture so defined is something that could be underpinned by either associative or cognitive mechanisms. (See Cameron Buckner's and Mike Dacey's chapters in the next section for different views about the distinction between associative and cognitive mechanisms.)

Rachael Brown continues the investigation of cognitive capacities involved in animal culture. In particular, she examines the relationship between social learning mechanisms and the development of traditions in animal societies. She argues that what appear to be complex cultural behaviors can be learned via simple forms of social learning. (Her discussion relates to Colin Allen's chapter on associative learning mechanisms in the next section.) Brown concludes that cumulative culture, which some theorists take to be unique to humans, can be had by animals thanks to a relatively simple social learning mechanism. Furthermore, she argues that as with humans, animal cultures can have an impact on group genetic evolution. Hence, without appeal to culture, we will not be able to explain certain biological differences between populations.

Maria Botero looks at the development of social understanding in the chimpanzee. Joint attention is thought by some to be an important aspect of human cognition and required for cooperation, but the existence of joint attention in other animals is a matter of some debate among empirical researchers. Botero argues that the typical emphasis on the visual modality ignores the other ways in which individuals can jointly attend to something. She thinks that nonhuman primate social cognition is better understood via the modality of touch, given the amount of time mothers and infants spend in physical contact, and the limited interest they have in eye gaze.

Laura Schlingloff and Richard Moore also focus on chimpanzee social cognition. They investigate the claim that chimpanzees engage in normative behavior, and that their culture includes social norms. By appealing to empirical evidence from captive and field research, and appealing to Cristina Bicchieri's account of social norms, Schlingloff and Moore conclude that chimpanzees do not fulfill the cognitively demanding requirements for social norms. Nonetheless, they suggest that apes may have a precursor to moral norms, which unlike conventional social norms, may be based on general empathic and prosocial capacities. While the current empirical work is suggestive, they think it is premature to draw conclusions about the existence of moral norms in chimpanzees.

While the other chapters in this section focus on social cognition in great apes and birds, the final chapter examines the possibility that coordination among individuals can result in the creation of a new mind that is constituted by the coordinators. Bryce Huebner examines this possibility by looking at the swarming behavior of desert locusts, the schooling behavior of golden shiner fish, and army ant foraging behavior. He suggests that these and other organisms act together with contextualized self-interest for the group as a unified cognitive system.

Association, simplicity, and modeling

The chapters in this section cluster around three issues: What is association, and how does it differ from cognition? What makes one explanation of animal behavior simpler than another, and on what grounds, if any, are simpler explanations to be preferred? How is animal behavior best modeled, and how should those models be interpreted and applied?

Colin Allen's chapter focuses on the nature of association. He is concerned that many philosophers believe that associative learning is a dead research program – indeed, one that has been dead since Chomsky famously critiqued Skinner over fifty years ago. But Allen argues that modern approaches to associative learning belie this assumption, and have much to offer philosophers. Allen focuses on two distinctions within associative learning theory: the distinction between delay conditioning and trace conditioning, which he suggests may have relevance to our understanding of conscious awareness; and the distinction between instrumental and operant conditioning, which may mark an important psychological boundary between various taxa. (There are interesting points of contact here to Godfrey-Smith's contribution.)

Cameron Buckner and Mike Dacey are both motivated by a problem they find in comparative psychology. The problem is that of selecting between associative and cognitive models of animal behavior. On the standard assumption, associative models are simpler and are thus to be preferred. But this is problematic since it seems that, for any behavior, it is always possible to amend some associative model or other to explain it. So there is an ersatz conflict between associative and cognitive models.

Buckner and Dacey differ, however, in the solutions they recommend to address this problem. Buckner argues that the old association/cognition distinction should be replaced with a new one that is grounded in two distinct memory systems. Those who debate whether a given behavior is best explained by an associative or cognitive mechanism can thus be interpreted as fruitfully debating whether the behavior is best explained by one type of memory system or the other. Dacey, by contrast, argues that associative models do not describe a special type of process (an "associative" process). Rather, they are highly abstract, partial descriptions of causal relations between representations. So on Dacey's view, associative models are compatible with processes that are typically thought of as cognitive (e.g., the application of a rule in an algorithm), but they differ from cognitive models in that they are pitched at a different level of abstraction.

Like Buckner and Dacey, Irina Mikhalevich is concerned with the conflict between putatively simple models, such as associative models, and putatively complex models. She argues that the widespread preference for simplicity has unjustifiably biased animal cognition researchers in favor of associative models, leading to a misapplication of resources. To combat this bias, she recommends that researchers make use of more quantitative cognitive models and that they reject simplicity as a criterion for deciding among models.

Simon Fitzpatrick also criticizes the way in which comparative psychologists have appealed to simplicity. He notes that such appeals often invoke *Morgan's Canon*, which holds that animal behavior should be explained in terms of "lower" faculties rather than "higher" faculties whenever possible. He then distinguishes four different interpretations of Morgan's Canon and argues that all of them should be rejected. Fitzpatrick recommends a principle he calls *Evidentialism* to replace Morgan's Canon.

David Kaplan investigates a different type of model: model organisms. Scientists have used fruit flies to study genetics, squid to study action potentials, mice to study learning, and so on. Scientists frequently use the findings from these studies to draw inferences about other animals, including humans. Kaplan argues that these inferences can be extremely shaky, as the selection of a model organism is usually based on practical considerations, such as its easy availability as a research subject. Kaplan argues that researchers should pay closer attention to evolutionary history in selecting model organisms in order to ensure that the models are indeed representative of the taxa about which the researchers want to draw conclusions.

Ethics

One question at the intersection of animal cognition and ethics is whether animals are moral patients. When we act, how should the impact of our actions on animals be taken into account? A second question is whether animals are moral agents. Are animals themselves capable of acting morally or immorally? The chapters in this section address both of these related questions.

Dale Jamieson argues that the backdrop for thinking about animals and ethics has been influenced recently by the view that animals have a type of moral agency. He then shows how this move to see animals as agents can help us to think differently about three important topics in animal ethics: suffering, captivity, and killing animals.

Mark Rowlands also addresses the issue of whether animals can participate in the moral sphere. Here he outlines his theory that some nonhuman animals are moral subjects, individuals who can be motivated to act for moral reasons. Moral subjects are not moral agents, who are responsible for their actions due to the ability to scrutinize their reasons and control their actions, but they are individuals who are motivated by their empathy for another, and whose behavior at least sometimes tracks moral facts. By carving out this middle ground between full moral agency (which Rowlands isn't sure that even humans enjoy) and moral patients, Rowlands identifies another way in which individuals can be moral.

Andrew Fenton's chapter considers the relationship between animal autonomy and the proper treatment of animals. He proposes that animals should be allowed the opportunity to consent to our treatment of them. In human research, we only use subjects who provide their consent to be a research subject. Fenton argues that the same should be true for other animals. He describes to what extent we can interpret animals' behavior as consent or dissent, and how we can design experiments such that animal subjects can choose whether or not to participate.

Lori Gruen considers another aspect of moral practice, namely empathy. In her chapter, she discusses the different types of empathy, examining which may be had by animals, including rats and chimpanzees, and which may be relevant for morality. She describes the importance of what she calls entangled empathy – an experiential process requiring emotion and cognition that perceives our relationships with others in such a way that we are responsive to each other's needs, interests, desires, vulnerabilities, hopes, and sensitivities. Gruen notes that this sort of empathy has been largely ignored by researchers examining empathic abilities in other animals.

Alasdair Cochrane examines an oft-stated distinction between animal welfare and animal rights approaches in animal ethics. He argues that this distinction fails because the notion of rights on the animal rights approach overstates the rights that animals have. Cochrane argues that animal rights are tied to animal interests, and that most animals have no interest in not being used, owned, or exploited. Since they lack those interests, they also lack the equivalent rights. The rights that animals have will provide the very same benefits they get on the welfare approach to animal ethics, which are already tied to animal interests.

Bernard E. Rollin's chapter examines the history of philosophers' and scientists' take on animal minds. In his analysis, the absence of thought and feeling in animals was never proved, even though it was widely accepted. The rejection of animal minds was due to the values inherent in our past scientific and philosophical cultures. He suggests that recent changes in the treatment of animals stem not from philosophical or scientific progress, but is rather a cultural change involving a change in values.

PART I

Mental representation

1

ARTHROPOD INTENTIONALITY?[1]

Andrew Knoll and Georges Rey

Introduction

A ubiquitous idiom in cognitive science is:

  x represents y

Thus, one reads of the visual system representing edges, surfaces, color and objects; birds representing the stars; bees the azimuth of the sun, and ants the direction of food from their nest. We will presume here that such talk treats the system as in some way mental, involving the puzzling phenomenon of intentionality: representations are *about* a certain subject matter, and they may be *non-factive*, *non-existential* and *aspective*: i.e., they can be *false*, represent *non-existing* things, and usually represent things "*as*" one way or another, e.g., a four-sided figure *as a square* or *as a diamond*. That is, representations have "correctness" (or "veridicality") conditions which specify when they're correct and in what way. We will regard those conditions as providing the "content" of the representation.[2]

 An obviously important question is when talk of such intentional representation is literally true, and when it is merely metaphorical or a *façon de parler*. Sunflowers "follow" the sun through the course of a day, presumably not because they literally represent the sun, but simply because cells on the sunless side of the stem grow faster, causing the plant to droop towards it.[3] Drooping sunflowers at night don't *misrepresent* the position of the sun.

 In this short entry, we want to address this question by focusing on some of the simplest animal "minds" that have so far been investigated: those of arthropods, specifically ants and bees. This is partly because their relative simplicity permits a clearer understanding of what's relevant to literal intentional ascription than is easy to acquire of more complex animals, particularly human beings; and partly because they seem very near – or past – the limits of such ascription. Getting clearer about them should help clarify what's essential in the more complex cases. Moreover, ants and bees have been the subject of quite exciting, detailed research, with which we think any philosopher of mind ought to be acquainted.

 Whether a system has literal intentionality has sometimes been thought to turn on its cognitive architecture. For example, Carruthers (2004) argues that some insects (ticks, caterpillars, Sphex and digger wasps) have an inflexible architecture, which is unamenable to explanation in terms of intentional attitude states, while the behavior of insects that exhibit *flexible* navigational capacities, such as honeybees, is best explained in terms of practical syllogisms operating over states with intentional content. We agree with Carruthers' general point that the flexibility of a system may be a good guide to whether it involves states with intentional content. But we think that much turns on the details of this flexibility, in particular on how much it involves a certain kind of *information integration*, which we think in turn requires the features of intentionality we have mentioned. The empirical case is still out on the cognitive architecture of ants and bees; however, there is a *prima facie* case that some ant navigation involves a flexible architecture that doesn't require intentional explanation, while the honeybees have one that does.

The desert ant (*Cataglyphis fortis*)

First, consider the desert ant, *Cataglyphis fortis*, which lives in the relatively featureless Tunisian desert. It goes on meandering foraging expeditions from its nest that can cover 100m. After finding food, it can return on a direct path to its nest, despite its tortuous outbound route.

Cataglyphis relies on several systems to perform its navigational feats, including a sun compass, wind compass, odor beaconing system, and retinotopic landmark guidance system. Its principle navigation system, however, is a "dead reckoning" or path integration ("PI"[4]) system. This system keeps track of the steps the ant has taken, and of the polarization of incoming light, which usually changes as a result of changes in the ant's direction of travel. By realizing a simple vector algebra, the system computationally transforms these correlates of distance and direction, and generates the vector sum of the distance-direction vectors that describe its outward walk. It then follows the inverse of that vector back to its nest.

Our question is whether ascribing states with intentional content to this computational process is part of the best explanation of the PI system. For Charles Gallistel (1990: 58–83), a representation just *is* a state in a computational system that stands in an isomorphic relation to the structure of the environment and functions to regulate the behavior of an animal in that environment. By these lights, because the ant has states that are functionally isomorphic to the distance and direction it traverses, it therefore has "representations" of distance and direction.

Tyler Burge (2010: 502) complains that such states are "representational" in name only. That is, the states are not about actual spatial distance and direction, in the interesting sense that they have correctness conditions that do any explanatory work. The ant would behave the same *whether or not* it had representations with those or any other correctness conditions.

One needs to be careful here. It just begs the question against Gallistel to claim that his "representations" play no explanatory role in his theory. Insofar as he thinks representations just *are* states isomorphically related to and triggered by environmental phenomena, they consequently play an explanatory role if the correlations do. Theoretical reduction is not elimination: if talk of "salt" can be replaced by talk of "NaCl," salt will play precisely the same explanatory role as NaCl! The substantive issue is whether properties that are arguably *constitutive* of being an *intentional* representation – e.g., the properties we mentioned at the start – are essential to the explanation. But we can give Gallistel the word "representation" for functional isomorphisms, and use "i-representation" for the representations that exhibit intentional properties.[5]

Burge's complaint is nevertheless on the right track. Isomorphic correlations don't exhibit the intentional properties that make the representational idiom distinctively interesting. Correlations are *factive* and relate *existing* phenomena: no state of an animal can be correlated with features of non-existent landscapes, but animals might represent them nonetheless. Moreover, if a state is sometimes mistakenly correlated with environmental features that *fail* to take an ant back to its nest, then that's as real a part of the correlation as features that *do* take it back.

This latter fact raises what has been called the "disjunction" problem (Fodor 1987), a consequence of an i-representation's non-factivity. If an i-representation can be erroneous, what determines when that might be? To take a much-discussed example, suppose a frog flicks its tongue at flies, but equally at beebees and mosquitos. Is the content of the relevant representation [fly], and the *beebees* are errors, or is it [*fly or beebee*] – "[flybee]"? – and flies and beebees are right and the *mosquitos* errors? Or perhaps it is merely [moving black dot], and all of those are correct but [moving square] would be wrong. Generally, any non-factive representation can be entokened under conditions $C_1 C_2 C_3 \ldots C_n$, for indefinitely large n: what determines which of these conditions are the correct ones and which mistakes?[26]

Many philosophers have proposed solving the disjunction problem by imposing further constraints on correlations or other natural relations – say, that they must be law-like, obtaining under "normal" circumstances (Dretske 1987); that they must be specified by an "interpretation function" (Cummins 1989); that the correctness conditions involve evolutionary selection (Millikan 1984; Dretske 1986; Neander 1995, 2017); or that erroneous conditions asymmetrically depend upon the correct ones (Fodor 1987, 1990). Any of these constraints might succeed abstractly in distinguishing correct from incorrect uses of an i-representation. But, although defining correctness conditions is certainly an important issue, Burge's point is an additional one. The question he raises is whether *any* assignment of correctness conditions, appropriately idealized or not, would be *explanatory*. We want to agree with Burge that, insofar as the ant seems *insensitive* to whether any of its states are in error, correctness conditions seem *irrelevant* to that explanation, however they might be defined.

Cataglyphis: navigation without i-representations

As we've noted, the ant's navigational capacities are sensitive to a wide variety of proximal inputs beyond those that factor directly into the PI system.[7] The ant can follow odor concentrations emanating from food and nests (Buehlmann, Hansson, and Knaden 2013, 2012); its antennae are sensitive to displacement, which ordinarily correlates well with wind direction, and which the ant can use to set its direction of travel (Müller & Wehner 2007; Wolf and Wehner 2000); and it has systems that track changes in polarized light and also photoscopic patterns that track the position of the sun in the sky (Wehner and Müller 2006). Additionally, it is able to perform its PI in three dimensions, when its foraging path takes it up and down hills, and even when it is forced to trip and stumble over corrugations on its foraging paths.[8] More surprisingly still, Steck, Wittlinger, and Wolf (2009) showed that amputation of *two* of the ant's six legs doesn't impede the ant's successful navigation, even though such amputations cause the ant to stumble and use irregular gaits.

The ant is also sensitive to visual stimuli that correlate with landmarks. The prevailing view is that it responds to stored retinotopic "snapshots" of landmarks in its terrain,[9] which it can match with current retinal stimuli in order to influence navigation in a variety of ways (Collett, Chittka, and Collett 2013). Cartwright and Collett (1983, 1987) have described an algorithm that operates only upon proximal retinal stimuli to implement these capacities.

It might be supposed that this sensitivity to a wide variety of stimuli is enough to establish that *Cataglyphis* makes use of intentional states, i-representing the wind direction, sun position, and landmarks that are germane to computing its location. This inference is too hasty. Insofar as intentionality is genuinely explanatory, its properties, e.g., non-factivity, should support counterfactuals, indicating how, *ceteris paribus*, the ant *would* respond if the representation were *false*.[10] On the face of it, if a system's computations are counterfactually defined *only* over purely proximal inputs, then it would behave the same whenever different distal stimuli had the same proximal effects – e.g., in the case of an ant navigating by PI, a vector trajectory toward the nest vs. the same trajectory away from the nest. The fact that it's a distal error would make no difference to the ant: it wouldn't lead the ant to correct it.[11] Classifying states of the ant as "true" or "false" relative to the distal stimuli they are responding to would capture no generalizations not already accounted for by their response to proximal stimuli.

Indeed, not being able to recover from error seems precisely to be *Cataglyphis'* plight. Ants that are displaced after finding food will walk in the direction that would have taken them back to their nest had they not been moved (Wehner and Srinivasan 1981). Ants that have pig bristle stilts attached to their legs after they find food end up overshooting their nest on their homebound walk, whereas ants whose legs are amputated end up undershooting it (Wittlinger, Wehner, and Wolf 2006, 2007). One might think, given enough time, the ants will eventually be able to recover from such displacements. But Andel and Wehner (2004) gathered data indicating that, even given ample time, ants can't so correct. They manipulated the ant's PI system so that it ran in the direction *away* from its nest upon getting food,[12] and then recorded the behavior of the ants for three minutes after they had executed this PI vector. For those three minutes, the ants did run back and forth parallel to their PI vector. But ants execute this back and forth after completing *all* of their PI walks, *whether or not* they succeed in taking them toward the nest. The behavior seems to be not a correction from error, but mere execution of the motor routine triggered by activation of the PI vector. The ants have been observed persisting in this motor routine for up to *two hours* without finding their nest upon having been displaced (Müller and Wehner 1994: 529). They seem to lack the cognitive resources to recover from error.

Of course, it's still possible in these instances that there just isn't enough information available to the ant to allow it to revise course. But there are instances in which the ants are unable to use available proximal stimuli to orient themselves even if those same stimuli *can* orient them in other circumstances. For example, ants deprived of polarized light can use the sun compass to navigate just as accurately to and from the nest. However, if an ant uses polarized light to chart a course from nest to food, and *then* is deprived of polarized light cues, it cannot use its sun compass to navigate back home, even though sun compass cues are still readily available (Wehner and Müller 2006). The ant can't use the sun compass to correct its course, though it could have had it been deprived of polarized light from the start. Perhaps it just doesn't *like* using the sun compass, or it falsely believes the sun compass is inaccurate under these conditions – but absent such alternate accounts, the best explanation is that the ant is not i-representing the direction to its nest, but executing a routine that's sensitive only to stimulation of the polarization detectors.

The similar Australian desert ant, *Melophorus bagoti*, also demonstrates insensitivity to stimuli that in other circumstances would allow it to recover from displacements (Wehner et al. 2006). These ants use their landmark guidance system to establish one habitual route from the nest to food, and another from the food to the nest. If displaced to any arbitrary point on their nest-bound route, the ants use their landmark guidance to navigate back to the nest. But if displaced from their nest-bound route to a spot on their food-bound route, they behave as though they have been displaced to an unknown location. They just walk on the trajectory output by the nest-bound PI vector – even though the surrounding landmarks should be sufficient to guide the ant back to its food source and thence back to the nest. Again, the ants seem to be relying on triggered motor routines that cannot be revised in light of new information. Whether states of the system are "correct" or "incorrect" will make no difference to the operation of the system in any counterfactual conditions. So, attributing i-representations to the ant's navigation system provides no explanatory gain.

The issues can get subtle: it turns out the ant exhibits *some* flexibility. For example, the PI and landmark guidance system do seem to interact. When the output of the PI system and that of the landmark guidance system conflict, ants steer a course intermediate between them (Collett 2012). This behavior might be thought to be evidence of the ant i-representing the locations of various landmarks, mapping them onto locations i-represented by its PI system, and then correcting its course when there is a mismatch from the i-representational output by these two systems. However, to the contrary, Collett proposes that the ant is simply computationally super-imposing the outputs of the two systems to arrive at this motor routine, a computation of what Burge (2010: 501) calls a "weighted average" that would appear not to require intentionality: the two systems don't permit the ant to *recover* from error, but just – again, fortuitously – *to avoid making errors* in the first place.

Similar points apply to the ant's supposed ability to use its wind compass to compensate for uncertainty in the PI system. When walking to a familiar food source, ants use their wind compass to walk to a position downwind of the food (Wolf and Wehner 2000). They then rely on the odor plumes emanating from the food to guide them the rest of the way, and walk in the direction of increasing odor concentration, changing how far downwind they walk as a linear function of the distance between the food and the nest. Wolf and Wehner (2005: 4228) conclude that this behavior may be driven by what "might be interpreted as the ants' own assessment of their navigation uncertainty": the ant correctly i-represents that its error in navigating to the food increases as the distance to the food increases, and compensates by aiming for a target downwind of the food just beyond the maximum possible error. That way, if the ant errs maximally in the upwind direction, it will still arrive downwind of the food. If it errs maximally in the downwind direction, it will still be in contact with odors that can guide it to the food.

Nonetheless, there's an alternative, non-intentional, explanation. Upon receiving wind stimuli from the ant's antennae, the PI system multiplies the direction component of the motor routine by a factor of the distance component. It's a happy accident that this factor corresponds to the ants' actual tendency to err, and that in so doing, it takes the ant to an area appropriately downwind of the food source. We need not suppose that the ant has i-representations of its own error factor, or of the distance of the food from the nest.

If this explanation is correct, the ant does manifest at least a degree of Carruthers' "flexibility," but, as the examples illustrate, this flexibility can be accomplished simply by rote, non-intentional operations over proximal stimuli. Wehner and colleagues[13] claim that the ant's integration of *all* its navigation systems is best understood in just this way, as a "toolkit" (Wehner 2009). Each "tool" – the PI system, polarization compass, sun compass, wind compass, and landmark guidance system – can be fully characterized in terms of computational processes operating over proximal inputs. Interactions among the systems are explained by taking the outputs from one system as inputs to another, which in turn trigger its operation. For example, whether input from the sun compass affects the output of PI depends on what input it's receiving from the polarized light compass. But, again, while such interactions decrease the likelihood of error, they don't require *recovery* from it, and so the intentional content of the input would still seem to be explanatorily inert.

Whether this "toolkit" architecture continues to hold under continued empirical scrutiny as the correct model of *Cataglyphis* cognition remains to be seen. But, at the least, Wehner's model shows us how it's *possible* for a creature to exhibit extensive cognitive integration and behavioral flexibility without having intentional states.

Honeybees: navigation with i-representations

In contrast to the toolkit architecture for the ant, Menzel and Giurfa (2001)[14] propose a more integrated architecture for the honeybee (*Apis mellifera*) that *does* seem best characterized in intentional terms. Honeybees have a similar suite of modular navigation systems as the ant: a polarization compass, an optic flow detector that correlates with speed and distance flown, a PI system that combines these inputs, a visual landmark guidance system, and the like. Whereas Wehner's ant architecture specifies how the deliverances of each subsystem supply input to others, Menzel and Giurfa propose that, in the honeybee, outputs of individual modular navigation systems enter into a common "central integration" space (CIS). The systems are free to influence one another in *indefinite* ways before outputting motor routines: deliverances from any one subsystem can, in principle, have an effect *at any point* on any other.

Evidence that bees employ such central integration comes essentially from two studies. The key finding in each is that bees evince systematic sensitivity to indefinite disjunctions of proximal stimuli. Menzel et al. (2005) displaced bees from locations in their foraging grounds to a variety of novel locations, taking care to shield them from visual stimuli during displacement. Upon release, most of the bees initially fly on a course that would have taken them back to the hive were they still at the point from which they had been displaced. So far, this is the same behavior displayed by *Cataglyphis* under analogous conditions. But, unlike the ants, the bees then change course and make their way back, either directly to the hive or to a previously encountered feeder, and thence on to the hive. They do this on the basis of specific input from release points that do not correspond to positions the bees have been at before, so it is impossible for them to have stored retinal snapshots that they can match to their current positions.[15] Unlike the ants, the bees seem sensitive to errors at arbitrarily different points in their flights and are able to recover from them, all of which invites explanation in terms of i-representation.

Moreover, bees also navigate in response to observing the famous "waggle dances," performed by conspecifics at the hive, which indicate the distance and direction from the hive to feeding locations.[16] In a second study, Menzel et al. (2011) discovered that bees who have been trained on a route from the hive to one feeder (FT), but then observe the dance of another bee at the hive indicating the distance and direction to a second feeder (FD), are able to pursue *novel shortcuts* between the two feeders (see Figure 1.1). In particular, bees can fly a route from the hive

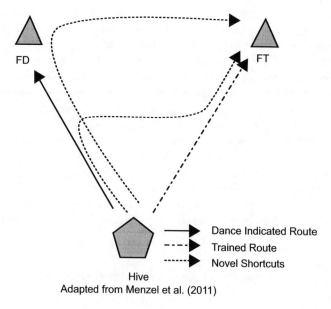

FD

FT

Dance Indicated Route
Trained Route
Novel Shortcuts

Hive
Adapted from Menzel et al. (2011)

Figure 1.1 Bees take novel shortcuts between a trained route to a feeder (FT) and dance-indicated route to another feeder (FD).

in the direction of FD, but then switch over mid-course and chart a path to FT. Furthermore, once the bees have arrived at either FD or FT, they are able to fly to the other feeder first before returning to the hive. Once again, their navigational capacity seems to elude generalization in terms of proximal stimuli alone. Exposure to the waggle dance eventuates not just in a particular motor routine, but rather a capacity that seems capable of taking the bee to the same location via indefinite different routes.

Distal i–representations provide a common coin that allows for the bees' recovery from error at arbitrarily different points, and therefore for generalizations about the operations of the CIS across an indefinitely large, disjunctive motley of proximal input.[17] Given the motley, there aren't law-like generalizations of the form: "Bees will modify their motor routine in response to *proximal stimuli of type x.*" Instead, such generalizations need to be of the form: "Bees will modify their motor routine in response to updated *distal representations of its location relative to the hive.*" Distal i–representations capture what's in common across different occasions, different bees and different proximal input.[18]

The role of i–representations is reinforced by consideration of further features of intentionality that we don't have space adequately to discuss: *non-existentiality* and sensitivity *to aspect*. It's certainly a plausible interpretation of the above experiments that the bees represent the feeders as such, and would continue to i–represent them even had they been removed. More interestingly, for an animal's responses to be fully effective, information from different input sources have to bear on the same *aspects* of the world, e.g., whether a distal object is represented, say, *as a feeder* and not *as a trap.* A distal object might in fact be both, and which of these the agent represents it *as* will make a difference to how this information is integrated with the rest of the animal's representations – in many instances, making a difference between life and death. These topics deserve much further discussion.[19] But, towards that, we conclude with impressive evidence of bees' susceptibility to perceptual illusions, specifically their sensitivity both to "non-existent" distal objects, and to the aspects under which they perceive them.

Van Hateren, Srinivasan, and Wait (1990) gathered data suggesting that bees are sensitive to Kanizsa rectangle illusions (see Figure 1.2).[20] Trained to associate sugar water with lines oriented in a particular direction, they responded to both genuine rectangles and Kanizsa figures oriented in the same direction – even though, in the latter case, there is no actual rectangle (occlude the "pacman" figures, and the appearance of a rectangle disappears). Bees weren't sensitive to collections of pacman figures at the same positions but which are rotated so as to disrupt the illusion. Their representations thereby exhibited all three of the features that are taken to be characteristic of intentionality: they were non-factive, indeed, erroneous ones of a *non-existent* object, which they saw *as* (or "*qua,*" or under the aspect of being) *rectangular.*[21]

Figure 1.2   A Kanizsa rectangle

Conclusion: (explanatory) i-representation iff cognitive integration?

We tentatively conclude that the evidence so far suggests that bees do seem to i-represent features of their distal environments, while desert ants do not. A further tentative conclusion we'd like to offer is that there is *no integration without i-representation*, whereby "integration" means the kind of responsiveness to indefinite ranges of proximal stimuli at indefinitely different points that is displayed by central integration systems. We are also inclined, even more tentatively, to propose the converse: that there is at least no *explanatory* i-representation without integration.[22] "Informational" systems that can be characterized in terms merely of many separate systems sensitive to a limited range of proximal stimuli do not require intentional explanation in and of themselves. Intentional explanation is only needed when the integration of information from different subsystems requires generalization over distal stimuli. The resulting i-representations are non-factive, non-existential and (plausibly) aspective, in the way that the states of bees, but not of the ants, seem to be.

Notes

1 We thank Carsten Hansen, Marc Hauser and Karen Neander for insightful comments.
2 The term "intentional(ity)" was resurrected from scholastic philosophy by the nineteenth-century Austrian philosopher Franz Brentano (1874/1995), who plausibly claimed that intentionality was a mark of the mental, and, more controversially, that it was irreducible to the physical (note that "intentional" here and below doesn't mean the usual "deliberate"). See Chisholm (1957) for the classic introduction of it to Anglo-American philosophy, and Jacob (2014) for a recent review of the literature.
3 See Whippo (2006).
4 "Path integration" is the usual term in the literature, as is the abbreviation "PI," which we adopt particularly to avoid confusion with our use of "integration" below for a particular sort of processing. See Srinivasan (2015) for a recent review of PI in ants and bees.
5 Rescorla (2013: 96) makes a similar allowance. As Gallistel notes, "representation" in mathematics is indeed used for mere isomorphism.
6 Fodor (1987) originally raised this problem, based on famous experiments of Lettvin, McCullough, and Pitts (1959/68). See Millikan (1989) and Neander (1995, 2017) for further discussion. It is virtually identical to the problem Kripke (1980/2004) claims to find in Wittgenstein (1953). Burge (2010: 322–323) dismisses the problem as "largely an artifact of reductive programs," or efforts to define the intentional in non-intentional terms. Although we don't share his dismissal of these efforts, we agree with him (2010: 298) that they are inessential to psychology: indeed, that "one could hardly have better epistemic ground to rely on a notion than that it figures centrally in a successful science" (2010: 298), whether or not it is reducible to physics (whatever that might actually amount to). But the disjunction problem is separate from reductionism: as the general form indicates, the problem arises for any representations that are not-factive, or, in Fodor's (1990: Ch. IV) term, "robust" – they can be entokened erroneously – as he claims any serious representation must be.
7 Burge (2010: 502) acknowledges as much, and was focusing on PI merely as a way of marking distinctions among bases for explanatory ascriptions of i-representations.
8 See Grah, Wehner and Ronacher (2005, 2007, 2008); Wohlgemuth, Ronacher, and Wehner (2001); Wohlgemuth, Ronacher, and Wehner (2002) and Wintergerst and Ronacher (2012) for the hill data; see Steck *et al.* (2009) for the corrugations.
9 See Wehner (2009: 88), Ronacher (2008: 59), Collett (2010) and Wystrach and Graham (2012: 16–17). We assume the "snapshots" are proximal patterns produced by landmarks, as are the patterns produced by their nests and prey.
10 Along lines of Pietroski and Rey (1995), we use "*ceteris paribus*" to rule out indefinitely many independent influences, e.g., memory dysfunction, change in motivation, motor inability: i.e., were no such factors at work, then the non-factivity should make a difference to the animal's behavior. Similar remarks apply to the non-existential and aspective properties, which there is not space to discuss (but see the brief discussion of illusions at the end).

11 Which is not to say that a creature recovering from error need have an i-representation of *(in)correctness* itself, à la Davidson (1975); just a sensitivity to when an i-representation does(n't) in fact apply. Could there be errors in *proximal* i-representations? Arguably, without distality there is no objective basis for an explanatorily relevant distinction between correct and incorrect (cp. Burge 2010: 396).

12 This particular experiment was on another, similar species of *Cataglyphis*: *C. bicolor*.

13 See Cruse and Wehner (2011); Ronacher (2008) and Wehner et al. (2006).

14 See also Giurfa and Menzel (2001); Wiener et al. (2011) and Giurfa and Menzel (2013).

15 For the record, Wehner (2009: 93), Cruse and Wehner (2011), and Collett, Chittka, and Collett (2013: R795–R797) dispute Menzel *et al.*'s claims, arguing that the bees' behavior could be explained with the same retinotopic landmark guidance systems they ascribe to the desert ant, which, we've seen, can be plausibly characterized in terms of non-intentional computations on proximal stimuli. For the sake of clarifying the distinctions we're after, we're going to stick with Menzel's theory, while acknowledging it hasn't been fully established.

16 We put aside whether responding to and performing these waggle dances requires i-representations (see Rescorla 2013, for discussion). Tautz *et al.* (2004) and Wray *et al.* (2008) cast doubt on the long reported result that bees reject as implausible dances indicating food in the middle of a lake (Gould and Gould 1982).

17 That is, the disjunction would consist of the motley proximal stimuli that have nothing in common other than they are evidence of the distal stimulus. Moreover, the disjunction could be indefinitely extended counterfactually, e.g., by increased sensitivity of the animal's receptors, or by further deliberation, linking new proximal evidence to the distal. The point is sometimes expressed in terms of such creatures having a "cognitive map" (see, e.g., Menzel *et al.* 2005, 2011).

18 Someone might think one could type individuate the content of the i-representations in terms of their computational role. But if different proximal states give rise to the same distal content in different bees, then explanatory generalizations across bees would be unlikely in the extreme – unless, of course, one distinguishes essential from accidental roles, which it's by no means clear it's possible to do in a principled way (see Fodor 1998).

19 As does another issue related to representations, the "systematicity" of bee navigation: e.g., [they can navigate right and then left] iff [they can navigate left and then right]. See Fodor (1987) for the general issue, and Tetzlaff and Rey (2009) for discussion of it in relation to the bees.

20 van Hateren *et al.* caution that their findings are preliminary; Horridge, Zhang, and O'Carroll (1992) show bees are sensitive to other illusory contours. See Rey (2012) for discussion of the significance of Kanizsa figures for theories of intentionality, and the problem of "non-existent objects."

21 Other examples are of cats trying to catch illusory snakes (https://youtu.be/CcXXQ6GCUb8) and dogs chasing illusory flying things (Dodman 1996). See Nieder (2002) for a review.

22 Note that the perceptual constancies stressed by Burge (2010: 408ff) as crucial to intentionality also involve generalizations over indefinite proximal stimuli, as in varying perspectival views of a shape.

References

Andel, D., and Wehner, R. (2004) "Path Integration in Desert Ants, *Cataglyphis*: How to Make a Homing Ant Run Away From Home," *Proceedings of the Royal Society B: Biological Sciences*, 271(1547), 1485–1489. doi:10.1098/rspb.2004.2749

Brentano, F. (1874/1995) *Psychology From an Empirical Standpoint* (A. Rancurello, D. Terrell, and L. McAlister, trans.), London: Routledge and Kegan Paul.

Buehlmann, C., Hansson, B. S., and Knaden, M. (2012) "Path Integration Controls Nest Plume Following in Desert Ants," *Current Biology*, 22, 645–649. doi:10.1016/j.cub.2012.02.029

——— (2013) "Flexible Weighing of Olfactory and Vector Information in the Desert Ant *Cataglyphis fortis*," *Biology Letters*, 9(3), 1–4. doi:10.1098/rsbl.2013.0070

Burge, T. (2010) *Origins of Objectivity*, Oxford: Oxford University Press.

Carruthers, P. (2004) "On Being Simple Minded," *American Philosophical Quarterly*, 41(3), 205–220.

Cartwright, B. A., and Collett, T. S. (1983) "Landmark Learning in Bees," *Journal of Comparative Physiology A*, 151(4), 521–543. doi:10.1007/bf00605469

——— (1987) "Landmark Maps for Honeybees," *Biological Cybernetics*, 57(1–2), 85–93. doi:10.1007/bf00318718

Chisholm, R. M. (1957) *Perceiving: A Philosophical Study*, Ithaca, NY: Cornell University Press.

Collett, M. (2010) "How Desert Ants Use a Visual Landmark for Guidance Along a Habitual Route," *Proceedings of the National Academy of Sciences*, *107*(25), 11638–11643. doi:10.1073/pnas.1001401107

—— (2012) "How Navigational Guidance Systems are Combined in a Desert Ant," *Current Biology*, *22*(10), 927–932. doi:10.1016/j.cub.2012.03.049

Collett, M., Chittka, L., and Collett, T. (2013) "Spatial Memory in Insect Navigation," *Current Biology*, *23*(17), R789–R800. doi:10.1016/j.cub.2013.07.020

Cruse, H., and Wehner, R. (2011) "No Need for a Cognitive Map: Decentralized Memory for Insect Navigation," *PLoS Computational Biology*, 7(3), e1002009. doi:10.1371/journal.pcbi.1002009

Cummins, R. (1989) *Meaning and Mental Representation*, Cambridge, MA: MIT Press.

Davidson, D. (1975) "Thought and Talk," in Samuel D. Guttenplan (ed.) *Mind and Language* (pp. 7–23), Oxford: Clarendon Press.

Dodman, N. (1996) *The Dog Who Loved Too Much*, New York: Bantam Books.

Dretske, F. (1986) "Misrepresentation," in R. Bogdan (ed.) *Belief: Form, Content, and Function* (pp. 17–36), Oxford: Oxford University Press.

—— (1987) *Explaining Behavior: Reasons in a World of Causes*, Cambridge, MA: MIT Press.

Fodor, J. A. (1987) *Psychosemantics*, Cambridge, MA: MIT Press.

—— (1990) *A Theory of Content and Other Essays*, Cambridge, MA: MIT Press.

—— (1998) *Concepts: Where Cognitive Science Went Wrong*, Cambridge, MA: MIT Press.

Gallistel, C. R. (1990) *The Organization of Learning*, Cambridge, MA: MIT Press.

Giurfa, M., and Menzel, R. (2013) "Cognitive Components of Insect Behavior," in R. Menzel and P. R. Benjamin (eds.) *Invertebrate Learning and Memory* (pp. 14–25), Amsterdam: Elsevier Associative Press.

Gould, J. L., and Gould, C. G. (1982). "The Insect Mind: Physics or Meta-Physics?" in D. R. Griffin (ed.) *Animal Mind – Human Mind* (pp. 269–298), Berlin: Springer-Verlag.

Grah, G., and Ronacher, B. (2008) "Three-Dimensional Orientation in Desert Ants: Context-Independent Memorisation and Recall of Sloped Path Segments," *Journal of Comparative Physiology A*, *194*(6), 517–522. doi:10.1007/s00359-008-0324-4

Grah, G., Wehner, R., and Ronacher, B. (2005) "Path Integration in a Three-Dimensional Maze: Ground Distance Estimation Keeps Desert Ants *Cataglyphis fortis* on Course," *Journal of Experimental Biology*, *208*(21), 4005–4011. doi:10.1242/jeb.01873

—— (2007) "Desert Ants Do Not Acquire and Use a Three-dimensional Global Vector," *Frontiers in Zoology*, *4*(1), 12. doi:10.1186/1742-9994-4-12

Horridge, G. A., Zhang, S. W., and O'Carroll, D. (1992) "Insect Perception of Illusory Contours," *Philosophical Transactions: Biological Sciences 337*(1279), 59–64.

Jacob, P. (2014) "Intentionality," in N. Zalta (ed.) *Stanford Encyclopedia of Philosophy* (Winter 2014 Edition), http://plato.stanford.edu/archives/win2014/entries/intentionality/

Kripke, S. (1980/2004) *Wittgenstein on Rules and Private Language: An Elementary Exposition*, Oxford: Oxford University Press.

Lettvin, J. Y., Maturana, H. R., McCullough, W. S., and Pitts, W. H. (1959/68) "What the Frog's Eye Tells the Frog's Brain," *Proceedings of the IRE, 47*, 1940–1951.

Menzel, R., and Giurfa, M. (2001) "Cognitive Architecture of a Mini-Brain: The Honeybee," *Trends in Cognitive Sciences*, *5*(2), 62–71. doi:10.1016/s1364-6613(00)01601-6

Menzel, R., Greggers, U., Smith, A., Berger, S., Brandt, R., Brunke, S., . . . Watzl, S. (2005) "Honey Bees Navigate According to a Map-Like Spatial Memory," *Proceedings of the National Academy of Sciences*, *102*(8), 3040–3045. doi:10.1073/pnas.0408550102

Menzel, R., Kirbach, A., Haass, W., Fischer, B., Fuchs, J., Koblofsky, M., . . . Greggers, U. (2011) "A Common Frame of Reference for Learned and Communicated Vectors in Honeybee Navigation," *Current Biology*, *21*(8), 645–650. doi:10.1016/j.cub.2011.02.039

Millikan, R. G. (1984) *Language, Thought, and Other Biological Categories: New Foundations for Realism*, Cambridge, MA: MIT Press.

—— (1989) "Biosemantics," *Journal of Philosophy, 86*, 281–297.

Müller, M., and Wehner, R. (1994) "The Hidden Spiral: Systematic Search and Path Integration in Desert Ants, *Cataglyphis fortis*," *Journal of Comparative Physiology, 175*, 525–530.

——— (2007) "Wind and Sky as Compass Cues in Desert Ant Navigation," *Naturwissenschaften, 94*(7), 589–594. doi:10.1007/s00114-007-0232-4

Neander, K. (1995) "Misrepresenting and Malfunctioning," *Philosophical Studies*, 79, 109–141.

——— (2017), *A Mark of the Mental: In Defense of Informational Teleosemantics*, Cambridge, MA: MIT Press.

Nieder, A. (2002) Seeing More Than Meets the Eye: Processing of Illusory Contours in Animals. *Journal of Comparative Physiology A: Neuroethology, Sensory, Neural, and Behavioral Physiology, 188*(4), 249–260.

Pietroski, P., and Rey, G. (1995) "When Other Things Aren't Equal: Saving *Ceteris Paribus* Laws from Vacuity," *The British Journal For the Philosophy of Science, 46*(1), 81–110. http://doi.org/10.1093/bjps/46.1.81

Rescorla, M. (2013) "Millikan on Honeybee Navigation and Communication," in D. Ryder, J. Kingsbury, and K. Williford (eds.) *Millikan and Her Critics*, Malden, MA: John Wiley & Sons.

Rey, G. (2012) "Externalism and Inexistence in Early Content," in R. Schantz (ed.) *Prospects for Meaning*, New York: deGruyter.

Ronacher, B. (2008) "Path Integration as the Basic Navigation Mechanism of the Desert Ant *Cataglyphis fortis*," *Myrmecological News, 11*, 53–62.

Srinivasan, M.V. (2015) "Where Paths Meet and Cross: Navigation by Path Integration in the Desert Ant and the Honeybee," *Journal of Comparative Physiology A, 201*(6), 533–546. doi:10.1007/s00359-015-1000-0

Steck, K., Wittlinger, M., and Wolf, H. (2009) "Estimation of Homing Distance in Desert Ants, *Cataglyphis fortis*, Remains Unaffected by Disturbance of Walking Behaviour," *Journal of Experimental Biology, 212*(18), 2893–2901. doi:10.1242/jeb.030403

Tautz, J., Zhang, S., Spaethe, J., Brockmann, A., Si, A., and Srinivasan, M. (2004), "Honeybee Odometry: Performance in Varying Natural Terrain," *PLoS Biology, 2*(7), 0195–0923.

Tetzlaff, M., and Rey, G. (2009) "Systematicity and Intentional Realism in Honeybee Navigation," in R. L. Lurz (ed.) *The Philosophy of Animal Minds* (pp. 72–88), Cambridge: Cambridge University Press.

van Hateren, J. H., Srinivasan, M.V., and Wait, P. B. (1990) "Pattern Recognition in Bees: Orientation Discrimination," *Journal of Comparative Physiology A, 167*, 649–654.

Wehner, R. (2009) "The Architecture of the Desert Ant's Navigational Toolkit," *Myrmecological News, 12*, 85–96.

Wehner, R., Boyer, M., Loertscher, F., Sommer, S., and Menzi, U. (2006) "Ant Navigation: One-Way Routes Rather than Maps," *Current Biology, 16*(1), 75–79. doi:10.1016/j.cub.2005.11.035

Wehner, R., and Müller, M. (2006) "The Significance of Direct Sunlight and Polarized Skylight in the Ant's Celestial System of Navigation," *Proceedings of the National Academy of Sciences, 103*(33), 12575–12579. doi:10.1073/pnas.0604430103

Wehner, R., and Srinivasan, M.V. (1981) "Searching Behaviour of Desert Ants," *Journal of Comparative Physiology, 142*(3), 315–338. doi:10.1007/bf00605445

Whippo, C.W. (2006) "Phototropism: Bending Towards Enlightenment," *The Plant Cell, 18*(5), 1110–1119. doi:10.1105/tpc.105.039669

Wiener, J., Shettleworth, S., Bingman, V. P., Cheng, K., Healy, S., Jacobs, L. F., . . . Newcombe, N. S. (2011) "Animal Navigation: A Synthesis," in R. Menzel and J. Fischer (eds.) *Animal Thinking: Contemporary Issues in Comparative Cognition*, Cambridge, MA: MIT Press.

Wintergerst, S., and Ronacher, B. (2012) "Discrimination of Inclined Path Segments by the Desert Ant *Cataglyphis fortis*," *Journal of Comparative Physiology A, 198*(5), 363–373. doi:10.1007/s00359-012-0714-5

Wittgenstein, L. (1953) *Philosophical Investigations*, New York: Macmillan.

Wittlinger, M., Wehner, R., and Wolf, H. (2006) "The Ant Odometer: Stepping on Stilts and Stumps," *Science, 312*(5782), 1965–1967. doi:10.1126/science.1126912

——— (2007) "The Desert Ant Odometer: A stride Integrator that Accounts for Stride Length and Walking Speed," *Journal of Experimental Biology, 210*(2), 198–207. doi:10.1242/jeb.02657

Wohlgemuth, S., Ronacher, B., and Wehner, R. (2001) "Ant Odometry in the Third Dimension," *Nature, 411*(6839), 795–798. doi:10.1038/35081069

——— (2002) "Distance Estimation in the Third Dimension in Desert Ants," *Journal of Comparative Physiology A, 188*(4), 273–281. doi:10.1007/s00359-002-0301-2

Wolf, H., and Wehner, R. (2000) "Pinpointing Food Sources: Olfactory and Anemotactic Orientation in Desert Ants, *Cataglyphis fortis*," *Journal of Experimental Biology*, *203*, 857–868.

———— (2005) "Desert Ants Compensate for Navigation Uncertainty," *Journal of Experimental Biology*, *208*(22), 4223–4230. doi:10.1242/jeb.01905

Wray, M. K., Klein, B. A., Mattila, H. R., and Seeley, T. D. (2008) "Honeybees Do Not Reject Dances for 'Implausible' Locations: Reconsidering the Evidence for Cognitive Maps in Insects," *Animal Behavior*, *76*, 261–269. doi:10.1016/j.anbehav.2008.04.005

Wystrach, A., and Graham, P. (2012) "What Can We Learn From Studies of Insect Navigation?" *Animal Behaviour*, *84*(1), 13–20. doi:10.1016/j.anbehav.2012.04.017

2

VISUAL IMAGERY IN THE THOUGHT OF MONKEYS AND APES

Christopher Gauker

Introduction

Explanations of animal problem-solving often represent our choices as limited to two: first, we can explain the observed behavior as a product of trained responses to sensory stimuli, or second, we can explain it as due to the animal's possession of general rules utilizing general concepts. My objective in this essay is to bring to life a third alternative, namely, an explanation in terms of imagistic cognition. The theory of imagistic cognition posits representations that locate objects in a multidimensional similarity space. It proposes that an animal's expectations can be explained on the basis of the similarity of novel objects to objects previously encountered. The animal can predict the behavior of the novel object by producing a *mental movie* of the novel object by *morphing* it into an object, the behavior of which has previously been observed.

After criticizing the theory of *concept abstraction*, I will identify some of the key elements of imagistic cognition. Then I will attempt to illustrate the utility of this conception of cognition by using it to explain the combination of successes and failures observed in monkeys in tool-mediated retrieval tasks (Fujita et al. 2003; Fujita et al. 2011) and in great apes in trap tube and trap table experiments (Martin-Ordas et al. 2008; Martin-Ordas et al. 2012).

Against abstraction

Many students of animal cognition regard their task as that of exploring the extent to which nonhuman animals can form *abstract* concepts. The philosophical and psychological literature contains a variety of attempts to explain what abstract concepts might be and how they might be formed (e.g., Barsalou 1999; Gärdenfors 2000; Mandler 2004). If one wants to reject these, one has to explain carefully why they fail. I cannot do that here, but the basic problems should be familiar enough that a reminder will suffice to motivate a hunt for alternatives. (For a thorough critical review of a wide range of theories of concepts, see Gauker 2011.)

Historically, the common thread in attempts at defining abstraction, going back to Locke (1975 [1689]), is the idea that abstract ideas are formed by a process of *abstraction* from perceptual representations. There are at least three questions about this process that, as far as I can see, are never squarely addressed. The first is: How does the mind select a class of perceptions from which to make an abstraction? Why, for instance, might the mind abstract from perceptions of four poodles, rather than from three poodles and a cat? The answer cannot be that the mind recognizes that the poodles but not the cat have something in common, since the capacity to recognize that commonality is supposed to be the product of the process, not its impetus.

The second question is: Of all of the abstract ideas that might be abstracted from the perceptions of, for example, four poodles, how does the mind choose the ones to abstract? Some of the endless possibilities are: *one-of-these-four-things, poodles, furry things, pets, barky pets, mammals, self-mover*. The third question is: If the idea to be abstracted is not already present in the perceptual representation, how can the mind abstract it? And if it is already present in the perceptual representations, how did the mind acquire the capacity to form such concept-containing perceptual representations in the first place? Of course, these questions are even more difficult when we cannot suppose that spoken language mediates the process.

The red herring of abstraction leads to false dichotomies. Many authors in the field of animal cognition cast the choice of explanations as exclusively a choice between the supposition that the animal relies on associations between sensory experiences, and the supposition that the animal grasps general rules by means of abstract concepts. For instance, after describing some tool-using behavior in animals, Seed and Byrne write:

> Behavior like this raises the intriguing possibility that animals represent the physical properties and forces involved in the tool-using event in an abstract, conceptual way: in terms of properties such as rigidity, continuity and connectedness. The simpler alternative is that the animals' thinking is grounded in perceptual features of the objects (their shape, feel and spatial orientation).
>
> (Seed and Byrne 2010: R1034)

(Compare, for example, Hauser 1997: 289; Call 2010: 83; Seed et al. 2011: 90; Mayer et al. 2014: 1; Albiach-Serrano et al. 2015: 176.) The dichotomy is false, because, as we will see, it ignores the possibility of distinctively cognitive activity at the level of imagistic representation.

The elements of imagistic cognition

There are no off-the-shelf theories of imagistic cognition. Early work on mental rotation, especially that by Shepard and Metzler (1971), reawakened the field of psychology to the possibility of imagistic problem solving. The ensuing debate, represented, for example, in Pylyshyn's critique (1973) and Kosslyn's defense (1975), was focused on the question of whether mental imagery is real. Regrettably, this debate never blossomed into a research program aimed at identifying the kinds of problems that can be solved by means of imagistic cognition.

Here is a partial list of cognitive problems that might be solvable by means of mental imagery: 1) Figuring out how objects come apart and go together. If I need to replace a faulty washer in a faucet, I can take the washer apart, record a mental movie of the parts coming apart, and then play that mental movie in reverse in order to put the faucet back together again. 2) Object tracking. Within limits, we can keep track of objects as they move around in space, even while they undergo certain changes (Scholl 2001). 3) An elementary grasp of causal relations. Our imagistic grasp of certain patterns of motion (such as those studied by Michotte 1963) can qualify as an elementary grasp of causal relations. 4) An imagistic representation of similarities. On the basis of an imagistic representation of an unfamiliar thing x and its behavior, we may represent x as more like a familiar thing y than like a familiar thing z, and on that basis form an imagistic expectation of what it will do.

Any deeper understanding of imagistic cognition will rely on an account of *imagistic representation*. Imagistic representation, I suggest, has two main aspects. The first aspect consists in the representation of spatial configuration. Spatial configurations consist of discrete entities, their shapes, their parts, their surfaces, and the configuration of the parts of each object and the arrangement of the objects relative to one another. We may suppose that spatial configuration is represented by virtue of an isomorphism between the elements of the representation and their relations to one another, and the elements of the scene represented and their spatial relations to one another.

The second aspect consists in the representation of an object's location in a many-dimensional space of graded qualities. The representation itself can be said to have a location in a *perceptual similarity* space. A perceptual similarity space is an aspect of, or model of, cognitive function, although it does not correspond directly to neurological properties. Each dimension is a measure of some more-or-less continuously variable, perceptible quality that an observable object or arrangement of objects might have. For example, there will be a number of dimensions that measure the various aspects of color. There will be dimensions that measure various aspects of shape. Beyond these, there will be dimensions that measure qualities that less readily come to mind, such as jerkiness of motion. The motion of a squirrel is jerkier than the motion of a cat. (Mandler [2004] emphasizes the role that jerkiness of motion plays in an infant's representation of animacy.)

My assumption is that perception can be modeled, in part, as the recording of a *mark* in perceptual similarity space. Points in perceptual similarity space correspond to points in objective quality space, the dimensions of which measure qualities that the perceived object actually has. Accordingly, a perception, considered as a mark in perceptual similarity space, can be said to represent the location of the perceived object in objective quality space. If mark x is closer to mark y than to mark z in perceptual similarity space, then the mind represents x as more similar, all things considered, to y than to z. If an act of perception results in a mark's being recorded in a biologically abnormal way, then the mark may be said to misrepresent. Further, the geometry of perceptual similarity space may not exactly match the geometry of objective quality space, and that disparity can be the source of persistent illusions, such as the Müller-Lyer illusion. (For a fuller exposition of the ideas in this paragraph, see Gauker 2011, Chapter 6.)

Not only perceptions, due to sensory contact with external objects, can be modeled as marks in perceptual similarity space. Also endogenously generated mental images of objects and scenarios can be so modeled. One means by which the mind might generate mental images is to start with a perception and "translate" it some distance across one or more dimensions of similarity space. For instance, a perception of a blue cube may be translated along the color dimensions to produce a mental image of a red cube. A perception of a slinkily moving cat may be translated across the jerkiness-of-motion dimension to produce a mental image of a jerkily moving cat. Call this process of generating mental images by translating perceptions across dimensions of perceptual similarity space *imagistic morphing*.

When an object is observed as it undergoes changes over time, these observations leave a trail of marks in perceptual similarity space, which we can call a *mental movie*. Just as a mental image can be produced by translating a perception across dimensions of similarity space, so too a whole course of events can be imagined by translating a mental movie across some dimensions of perceptual similarity space. For instance, having seen a ballet dancer execute a piroutte, we can imagine a panda bear executing a pirouette by morphing our image of the panda bear into our image of the ballet dancer. Furthermore, if we can form two such mental movies, one of which *ends* in a given mental image x and the other of which *begins* with mental image x, then we can link the two to form a mental movie of the one course of event followed by the other. Having imagined a panda bear executing a pirouette turn and a panda executing a fouette turn, we can imagine a panda bear executing first the pirouette and then moving directly on to the fouette.

There will be a distinction between mental morphings that we regard as realistic and those that we regard as fantastic. If we imagine a wine glass falling, shattering, and splattering wine all over the place, we will regard that as something that could happen, even if we have never seen it, and we will take care to make sure it does not. But if we imagine a wine glass falling and, on the way down, turning into a bird and flying away, we do not open the windows to let the bird out. I will assume that, in general, there is a difference between courses of imagination that we regard as realistic and those that we regard as fantastic.

Transfer in tool-mediated retrieval

In this section, I attempt to explain the results of a series of experiments carried out by Kazuo Fujita and Hika Kuroshima and colleagues (Fujita et al. 2003; Fujita et al. 2011), in which capuchin monkeys learned to use various hook-shaped tools in order to drag food to themselves. (Fujita et al. 2003 builds on paradigms reported in Hauser 1997 and Hauser et al. 1999.) The interesting observation is that, having learned to solve one sort of problem, the monkeys were quickly able to solve similar problems. I will suggest that their quick transfer may be attributed to imagistic morphing.

In all of the tasks to be reported here, four capuchin monkeys (the same four in all experiments) were confronted with a tray containing two "lanes" in which hook-shaped tools had been laid. In each trial, in one lane a piece of food was positioned so that the monkey could obtain it by pulling on the tool, and in the other lane a piece of food was positioned so that the monkey could not obtain the food by pulling on the tool.

In experiment 1 in Fujita et al. 2003, the monkeys had to choose between two black cane-shaped tools (see Figure 2.1, Exp 1). There were 12 different configurations, training sessions consisted of 12 trials each, and the monkeys reached criterion (10 correct choices out of 12) within 15 to 19 sessions. In experiment 2, the black tools were replaced with similarly shaped red or blue tools. For each color, all four monkeys immediately transferred the skill they had acquired in experiment 1 to the new condition involving tools of a different color.

In experiment 3, the cane-shaped tools were replaced with parabola-shaped tools (Figure 2.1, Exp 3). The monkeys reached criterion in this new task within two sessions. In some of the trials in this experiment, the food was oriented with respect to the tool so that it was inside the parabolic shape of the tool but pulling the tool would not bring the food (see the second example in Figure 2.1, Exp 3). The monkeys reliably chose the correct tool even in trials of this kind. In experiments 4 and 5, tools of two further shapes were used (Figure 2.1, Exp 4 and Exp 5), and the monkeys readily chose the correct tools in these tasks.

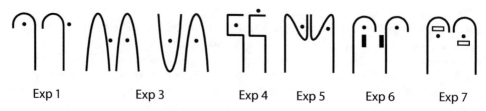

Figure 2.1 The tools used in the experiments in Fujita et al. 2003, with samples of arrangements of tool, food and (in experiments 6 and 7) hindrances.

In experiments 6 and 7, hindrances were added to the lanes. In experiment 6, the hindrance was a small block secured to the tray, which, depending on orientation, might or might not prevent the monkey from using the tool to obtain the food (see Figure 2.1, Exp 6). In experiment 7, the hindrances were holes in the tray that the food could fall into (see Figure 2.1, Exp 7). The monkeys did not reliably solve these tasks.

The task of pulling food past a hindrance was further explored in Fujita et al. 2011. In experiment 1, the four monkeys learned to obtain the food in trials in which either an obstacle (as in Fujita et al. 2003, experiment 6) or a trap (as in Fujita et al. 2003, experiment 7) could prevent the use of one of the two tools. The monkeys were not immediately successful in these tasks but learned to reliably choose correctly within about 10 sessions. In experiment 2, the three monkeys that were first trained on the obstacle task were tested on a different set of obstacle tasks (different configurations of obstacle, food and tool), and the one monkey that was first trained on the trap task was tested on a different set of trap tasks. Two learned to choose correctly in the new set within one session, and two learned to choose correctly in the new set within two sessions. In experiment 3, the three monkeys that were first trained on the obstacle task were tested in two sessions for each of the two sets of trap tasks, and the one monkey that was first trained on the trap task was tested in two sessions for each of the two sets of obstacle tasks. The combined scores for all four sessions were significantly above chance for all four monkeys. Experiment 4 tested the transfer of the monkey's skills in avoiding hindrances to a similar task using a tool of a different shape, and again achieved positive results.

Fujita et al. conclude from the second set of experiments, in their 2011 paper, that the monkeys "abstracted" a general rule that allowed them to choose the tool that allowed them to obtain the food despite the hindrance. However, the rule, as they formulate it, contains two parts, one part pertaining to the obstacle tasks and one part pertaining to the trap task (2011: 16). Since the rule has two parts, it is unclear how it captures the understanding that apparently transfers from the one task to the other. In any case, they describe themselves as having provided evidence for an explanation in terms of general rules, as opposed to "stimulus generalization" (Fujita et al. 2011: 16). Fujita et al. (2011) do not consider the possibility of an explanation in terms of imagistic cognition.

A hypothesis that takes us some distance toward explaining the results obtained is that the monkeys were able to imagistically morph new tasks into tasks that they had already learned to solve. Having learned to use the cane-shaped tool in experiment 1 of the 2003 paper, they were quickly able to learn to use tools of other colors and shapes by imaginatively morphing the color or shape of the tool in the second task to fit the colors or shapes of the tools in the earlier tasks. Granted, the hypothesis is in one way incomplete. In experiment 3, the monkeys were able to choose the correct tool (but not quite as reliably) even when, in both options, the food lay within the curve formed by the tool. It is not easy (but also not impossible) to see how a solution to this problem could be obtained by morphing the new configurations into configurations with the cane-shaped tools.

On this account, it is not surprising that the monkeys did not readily transfer their skills to the tasks that included hindrances (experiments 6 and 7 of Fujita et al. 2003). The effect of the hindrance could not be predicted on the basis of imagistically morphing the arrangements of tool and food in the tasks with hindrances into arrangements without hindrances. However, the imagistic morphing hypothesis can take us some distance toward explaining why, in the experiments in Fujita et al. 2011, the monkeys were able to transfer their skills on one set of hindrance tasks to a new set of hindrance tasks of the same kind (either obstacle or trap tasks) (experiment 2), and why they were able to transfer their skills to a differently shaped tool (experiment 4). Namely, the configurations in the new sets could generally be recognized as morphed versions of configurations in the old sets.

The imagistic morphing hypothesis might likewise explain why the monkeys (three of them) were able to transfer their skills on the obstacle task to the trap task and (in the fourth case) on the trap task to the obstacle task (Fujita et al. 2011, experiment 3). Namely, an obstacle in a lane can be imagistically morphed into a trap in the lane, and conversely. Granted, this explanation must be tempered by the realization that an obstacle and a trap do not behave in every way alike, because an obstacle behind the food will prevent a tool from being pulled to the food, but a trap behind the food will not prevent the tool from being pulled to the food (as Fujita et al. 2011 emphasize, p. 15). It is possible that morphing in these cases provides the start on a solution, which then must be completed by independent learning.

Transfer in trap-platform tasks

An important line of research into the tool-using abilities of apes and monkeys was initiated by Elisabetta Visalberghi and Luca Limongelli, working first with capuchin monkeys (Visalberghi and Limongelli 1994) and subsequently with chimpanzees (Limongelli et al. 1995). Limongelli et al. (1995) studied whether chimpanzees were able to use a rod to push a reward out of a transparent tube, and in so doing avoid pushing the food into a trap at the bottom of the tube. Only two of five chimpanzees were able to learn to do this, but both of them quickly transferred this skill to a second version of the task in which the trap was not at the center of the tube but displaced from the center.

In their study of monkeys, Visalberghi and Limongelli (1994) had asked what would happen if the trap tube were rotated 180 degrees so that the trap was still present but upside down and no longer functional. Only one monkey had learned to solve the original task with the functional tube, and that monkey continued to avoid pushing the food past the trap even when it was no longer functional, rendering it uncertain whether the monkey understood the function of the trap. Limongelli et al. did not try this version of the task on their chimpanzees. Reaux and Povinelli (2000), after successfully training one chimpanzee to solve the original trap-tube test (three others failed to learn it), administered the upside-down version of the trap-tube test to that one chimpanzee and found that she likewise continued to avoid the trap, even when it was no longer functional.

The fact that an animal avoids even the nonfunctional trap does not show that the animal does not understand the function of the trap when it is functional. Silva et al. (2005) showed that even adult humans are strongly biased to insert the rod in the end of the tube furthest away from the reward, even when there is no functional trap that has to be avoided. We would not want to infer from that that the humans do not understand the function of the traps. Moreover, subsequent researchers were able to obtain greater success in teaching great apes to avoid traps when certain predispositions were accommodated and complications were minimized. Mulcahy and Call (2006) obtained better results in the trap-tube test when they allowed their chimpanzees to rake the reward toward them through the tube rather than requiring them to push it away from themselves. Seed et al. (2009) showed that chimps could learn to avoid traps more readily when they were allowed to push the food along the length of the tube using their fingers (inserted through finger holes placed along the length of the tube) rather than using a tool.

Povinelli and Reaux (2000) also pioneered the use of a different kind of trap test, involving tables with two lanes along which an animal can rake food toward itself. One of the lanes has to be avoided because a trough runs across it into which the food will fall. Povinelli and Reaux had only limited success in training chimpanzees to perform this task, but a subsequent study by Girndt et al. (2008) showed that chimpanzees' performance on this sort of task could be improved by giving the chimpanzee only one tool and letting it decide for itself which lane to apply it to.

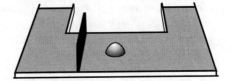

Figure 2.2   The trap platform is depicted on the left, the barrier platform on the right. The chimpanzee sat on the far side of the platform with the grill of its cage separating it from the platform.

The paradigm of trap tables was extended by Martin-Ordas et al. (2008), who invented the trap platform, which is a U-shaped platform divided by a trap (see Figure 2.2). A reward can be placed at the "bottom" of the U and, provided no hindrance is present, raked in along either branch. The trap platform contains a break between the two branches positioned off-center from the bottom of the U. The subject must rake the food along the branch that does not take it over the trap. A population of 20 apes (chimpanzees, bonobos, orangutáns and gorillas) received three 12-trial sessions with the trap platform and three sessions with a version of the trap-tube test. Half experienced the trap-platform task first and half experienced the trap-tube test. Twelve out of their population of 20 great apes learned to solve the trap-platform task. The apes were slower and less successful in solving the trap-tube test. No significant correlation between successful learning in the trap-platform test and successful learning in the trap-tube test was found. On this basis, Martin-Ordas et al. report failure to find transfer of skills from one task to the other (2008, p. 245).

A major step forward in demonstrating transferable skills was taken by Martin-Ordas et al. (2012) when they compared ape performance on three tasks: a hindrance-free U-shaped platform, the trap platform described above, and a barrier platform in which a barrier was placed across the width of the platform, over which the reward could not be dragged (see Figure 2.2). Martin-Ordas et al. discovered that apes who had been trained on the trap platform quickly learned to succeed on the barrier platform and conversely, but apes who had been trained on a platform with no hindrance did not as quickly learn either the trap-platform or the barrier-platform task. In other words, skill in avoiding one kind of hindrance transferred to the other kind of hindrance.

Why did the skill in avoiding the trap on the platform not transfer to the trap-tube task (in the Martin-Ordas et al. 2008 study), while skill in avoiding the trap on the platform transferred to the barrier platform, and vice versa (in the Martin-Ordas et al. 2012 study)? The answer, I would like to suggest, lies in *imaginative morphability*.

In the Martin-Ordas et al. 2008 study, the trap platform and the trap tube look quite different. The former is flat and broad. The latter is a transparent tube into which a tool has to be inserted. In the platform task, the trap was just a gap dividing the surface of the platform. In the Martin-Ordas et al. 2008 version of the trap tube, the trap was a large black box beneath the tube. It would take a kind of morphing genius to imagine the trap-laden tube morphing into the gappy platform. It is not surprising that the chimpanzees could not do this.[1]

By contrast, the trap platform and the barrier platform were visually quite similar. From a topological point of view, the trap platform and the barrier platform are fundamentally different, since the former and not the latter contains a gap. But for imaginative morphing, they are really quite similar. Both the trap and the barrier represent an edge at which motion of the food (dragged across the surface) comes to an end. One might even say that the barrier and the gap can be perceived as raised or sunken surfaces that may be imaginatively morphed into one another by imagining the upper edge of the barrier to descend below the surface of the platform, and conversely. Thus, on the hypothesis that chimpanzees can engage in imaginative morphing, it is perhaps explicable that an acquired skill in performing the trap-platform task would transfer to the barrier-platform task, and conversely.

Directions for future research

At this point, the hypothesis that monkeys and apes solve problems by imaginative morphing must be deemed highly speculative. However, it does suggest directions for future research. A possible test of the theory would be to test whether the morphing tendencies of monkeys and apes can be exploited in order to fool them into making wrong choices. A further question would be whether monkeys and apes can learn to solve difficult problems if they first learn to solve simpler problems, such that the solution to the difficult problem might be obtained by imaginatively morphing the solutions to the simpler problems. Another question would be whether monkeys and apes can be educated to utilize their imaginative morphing skills more fully.

Note

1 Taylor et al. (2009) report that New Caledonian crows transfer their ability to solve a trap-tube task to a trap platform. But the construction of their trap-platform task is such that, from the point of view that the crows must adopt in solving these two tasks, the tasks look quite similar.

References

Albiach-Serrano, A., C. Sebastián-Enesco, A. Seed, F. Colmenares, and J. Call (2015) "Comparing Humans and Nonhuman Great Apes in the Broken Cloth Problem: Is Their Knowledge Causal or Perceptual?," *Journal of Experimental Child Psychology* 139: 174–189.

Barsalou, L. W. (1999) "Perceptual Symbol Systems", *Behavioral and Brain Sciences* 22: 577–609.

Call, J. (2010) "Trapping the Minds of Apes: Causal Knowledge and Inferential Reasoning About Object-Object Interactions," in E. Lonsdorf, S. Ross, and T. Matsuza (eds.), *The Mind of the Chimpanzee: Ecological and Experimental Perspectives*, Chicago: University of Chicago Press, pp. 75–84.

Fujita, K., H. Kuroshima, and S. Asai (2003) "How Do Tufted Capuchin Monkeys (*Cebus apella*) Understand Causality Involved in Tool Use?," *Journal of Experimental Psychology: Animal Behavior Processes* 29: 233–242.

Fujita, K., Y. Sato, and H. Kuroshima (2011) "Learning and Generalization of Tool Use by Tufted Capuchin Monkeys (*Cebus apella*) in Tasks Involving Three Factors: Reward Tool, and Hindrance," *Journal of Experimental Psychology: Animal Behavior Processes* 37: 10–19.

Gärdenfors, P. (2000) *Conceptual Spaces*, Cambridge, MA: MIT Press.

Gauker, C. (2011) *Words and Images: An Essay on the Origin of Ideas*, Oxford: Oxford University Press.

Girndt, A., T. Meier, and J. Call (2008) "Task Constraints Mask Great Apes' Ability to Solve the Trap-Table Task," *Journal of Experimental Psychology; Animal Behavior Processes* 34: 54–62.

Hauser, M. (1997) "Artifactual Kinds and Functional Design Features: What a Primate Understands Without Language," *Cognition* 64: 285–308.

Hauser, M., J. Kralik, and C. Botto-Mahan (1999) "Problem Solving and Functional Design Features: Experiments on Cotton-top Tamarins, *Saguinus oedipus oedipus*," *Animal Behavior* 57: 565–582.

Kosslyn, S. (1975) "Information Representation in Visual Images," *Cognitive Psychology* 7: 341–370.

Limongelli, L., S. Boysen, and E. Visalberghi (1995) "Comprehension of Cause-Effect Relations in a Tool-Using Task by Chimpanzees (*Pan troglodytes*)," *Journal of Comparative Psychology* 109: 18–26.

Locke, J. (1975 [1689]) *An Essay on Human Understanding*, ed. P. Nidditch, Oxford: Oxford University Press.

Mandler, J. (2004) *The Foundations of Mind: Origins of Conceptual Thought*, Oxford: Oxford University Press.

Martin-Ordas, G., J. Call, and F. Colmenares (2008) "Tubes, Tables and Traps: Great Apes Solve Two Functionally Equivalent Trap Tasks But Show No Evidence of Transfer Across Tasks," *Animal Cognition* 11: 423–430.

Martin-Ordas, G., F. Jaek, and J. Call (2012) "Barriers and Traps: Great Apes' Performance in Two Functionally Equivalent Tasks," *Animal Cognition* 15: 1007–1013.

Mayer, C., J. Call, A. Albiach-Serrano, E. Visalberghi, G. Sabbatini, and A. Seed (2014) "Abstract Knowledge in the Broken-String Problem: Evidence From Nonhuman Primates and Preschoolers," *Plos One* 9: 1–7.

Michotte, A. (1963) *The Perception of Causality*, trans. T. R. Miles and Elaine Miles, Methuen, MA: Routledge.

Mulcahy, N., and J. Call (2006) "How Great Apes Perform on a Modified Trap-Tube Task," *Animal Cognition* 9: 193–199.

Povinelli, D., and J. Reaux (2000) "The Trap-Table Problem," in Daniel J. Povinelli (ed.), *Folk Physics for Apes: The Chimpanzee's Theory of How the World Works*, Oxford: Oxford University Press, pp. 132–148.

Pylyshyn, Z. (1973) "What the Mind's Eye Tells the Mind's Brain: A Critique of Mental Imagery," *Psychological Bulletin* 80: 1–25.

Reaux, J., and D. Povinelli (2000) "The Trap-Tube Problem," in Daniel J. Povinelli (ed.), *Folk Physics for Apes: The Chimpanzee's Theory of How the World Works*, Oxford: Oxford University Press, pp. 108–131.

Scholl, B. (2001) "Objects and Attention: The State of the Art," *Cognition* 80: 1–46.

Seed, A., and R. Byrne (2010) "Animal Tool-Use," *Current Biology* 20: R1032–R1039.

Seed, A., J. Call, N. Emery, and N. Clayton (2009) "Chimpanzees Solve the Trap Problem When the Confound of Tool-use Is Removed," *Journal of Experimental Psychology: Animal Behavioral Processes* 35: 23–34.

Seed, A., D. Hanus, and J. Call (2011) "Causal Knowledge in Corvids, Primates, and Children: More Than Meets the Eye?," in T. McCormack, C. Hoerl, and S. Butterfill (eds.), *Tool Use and Causal Cognition*, Oxford: Oxford University Press, pp. 89–110.

Shepard, R., and J. Metzler (1971) "Mental Rotation of Three-dimensional Objects," *Science* 171: 701–703.

Silva, F., D. Page, and K. Silva (2005) "Methodological-Conceptual Problems in the Study of Chimpanzees' Folk Physics: How Studies With Adult Humans Can Help," *Learning and Behavior* 33: 47–58.

Taylor, A. H., G. R. Hunt, F. S. Medina, and R. D. Gray (2009) "Do New Caledonian Crows Solve Physical Problems Through Causal Reasoning?" *Proceedings of the Royal Society* 276: 247–254.

Visalberghi, E., and L. Limongelli (1994) "Lack of Comprehension of Cause-Effect Relations in Tool-Using Capuchin Monkeys (*Cebus apella*)," *Journal of Comparative Psychology* 108: 15–22.

3

MAPS IN THE HEAD?

Michael Rescorla

Any creature that travels through space needs some ability to navigate. The psychologist Edward Tolman (1948) proposed that rats navigate using *cognitive maps*. His proposal flouted the behaviorist consensus of his day, which sought to explain all mental and behavioral phenomena in terms of stimulus–response associations, without recourse to mental representations. Numerous scientists have subsequently pursued the cognitive map hypothesis as applied to diverse species, with especially notable contributions by O'Keefe and Nadel (1978) and Gallistel (1990). What could it possibly mean to say that an animal has a map inside of its head? And why should we believe any such thing? The present entry will pursue these questions.

Map-based navigation

Scientists standardly distinguish four main animal navigation strategies. Each strategy is an instance or an analogue of a human navigation strategy:

Beaconing, i.e. travel to a goal using sensory input that emanates from the goal. For example, you might walk towards a nearby tree, using its visually perceived distance to guide your approach. Beaconing has limited utility, because it only helps you travel to a destination that currently impinges on your sensory apparatus.

Route following: We frequently navigate by following a series of instructions (e.g. "Turn left at the fork in the road"). Similarly, many species conform to sensorimotor routines, whereby a specific sensory stimulation triggers a specific behavioral response. For example, honeybees can store retinal "snapshots" of the environment as seen from various locations, and they can learn to fly in some direction when confronted with a snapshot (Collett and Collett 2002). Honeybees can chain together such sensorimotor routines: an initial stimulus triggers some motor behavior until a new stimulus triggers a new motor behavior, and so on.

Dead reckoning uses self-motion cues to maintain a running record of position. Dead reckoning is ubiquitous among nonhuman vertebrates and invertebrates (Gallistel 1990: 57–102). Even the humble desert ant has impressive dead-reckoning capacities. Using dead reckoning, the desert ant can travel long, circuitous routes and then return directly home along a straight path.

Map-based navigation, i.e. navigation using a cognitive map. This is the most controversial of the four navigation strategies. Scientists continue to debate the extent, if any, to which cognitive maps figure in human and nonhuman navigation. What counts as "map-like" mental representation also remains unclear.

As Bermúdez (1998: 203–207) and Kitchin (1994) emphasize, a persistent problem in the scientific literature is that different authors use the phrase "cognitive map" in different ways. In Rescorla 2009, I distinguished two notable usages. A *cognitive map in the loose sense* is a mental representation that represents geometric aspects of the environment. Those aspects may be *metric* (e.g. distances and angles), *topological* (e.g. connectedness and adjacency), or otherwise. A *cognitive map in the strict sense* is a mental representation that has the same basic representational properties and mechanisms as ordinary concrete maps. A cognitive map in the strict sense has the same representational format as a concrete map, while a cognitive map in the loose sense merely encodes the same information, possibly in a different way than a concrete map would encode it.

Evidence for cognitive maps in the loose sense

To defend the existence of cognitive maps, scientists usually cite evidence that animals take novel detours and shortcuts. Tolman (1948) argued thus based on his study of rats traveling through mazes. Kramer (1957) independently argued along similar lines for pigeons navigating through nature. A recurring experimental paradigm in both laboratory and field work is to displace the animal to an unfamiliar release point within a familiar environment. In many cases, the animal travels directly from the release point to a goal (e.g. the location of some reward). This is advanced as evidence that the animal located itself on a cognitive map and thereby computed a route from the release point to the goal. Researchers have developed these ideas in considerable detail for various species (Gallistel 1990; Jacobs and Menzel 2014; O'Keefe and Nadel 1978; Weiner et al. 2011), including rats (Geva-Sagiv et al. 2015; Morris 1981), pigeons (Bingman 2011; Schiffner and Wiltschko 2013; Wallraf 2005), and honeybees (Menzel and Greggers 2015; Cheeseman et al. 2014).

Critics respond that novel routes can often be explained without positing cognitive maps (Bennett 1996; Collett et al. 2013; Mackintosh 2002). For example, Cheung et al. (2014) claim that any novel routes taken by honeybees may simply reflect route following, in which the bee tries to minimize discrepancies between stored snapshots and its current panoramic view of the environment. Critics also adduce experimental evidence that certain animals, including honeybees (Dyer 1991; Wehner et al. 1990) and rats (Whishaw 1991), sometimes do *not* take shortcuts when doing so would be advantageous. Critics conclude that cognitive maps are not needed to explain whatever novel routes animals actually take.

Despite such controversies, a broad, albeit non-unanimous, consensus has emerged over the past few decades: many mammals take some novel routes best explained by positing mental representations that represent metric aspects of the environment, including distances between locations (Gallistel and Matzel 2013; Jacobs and Menzel 2014; Weiner et al. 2011). A good illustration is an experiment on golden hamsters performed by Etienne et al. (1998). Hamsters lived in a 180-cm-diameter circular arena containing four identical, symmetrically placed cylinders. They learned that one cylinder, distinguishable from the others only by its location, contained food. Upon being lured to a location within the arena, hamsters could navigate directly towards the food-containing cylinder, even in the dark. How did the hamsters do this? They had no access to sensory cues that might inform beaconing or route following. Dead reckoning surely played a large role, enabling the hamster to estimate its current position. But dead reckoning taken on its own would not enable the hamster to compute a course to the cylinder. Evidently, the hamster mentally represented the cylinder's position, integrated that representation with the deliverances of dead reckoning, and thereby computed a route to the cylinder.

A recent field illustration of map-based mammalian navigation features the Egyptian fruit bat (Tsoar et al. 2011). Using GPS technology, researchers tracked flight paths of bats. When displaced to a desert area 44 km outside their normal flight range, bats showed a remarkable ability to navigate directly to one of two goals: a familiar feeding site or the home cave, depending on whether they were hungry. This astonishing feat cannot be explained in terms of beaconing (distinctive sensory cues to the goal were not available), dead reckoning (bats were transported inside a cloth bag, so they could not dead reckon), or route following (the release point was far outside the bats' visually familiar area, so it is not plausible that they had acquired suitable sensorimotor routines). Tellingly, bats were initially quite disoriented when released inside a large crater, but they became well-oriented upon exiting the crater. The bats apparently determined their current position using visual landmarks that were only visible upon exiting the crater (e.g. city lights). On that basis, they computed a route to the goal. An explanation along these lines presupposes that bats have a large-scale representation of landmark locations.

Localization and mapping

How do animals construct and update cognitive maps? The answer depends heavily on psychological, physiological, and environmental details for each species. We are only beginning to understand these matters. However, some general features of map-based mammalian navigation are relatively well-established.

Any animal that represents the spatial layout of its environment must have at its disposal mental *coordinates* that represent locations in the environment (Gallistel and Matzel 2013). Researchers standardly distinguish between *allocentric* and *egocentric* coordinates. Allocentric coordinates are anchored to the external environment (e.g. the sun or the animal's home). Egocentric coordinates are anchored to the creature's body. Map-based navigation uses allocentric rather than egocentric coordinates, because it requires representations of landmark position that remain relatively stable as the animal moves.

We know through introspection that humans perceive the egocentric distances and directions of objects. There is also experimental evidence that many animal species, from insects to mammals, perceive egocentric distance and direction (Kral 2003). Mammalian navigation draws crucially upon perceptual estimates of egocentric position:

- *Localization*, i.e. estimation of one's own allocentric position. Dead reckoning is a widely employed localization strategy. However, dead reckoning is fallible and noisy, rendering it unreliable over long periods. Accordingly, many species employ an additional localization strategy called *piloting* (Gallistel 1990). Piloting estimates current position by observing landmarks whose positions are represented on the allocentric cognitive map. Given the egocentric positions of suitably situated landmarks, and given the allocentric positions of those landmarks, it is basic trigonometry to compute one's current position.[1]
- *Mapping*. Perception supplies egocentric estimates of landmark positions, and dead reckoning supplies an allocentric estimate of one's position and orientation. Combining these estimates, one can form allocentric estimates of landmark positions. One thereby converts egocentric spatial representations into an allocentric cognitive map. Gallistel (1990) reviews evidence that map construction along these lines occurs in various species.

Localization and mapping deploy *coordinate transformations* between egocentric spatial representations and allocentric representations. A coordinate transformation converts a representation in one coordinate system into a representation in a different coordinate system.

Mapping relies on dead reckoning, which becomes increasingly unreliable as uncorrected errors accumulate. Piloting can correct those errors, but piloting presupposes an allocentric cognitive map. For that reason, localization and mapping are intertwined. The animal must estimate its current allocentric position while *simultaneously* estimating allocentric landmark positions. To solve this simultaneous estimation problem, the animal must somehow integrate the dead-reckoning estimate with perceptually based egocentric position estimates and with any past allocentric landmark position estimates.

An analogous estimation problem arises in *robotics*, where it is called the *simultaneous localization and mapping* (SLAM) problem. An autonomous navigating robot must estimate its own position along with the positions of salient landmarks. The most successful robotics solution is grounded in *Bayesian decision theory*, a mathematical theory of reasoning and decision-making under uncertainty. On a Bayesian approach, the robot maintains a probability distribution over possible maps of the environment, using self-motion cues and sensory input to update probabilities as it travels through space. Bayesian robotic navigation algorithms have achieved notable success (Thrun et al. 2005). Given how well Bayesian solutions to SLAM work within robotics, it is natural to conjecture that some animals use Bayesian inference when navigating (Gallistel 2008; Rescorla 2009). Scientists have recently begun offering Bayesian models of animal navigation (Cheng et al. 2007; Cheung et al. 2012; Madl et al. 2014; Madl et al. 2016; Penny et al. 2013). The models look promising, although this research program is still in its infancy.

Neurophysiological underpinnings

How are cognitive maps realized in the brain? What neural processes implement mapping, localization, and route planning? While we do not have complete answers to these questions, we know a lot about the neural states and processes that underlie mammalian map-based navigation.

O'Keefe and Dostrovsky (1971) discovered that the rat hippocampus contains *place cells*, each responding selectively to a specific spatial location. On that basis, O'Keefe and Nadel (1978) proposed that the hippocampus provides the neural substrate for cognitive mapping. This work generated a huge surge of interest in cognitive maps, especially among neuroscientists.

Ensuing research discovered several other notable cells (Moser et al. 2008):

- Several areas in the rat brain contain *head direction cells* (Taube 2007). A head direction cell fires when the rat's head is at a certain angle with respect to an external reference direction.
- The rat entorhinal cortex contains *grid cells* (Hafting et al. 2005), each responding selectively to multiple spatial locations in the available environment. The locations where a cell fires form a periodic grid that covers the environment. Different cells generate grids with different scales and different orientations. Metric information about the physical environment can be extracted from the firing patterns of grid cells (Moser and Moser 2008).
- The rat entorhinal cortex contains *border cells* (Solstad et al. 2008), each of which fires when the rat is near a border oriented in a certain direction.

Edvard Moser, May-Britt Moser, and John O'Keefe shared the 2014 Nobel Prize in Physiology or Medicine for their work in this area.

Neuroscientists have developed detailed mathematical models describing how place cells, grid cells, and other such cells support navigation (e.g. Bush et al. 2015; Cheng and Frank, 2011; McNaughton et al. 2006; Solstad et al. 2006). In many cases, the models are reasonably well-integrated with cognitive-level theories that allude to cognitive maps, dead reckoning, localization, mapping, path planning, coordinate transformations, probability distributions, etc. However, just as we are far from completely understanding the mental processes through which mammals form, update, and deploy their cognitive maps, so are we far from completely understanding the neural implementation of those mental processes.

Cartographic representation

The phrase "cognitive map" naturally suggests that these mental representations resemble ordinary concrete maps in important respects. To what extent, and in what ways, do cognitive maps resemble concrete maps? Are they cognitive maps in the *strict* sense?

Although many aspects of cartographic representation remain ill-understood, we can isolate four important properties of the concrete maps employed within human society:

(1) *Maps represent geometric aspects of physical space.* A map represents the layout of entities in space. The map thereby represents geometric relations among those entities. Maps vary in precisely which geometric relations they represent. City maps represent metric structure, while subway maps only represent topological structure.

(2) *Maps have veridicality-conditions.* A map is evaluable as veridical or non-veridical, depending on how the world is. The map is veridical only when it correctly represents geometric relations among entities. Thus, it is veridical under certain conditions, non-veridical under others.

(3) *Maps have geometric structure.* A map does not merely *represent* geometric structure. The map itself is geometrically structured. For example, a city map has metric structure. A map's geometric structure is representationally significant, as clause (4) elucidates.

(4) *A map is veridical only if it replicates salient geometric aspects of the region that it represents.* Informally, a map purports to replicate relevant geometric aspects of physical space. More formally, a map is veridical only if there exists a structure-preserving function from the map to the region that it represents. For example, a city map is veridical only when distances on the map are proportional to distances in the physical environment.

I do not advance properties (1)–(4) as a finished theory of cartographic representation, but rather as a springboard for further inquiry. For present purposes, the key point is that a mental representation should share properties (1)–(4) to the extent that it counts as a cognitive map *in the strict sense.* Does animal navigation feature mental representations with properties (1)–(4)?

We have already canvassed evidence that mammalian navigation uses cognitive maps in the loose sense, i.e. mental representations with property (1). However, this commonality is less impressive than it may initially appear, because it hinges on the unexplicated term "represent." Philosophers and psychologists have proposed many different theories of representation (e.g. Burge 2010; Davidson 2001; Fodor 1990; Gallistel 1990; Millikan 1984), and the theories vary wildly in how much is required for one entity to "represent" another. Saying without further elucidation that a map "represents" geometric aspects of the environment does not tell us much.

In effect, (2) provides one way of glossing (1). An advantage of (2) over (1) is that (2) uses the relatively well-understood notion *veridicality-condition*, which has long been a staple of philosophical research into representation. Many important mental states have veridicality-conditions. To illustrate:

- Beliefs are evaluable as true or false. For example, my belief *that Barack Obama is president* is true iff Barack Obama is president. So beliefs have truth-conditions.

- Desires are evaluable as fulfilled or unfulfilled. For example, my desire *to eat chocolate* is fulfilled only if I eat chocolate. So desires have fulfillment-conditions.
- Perceptual states are evaluable as accurate or inaccurate. For example, my perceptual experience *as of a red sphere located a certain egocentric distance from me* is accurate only if a red sphere is located a certain egocentric distance from me. So perceptual states have accuracy-conditions.

Truth, fulfillment, and accuracy are species of veridicality. So beliefs, desires, and perceptual states all have veridicality-conditions. As (2) asserts, concrete maps also have veridicality conditions. If you do not recognize that concrete maps may be veridical or non-veridical (that a map may or may not *correctly* represent the region that it represents), then you have missed a fundamental aspect of our navigational and cartographic practices.

Do *cognitive* maps have veridicality-conditions? It is far from clear how to answer this question. The strategy I will now pursue is to reflect on the role played by veridicality-conditions within psychological explanation.

The explanatory role of veridicality-conditions

Intentional explanation is explanation that cites veridicality-conditions or representational properties that contribute to veridicality-conditions. The most familiar example is *folk psychology*: our everyday practice of citing beliefs, desires, and other mental states to explain mental and behavioral outcomes. Folk psychology routinely identifies mental states through their veridicality-conditions. For example, we might identify a belief as the belief *that Obama is president*, thereby specifying a condition that must obtain for the belief to be true. Or we might identify a desire as a desire *to eat chocolate*, thereby specifying a condition that must obtain for the desire to be fulfilled.

Taking inspiration from folk psychology, cognitive science offers numerous intentional explanations. For example, *perceptual psychology* studies how the perceptual system transits from proximal sensory stimulations (e.g. retinal stimulations) to perceptual states that estimate shapes, sizes, colors, locations, and other observable properties. A perceptual state is veridical only if perceived objects have the estimated shapes, sizes, colors, locations, and other such properties. The science identifies perceptual states through representational properties that contribute to veridicality-conditions – e.g. through specific shapes, sizes, colors, and locations estimated by the perceptual system (Burge 2010; Rescorla 2015). Intentional explanations of perception have proved enormously fruitful, illuminating a wide range of perceptual phenomena.

Does cognitive science offer successful intentional explanations of animal navigation? While there is room for healthy debate here, my own view is that intentional discourse contributes serious explanatory value at least when applied to *mammalian* map-based navigation. Scientific research into mammalian navigation hinges upon a straightforward thought: mammalian cognitive maps are *estimates*. They estimate geometric aspects of the environment, including the spatial layout of landmarks. An estimate is evaluable as veridical or non-veridical. Cognitive science identifies mammalian cognitive maps at least partly through their veridicality-conditions, i.e. through the conditions that they estimate as obtaining. By identifying cognitive maps in this way, the science delineates systematic patterns of interaction between allocentric cognitive maps, egocentric perceptual states, and actions.

To illustrate, consider *coordinate transformations* between allocentric and egocentric representations. As we have seen, these coordinate transformations underwrite mammalian localization and mapping. They also underwrite the interface between cognitive maps and action: to travel towards a goal, the animal often converts its allocentric representation of the goal into an egocentric representation with immediate consequences for action (Gallistel 1999). Overall, coordinate transformations figure pivotally in scientific theorizing about mammalian navigation (Madl et al. 2015; Shadmehr and Mussa-Ivaldi 2012: 35–66; Wilber et al. 2014), including some impressively detailed computational models (Byrne et al. 2007; Sheynikhovich et al. 2009; Touretzky and Redish 1996).

A coordinate transformation *preserves veridicality* when it carries veridical representations into veridical representations. Virtually all scientific treatments presume that mammalian coordinate transformations typically preserve veridicality, at least approximately. Given a veridical allocentric cognitive map, the relevant coordinate transformations typically yield veridical (or approximately veridical) egocentric representations of landmark positions. Given veridical egocentric representations of landmark positions, and given a veridical estimate of one's own allocentric position and orientation, the relevant coordinate transformations typically yield veridical (or approximately veridical) allocentric representations of landmark positions. Approximate veridicality-preservation is a core presupposition of scientific research into mammalian navigation, including the aforementioned computational models. This core presupposition, although not often made explicit, guides the construction of detailed theories describing how cognitive maps interact with perception and action. It also helps us explain the extraordinary success with which mammals navigate. Veridical egocentric perceptual estimates, combined with veridical estimates of the animal's position and heading, tend to cause veridical allocentric maps. Veridical allocentric cognitive maps tend to cause veridical egocentric representations, which in turn tend to cause successful actions.[2]

Researchers have developed this explanatory strategy with increasing experimental and theoretical sophistication over ensuing decades. The strategy presupposes that cognitive maps have veridicality-conditions. After all, a coordinate transformation can only preserve veridicality if the representations over which it operates have veridicality-conditions.

I favor a broadly *scientific realist* viewpoint: explanatory success is a *prima facie* guide to truth. From a scientific realist viewpoint, successful intentional explanation provides reason to attribute veridicality-conditions. For example, the explanatory success of perceptual psychology provides reason to attribute veridicality-conditions to perceptual states (Burge 2010; Rescorla 2015). Likewise, successful intentional explanations of mammalian navigation provide reason to attribute veridicality-conditions to mammalian cognitive maps. I conclude that (2) applies to mammalian cognitive maps.[3]

Bayesian models of mammalian navigation provide further evidence for this conclusion. The basic idea behind Bayesian models is that the navigational system maintains a probability distribution over a *hypothesis space*. Each hypothesis represents some aspect of the spatial environment. One such hypothesis might represent that a certain landmark has a certain allocentric location. Another hypothesis might represent that the animal itself has a certain allocentric location. Hypotheses of this kind are incorporated into cognitive maps, which estimate overall spatial layout. The probability assigned to a cognitive map is determined by the probabilities assigned to component hypotheses. The navigational system regularly updates its probabilities in light of perceptual input and self-motion cues. In this manner, localization and mapping become exercises in statistical inference.

How should we understand the "hypotheses" to which probabilities get assigned? Current Bayesian models identify the hypotheses through representational properties that contribute to veridicality-conditions. For example, when we identify a hypothesis *as* representing that a landmark has a certain allocentric location, we cite a condition that must be satisfied for the overall cognitive map to be veridical: that the landmark has the hypothesized location. We thereby identify the hypothesis in intentional terms. Bayesian models describe how probabilities over hypotheses *as identified in intentional terms* change in light of perceptual input and self-motion cues. The science presupposes that mammalian navigation deploys cognitive maps with veridicality-conditions, and it describes probabilistic inference over hypotheses *identified by how the hypotheses contribute to cognitive maps' veridicality-conditions*. Hence, the science presuppose that (2) applies to mammalian cognitive maps. The success of the Bayesian research program provides further reason to attribute veridicality-conditions to mammalian cognitive maps. As the research program accrues more explanatory success, the case for an intentional analysis of mammalian navigation should grow commensurately stronger.

Geometrically structured mental representations?

I now consider the representational *format* of cognitive maps. Do they have representationally significant geometric structure? More precisely, do they share properties (3) and (4) with ordinary concrete maps?

Even if we grant that an animal mentally represents geometric structure, why should we hold that the animal uses geometrically structured mental representations? What would it even mean to ascribe geometric structure to a mental representation? Pylyshyn (2007: 80–81) warns against the *intentional fallacy* – the fallacy of confusing properties of a representation with properties of what it represents. Mental representations of color are not colored. Mental representations of loudness are not loud. Why should mental representations of geometric structure be geometrically structured? Surveying a range of navigational behaviors, Pylyshyn concludes (2007: 178): "however impressive these behaviors may be, and even when they reveal something about the content of the representation (what information must have been encoded), they reveal little about the form of the representation involved that makes it maplike."

Any theorist who posits cognitive maps in the strict sense must answer Pylyshyn's challenge. Note furthermore that cognitive maps do not seem to have literal spatial structure in the brain. In particular, nearby place cells do not correspond to nearby locations in physical space. Thus, any satisfying theory of geometrically structured cognitive maps must articulate a notion of "geometric structure" much more abstract than literal spatial structure in the brain.

In this connection, it is helpful to recall the highly abstract character of modern mathematical geometry. The standard modern procedure is to isolate axioms of geometric structure, such as metric or topological structure. For example, a *metric space* is an ordered pair (X, d), where X is any set and d is a function from $X \times X$ to the real numbers such that, for all elements a, b, and c in X:

$d(a, b) \geq 0$
$d(a, b) = 0$ if and only if $a = b$
$d(a, b) = d(b, a)$
$d(a, c) \leq d(a, b) + d(b, c)$.

A metric space may be composed of any entities whatsoever. What matters is not the set X itself, but rather the relations between X's elements. Moral: *any* entities may be enveloped within a metric structure.

In principle, then, it makes sense to talk about geometric structure over the mental coordinates that appear on a cognitive map. Indeed, if C is a set of mental coordinates, then there are infinitely many metric spaces (C, d). Obviously, most of these metric spaces are irrelevant to the animal's navigation and hold no interest for cognitive science. Can we isolate some useful sense in which the animal's psychology instantiates a geometric structure over *C*? If so, does the resulting geometric structure contribute to veridicality-conditions as (4) dictates?

Several authors have explored how something like properties (3) and (4) might be true of cognitive maps (e.g. Brecht et al. 2014; Heck 2007; Muller et al. 1996; Rescorla 2009; Shea 2014; Terrazas et al. 2005). The basic idea behind most treatments is that functionally significant neural or psychological relations among mental coordinates induce geometric structure over the cognitive map, where this structure represents geometric relations in physical space. For example, Shea (2014) suggests that place cells may have a co-activation structure that represents proximity relations in physical space. An important task for future scientific and philosophical research is to investigate suggestions along these lines. Doing so should illuminate whether, and in what sense, cognitive maps have representationally significant geometric structure.

Conclusion

Cognitive maps figure pivotally in navigation across a range of species. Numerous navigational phenomena are difficult or impossible to explain unless we posit cognitive maps in the loose sense. Animal navigation therefore provides strong evidence for a broadly representationalist approach to psychology. A vast interdisciplinary literature spanning many decades provides great insight into the nature of cognitive maps, their neurophysiological underpinnings, and the psychological processes in which they participate. We understand quite a bit about cognitive maps, as compared with most other mental representations posited by philosophers and scientists. Nevertheless, numerous questions remain about their format, content, psychological role, and neural basis. This entry will have served its purpose if you feel moved to investigate further.

Acknowledgments

I presented some of this material at the workshop "Mental Representation – Naturalistic Approaches" hosted by the Institute of Philosophy, University of London. Thanks to all participants for their helpful feedback, especially Kathryn Jeffery, Peter Godfrey-Smith, David Papineau, Jesse Prinz, and Nicholas Shea.

Notes

1 Honeybees can perceptually estimate the egocentric distances and directions of landmarks. As Burge (2010: 508) emphasizes, the resulting perceptual estimates do not appear to exert much impact upon honeybee localization. Honeybee localization seems to operate primarily through dead reckoning, with periodic resets of the odometer when the bee encounters a familiar landmark (Srinivasan 2011).

2 Do coordinate transformations between egocentric and allocentric representations play a significant role in honeybee navigation? The answer is unclear. By comparison with scientific theorizing about mammalian navigation, scientific theorizing about honeybee navigation assigns relatively little weight to coordinate transformations. For example, as mentioned in note 1, honeybees do not seem to localize based upon egocentric perceptually-based representations of landmark distances and directions. Thus, my argument in the main text does not readily generalize from mammals to honeybees. In general, it is unclear whether attribution of veridicality-conditions adds explanatory value to the scientific study of honeybee navigation (Burge 2010: 509–514; Rescorla 2013).

3 Philosophers sometimes suggest that non-intentional discourse can reproduce any explanatory benefits afforded by intentional explanation (Field 2001; Stich 1983). They claim that we can eliminate intentional locutions from cognitive science, without explanatory loss. In (Rescorla 2015), I argue that such claims are implausible when applied to intentional explanations of human perception. I think they are

also implausible when applied to intentional explanations of mammalian map-based navigation. For present purposes, I must leave my assessment undefended.

Further reading

C. R. Gallistel's *The Organization of Learning* (1990) remains an outstanding introduction to cognitive maps. Madl et al. (2015) survey numerous computational models of navigation. Neurophysiological models of mammalian navigation are helpfully discussed in Talfan Evans, Andrej Bicanski, Daniel Bush, and Neil Burgess's "How Environment and Self-Motion Combine in Neural Representations of Space," *The Journal of Physiology* 594 (2016): 6535–6546; and in Lisa Giocomo, May-Britt Moser, and Edvard Moser's "Computational Models of Grid Cells," *Neuron* 71(2011): 589–603. Gareth Evans's *The Varieties of Reference* (Oxford: Clarendon Press, 1982) argues that cognitive maps undergird fundamental aspects of human thought. Chapter 10 of Tyler Burge's *Origins of Objectivity* (2010) analyzes cognitive maps from a representationalist perspective, with particular emphasis on relations to perceptual representation. Other notable philosophical treatments include José Luis Bermúdez's *The Paradox of Self-Consciousness* (Cambridge, MA: MIT Press, 1998); Elisabeth Camp's "Thinking With Maps," *Philosophical Perspectives* 21 (2007): 145–182; John Campbell's *Past, Space, and Self* (Cambridge, MA: MIT Press, 1994); and Ruth Millikan's *Language: A Biological Model* (Oxford: Oxford University Press, 2005).

References

Bennett, A. (1996) "Do Animals Have Cognitive Maps?," *The Journal of Experimental Biology* 199, pp. 219–224.

Bermúdez, J. L. (1998) *The Paradox of Self-Consciousness*, Cambridge, MA: MIT Press.

Bingman, V. (2011) "Making the Case for the Intelligence of Avian Navigation," in R. Menzel and J. Fischer (eds.) *Animal Thinking*, Cambridge, MA: MIT Press.

Brecht, M., Ray, S., Burgalossi, A., Tang, Q., Schmidt, H., and Naumann, R. (2014) "An Isomorphic Mapping Hypothesis of the Grid Representation," *Philosophical Transactions of the Royal Society B* 369, pp. 1–10.

Burge, T. (2010) *Origins of Objectivity*, Oxford: Oxford University Press.

Bush, D., Barry, C., Manson, D., and Burgess, N. (2015) "Using Grid Cells for Navigation," *Neuron* 87, pp. 507–520.

Byrne, P., Becker, S., and Burgess, N. (2007) "Remembering the Past and Imagining the Future: A Neural Model of Spatial Memory and Imagery," *Psychological Review* 114, pp. 340–375.

Cheeseman, J., Millar, C., Greggers, U., Lehmann, K., Pawley, M., Gallistel, C. R., Warman, G., and Menzel, R. (2014) "Way-Finding in Displaced Clock-Shifted Bees Proves Bees Use a Cognitive Map," *Proceedings of the National Academy of Sciences* 111, pp. 8949–8954.

Cheng, K., Shuttleworth, S., Huttenlocher, J., and Rieser, J. (2007) "Bayesian Integration of Spatial Information," *Psychological Bulletin* 13, pp. 625–637.

Cheng, S., and Frank, L. (2011) "The Structure of Networks that Produce the Transformation From Grid Cells to Place Cells," *Neuroscience* 197, pp. 293–306.

Cheung, A., Ball, D., Milford, M., Wyeth, G., and Wiles, J. (2012) "Maintaining a Cognitive Map in Darkness: The Need to Fuse Boundary Knowledge with Path Integration," *PLoS Computational Biology* 8, p. e1002651.

Cheung, A., Collett, M., Collett, T., Dewar, A., Dyer, F., Graham, P., Mangan, M., Narendra, A., Philippides, A., Stürzl, W., Webb, B., Wystrach, A., and Zeif, J. (2014) "Still No Convincing Evidence for Cognitive Map Use By Honeybees," *Proceedings of the National Academy of Sciences* 111, pp. e4397–e4397.

Collett, M., Chittka, L., and Collett, T. (2013) "Spatial Memory in Insect Navigation," *Current Biology* 23, pp. R789–R800.

Collett, T. S., and Collett, M. (2002) "Memory Use in Insect Visual Navigation," *Nature Reviews Neuroscience* 3, pp. 542–552.

Davidson, D. (2001) *Subjective, Intersubjective, Objective*, Oxford: Clarendon Press.

Dyer, F. (1991) "Bees Acquire Route-Based Memories But Not Cognitive Maps in a Familiar Landscape," *Animal Behavior* 41, pp. 239–246.

Etienne, A., Maurer, R., Berlie, J., Reverdin, B., Rowe, T., Georgakopoulos, J., and Séguinot, V. (1998) "Navigation Through Vector Addition," *Nature* 396, pp. 161–164.

Field, H. (2001) *Truth and the Absence of Fact*, Oxford: Oxford University Press.

Fodor, J. (1990) *A Theory of Content and Other Essays*, Cambridge, MA: MIT Press.

Gallistel, C. R. (1990) *The Organization of Learning*, Cambridge, MA: MIT Press.

——— (1999) "Coordinate Transformations in the Genesis of Action," in B. Bly and D. Rumelhart (eds.) *Cognitive Science: Handbook of Perception and Cognition*, 2nd ed., New York: Academic Press.

——— (2008) "Dead Reckoning, Cognitive Maps, Animal Navigation, and the Representation of Space: An Introduction," in M. Jeffries and W.-K. Yeap (eds.) *Robotics and Cognitive Approaches to Spatial Mapping*, Berlin: Springer.

Gallistel, C. R., and Matzel, L. (2013) "The Neuroscience of Learning: Beyond the Hebbian Synapse," *Annual Review of Psychology* 64, pp. 169–200.

Geva-Sagiv, M., Las, L., Yovel, Y., and Ulanovsky, N. (2015) "Spatial Cognition in Bats and Rats: From Sensory Acquisition to Multiscale Maps and Navigation," *Nature Reviews Neuroscience* 16, pp. 94–108.

Hafting, T., Fyhn, M., Molden, S., Moser, M.-B., and Moser, E. (2005) "Microstructure of a Spatial Map in the Entorhinal Cortex," *Nature* 436, pp. 801–806.

Heck, R. (2007) "Are There Different Kinds of Content?" in B. McLaughlin and J. Cohen (eds.) *Contemporary Debates in Philosophy of Mind*, Malden, MA: Blackwell.

Jacobs, L., and Menzel, R. (2014) "Navigation Outside of the Box: What the Lab Can Learn From the Field and What the Field Can Learn from the Lab," *Movement Ecology* 2, pp. 1–22.

Kitchin, R. (1994) "Cognitive Maps: What Are They and Why Study Them?" *Journal of Environmental Psychology* 14, pp. 1–19.

Kral, K. (2003) "Behavioral-Analytic Studies of the Role of Head Movements in Depth Perception in Insects, Birds, and Mammals," *Behavioral Processes* 64, pp. 1–12.

Kramer, G. (1957) "Experiments in Bird Orientation and their Interpretation," *Ibis* 99, pp. 196–227.

Mackintosh, N. J. (2002) "Do Not Ask Whether They Have a Cognitive Map, But How They Find Their Way About," *Psicológica* 23, pp. 165–185.

McNaughton, B., Battaglia, F., Moser, E., and Moser, M.-B. (2006) "Path Integration and the Neural Basis of the 'Cognitive Map'," *Nature Reviews Neuroscience* 7, pp. 663–678.

Madl, T., Chen, K., Montaldi, D., and Trappl, R. (2015) "Computational Cognitive Models of Spatial Memory in Navigation Space: A Review," *Neural Networks* 65, pp. 18–43.

Madl, T., Franklin, S., Chen, K., Montaldi, D., and Trappl, R. (2014) "Bayesian Integration of Information in Hippocampal Place Cells," *PloS One* 9, p. e89762.

——— (2016) "Towards Real-World Capable Spatial Memory in the LIDA Architecture," *Biologically Inspired Cognitive Architectures* 16, pp. 87–104.

Menzel, R., and Greggers, U. (2015) "The Memory Structure of Navigation in Honeybees," *Journal of Comparative Physiology A* 201, pp. 547–561.

Millikan, R. (1984) *Language, Thought, and Other Biological Categories*, Cambridge, MA: MIT Press.

Morris, R. (1981) "Spatial Localization Does Not Require the Presence of Local Cues," *Learning and Motivation* 12, pp. 239–260.

Moser, E., Kripff, E., and Moser, M.-B. (2008) "Place Cells, Grid Cells, and the Brain's Spatial Representation System," *Annual Reviews Neuroscience* 31, pp. 69–89.

Moser, E., and Moser, M.-B. (2008) "A Metric for Space," *Hippocampus* 18, pp. 1142–1156.

Muller, R., Stead, M., and Pach, J. (1996) "The Hippocampus as a Cognitive Graph," *The Journal of General Physiology* 107, pp. 663–694.

O'Keefe, J., and Dostrovsky, J. (1971) "The Hippocampus as a Spatial Map: Preliminary Evidence from Unit Activity in the Freely-moving Rat," *Brain Research* 34, pp. 171–175.

O'Keefe, J., and Nadel, L. (1978) *The Hippocampus as a Cognitive Map*, Oxford: Clarendon University Press.

Penny, W., Zeidman, P., and Burgess, N. (2013) "Forward and Backward Inference in Spatial Cognition," *PLoS Computational Biology* 9, pp. e1003383.

Pylyshyn, Z. (2007) *Things and Places*, Cambridge, MA: MIT Press.

Rescorla, M. (2009) "Cognitive Maps and the Language of Thought," *The British Journal for the Philosophy of Science* 60, pp. 377–407.

——— (2013) "Millikan on Honeybee Navigation and Communication," in D. Ryder, J. Kingsbury, and K. Williford (eds.) *Millikan and Her Critics*, Malden, MA: Wiley-Blackwell.

——— (2015) "Bayesian Perceptual Psychology," in M. Matthen (ed.) *The Oxford Handbook of the Philosophy of Perception*, Oxford: Oxford University Press.

Schiffner, I., and Wiltschko, R. (2013) "Development of the Navigational System in Homing Pigeons: Increase in Complexity of the Navigational Map," *Journal of Experimental Biology* 216, pp. 2675–2681.

Shadmehr, R., and Mussa-Ivaldi, S. (2012) *Biological Learning and Control*, Cambridge, MA: MIT Press.

Shea, N. (2014) "Exploitable Isomorphism and Structural Representation," *Proceedings of the Aristotelian Society* 114, pp. 123–144.

Sheynikhovich, D., Chavarriaga, R., Strösslin, T., Arlea, A., and Gerstner, W. (2009) "Is There a Geometric Module for Spatial Orientation? Insights From a Rodent Navigation Model," *Psychological Review* 116, pp. 540–566.

Solstad, T., Boccara, C., Kropff, E., Moser, M.-B., and Moser, E. (2008) "Representation of Geometric Borders in the Entorhinal Cortex," *Science* 322, pp. 1865–1868.

Solstad, T., Moser, E., and Einevoll, G. (2006) "From Grid Cells to Place Cells: A Mathematical Model," *Hippocampus* 16, pp. 1026–1031.

Srinivasan, M. (2011) "Honeybees as a Model for the Study of Visually Guided Flight, Navigation, and Biologically Inspired Robotics," *Physiological Review* 91, pp. 413–460.

Stich, S. (1983) *From Folk Psychology to Cognitive Science*, Cambridge, MA: MIT Press.

Taube, J. (2007) "The Head Direction Signal: Origins and Sensory-Motor Integration," *Annual Review of Neuroscience* 30, pp. 181–207.

Terrazas, A., Krause, M., Lipa, P., Gothard, K., Barnes, C., and McNaughton, B. (2005) "Self-Motion and the Hippocampal Spatial Metric," *The Journal of Neuroscience* 25, pp. 8085–8096.

Thrun, S., Burgard, W., and Fox, D. (2005) *Probabilistic Robotics*, Cambridge, MA: MIT Press.

Tolman, E. (1948) "Cognitive Maps in Rats and Men," *Psychological Review* 55, pp. 189–208.

Touretzky, D., and Redish, A. D. (1996) "A Theory of Rodent Navigation Based on Interacting Representations of Space," *Hippocampus* 6, pp. 247–270.

Tsoar, A., Nathan, R., Bartan, Y., Vyssotski, A., Dell'Omo, G., and Ulanovsky, N. (2011) "Large- Scale Navigational Map in a Mammal," *Proceedings of the National Academy of Sciences* 108, pp. E718–E724.

Wallraf, H. (2005) *Avian Navigation: Pigeon Homing as a Paradigm*, New York: Springer.

Wehner, R., Sleuler, S., Nievergelt, C., and Sha, D. (1990) "Bees Navigate By Using Vectors and Routes Rather Than Maps," *Naturwissenshaften* 10, pp. 479–482.

Weiner, J., Shettleworth, S., Bingman, V., Cheng, K., Healy, S., Jacobs, L., Jeffery, K., Mallot, H., Menzel, R., and Newcombe, N. (2011) "Animal Navigation: A Synthesis," in R. Menzel and J. Fischer (eds.) *Animal Thinking*, Cambridge, MA: MIT Press.

Whishaw, I. (1991) "Latent Learning in a Swimming Pool Place Task by Rats: Evidence for the Use of Associative and Not Cognitive Mapping Processes," *The Quarterly Journal of Experimental Psychology* 43, pp. 83–103.

Wilber, A., Clark, B., Forster, T., Tatsuno, M., and McNaughton, B. (2014) "Interaction of Egocentric and World-Centered Reference Frames in the Rat Posterior Parietal Cortex," *The Journal of Neuroscience* 34, pp. 5431–5446.

4

DO NONHUMAN ANIMALS HAVE A LANGUAGE OF THOUGHT?

Jacob Beck

1 Introduction

In the second half of the 20th century, behaviorism slowly gave way to the computational and representational paradigm of cognitive science. Human language may have been the first beneficiary, but it wasn't the last. Even much animal cognition came to be routinely explained in computational and representational terms (Gallistel 1990).

One influential, if controversial, idea that accompanied the ascendency of cognitive science is the language of thought hypothesis (LOTH), which maintains that mental representations are formatted like sentences (Fodor 1975). Because we human animals speak a public language, there has always been a special reason to accept LOTH as true of us. Our linguistic utterances are naturally construed as direct translations of our internal thoughts, which suggests that our internal thoughts mirror the structure of their public-language expressions.

When it comes to nonhuman animals (hereafter: animals), this special reason is missing. Insofar as animals communicate, they do so without employing the richly structured public languages that humans employ. One might therefore be tempted to infer that animals' mental representations have a nonlinguistic format – for example, an imagistic, map-like, or analog format. But this conclusion does not follow of necessity. The language of thought hypothesis for animals (LOTHA) could be true even if animals lack a public language in which to express their thoughts.

This chapter has two aims. The first is to review evidence that animals have at least some representations with a nonlinguistic format. The second is to argue that although we don't know enough as of yet to determine whether LOTHA is true, there is a clearly defined research program into the logical abilities of animals that can help to deliver an answer.

2 LOTHA

Sometimes LOTH is interpreted to mean only that cognizers have mental representations that are *compositional*. The representations consist of atomic parts that compose into complexes such that the contents of the atomic parts determine the contents of the complexes in a rule-governed way. But the common refrain that mental states are relations to LOT *sentences* suggests that proponents of LOTH often have something stronger in mind. According to this stronger conception, LOT representations exhibit the same basic representational and compositional properties as paradigmatic sentences (cf. Camp 2007 on "Weak-LOT" vs. "Strong-LOT").

We can make this stronger conception more precise by noting two properties of paradigmatic sentences. First, the constituents of sentences bear an *arbitrary* relation to their referents. There is nothing intrinsic to the English word "dog" that makes it especially well suited to represent dogs as opposed to cats or anything else. By contrast, a picture of a dog is especially well suited to represent dogs because it resembles dogs. Second, sentences have *logical form*. Their basic compositional mechanisms include predication and logical constants, such as negation, disjunction, implication, identity, universal quantification, and existential generalization (cf. Burge 2010a: 542–5 and Burge 2010b on "propositional thought"). Proponents of LOTH often emphasize this feature of sentences. For example, Margolis and Laurence (2007: 562) write that LOTH is committed to a "language-like syntax" that "incorporates, at the very least, a distinction between predicates and subjects, and that includes logical devices, such as quantifiers and variables."

In evaluating LOTHA, I will interpret it in this stronger sense. So interpreted, LOTHA contrasts with other accounts of animal cognition that are compatible with the representational and computational paradigm that dominates cognitive science (and is assumed here). For example, Rescorla (Chapter 3 in this volume) reviews evidence that animals navigate using cognitive maps, which, if interpreted in what he calls the "strict sense," have geometric rather than logical form. Similarly, Gauker (Chapter 2 in this volume) argues that animals' tool use and physical reasoning can be explained by imagistic representations, which are bereft of general concepts of the sort associated with predicates. If these hypotheses are correct, animals have at least some cognitive representations that defy LOTHA.

LOTHA is of interest, in part, because it provides a way to understand, from within the representational and computational paradigm of contemporary cognitive science, the question whether human and animal cognition differ in kind or only degree. If humans have a LOT but animals do not, then there is a clear sense in which human cognition has a fundamentally different representational format from animal cognition. By contrast, if humans and animals both have a LOT, then it remains an open possibility that, at least from the perspective of contemporary cognitive science, human and animal cognition differ only in degree.

3 Analog magnitude representations

Insofar as we can fully explain animal cognition by appeal to representations with a nonlinguistic format, such as cognitive maps and imagistic representations, we have reason to be skeptical of LOTHA. In this section, I want to briefly review evidence for one additional, but oft-overlooked type of nonlinguistic representation: *analog magnitude representations*. Hundreds of studies indicate that a wide range of animals, including mammals, birds, and fish, can represent numerosities, durations, rates, distances, sizes, and other worldly magnitudes (Gallistel 1990; Beck 2015). As an illustration, I'll review a now-classic set of experiments on rats.

After training rats to press the left lever in response to a two-second sequence of two tones and the right lever in response to an eight-second sequence of eight tones, Meck and Church (1983) tested the rats on intermediate stimuli, either holding duration constant at four seconds while varying the number of tones or holding number constant at four tones while varying the duration of tones (Figure 4.1). When duration was held constant, the rats were most likely to press the left lever in response to two or three tones and most likely to press the right lever in response to five, six, or eight tones, suggesting that they represented the numerosity of the tones. When number was held constant, the rats were most likely to press the left lever in response to a two- or three-second tone and most likely to press the right lever in response to a five-, six-, or eight-second

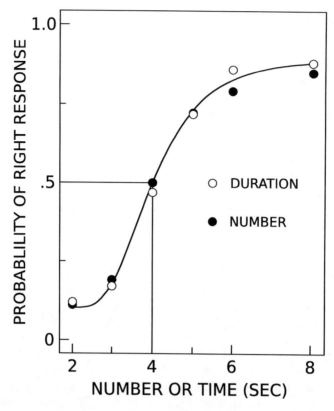

Figure 4.1 The probability that the rat will press the right lever as a function of the duration or number of tones. Redrawn from Meck and Church (1983).

tone, suggesting that they also represented the duration of the tones. By contrast, the rats were equally likely to press the right and left levers when presented with a four-second sequence of four tones. At first blush, it may seem surprising that rats treat four (the geometric mean), rather than five (the arithmetic mean), as the point of subjective equality between two and eight. This result makes perfect sense, however, if the rats represent magnitudes in terms of ratios, since 2:4 = 4:8.

Do the rats in these experiments really represent duration and numerosity? Or can their behavior be explained more simply in terms of low-level acoustic properties that correlate with duration and numerosity? One reason to think rats represent duration and numerosity themselves is that they transfer their training across modalities. For example, when rats are trained on auditory stimuli as summarized above and then presented with flashes of light (visual stimuli), they'll press the left lever when presented with a two-second light and press the right lever when presented with an eight-second light (Meck and Church 1982). Since vision and audition operate over disparate low-level sensory stimuli, these results support the hypothesis that rats really are glomming onto the abstract properties of duration and numerosity.

There are at least three related reasons to think that animals' magnitude representations are nonlinguistic. First, they have a nonarbitrary, analog format (Beck 2015). Animals' magnitude discriminations are ratio sensitive: as the ratio of two magnitudes approaches one, the ability to discriminate them deteriorates. Rats thus find it easier to discriminate three tones from four tones than four tones from five tones. (This is why the rats in Meck and Church's study treat five as more similar to eight than to two.) On the assumption that magnitude representations involve some internal magnitude (say, neural firing rate) that increases or decreases in proportion to the magnitude represented (say, number of tones), and are thus a direct analog of the magnitudes they represent, this ratio sensitivity is exactly what one would predict. As the ratio of two external magnitudes approaches one, the ratio of the internal magnitudes will follow suit. Thus, assuming some noise in the system, the internal magnitudes will themselves become increasingly difficult to discern, leading to discrimination errors of the magnitudes they represent. Because of their arbitrary referential relation, paradigmatic linguistic representations are not analog in this sense. For example, there is no property of Arabic numerals or English number words that increases as the number represented increases: "9" is not intrinsically more similar to "7" than to "5," and "nine" is not intrinsically more similar to "seven" than to "five."

Second, because they exhibit logical form, LOT representations are systematically recombinable like the words in a sentence (Fodor 1987). Thus, given LOTH, if you can think that Amy likes Ben and that Ben likes Cam, then you can also think that Amy likes Cam. It is doubtful that analog magnitude representations are systematically recombinable in this way. For example, although a rat can form representations with something like the content that 9 tones are fewer than 18 tones and that 10 tones are fewer than 20 tones, it is questionable whether it can form representations with anything like the content that 9 tones are fewer than 10 tones or that 18 tones are fewer than 20 tones (Beck 2012a). The reason, once again, is that magnitude discriminations are ratio sensitive, and as the ratio of two magnitudes approaches one, the ability to discriminate them deteriorates. When the ratio of two numbers is close enough to one, rats cannot reliably represent the numbers as distinct.

A final reason to doubt that analog magnitude representations have a linguistic format is that the computations they enter into can be fully described without any appeal to logical constants such as negation, disjunction, or identity. Rather, the computations that analog magnitude representations enter into are arithmetic. They include addition, subtraction, multiplication, division, and comparison (or primitive analogs thereof). For example, animals might divide a numerical representation by a duration representation to yield a representation of the rate of return of a given feeding source, and then compare the result to its representation of the rate of return of a second feeding source in order to help it decide which source to visit. Logical constants play no role in this explanation (Beck 2015).

4 Logical inference as a test for LOTHA

The existence of various types of nonlinguistic representations – cognitive maps, mental images, analog magnitude representations – places pressure on LOTHA. The more that intelligent animal behavior can be explained through various types of nonlinguistic representation, the less theoretical work there is left over for LOTHA to do.

Still, we are a long way from being certain that all of animal cognition can be explained by appeal to nonlinguistic representations, and the mere fact that some aspects of animal cognition have been so explained is hardly reason to conclude that animal minds are bereft of any sentence-like representations. It is thus worth considering whether there aren't more direct ways to test LOTHA.

I want to suggest that we can gain some traction on this issue from the idea that the inferences a thinker is capable of undertaking form a window into the structure of the thinker's thoughts (Evans 1985: 337; Burge 2010a: 542–7; Beck 2012b: 225–6). If a thinker's cognition is supported by a LOT, and thus by representations with logical form, we should expect that thinker to be capable of engaging in logical inferences. This suggests that we can test LOTHA by testing an animal's facility with logic.

In the next section, I will review one experimental paradigm that has been put to use to test the logical abilities of animals. First, however, I want to note, if only to set aside, five complications that attend to the strategy of using logical inference as a test for LOTHA.

The first complication derives from alternatives to LOTH for which talk about the "format" of a thinker's mental representations seems to have no place. Chief among these are connectionist networks. It is trivial to get connectionist networks to compute logical functions. But because the representations in a connectionist network can be distributed across the network, questions about their format are arguably misplaced.

This complication deserves more attention than I have space for here, so I'll have to settle for three brief comments. First, while it is uncontroversial that connectionist networks can compute logical functions, it is far less clear whether they can do so without *implementing* a LOT.[1] Second, my main concern here is not to resolve the question of whether LOTHA is true, but to show how it can be approached empirically, and connectionist models can surely be empirically tested. Third, whether or not the ability to draw logical inferences is evidence *for* LOTHA, the inability to draw logical inferences is surely evidence *against* LOTHA. For those interested in the status of LOTHA, there is thus good reason to examine animals' logical abilities regardless of what one thinks of the relation between LOTH and connectionism.

A second complication derives from *hybrid* formats that combine linguistic and nonlinguistic elements, such as Venn diagrams that are outfitted with special symbols (Peirce 1933; Shin 1994) or maps that have markers for negation or disjunction (Camp 2007). Such hybrid formats have been pursued in psychology under the guise of mental-models theory, which posits imagistic representations that are supplemented with arbitrary symbols (Johnson-Laird 2006). In some sense, hybrid representations such as mental models are sentence-like since they have arbitrary symbols that represent logical constants. But they also have components (e.g., imagistic elements) that are nonlinguistic. As with connectionist networks, it thus isn't always clear whether hybrid mental representations ought to count as implementing LOTH or competing with it. But one thing that *is* fairly clear is that, as with connectionist models, mental models can be empirically evaluated. It should thus be possible to empirically distinguish mental models from a purer form of LOTHA. Furthermore, whatever one thinks of the relation between LOTHA and mental models, the inability to draw logical inferences would surely count as evidence *against* LOTHA.

Third, performance on logical reasoning tasks is a function not only of a thinker's logical concepts, but also of various additional factors such as attention, working memory, and background beliefs. Thus, while possessing logical concepts plausibly entails the *capacity* to draw certain inferences, it does not entail the *successful exercise* of that capacity. A thinker could possess a logical concept and yet fail this or that logical reasoning task. But by testing a thinker in a wide variety of inference tasks that require the same logical concept but place varying demands on performance factors, it should be possible to tease conceptual competence apart from performance.

A fourth complication is that the kingdom of animals is diverse, and there is every reason to think that reasoning abilities will vary across species. This means that in the long run, empirical research into the logical abilities of animals should sample from a diversity of species. Here, however, I focus on the question of how the logical abilities of *any* nonlinguistic species can be empirically tested.

A final complication is that logic is not monolithic. There are many forms of logical inference. In the long run, there is no reason to limit an inquiry to this or that form of inference. If we want a full picture of the contours of the format of animal cognition, we should test as large a variety of inferences as is feasible. In the more medium term, however, we would do best to focus our efforts on nontrivial but fairly basic forms of inference. One such form that has the advantage of having been extensively studied is the disjunctive syllogism, *modus tollendo ponens*, or reasoning by exclusion.[2]

P or Q
Not P
Q

In the following section, I focus on how we can tell whether animals can execute inferences of this form.

5 One cup, two cups, three cups, four

A now-standard tool researchers have used to probe animals' capacity to reason by exclusion is the "two-cups task." An animal is presented with two opaque cups, A and B, and shown that both are initially empty. The animal sees the experimenter bait one of the cups with food, but a barrier prevents it from seeing which cup was baited. In the crucial condition, the experimenter reveals that cup A is empty and then allows the animal to choose a cup for inspection. If the animal is capable of executing a disjunctive syllogism, it should choose cup B. It should reason: *The food is either in cup A or in cup B; it's not in cup A; so it's in cup B.*

Several species have succeeded at this task, including great apes (Call and Carpenter 2001; Call 2004), monkeys (Grether and Maslow 1937; Petit et al. 2015; Marsh et al. 2015), ravens (Schloegl et al. 2009), and dogs (Erdőhegyi et al. 2007). Does that mean that these species can execute disjunctive syllogisms?

Surely not. No single task is ever sufficient to establish a conceptual ability. There are, as always, competing interpretations that need to be evaluated. In the remainder of this section, I discuss three such interpretations and indicate how further experiments might address them. My aim is to show how empirical evidence can, in principle, be used to decide among competing interpretations, not to defend any one interpretation in particular.

5.1 Avoid the empty cup

First, animals could succeed on the two-cup task by following the simple heuristic: *avoid the empty cup.* According to this interpretation, it's not that animals search in cup B because they infer that cup B has food. Rather, they search in cup B because they see that cup A is empty, want to avoid empty cups, and cup B is the only other hiding place in view.

In order to evaluate this interpretation, Call (2016) has developed a three-cup task. Subjects see the experimenter place food in either cup A or cup B, but not in cup C. The experimenter then reveals that cup A is empty. If the subjects only avoid the empty cup, they should have no preference as between cups B and C. But if they execute a disjunctive syllogism, they should choose cup B, reasoning that it was in A or B, not in A, and thus must be in B. As of this writing, Call was still in the process of collecting data on great apes, and so the results are not yet known. But the design of the study clearly illustrates how the avoid-the-empty-cup heuristic can be empirically distinguished from exclusionary reasoning.

5.2 Maybe A, maybe B

A second competing explanation of the two-cup task, suggested by Mody and Carey (2016), is that subjects represent each cup as a possible location of food and then eliminate cup A when it is shown to be empty. Unlike in a disjunctive syllogism, this does not lead subjects to conclude that the food is definitely in cup B. They don't update their representations of cup B at all. It's just that once cup A is eliminated, cup B is the only location remaining in which food is represented as possibly being present, and so subjects choose it. Mody and Carey call this the "maybe-A-maybe-B" interpretation.

Notice that the three-cup task doesn't distinguish the maybe-A-maybe-B interpretation from the disjunctive-syllogism interpretation. When subjects see food hidden in cup A or cup B, they represent the food as maybe in A and maybe in B. By contrast, they do not represent food as maybe in C. So when A is shown to be empty, they eliminate that cup, leaving cup B as the only cup represented as possibly containing the food. So both the maybe-A-maybe-B interpretation and the disjunctive-syllogism interpretation predict that subjects should choose cup B in the three-cup task.

To make headway, Mody and Carey add a fourth cup. The child (Mody and Carey ran their study on human children) sees the experimenter place one sticker in either cup A or cup B and another sticker in either cup C or cup D. The experimenter then reveals that cup A is empty and allows the child to select a cup for search. If the maybe-A-maybe-B interpretation were correct and the child never updated her representation of B upon learning that A is empty, she should be equally likely to choose B, C, or D. But if the disjunctive-syllogism interpretation were correct, then when the child was shown that A is empty, she should update her representation of B as definitely containing a sticker, and should thus prefer to search in that cup. Mody and Carey found that 2.5-year-old children failed at this task even though they succeeded at the two-cup task. By contrast, three- to five-year-old children succeeded at both tasks. The four-cup task has yet to be run on nonhuman animals, but it surely could be in principle.

5.3 Probabilistic reasoning

A third alternative to the disjunctive-syllogism interpretation, articulated by Rescorla (2009), maintains that animals use cognitive maps to represent the possible locations of objects, tag the maps with subjective probabilities of how likely they are to be accurate, and then update those probabilities in accordance with Bayes' Law. In the two-cup task, when animals initially see the food hidden, they represent cups A and B as equally likely to contain food. When cup A is then shown to be empty, they raise the probability that food is in cup B and lower the probability that it's in A. But contrary to the disjunctive-syllogism interpretation, there is no deterministic inference that cup B definitely contains food. Yet because Rescorla further assumes that animals will conform to expected utility theory and thus search in the location that is most likely to contain food, their behavior will be indistinguishable from that of a subject who reasons by way of the disjunctive syllogism. When cup A is shown to be empty, they'll always choose cup B.

Of all the alternative interpretations we have thus far considered, this one seems to be the most difficult to test. Mody and Carey (2016: 46) claim that their results from the four-cup task tell against it since "3- to 5-year-old children chose the target cup [cup B] just as often in test trials as they did in training trials, in which they could directly observe that a sticker was being hidden there." But if the children are conforming to expected utility theory, that's exactly what one would predict. In the four-cup study, cup B is the most likely to contain a sticker. So if children approach the task using probabilistic representations and a decision procedure that has them select the greatest expected payoff, they'll choose cup B as surely as if they saw the sticker there directly.

How, then, can we test between the probabilistic and deductive alternatives? As Rescorla knows, the proposal that thinkers use probabilistic representations only generates predictions about behavior when tied to an assumption about how those representations figure into practical reasoning. Rescorla, as we've seen, assumes a version of expected utility theory, whereby thinkers try to maximize their expected payoffs. Yet this, too, is an empirical assumption – one that can be, and has been, subjected to its own tests. As it happens, one of the more interesting findings to emerge from the animal cognition literature over the past few decades is that there are circumstances in which animals systematically *violate* expected utility theory.

A fish tank contains two feeding tubes: one that releases a food morsel every second and another that releases a food morsel every two seconds. Fish that obeyed expected utility theory would spend all of their time in front of the first tube. But that's not what fish actually do. Instead, they spend two-thirds of their time in front of the first tube and one-third of their time in front of the second tube. In other words, they adopt a probability matching decision procedure (Godin and Keenleyside 1984). While initially puzzling, this procedure has clear selection benefits for group foragers. A lone fish that adopted a probability matching strategy while its peers all conformed to expected utility theory would reap a superior harvest.

The tendency to follow a probability matching strategy in certain circumstances is widespread throughout the animal kingdom. (Even humans sometimes display this tendency, which is one reason casinos are so profitable.) This gives us a wedge to distinguish between the probabilistic and deductive interpretations. All we need to do is run a version of the four-cup task for animals when we have independent evidence that they are disposed to adopt a probability matching decision procedure over their probabilistic representations.

For example, we might begin by putting up a barrier that covers all four cups and hiding food in a way that prevents the animal from telling which of cups A, B, C, or D it is hidden in. We could then privilege cup A by hiding the food in it on 40 percent of trials (and hiding the food in cups B, C, and D on 20 percent of trials each). On each trial, the animal chooses a cup and keeps the food if it guesses correctly. Over time, we could see how the animal responds. If, as seems likely, it adopts a probability matching strategy, it should eventually learn to choose cup A 40 percent of the time and each of the other cups 20 percent of the time. We can then continue to a version of the four-cup task in which the animal sees one piece of food hidden in A or B, a second piece hidden in C or D, and is then shown that A is empty. Given Bayes' Law and reasonable background assumptions, the animal should assign a very high probability to food being in cup B, and lower probabilities of roughly .5 each to food being in cup C or in cup D. Given a probability matching strategy, it should thus choose cup B more often than it chooses C and more often than it chooses D, but not more often than it chooses C or D. If the animal is executing a disjunctive syllogism, however, it should choose cup B almost all of the time (or, allowing for performance errors, about as often as when it directly sees the food hidden in B).[3]

6 Conclusion

We began with the question: Is LOTHA true? That is: do animals have sentence-like mental representations – mental representations with an arbitrary referential relation and logical form? As we saw in our discussion of analog magnitude representations, there is evidence that at least some animal mental representations are *not* sentence-like. But of course that doesn't settle the question of LOTHA since animals could have sentence-like representations in addition. We thus sought out a more direct way of evaluating LOTHA.

This led us to examine experiments that test whether animals are capable of logical inferences such as the disjunctive syllogism. Such experiments are always open to alternative interpretations. Thus, no single experiment can hope to settle the matter on its own. But by developing a series of experiments that are designed to pit two or more competing interpretations against one another, we saw how we can acquire empirical evidence that enables us to rationally decide among competing interpretations. As a result, we can begin to see – modulo the challenges identified in Section 4 – how empirical methods can help to reveal whether LOTHA is true.[4]

Notes

1 This is a delicate issue. For an overview and references, see Aydede (2015: §8).
2 One indication of the nontriviality of this form of inference is that it presupposes the conceptual resources to express all possible truth-functions in propositional logic.
3 Bermúdez (2003) suggests a fourth alternative interpretation that I lack the space to properly discuss. Animals could solve the various cup tasks without a genuine negation operator by employing contrary representations, such as *present* and *absent*. For a response, see Burge (2010b: 62–3).
4 Thanks to Kristin Andrews, Roman Feiman, and Christopher Peacocke for helpful comments, and to Matthew Cutone for assistance with Figure 4.1.

Further reading

S. Shettleworth, *Cognition, Evolution, and Behavior* (New York: Oxford University Press, 2010) is a comprehensive textbook on animal cognition that covers both behaviorist and computational/representational approaches. C. J. Völter and J. Call, "Causal and Inferential Reasoning in Animals," in G. M. Burghardt, I. M. Pepperberg, C. T. Snowdon, and T. Zentall (Eds.), *APA Handbook of Comparative Psychology Vol. 2: Perception, Learning, and Cognition*, pp. 643–671 (Washington, DC: American Psychological Association, 2017), reviews empirical research on exclusionary reasoning. Chapter 4 of K. Andrews, *The Animal Mind: An Introduction to the Philosophy of Animal Cognition* (New York: Routledge, 2015) contains an accessible introduction to many of the issues discussed here, including logical reasoning in animals.

References

Aydede, M. (2015) "The Language of Thought Hypothesis," in E. N. Zalta (ed.) *The Stanford Encyclopedia of Philosophy* (Fall 2015 Edition), http://plato.stanford.edu/archives/fall2015/entries/language-thought/
Beck, J. (2012a) "The Generality Constraint and the Structure of Thought," *Mind* 121: 563–600.
——— (2012b) "Do Animals Engage in Conceptual Thought?" *Philosophy Compass* 7: 218–229.
——— (2015) "Analogue Magnitude Representations: A Philosophical Introduction," *British Journal for the Philosophy of Science* 66: 829–855.
Bermúdez, J. L. (2003) *Thinking Without Words*, New York: Oxford University Press.
Burge, T. (2010a) *Origins of Objectivity*, New York: Oxford University Press.
——— (2010b) "Steps Towards Origins of Propositional Thought," *Disputatio* 4: 39–67.
Call, J. (2004) "Inferences About the Location of Food in the Great Apes (Pan Paniscus, Pan Troglodytes, Gorilla Gorilla, and Pongo Pygmaeus)," *Journal of Comparative Psychology* 118: 232–241.
——— (2016) "Avoiding the Empty Cup: Is There Anything More to Apes' Inferential Reasoning?" Talk delivered at the Origins of Logical Reasoning Workshop, York University, Toronto.
Call, J., and Carpenter, M. (2001) "Do Apes and Children Know What They Have Seen?" *Animal Cognition* 3: 207–220.
Camp, E. (2007) "Thinking With Maps," *Philosophical Perspectives* 21: 145–182.
Erdőhegyi, Á., Topál, J., Virányi, Z., and Miklósi, Á. (2007) "Dog-Logic: Inferential Reasoning in a Two-Way Choice Task and Its Restricted Use," *Animal Behaviour* 74: 725–737.

Evans, G. (1985) "Semantic Theory and Tacit Knowledge," in G. Evans (ed.) *Collected Papers*, New York: Oxford University Press, 322–342.

Fodor, J. (1975) *The Language of Thought*, New York: Crowell.

——— (1987) *Psychosemantics: The Problem of Meaning in the Philosophy of Mind*, Cambridge, MA: MIT Press.

Gallistel, C. R. (1990) *The Organization of Learning*, Cambridge, MA: MIT Press.

Godin, J. J., and Keenleyside, M. H. A. (1984) "Foraging on Patchily Distributed Prey By a Cichlid Fish (Teleosti, Cichlidae): A Test of the Ideal Free Distribution Theory," *Animal Behaviour* 32: 120–131.

Grether, W. F., and Maslow, A. H. (1937) "An Experimental Study of Insight in Monkeys," *Journal of Comparative Psychology* 24: 127–134.

Johnson-Laird, P. (2006) *How We Reason*, New York: Oxford University Press.

Margolis, E., and Laurence, S. (2007) "The Ontology of Concepts – Abstract Objects or Mental Representations?" *Noûs* 41: 561–593.

Marsh, H. L., Vining, A. Q., Levendoski, E. K., and Judge, P. G. (2015) "Inference by Exclusion in Lion-Tailed Macaques (Macaca Silenus), a Hamadryas Baboon (Papio Hamadryas), Capuchins (Sapajus Apella), and Squirrel Monkeys (Saimiri Sciureus)," *Journal of Comparative Psychology* 129: 256–267.

Meck, W. H., and Church, R. M. (1982) "Abstraction of Temporal Attributes," *Journal of Experimental Psychology: Animal Behavior Processes* 8: 226–243.

——— (1983) "A Mode Control Model of Counting and Timing Processes," *Journal of Experimental Psychology: Animal Behavior Processes* 9: 320–334.

Mody, S., and Carey, S. (2016) "The Emergence of Reasoning by the Disjunctive Syllogism in Early Childhood," *Cognition* 154: 40–48.

Peirce, C. S. (1933) *Collected Papers*, Cambridge, MA: Harvard University Press.

Petit, O., Dufour, V., Herrenschmidt, M., De Marco, A., Sterck, E. H., and Call, J. (2015) "Inferences About Food Location in Three Cercopithecine Species: An Insight Into the Socioecological Cognition of Primates," *Animal Cognition* 18: 821–830.

Rescorla, M. (2009) "Chrysippus' Dog as a Case Study in Non-Linguistic Cognition," in R. Lurz (ed.) *The Philosophy of Animal Minds*, New York: Cambridge University Press, 52–71.

Schloegl, C., Dierks, A., Gajdon, G. K., Huber, L., Kotrschal, K., and Bugnyar, T. (2009) "What You See Is What You Get? Exclusion Performances in Ravens and Keas," *PLoS ONE* 4: e6368.

Shin, S. (1994) *The Logical Status of Diagrams*, Cambridge: Cambridge University Press.

5

ANIMAL MINDS IN TIME

The question of episodic memory

Christoph Hoerl and Teresa McCormack

In his book *Matter and Memory*, Henri Bergson writes:

> When a dog welcomes his master, barking and wagging his tail, he certainly recognizes him; but does this recognition imply the evocation of a past image …? [The] past does not interest the animal enough to detach it from the fascinating present [. . .]. To call up the past in the form of an image, we must be able to withdraw ourselves from the action of the moment, we must have the power to value the useless, we must have the will to dream. Man alone is capable of such an effort.
>
> (Bergson 1911: 93f.)

Bergson's words evoke a trope that can be found in the works of philosophers as diverse as Aristotle (1930: 453a4–13), Friedrich Nietzsche (1983: 60f.), and Daniel Dennett (2005: 168f.). The idea is that there is a deep discontinuity between us and the rest of the animal kingdom when it comes to the role of time in our mental lives: nonhuman animals are, in some sense, cognitively stuck in the present. This idea has recently received fresh attention, and is now typically framed in terms of the question as to whether animals are capable of having *episodic memories* (Tulving 2001). The thought, in short, is that the human capacity to consciously recollect particular past events constitutes an important way in which we can cognitively transcend the present. As it is sometimes put, it constitutes a form of 'mental time travel'. And the question is whether nonhuman animals, too, are capable of mentally transporting themselves to another time in this way.

A background issue: the question of function

Bergson's remark about "the power to value the useless" was perhaps not meant entirely literally. It can more plausibly be seen as a rhetorical device aimed at drawing attention to a key issue in the background of the question as to whether animals have episodic memories – the question of the *function* of episodic memory. Much human reminiscing about times gone by seems to serve no useful practical purpose. And even when episodic memories contain useful information about events or situations of a type we may encounter again, this information could arguably equally well be carried by other forms of memory, in which only generic knowledge is retained. So there is a genuine question as to whether there is ever any specific point to being able to cast one's mind back to a particular past event as such, given that *that particular event* will never come round again.

If there is no easily identifiable, distinct adaptive function that episodic memory can be seen to serve, this obviously also makes it difficult to come up with experimental paradigms that hold the potential to yield unambiguous evidence of the presence of episodic memories in animals. It is therefore a hopeful sign that the question of the function of episodic memory has recently moved into the forefront of attention in the context of research on 'mental time travel' more generally conceived, which views episodic memory as part of a larger functional system that also includes capacities for specific forms of future directed thinking (Boyer 2008; Hoerl and McCormack 2016; Klein 2016; Schacter et al. 2007). A clear consensus has yet to emerge from this literature as to how precisely the function of episodic memory is to be construed, but we will briefly mention one particular suggestion at the end of this chapter.

For the moment, one important thing to note is that what we are calling the question of function, as we understand it, is not answered by saying that episodic memory is memory for particular past events, or that it involves the retention of information, as it is sometimes put, about 'what' happened, 'where' and 'when'. For that just raises the question of function again, i.e. the question as to what the benefit is, to the individual, of being able to retain such information. This point, we believe, sometimes gets lost in what has perhaps been the predominant strand of debate in the recent literature on animal episodic memory. As a result, even though there remains deep disagreement on the question as to whether animals can be credited with episodic memory, there is in fact something of an unhealthy consensus regarding the way the terms of the debate are framed. As we discuss in more detail below, it is typically assumed on all sides that certain animal experiments have successfully demonstrated that animals can retain information about 'what', 'where' and 'when', and debates have mainly focused on whether this is sufficient to also demonstrate that they possess episodic memory. We want to make a case for shifting the focus of the debate elsewhere.

Is "the only thing missing" evidence of conscious phenomenology of recollection?

It is a series of studies on scrub jays carried out by Nicola Clayton and her colleagues that is largely responsible for the recent surge of interest in the question as to whether animals have episodic memories (Clayton and Dickinson 1998; de Kort et al. 2005; Griffiths et al. 1999). Western scrub-jays are food-caching birds who have a strong preference for eating worms over eating nuts. But worms are perishable, whereas nuts are relatively nondegradable. Clayton and her colleagues exploited these facts in creating a setup in which a group of scrub jays could learn that worms were still fresh four hours after caching, whereas they had decayed and become inedible after 124 hours. The jays were given opportunities on different occasions to cache either one or the other food source, and later to retrieve their caches. What the researchers found was that the birds were sensitive, at recovery, to how long ago they had cached the worms. If they had cached the nuts some time ago, and the worms just four hours ago, they tried to retrieve the worms. If they had cached the worms 124 hours ago, they tried to retrieve the nuts, leaving the caching site of the worms undisturbed.

In interpreting these findings, Clayton et al. (2003: 686) draw a contrast between, as they call it, "phenomenological and behavioral criteria for episodic memory", respectively, pointing out that much of the literature characterizing episodic memory in humans focuses on its distinct phenomenology as a conscious phenomenon. What they claim is that their study demonstrates that the jays can remember 'what' they cached, 'where' and 'when', thus providing behavioral evidence for memory that is, they say, at least 'episodic-like' in these respects, even though the study leaves open whether the jays also have the same phenomenology of mentally re-experiencing the past that humans enjoy when they recollect events in episodic memory.

Interestingly, this general analysis of Clayton and Dickinson's study is in fact *shared* by many of those authors who are skeptical about the existence of episodic memory in animals. In the view of the latter, the conscious experience of mentally re-experiencing the past is essential to episodic memory, and because it is not clear whether the jays have this experience, we lack evidence that they have episodic memory. Here, for instance, is Endel Tulving's assessment of the significance of Clayton and Dickinson's study:

> The ingenious and convincing demonstrations of the 'what, where, when' memory in scrub jays by Clayton and her colleagues come very close to clinching the case for the jays' episodic memory. The only thing missing is evidence that they have human-like conscious recollections of their worm and nut caching activities.
>
> (Tulving 2001: 1512)

Similarly, Thomas Suddendorf and his colleagues, who have been amongst the most vigorous defenders of the claim that episodic memory is unique to humans (Suddendorf and Busby 2003; Suddendorf and Corballis 2007), seem in agreement with Clayton and her colleagues regarding the basic dialectical situation, which they describe as having to define episodic memory either "in terms of the information encoded" (Suddendorf and Busby 2003: 392), or in terms of the phenomenology of traveling back in time, where these are seen as mutually exclusive options, because one "can know what happened where and when without being able to remember the event (e.g. your birth) and, conversely, one can travel back in time without access to accurate when and where information" (Suddendorf and Busby 2003: 392).

We believe that this is an unhelpful way of framing the dialectic of the debate over the question as to whether animals are capable of episodic recollection. Take, for instance, the stance taken by Clayton and her colleagues. Although they are not officially committing themselves either way, there are essentially two ways in which this stance might be fleshed out. Either it implies that it is indeed possible for animals to engage in much the same kinds of information processing as humans, but without the conscious phenomenology that accompanies it in humans. Or the view is that, because their study provides the best available evidence for animal episodic memory, we should also accept that such memory is accompanied by the same phenomenology that accompanies human episodic recollection (Eichenbaum et al. 2005 explicitly take a position along those lines).

Note that if either of these was in fact the target view at stake in the debate, it would actually render it mysterious why it is the question of animal *episodic memory*, specifically, that is supposed to be of special interest in that debate. The first view just described effectively relies on something like the philosophical 'zombie hypothesis' in the literature on physicalist approaches to consciousness, according to which it is possible for an organism to show exactly the same behavior as a conscious human being, but without enjoying any conscious phenomenology. Conversely, on the second view, it is those who question the existence of animal episodic memory who are effectively portrayed as relying on something like this hypothesis. But the zombie hypothesis is a completely general skeptical hypothesis, covering all forms of activity that typically involve conscious awareness in humans. So it is unclear what the dialectical benefit would be (to either side) in trying to invoke it to make a point specifically about episodic memory.

We believe that the existing focus on a supposed dichotomy between information-based and consciousness-based approaches to episodic memory anyway misrepresents some of the arguments that are being made, including arguments by some of the researchers who subscribe to the idea of such a dichotomy. As we want to argue, what should really be at issue is whether it is even correct to describe Clayton and Dickinson's study as demonstrating the existence of a form of memory in which information about 'what', 'where' and 'when' is retained.

Being sensitive to time without representing the past

Somewhat contrary to their own claim that "[t]he current evidence suggests that scrub jays [. . .] can encode, store and use information about *what* they cached *where* and *when*" (2003: 394), Suddendorf and Busby at one point also write that the cognitive processes governing the behavior exhibited in Clayton and her colleagues' studies "need not be *about* the past at all" (Suddendorf and Busby 2003: 392). Following Dretske (1982), they explain:

> [E]vent A might cause cognitive change B that affects behavior C at a later point in time, but this need not imply that B carries any information about A itself – the mediator B might be causal rather than informational. Thus, although jays perform actions C (recovery) that make sense only in the light of A (caching what, where and when) it need not imply that B represents the past event A.
>
> (Suddendorf and Busby 2003: 392)

On the face of it, this would seem to be a way of arguing against the claim that Clayton and her colleagues have demonstrated episodic memory in animals that does not rely on considerations about phenomenology. Instead, it concerns what it means to say that an organism has information about or represents something. But how can we flesh out Suddendorf and Busby's remark further, to see how exactly the rather abstract thought they sketch might apply to this particular case? The jays studied by Clayton et al. are clearly sensitive to the temporal interval that has elapsed since they cached the worms. So what grounds might there be for thinking that they nevertheless do not represent the worm-caching event as lying at the far end of that interval, in a way that would warrant describing them as remembering 'when' the caching happened?

In general, we can distinguish between two quite different ways in which an individual's cognitive state might be sensitive to the passing of time. One of them involves explicitly representing events as happening at an array of different times. By contrast, in what we have elsewhere referred to as *temporal updating* (Hoerl 2008; Hoerl and McCormack 2011; McCormack and Hoerl 2005), the individual just operates with a model of its *current* environment, which is updated in ways that are sensitive to the passing of time, but with each update simply replacing its predecessor. In its simplest form, such updating would consist in changing the model in response to new perceptual information that conflicts with the previous model. But temporal updating could also, for instance, explain certain basic forms of sequential learning. Becoming sensitive to the sequence in which a familiar set of events typically unfolds might simply be a matter of acquiring a routine for serially updating one's model of one's current environment, so that representations of the relevant events come to succeed each other in the right order in successive instantiations of that model.

So the general thought here would be that some forms of sensitivity to the passing of time can be explained by appealing to processes governing how the individual's model of the environment gets updated over time, where this is to be contrasted with the idea that temporal relations are themselves represented in that model. Is there also an explanation of the scrub jays' caching behavior available that relies only on the idea of temporal updating? Note that one thing that should be uncontroversial is that their behavior must, in part, be governed by a mechanism that can keep track of intervals of time. Unless we postulate the existence of some kind of internal interval timer that is causally responsive to the amount of time that has elapsed since the caching took place, it remains mysterious how the jays can show differential behavior depending on the length of that interval. But, given that the behavior must be based on the use of such a timer, we can once again distinguish two different mechanisms by which its workings could influence behavior (see also McCormack 2001 and Hoerl 2008). One of these involves producing mental representations in which the caching and the interval elapsed since figure – as implied by the idea of a memory for 'what', 'where' and 'when'. Yet, in line with the idea of temporal updating, there is also another, simpler, mechanism by which such a timer could have an impact on behavior, *viz.* by determining how long aspects of the individual's model of its environment will be maintained in existence. In other words, what the timer would determine is how long the presence of the worms (or worms-as-food) in their caching location would continue to figure in the jays' model of their current environment before disappearing from that model. It is in this sense that the processes governing the birds' behavior "need not be *about* the past", as Suddendorf and Busby put it.

Event-independent thought about times

If the considerations presented in the previous section are along the right lines, the crucial question they raise is how exactly human temporal cognition goes beyond mere temporal updating, and whether there is any evidence that can bear on the question as to whether animals, too, can engage in modes of temporal cognition that go beyond temporal updating.

Elsewhere, we have argued that one distinctive feature of mature human temporal cognition is that it involves *event-independent* thought about times (Hoerl and McCormack 2011; McCormack and Hoerl 2008), i.e. the idea of time as a framework of positions at which different events can be located. Episodic memory can be seen as one manifestation of such event-independent thought about times, insofar as it involves the ability to retain information about events that are no longer part of one's environment specifically by cognitively placing those events at other times. This arguably requires the ability to make those other times an object of thought in their own right, rather than just retaining features of the events in question that might still be of relevance to how the world is now.

Thus, at least one important aspect of the question as to whether nonhuman animals have episodic memories is whether they can engage in event-independent thinking about time, rather than just relying on temporal updating. Is there any existing research that might help in answering this question? We will conclude by briefly considering two such lines of research, which may also help to clarify what exactly the question consists in.

One relevant line of research concerns the question as to whether animals can experience *regret*. As we have argued in more detail elsewhere, regret involves event-independent thinking about past times, and indeed one key function of episodic memory may in fact lie in underpinning the ability to experience regret (Hoerl and McCormack 2016). Regret is sometimes referred to as a *counterfactual emotion*, as it turns crucially on a grasp of the idea that what one did at a certain point in the past was not the only option available at that time, and that one's making a different choice might have led to a different, better, outcome. This also, arguably, means that regret involves the ability to think of the time when the past choice was made independently of thinking just of that choice and its outcome.

In order to investigate whether rats can experience regret, Steiner and Redish (2014) constructed a spatial decision-making task in which rats could sequentially visit four different food locations, each with a different kind of food. When entering each food location, the rats heard a tone that was gradually decreasing in pitch, with the pitch of the tone indicating the delay the rat had to wait until gaining access to the food at that location. The delays, lasting between 1 and 45 seconds, were selected pseudorandomly, and if the rat left the location before the delay was over, the countdown stopped and the rat had to move on to another location for food.

After determining the rats' food preferences, and the threshold duration each rat was prepared to wait for each foodstuff on each day, the researchers analyzed in particular those sequences in which rats abandoned waiting for one type of food, even though the delay, on that occasion, was below the threshold for that type, and the delay for the next type of food then turned out to be greater than the threshold for that type. As they explain, this kind of sequence can be interpreted as one "in which the rat skipped a low-cost offer, only to find itself faced with a high-cost offer" (Steiner and Redish 2014: 998). This was compared with sequences in which the rat took the first, low-cost, offer, and then encountered a high-cost one, and sequences in which both offers were high-cost, and the rat skipped the first one, only to find itself faced with another high-cost one. As Steiner and Redish argue, these latter two control conditions are ones that might prompt disappointment or frustration, but, unlike the first, are not potentially regret-inducing, because the rat acts correctly, given its preferences and the relevant thresholds.

Steiner and Redish found that the rats treated the potentially regret-inducing sequences differently from each of the two types of control sequence. Specifically, in the former, they "paused and looked backwards towards the previous option" (Steiner and Redish 2014: 998), which they had abandoned. This was accompanied by neurophysiological activity that corresponded to the missed action.

Steiner and Redish's interpretation is that the rats experienced regret at their past decision to leave the previous food location rather than waiting out the delay. This implies ascribing to them the capacity to turn their minds back to the past in quite a robust sense, i.e. to genuinely revisit a *past time* in their thinking, insofar as they can think of it both as the time they made a certain choice, but also a time at which another choice, too, could have been made. This is an intriguing suggestion, particularly in the light of research that suggests that regret is a cognitively sophisticated emotion that is late-developing in children (O'Connor et al. 2012, 2014; Weisberg and Beck 2010). It is largely because of its counterfactual element that regret is viewed as cognitively sophisticated, and a key challenge facing a regret-based interpretation of animal behavior is to provide convincing evidence that the behavior in question is indeed underpinned by counterfactual thought.

In typical human studies of regret (e.g., Camille et al. 2004; Mellers et al. 1999), participants are faced with a choice (e.g., between a safe and a risky gamble in a trial of a gambling task), and at that choice point, they do not know what outcome would result from the choice they could take but subsequently reject. Only once they have made their actual choice and have found out the outcome resulting from that choice are they provided with information about the outcome the rejected choice would have yielded, which on a regret trial turns out to be better than that of the actual choice. This makes it more difficult to explain the subsequently reported negative emotion without appealing to participants entertaining a counterfactual about a past state of affairs (i.e. what would have happened if they had chosen differently), because participants' motivational state, experience, intention and decision are, up until that point, potentially identical to those in a control trial in which exactly the same choice is made but the actual outcome is better than or equivalent to the outcome of the other choice (and also to those in a so-called 'partial feedback' trial in which participants never find out the outcome associated with the nonchosen option). This is not the case in Steiner and Redish's study, where the previous experience and presumably motivational state of the animal differs by definition across 'regret' and control trials. This makes it somewhat harder to argue that the rats must be entertaining a counterfactual.[1]

The example of regret serves to demonstrate that focusing on the significance of event-independent thought about time is useful in broadening the scope of the studies that can be considered to be relevant to assessing animals' temporal abilities. We finish by describing a study that can be interpreted as examining another type of behavior requiring event-independent thought about time in a different species, i.e. great apes. Adapting a procedure first used by Beck et al. (2006) to test children, Redshaw and Suddendorf (2016) showed apes a forked tube apparatus with one opening at the top but two openings at the bottom and demonstrated that a grape dropped into the top opening could emerge from either bottom opening, it being apparently random from which it would emerge on each occasion. The apparatus was then moved closer to the apes, so that they had the opportunity to catch the grapes as they emerged from the bottom opening; otherwise, the grapes would roll out of reach. The experimenters found that none of a number of great apes they tested spontaneously covered *both* bottom openings on their first trial, and only one of them did so at all on the initial twelve test trials, but subsequently regressed to covering only one opening.

That apes fail this relatively simple task seems to point to a fairly basic limitation in the ability to think about the future. Specifically, what they seem to lack is the ability to apply the equivalent of the type of thinking about the past that we have argued is involved in regret. The grape dropped into the apparatus is clearly part of their model of the world, even after it has disappeared in the top opening, but it appears that they cannot think of the time at which it will re-emerge as a time at which it will emerge from one of the bottom openings, but at which it could emerge from either one of them. Thus, Redshaw and Suddendorf's study might be taken to be indicative of an inability to engage in event-independent thought about times, indicating instead that apes' cognitive abilities with respect to time are limited to mere temporal updating.

Conclusion

Are animals cognitively stuck in the present, or are they, like us, able to mentally revisit particular past events in episodic memory? In this chapter, we have made a case for shifting the existing focus of debate on this issue from considerations about the phenomenology of episodic recollection to the question as to whether there is evidence that animals are capable of event-independent thinking about times, or whether they are capable of temporal updating only. In temporal updating, there may be a variety of mechanisms by which the passing of time can influence the model of its environment that an individual operates with. Yet, this does not mean that time itself – the past and the future alongside the present – figures in that model. Episodic memory, by contrast, involves retaining information about events specifically by cognitively placing them at a past time. This, we have suggested, requires making that past time an object of thought in its own right, as one that could also have been filled with different events. As such, episodic memory is distinct from other ways of retaining or being sensitive to information over time not just in virtue of its phenomenology, but also in the way in which it is bound up with quite sophisticated abilities to think about the possible as well as the actual, which remain to be demonstrated in nonhuman animals.

Note

1 It may be possible to design rat experiments that more closely resemble the human tasks in this respect, given the emerging body of research on the effects of entirely fictive rewards on animal behavior (Hayden et al. 2009; Kim et al. 2015).

Further reading

J. Bennett, *Rationality* (Indianaplois, IN: Hackett Publishing Company, 1989) provides a thought experiment intended to establish that "there is no non-linguistic way of manifesting knowledge of just some fact about one's past" (p. 88). Chapter 5 of T. Suddendorf, *The Gap: The Science of What Separates Us from Other Animals* (New York: Basic Books, 2013) critically reviews empirical work claimed to provide evidence for the existence of animal episodic memory. Less-skeptical views about animal memory can be found in part 6 of K. Michaelian, S. Klein, and K. Szpunar (eds.), *Seeing the Future: Theoretical Perspectives on Future-Oriented Mental Time Travel* (Oxford: Oxford University Press, 2016).

References

Aristotle. (1930). On memory and reminiscence (J. I. Beare, Trans.). In W. D. Ross (Ed.), *The works of Aristotle* (vol. 3). Oxford: Oxford University Press.

Beck, S. R., Robinson, E. J., Carroll, D. J., and Apperly, I. A. (2006). Children's thinking about counterfactuals and future hypotheticals as possibilities. *Child Development, 77*(2), 413–426.

Bergson, H. (1911). *Matter and memory* (N. M. Paul and W. S. Palmer, Trans.). London: George Allen and Unwin.

Boyer, P. (2008). Evolutionary economics of mental time travel? *Trends in Cognitive Sciences, 12*(6), 219–224.

Camille, N., Coricelli, G., Sallet, J., Pradat-Diehl, P., Duhamel, J. R., and Sirigu, A. (2004). The involvement of the orbitofrontal cortex in the experience of regret. *Science, 304*(5674), 1167–1170.

Clayton, N. S., Bussey, T. J., and Dickinson, A. (2003). Can animals recall the past and plan for the future? *Nature Reviews: Neuroscience, 4*(8), 685–691.

Clayton, N. S., and Dickinson, A. (1998). Episodic-like memory during cache recovery by scrub jays. *Nature, 395*(6699), 272–274.

de Kort, S. R., Dickinson, A., and Clayton, N. S. (2005). Retrospective cognition by food-caching western scrub-jays. *Learning and Motivation, 36*(2), 159–176.

Dennett, D. C. (2005). *Sweet dreams: Philosophical obstacles to a science of consciousness.* Cambridge, MA: MIT Press.

Dretske, F. (1982). The informational character of representations. *Behavioral and Brain Sciences, 5*(3), 376–377.

Eichenbaum, H., Fortin, N. J., Ergorul, C., Wright, S. P., and Agster, K. L. (2005). Episodic recollection in animals: "If it walks like a duck and quacks like a duck. . .". *Learning and Motivation, 36*(2), 190–207.

Griffiths, D., Dickinson, A., and Clayton, N. (1999). Episodic memory: What can animals remember about their past? *Trends in Cognitive Sciences, 3*(2), 74–80.

Hayden, B. Y., Pearson, J. M., and Platt, M. L. (2009). Fictive reward signals in the anterior cingulate cortex. *Science, 324*(5929), 948–950.

Hoerl, C. (2008). On being stuck in time. *Phenomenology and the Cognitive Sciences, 7*(4), 485–500.

Hoerl, C., and McCormack, T. (2011). Time in cognitive development. In C. Callender (Ed.), *The Oxford handbook of philosophy of time.* Oxford: Oxford University Press.

Hoerl, C., and McCormack, T. (2016). Making decisions about the future: Regret and the cognitive function of episodic memory. In K. Michaelian, S. Klein, and K. Szpunar (Eds.), *Seeing the future: Theoretical perspectives on future-oriented mental time travel* (pp. 241–266). Oxford: Oxford University Press.

Kim, K. U., Huh, N., Jang, Y., Lee, D., and Jung, M. W. (2015). Effects of fictive reward on rat's choice behavior. *Scientific Reports, 5*, 8040.

Klein, S. B. (2016). Autonoetic consciousness: Reconsidering the role of episodic memory in future-oriented self-projection. *Quarterly Journal of Experimental Psychology, 69*(2), 381–401.

McCormack, T. (2001). Attributing episodic memory to animals and children. In C. Hoerl and T. McCormack (Eds.), *Time and memory: Issues in philosophy and psychology.* Oxford: Oxford University Press.

McCormack, T., and Hoerl, C. (2005). Children's reasoning about the causal significance of the temporal order of events. *Developmental Psychology, 41*(1), 54–63.

McCormack, T., and Hoerl, C. (2008). Temporal decentering and the development of temporal concepts. *Language Learning, 58*(SUPPL. 1), 89–113.

Mellers, B. A., Schwartz, A., and Ritov, I. (1999). Emotion-based choice. *Journal of Experimental Psychology: General, 128*(3), 332–345.

Nietzsche, F. W. (1983). *On the uses and disadvantages of history for life Untimely Meditations.* Cambridge: Cambridge University Press.

O'Connor, E., McCormack, T., and Feeney, A. (2012). The development of regret. *Journal of Experimental Child Psychology, 111*(1), 120–127.

O'Connor, E., McCormack, T., and Feeney, A. (2014). Do children who experience regret make better decisions? A developmental study of the behavioral consequences of regret. *Child Development, 85*(5), 1995–2010.

Redshaw, J., and Suddendorf, T. (2016). Children's and apes' preparatory responses to two mutually exclusive possibilities. *Current Biology, 26*(13), 1758–1762.

Schacter, D. L., Addis, D. R., and Buckner, R. L. (2007). Remembering the past to imagine the future: The prospective brain. *Nature Reviews Neuroscience, 8*(9), 657–661.

Steiner, A. P., and Redish, A. D. (2014). Behavioral and neurophysiological correlates of regret in rat decision-making on a neuroeconomic task. *Nature Neuroscience, 17*(7), 995–1002.

Suddendorf, T., and Busby, J. (2003). Mental time travel in animals? *Trends in Cognitive Sciences, 7*(9), 391–396.

Suddendorf, T., and Corballis, M. C. (2007). The evolution of foresight: What is mental time travel, and is it unique to humans? *Behavioral and Brain Sciences, 30*(3), 299–313.

Tulving, E. (2001). Episodic memory and common sense: How far apart? *Philosophical Transactions of the Royal Society of London B: Biological Sciences, 356*(1413), 1505–1515.

Weisberg, D. P., and Beck, S. R. (2010). Children's thinking about their own and others' regret and relief. *Journal of Experimental Child Psychology, 106*(2), 184–191.

6

NOVEL COLOURS IN ANIMAL PERCEPTION

Mohan Matthen

Studies of animal cognition are often about an evolutionary *scala naturae* – about the degree to which other animals approximate to mental functioning we know best in ourselves. Do they have a grasp of predication? Are they self-aware? Do they have a sense of the future?

In this entry, I am concerned with a different sort of question. All animals perceive, but they often perceive differently. My assumption is that perception serves nonhuman animals just as well as it does humans. Within the parameters set by this assumption, we can ask: What is the significance of a different way of perceiving? My example is colour, which I contrast with acoustic pitch. I will show that the colours animals perceive are different from those that humans do, but that pitch is the same across the board. I'll try to explain this and to draw some conclusions about perceptual qualities in general.

I Novel colours

Some animals sense *novel colours* (Thompson 1992, Matthen 1999) – colours that humans don't perceive. For example, chickens are tetrachromats. They have four different classes of cone cells while humans have only three, three opponent processes while humans have only two (Osorio et al. 1999). (Details and explanations later.) The colours that result are quite different from those that humans experience. These colours are not merely more fine-grained – it's not just that birds can distinguish by colour some things that look the same to us (though this is also true). Nor is it just that they see beyond the extremes of the spectrum visible to humans – it is true that birds are sensitive to ultraviolet, but this is not my focus here. The point of interest for me here is that bird colours are removed from such determinants of human colour experience as the red-green, blue-yellow hue palette. The colour properties birds see are different from those we see.

What colour does a bird see when it looks at turmeric powder? The point I want to make is that it can't be *orange*, which is what trichromatic humans see. *Orange* is the colour we experience as reddish and yellowish in more or less equal proportions. But the red-green, blue-yellow hue dimensions thrown up by our three cone cells and two opponent processes do not define bird colour-experience.[1] (These processes give the bird a richer palette of colour experience; on the flip side, colour deficiencies such as protanopia diminish colour experience in some humans.) And the same goes for other bird colour-experiences. Bird colours are defined by different hue dimensions. Consequently, birds don't experience orange and other colours that humans do; conversely, humans don't experience the colours that birds do. (For more on the structure of colour, see Matthen forthcoming.)

A caveat before we continue. I said that bird colour-*experience* is different from ours, and concluded that birds don't experience the same colours. There's a lacuna in this inference: it doesn't rule out the possibility that birds have different experience of the same colours. Consider motion: when I throw a ball to you, you experience it as approaching and I as retreating. In other words, you and I experience the same motion differently. Could birds and humans, similarly, experience the same colours differently? Let's hold this possibility in abeyance until the end of Section II, when we will have a bit more apparatus at hand.

Here, however, is a preliminary conclusion:

Proposition 1 Bird colour-experience is different from human.

As an aside, Proposition 1 is a problem for those who would define colour as a disposition to evoke a specific kind of experience. For it invites the question: Why does the kind of experience that birds have count as colour experience? Since the colour experiences in question are different, the question arises: why are novel colours colours at all?

II Perceptual grasp of colour

Colours are *properties*, commonalities among multiple concrete individuals. Orange is a colour that *this* mound of turmeric powder has; it is also present in *that* heap of turmeric. This is what it means to say it is a property.

Perception gives us direct visual experience of the colours – "direct" in the sense that we do not see them by seeing something else. Some argue that we see polygons *indirectly*, because we see them *by* seeing their sides. Whether this is correct or not regarding polygons, the point about colours is that there is no such intermediary. It is not by construction or learning that we see the colour of turmeric, but just by seeing.

The directness of colour perception has prompted certain well-known doctrines about the nature of colour. G. E. Moore (1903, 10) says that the colours are simple, undefinable qualities known by perception. This is not exactly correct. As I said earlier, colours have component structure: orange consists of the reddish and yellowish hue dimensions in more or less equal parts. In this sense, at least, they are not simple. Still, Moore points to an important truth: the colours cannot be defined except in chromatic terms, i.e., in terms of directly perceived qualities such as hue and lightness.

Bertrand Russell (1912) propounds a view similar to that of Moore. He thought that colours were sense data known by acquaintance. "I know the colour perfectly and completely when I see it, and no further knowledge of it itself is even theoretically possible," he wrote (47). Russell's point is that if colour is a perceptual property, then nonperceptual knowledge about it must originate in correlations that we discover. These correlations do not constitute "knowledge of [colour] *itself*." Orange is reddish yellow; this is its directly perceived chromatic essence. Orange has a wavelength of around 600 nm; this is a contingently correlated physical fact not knowable by perception alone. We know a colour "perfectly and completely" when we directly perceive its chromatic essence.

The Moore-Russell doctrine stands on a simple foundation: perception is self-contained. We go beyond perception when we investigate physical causes. With colour, perception reveals a system of properties constituted by the hue and lightness. There is nothing else to know about its intrinsic nature.

Mark Johnston (1992) formulates another central doctrine: colour causally explains colour experience. He suggests that this sits uncomfortably with the Moore-Russell doctrine. Scientists causally explain colour experience by reference to physical quantities, such as wavelength or reflectance, or physically realized "dispositions to appear colored" (Johnston 1992: 224). It follows, Johnston says, that colour must be some such quality. But these qualities are not perfectly and completely known by perception (225). So, Johnston concludes, we should "abandon or weaken" the Moore-Russell doctrine (228).

This reasoning rests on a mistaken assumption. We explain colour experience by chromatic properties. For instance, we say that turmeric *looks* orange (an experience) *because* (causal explanation) it *is* orange and white light is shining on it. It is true that science amplifies this explanation in terms of wavelength and the like, but it does not do so by *identifying* colours with these physical quantities. Science only demands that there be *law-like correlations* between physical quantities and the colours. Psychophysics provides these correlations. Psychophysics goes beyond mere perception. There is no reason to weaken the Moore-Russell doctrine.

This gives us the argument that we earlier were missing about the novel colours. Perception serves chickens as well as it serves us. So we should assume that they have the same kind of perceptual access to the colours they directly experience as we do to ours – they, too, enjoy perfect and complete grasp of perceptual qualities. But bird colours have a different chromatic character than those that we perceive. Thus, we have:

> *Proposition 2* Since colours are defined by chromatic character, bird colours are different from human.

Note that this argument does not simply go from different experience to different thing experienced. Rather, it uses the Moore-Russell doctrine as an additional premise.

III Auditory perception: a sideways glance

Auditory pitch (high/low) and loudness are also perceptual qualities, this time of audition. The Moore-Russell doctrine implies that we know them by hearing them (though I don't think we know either pitch or loudness *completely*[2]). But as I shall show in this section and the next two, colour and pitch are very different cases. Colour and auditory pitch are both wavelength-related property systems. But our perceptual systems relate to the underlying wavelengths in different ways. The way wavelength sensitivity works in the case of colour is what makes novel colours possible. There is no such thing as novel auditory pitch (at least not in cochlea-based auditory systems). (This should be somewhat qualified. Pitch has attending characteristics that can vary from organism to organism. My point is that its correspondence to wavelength cannot vary.)

Here's how the auditory system measures wavelength. Sound waves are converted to pressure waves in the fluid of the middle ear; these are conveyed to the cochlea of the inner ear. According to Georg von Békésy's now widely accepted "place theory" (http://tinyurl.com/okumo), different parts of the cochlea (and of its basilar membrane) are sensitive to different sound frequencies. (See Figure 6.1.) Taken as a whole, the cochlea is a coiled organ; each place on this organ corresponds to a frequency, and the strength of response at this place indicates the amplitude of the corresponding frequency. Thus, the cochlea is, as the jargon goes, "tonotopic"; its places correspond to tones. Cochlear hair cells transduce this information and send it through a number of subcortical relay stations through to the auditory cortex. The primary auditory cortex is likely not concerned with tone as such, but rather with characteristics of sound that

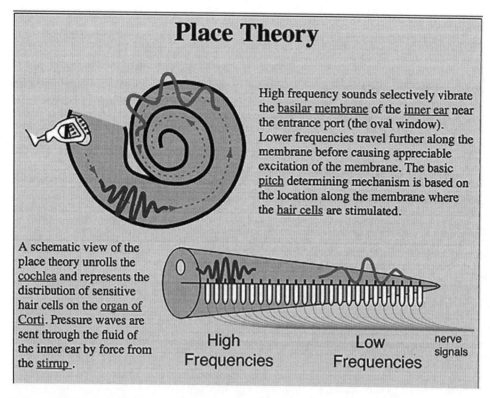

Figure 6.1   Place theory of pitch perception

Source: From HyperPhysics by permission of Rod Nave.

enable us to identify environmental events of different kinds. Nevertheless, it does retain some of the tonotopic organization of the cochlea and reflects the wavelength composition of ambient sound. (For a recent review, see King and Nelken 2009.)

Our experience of pitch and volume derives from this mechanism. The auditory system and the speech perception system extract detailed information from the incoming acoustic signal. From the single amalgamated signal, they reconstruct the spatial array of individual sources of sound. For example, they separate out the many voices and other sounds at a cocktail party, and differentiate human voices from other kinds of sounds such as those of people walking about and wine glasses tinkling against one another. But whatever else we might experience in audition, we also perceive pitch and volume. It is not clear that the pitch and volume that we hear corresponds cleanly to the composition of sounds; for instance, one voice may be more high-pitched than another, even though both consist of many tones. Nonetheless, we perceive environmental sources of sounds as being, among other things, high or low and loud or soft.

Pitch and loudness are directly perceived in the way that Moore and Russell say colour and brightness are (though in this case the resulting knowledge is incomplete – see note 2). We know what we know of them by hearing them, and no other source of knowledge of them themselves is even theoretically possible.

Here, however, is something audition *doesn't* tell us: because pitch and loudness trace back to the tonotopic organization of the cochlea, their auditory inter-relations mirror the physical structure of frequency and volume.[3] This representational structure is dictated by the cochlea.

(It is possible, in some sense, for auditory perception not to be cochlea based, but the resulting qualities would have a very different perceived character than pitch and loudness.)

This imposes a constraint on "novel" pitch and volume. Some animals may experience finer gradations of pitch; some may sense higher or lower frequencies than humans can. However that might be, high/low and loud/soft always correspond in the same way to the physical parameters of frequency and volume in sound. The physical structure of sound constrains the perceptual structure of auditory qualities. As we shall see, this marks a contrast between colour vision and audition.

Proposition 3 Pitch and loudness cannot structurally vary across animals because they are constrained by physical acoustic relations in sound.

IV How the eye measures colour

Now let's return to colour and the visual system. Colour is extraordinarily vivid to those of us who see it, and some think that it is the basic visual datum from which all visual objects are constructed – "If it be perceiv'd by the eyes, it must be a colour," Hume (1739/1978: 16) wrote. Whatever Hume might have meant and however he might be vindicated, we should beware of assuming that colour is functionally primary for vision. The business of vision is space; colour is an add-on. And this has important implications for how colour is processed by the visual system.

Because vision is primarily for space, the retina is *topo*topically organized; each place on the retina corresponds to a place in the two-dimensional image produced by the corneal lens. Colour sensitivity would be improved by adding cone-cells, but this reduces spatial resolution, since more cells have to be packed into each location. Birds are tetrachromats; humans are normally trichromats – in each case, the limitations on colour resolution are an evolutionary compromise between the needs of spatial vision and those of colour vision.

This brings us to the cone-cells. Animals with colour vision – honeybees, birds, humans, etc. – possess several photoreceptor cell types, each differentially sensitive to light in a subregion of the visual spectrum. Figure 6.2 shows the spectral sensitivity of the three human cone-cells. Each place in the colour-sensitive portion of the retina contains these three cone-cells.

The cone-cells are sensitive to broad wavebands. The L (or long wavelength) cone emits a response when light of just about any frequency is incident upon it, but if we pick a threshold of 25% of peak response, then it responds to light between 500 and 650 nm, or about half of the visible spectrum. The output of each cone-cell is proportionate to the integrated sum of signal strength at each wavelength multiplied by cone-cell sensitivity at that wavelength. Cone-cells are distinguished one from another by a response curve more than by peak sensitivity. The M-cone is only slightly shifted from the L-cone, as it results from a genetic modification of the latter. Kainz et. al 1998 and Surridge et al. 2003 are good reviews.)

The output of the cone-cells is not wavelength-specific in the way that the output of the cochlea is. With regard to environmental discrimination, this has the negative consequence that there are signals that are different in wavelength composition, but nonetheless equivalent with respect to their effect on the cone-cells. For example, since light of 525 nm and 625 nm both affect the L-cone, we can get the same L-response by manipulating strength at one frequency to compensate for changes at the other. This kind of equivalence among distinct light signals is called "metamerism."

Though wavelength discrimination is limited by metamerism, it is surprisingly fine. Consider two monochromatic beams of light at 575 and 525 nm, the second twice as strong as the first.

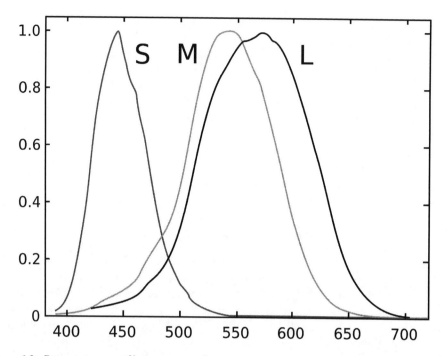

Figure 6.2 Response curves of human cone-cells

Source: From the Wikipedia article on cone-cells under the Creative Commons licence.

These beams will have the same effect on the L-cone, since the strength of the second beam compensates for the lower response-sensitivity of this cone at 525 nm. However, the two beams have a completely different effect on the M-cone, which has roughly the same sensitivity at these two wavelengths, and thus responds much more strongly to the stronger 525-nm beam. Thus, the two beams are distinguished by their aggregate effect on the three cones.

In this manner, take the ordered triple of the three cone-cell responses, $<x, y, z>$. The responses to two signals is different if they produce a different effect on even one cell. In consequence, given just three cones, discrimination for monochromatic beams is close to perfect over a long-enough series of "same–different" discrimination trials (Hardin 1988). Cone-cell activation is always different for different monochrome lights. (Figure 6.3 maps these differences for equal-strength beams.)

The points made in the immediately preceding paragraphs fit oddly with each other. On the one hand, cone-based colour vision is capable of making a very large number of distinctions: over a long-enough series of discrimination trials, light of any given wavelength is discriminable from light of any other at equal strength. On the other hand, because of metamerism, colour vision *fails* to discriminate signals with very different wavelength-amplitude profiles. You could put it this way: there are very many colours – in some ways of looking at it, an infinite number of them – but in any given illumination, there are things of different spectral composition that look the same. The colours are a mash-up. Figure 6.3 makes it look as if colour difference is wavelength difference, but this is only because of background constraints.

Proposition 4 Auditory pitch corresponds very well to wavelength; colour does not.

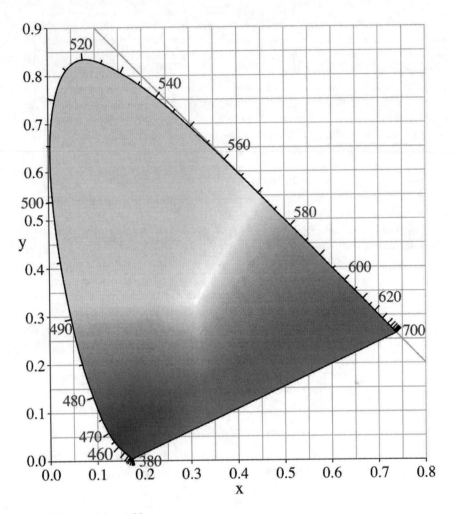

Figure 6.3 Colour and the visible spectrum

Source: By User: PAR (Own work) (Public Domain), via the Wikimedia Creative Commons Licence.

V Opponent processing vs. constancy processing

Before we can figure out the significance of Proposition 4, we need to look a little deeper into the operations of the colour vision system.

As explained in the preceding section, a light beam hitting the colour-sensitive portions of the retina will elicit a response from cone-cells of each of three types. These three response values jointly define what one might call the system's *first colour response* (FCR). Colour *experience* is extracted from the FCR by the operation of two functionally different processes, *opponent processing* and *constancy processing*.

Opponent Processing

Light reflected off natural objects is generally polychromatic, though not balanced across the spectrum. Consequently, it stimulates all three cones. A ripe tomato, for example, stimulates the

L-cone more than the S-cone. (Red light is long wavelength; blue is short.) But this does not mean that it *doesn't* stimulate the S-cone. Though it reflects 70% of the red light that falls on it, it still reflects 10% of the blue. In bright light, then, the red tomato might actually stimulate the S-cone more than a blue object does in dim light.

FCR reflects both the spectral composition and the brightness of light reflected off or emitted by environmental objects. Because of brightness, the three values tend to be correlated: bright polychromatic light produces a strong response from all; dim light evokes a weak response. So to gauge the tomato's colour, as opposed to the brightness of the illumination, the important thing is not the response elicited from each cone, but the *difference* between cone-cell responses. In any level of light bright enough to elicit *any* cone-cell response, white light reflected off the tomato will elicit a stronger response from the L and M (long and medium wavelength) cones than from the S. To detect this, the visual system *subtracts* the S-response from the sum of the L- and M-responses. It also calculates the difference between the L- and M-cone responses. This is called "opponent processing."

The hue dimensions – red-green and blue-yellow – correspond to these differences in cone-cell responses. For instance, something looks reddish if it elicits more response from the L- and M-cones than it does from the S-cone; it looks yellowish if the difference between the L- and M-cones is positive. It is important to note that opponent processing does not *add* information to the cone-cell responses; it merely extracts information that is already present. The function of opponent processing is to remove the correlated portions of cone-cell response, which are due to brightness, so as to arrive at the uncorrelated portion, which is due to wavelength.

One last fact: the two hue dimensions of colour derive from the opponent channels; brightness derives from the sum. Experienced colour is hue plus brightness.

Constancy Processing

The same object reflects different colours when differently illuminated. The visual system is, however, able to reduce the effect of these changes. Objects look more or less the same colour and lightness in good viewing conditions, i.e., when the illumination is more or less white and reasonably bright. Processing for this kind of constancy makes certain "assumptions" – for example, that the brightest object in a scene is white. These assumptions arise from successful processing strategies pursued in evolutionary time. Thus, there is added information in constancy processing (for example, the "information" that the brightest object in any scene is white).

Proposition 5 a) Colour properties are defined by opponent process functions. b) The attribution of colour properties to individual objects across different conditions of illumination results from constancy processing.

VI Colour properties

One can think of the output of opponent processing in two ways.

One way is to think of it as a valiant attempt at wavelength readout, given not very good apparatus. Figure 6.3 suggests this picture: in that diagram, the <x,y> value of 700 nm is <0.74, 0.27>. So, one might think: if something matches this point, it looks 700-nm red, though the look might merely be metameric and thus misleading.

But this gets it backwards. The colours are calibrated by the $<x, y>$ coordinates of Figure 6.3 (and an additional dimension that need not concern us here). (There are other systemizations of colour experience as well; for present purposes, the differences are not important.) Monochrome beams of light and other light beams can be placed in the $<x, y>$ matrix; light of 700 nm is red. But it is the $<x, y>$ matrix that is directly given; it marks the colour properties we perceive directly.

Here is a better way of thinking about colour properties. They are simply the values that opponent processing computes. Or to put it differently, each colour-vision system, with its proprietary system of cones and opponency functions, generates its own system of colour properties. This, I take it, is what lies behind Byrne and Hilbert's (2003) characterization of colour representation:

> Objects are represented as having proportions of "hue" magnitudes . . . if an object is perceived as orange, then it is represented as having a value of R that is approximately 50 percent of its total hue, and similarly with Y . . . If [it] is perceived as purple, it is seen as having R and B in a similar proportion.
>
> (Byrne and Hilbert 2003, 14)

Byrne and Hilbert define the variables R, Y, etc., in terms of opponent values. The details are unimportant here, but let's just say that the red-green, blue-yellow, and black-white dimensions of colour are hue "magnitudes" defined by functions of L-, M-, and S-cone responses. Colour properties are just triples of these magnitudes. Simplifying greatly: colour properties are functions of the three cone responses. Different animals (and perhaps even different individual humans) use differently tuned cones and different opponent functions, resulting in individually tailored colour schemes. This is what makes novel colours possible.

Think back to audition; when we perceive pitch and loudness, we directly perceive structural properties of frequency and volume. Byrne and Hilbert are proposing, in effect, that when we perceive colour, we directly perceive a property defined in terms of cone-cell response differences. Notice that by their proposal, they are committed to bird colours being different from human trichromat colours. This is, I believe, a revolutionary consequence. (They take their proposal in a physicalist direction, but I won't go into that here.)

To clarify, looking a certain colour is not a matter of evoking a certain cone response. For as we noted earlier, *constancy processing* adjusts apparent colour so that it is more or less constant in varying illumination conditions. Consider a pale yellow object like a lemon. When it is under leaf colour, the light falling on it is tinged with green; when it is under a bright blue sky, the light falling on it is yellow-deficient; at sunset, it is irradiated with red-tinged light. Consequently, the light received from the lemon will vary from greenish under the tree, to darker under the blue sky, to more orange at sunset. In these different conditions, the lemon has a different effect on the cone cells. Constancy processing modifies and adjusts the cone-cell response so that it varies less than the light received changes. It looks more or less the same shade of yellow in all three conditions.

Summarizing

There are three cone cells, each of which has a certain response range.
Colour is defined by chromatic *dimensions* that we directly experience.

The chromatic dimensions are functions of cone-cell responses.
An object appears to have colour *C* if it visually appears to have the chromatic dimensions that define *C*.

A closing remark. I have said what it is to appear a certain colour, but what is it to *be* a certain colour? Something that looks orange *is* orange if it actually is the colour it looks to be. But what is it to be this colour in actuality, as opposed to merely looking that way? I would urge that this is not perceptually given. Being a certain colour is to look that colour in circumstances *C*: for instance, in white light or in good light, etc. But surprising facts have been uncovered about colour appearance: things look different when in certain situations of contrast, or when viewed obliquely, etc. We learn how to make colour judgements, but artists and scientists can still surprise us.

Proposition 6 Colour properties do not correspond to wavelength or other physical quantities. They are the outputs of opponent processing.

VII Conclusion: novel colours again

Is turmeric human-orange or bird-orange (where the latter is the name I give to whatever colour a bird sees when it looks at turmeric)? The question is based on the idea that we have to choose. Perhaps we *would* have to choose if colour were defined in terms of an external quality such as wavelength; then different colour systems would arguably be incompatible. But we have seen that colour doesn't do this. The colour properties humans see are defined by the chromatic dimensions that arise from their cone-cells and opponent functions; the colour properties birds see are similarly defined. These are simply different ways to partition the domain of surfaces. Turmeric is rightly classified as human-orange by humans and as bird-orange by birds. Human and bird visual systems have different ways of partitioning surfaces.

Sensory systems assign worldly objects to categories. There are two kinds of constraints on this function.

First, sensory systems must assign relevantly similar objects to the same categories. A coloured object sends different light to the eye in different conditions of illumination, and the visual system gets it wrong if it does not generate the same experience in all of these conditions. Getting this right is the function of *constancy processing*. (See section V above.)

The second kind of constraint has to do with the correspondence between sensory properties and the physical world. As we saw, high and low pitch corresponds to high and low acoustic frequency. An auditory system would be nonfunctional if it violated this correspondence. We have seen that colour does not correspond to physical properties in the way that pitch does. Consequently, it should not be thought of as violating its function if there is a failure of correspondence. Bird colours are just as much out of correspondence with physical wavelength-related properties as human colours are. But neither of these perceptual categories are nonfunctional as a result. As we said at the outset, perception serves animals differently from humans, but equally well.

Proposition 7 Novel colours constitute a different but equally valid system of assigning objects to perceptual categories as human colours.

Notes

1   It's important to remember here that we are *not* talking about mixing pigments or filters, but rather about *phenomenal* components of colour experience. Orange is experienced as a mixture of reddishness

and yellowishness. It is also important to distinguish between the *colour*, red, and the *hue dimension*, reddishness. Orange is redd*ish*, but not red; in the Swedish Colour System, it is 50% **R** and 50% **Y**.

2   Presumably, only those with "perfect pitch" know it *completely* by hearing. Most of us hear pitch (and also loudness) only relationally – we don't have a perceptual schema for all pitch qualities, within which we can place notes that we hear. Arguably, trichromats have "perfect colour," or something close to it – we *do* have a perceptual schema for colour. (The Munsell and Natural Colour System are attempts to capture this schema; see Matthen forthcoming.) This is a difference between the two cases that I won't explore further here.

3   There is constancy processing in sound analogous to that described in Section V for colour. Consequently, the auditory system may use pitch cues to adjust loudness and vice versa. This doesn't add new structure to auditory properties; it is rather an adjustment of how particular sounds are assigned to those properties.

Further reading

For more about colour vision in other animals, see the classic work by G. H. Jacobs, *Comparative Color Vision* (New York: Academic Press, 1981), and also J. F. Nuboer, "A Comparative View of Colour Vision" (*Netherlands Journal of Zoology* 36, 1986: 344–380), as well as Osorio et al. 1999. Important discussions of the evolution of colour vision are found in B. C. Regan et al., "Fruits, Foliage, and the Evolution of Colour Vision" (*Philosophical Transactions of the Royal Society of London B* 356, 2001: 229–283) and N. J. Dominy and P. W. Lucas, "Ecological Importance of Trichromatic Vision in Primates" (*Nature* 410, 2001: 363–366), as well as Surridge et al. 2003. A superb account of colour structure is found in H. Arnkil, *Colours in the Visual World* (Helsinki: Aalto ARTS Books, 2013), Chapter 7. Philosophical discussion of these issues is found in M. Matthen, *Seeing, Doing, and Knowing* (Oxford: Clarendon Press, 2005).

References

Byrne, Alex, and David Hilbert (2003) "Color Realism and Color Science," *Brain and Behavioral Sciences* 26: 3–64.

Hardin, C. L. (1988) "Phenomenal Colors and Sorites," *Noûs* 22: 213–234.

Hume, D. (1739/1978) *A Treatise of Human Nature*. L. A. Selby-Bigge and P. H. Nidditch (eds.) New York: Oxford University Press.

Johnston, Mark (1992) "How to Speak of the Colours," *Philosophical Studies* 68: 221–263.

Kainz, Pamela M., Jay Neitz, and Maureen Neitz (1998) "Recent Evolution of Uniform Trichromacy in a New World Monkey," *Vision Research* 38: 3315–3320. doi:10.1016/S0042-6989(98)00078-9

King, Andrew J., and Israel Nelken (2009) "Unraveling the Principles of Auditory Cortical Processing: Can We Learn From the Visual System?" *Nature Neuroscience* 12: 698–701. doi: 10.1038/nn.2308

Matthen, Mohan (1999) "The Disunity of Color," *Philosophical Review* 108: 47–84.

Matthen, Mohan (forthcoming) "Unique Hues and Colour Experience," *Routledge Handbook of the Philosophy of Colour.*

Moore, G. E. (1903) *Principia Ethica* Cambridge: Cambridge University Press.

Osorio, D., M. Vorobyev, and C. D. Jones (1999) "Colour Vision of Domestic Chicks," *Journal of Experimental Biology* 202: 2951–2959.

Russell, Bertrand (1912) *The Problems of Philosophy* Oxford: Oxford University Press.

Surridge, Alison K., Daniel Osorio, and Nicholas I. Mundy (2003) "Evolution and Selection of Trichromatic Vision in Primates," *Trends in Ecology and Evolution* 18: 198–205. doi:10.1016/S0169-5347(03)00012-0

Thompson, Evan (1992) "Novel Colors," *Philosophical Studies* 68: 321–349.

7

COLOR MANIPULATION AND COMPARATIVE COLOR

They're not all compatible

Derek H. Brown

Introduction

Comparative color vision has had a rich, positive impact on basic issues in the philosophy of color and philosophy of perception.[1] Most centrally, it has demonstrated an unexpected variety of color visual architecture and of uses to which color vision has and can be put by various animals. Architectural differences include differences in the numbers of cones, cone sensitivities (differences within the same range of the electromagnetic spectrum and by virtue of extending to different ranges), the processing of cone outputs, the presence and absence of oil droplets, and so on. The uses of color vision across species have some broad, uninformative commonalities (color vision helps creatures see) and differences that contain important lessons about both humans and nonhumans (see below). This knowledge has forced us to: more broadly conceive of what the *function* of color vision is within an organism or species; recognize substantive differences in color *perceptions* across species, fundamentally broader differences than we are forced to recognize within humanity; speculatively conclude that various nonhuman animals have categorically different color *experiences* from our own; and push color *ontology*, as many phenomena do, away from any simple form of color objectivism.

In this brief chapter, I must leave to one side many fascinating questions that have been studied in this area over the last twenty-five years. To facilitate this, I will make some simplifying assumptions.

Do nonhuman animals perceive colors at all? I suppose that at least some of them do. Justification for this stems from numerous factors, including the existence of visual systems that are not only wavelength sensitive (i.e., have numerous cones) but also exhibit opponent processing and color constancy. Those who wish to emphasize the importance of consciousness for color perception may wish to examine the animals with these kinds of visual systems to see which ones otherwise satisfy their preferred account of consciousness, and conclude that only these ones see colors. I am not opposed to this, but the issue will not substantively impact this work. For ease of discussion, I will be liberal and suppose that many of the species with these kinds of visual systems do have consciousness and see colors.

Are animal colors like human colors? Fortunately, this is treated in Mohan Matthen's Chapter 6 in this volume. As a simplifying assumption, I will suppose that Matthen is right that bird colors are distinct from human colors. More generally, I presume:

Disunity Hypothesis: architectural differences in color visual systems across different species in general yield disjoint *spaces* (*exclusion ranges, families, sets*) of colors for those species.[2]

Human colors are different from and do not overlap with pigeon colors, and so on for different pairs of species. The reader is invited to consult Matthen's chapter for a supporting argument.

Although Disunity takes no stance on the reality or instantiation of color, it raises difficult questions about it. One easy means of appreciating this is by appeal to the supposition that color experiences are of or about colors. Perceptual relationalists (/acquaintance theorists) presume, minimally, that the colors experiences are about are instantiated in our world. Representationalists presume, minimally, that the colors *veridical* experiences are about are instantiated in our world. I will work with the latter framework, though what follows is generalizable to the former.

Supposing Disunity obtains, is one of these color spaces uniquely correct of our world? More generally, are some spaces more correct than others? It is exceedingly difficult to single out a preferred space, in large part because it is difficult to single out a preferred color visual system. Different species are sensitive to different wavelength information and in different ways, and use it for different purposes (e.g., to learn different things about the world, to variously interact with it). If there is some unique color space of our reality, comparative color vision does a good job of hiding it from us. To take one fascinating class of examples (Akins and Hahn 2014: 154), a functioning visual system for underwater creatures helps them survive (eat and not be eaten) in their normal, water-laden environments. This means that the system can adequately interpret the light arrays coming through water in front of them. But water – even more so than air – acts as a kind of filter, and thus the wavelengths of light passing through shallower depths is more varied than those passing through deeper depths (where only the intermediate "blue" wavelengths are left). Interestingly, color visual systems are often suitably varied depending on whether the creature typically lives in shallower or deeper waters. Relatedly, creatures who typically look down into the ocean look into a dark background. To facilitate the perception of other life, their color visual systems often systematically normalize or "ignore" darkness and enhance lightness, thus increasing their sensitivity to food and prey. By contrast, creatures who typically look up look into a bright background. Their systems often normalize or "ignore" lightness and enhance darkness, so as to be sensitive to the darkened shadows things above them project downward.

The idea that one color visual system is uniquely correct, or even that one is more correct than another, stands in tension with the kinds of lessons we've learned from comparative studies. There is much to discuss here, but for simplicity I assume:

Ecumenicism: all species' color visual systems are equally correct/veridical.

Finally, given that my interest is primarily in what we can learn from cross-species studies, I will also for simplicity suppose a known falsity:

Within-species unity: there are no systemic variations in color vision across individuals within a species.

Philosophers of color have emphasized the importance of "normal" systemic variations in human color perception (the plethora of work on unique hue variations is a great source for this; see Tye 2006 and various *Analysis* articles that followed), and new ground has recently been broken on our understanding of less "normal" variations like color blindness (Broackes 2010). Working these topics into what follows would be a distraction. By contrast, nonsystemic, local variations in color experience within a species cannot be avoided without risking incoherence:

different individuals often view things from different locations, and in different conditions, and these factors can impact experienced and perhaps perceived color. These variations are assumed, though they will not play a substantive role in this discussion. What is *excluded* are variations that remain when members of the same species view the same thing at the same time in the same condition.

1 Pluralism and selectionism

Assume that one species' color experiences are generally veridical. Given Ecumenicism, this entails that others' are too, and given Disunity, it follows that there are numerous veridical color experiences from different color spaces. As above, I presume that a minimal condition on a color experience being veridical is that the color the experience is of or about is instantiated in our world. We now have:

Color Pluralism: colors from disjoint color spaces are instantiated in our world.[3]

While Pluralism places a significant constraint on color ontology, it nonetheless leaves many critical aspects of it underdetermined. For example, assuming that minds are in our world, Pluralism is mute with regard to the mind-(in)dependence of color. For example, color mentalists believe that colors are properties instantiated by minds (e.g., properties of sense-data, qualia, or neural states). Pluralism can be accommodated by holding that the minds of different species instantiate colors from different spaces. Assume that the minds of different species, while located in our universe, occupy distinct, non-overlapping, spatiotemporal regions (e.g., a human mind is never in the same place at the same time as a bird mind, and vice versa). It follows that, while Pluralism obtains, no part of the world instantiates more than one color (on a suitably restricted reading of "part").[4]

My interest is in the application of these considerations to *Color Objectivism*, which asserts that colors are mind-independent properties. Various species visually experience overlapping parts of the world (e.g., humans and birds both see at least some of the same trees). Since by hypothesis these experiences are generally veridical with regard to color, accommodating Pluralism now requires that the same part of the world can simultaneously instantiate more than one color. Put succinctly, a uniform object can simultaneously instantiate different colors. Is this plausible?

The matter concerns our commitments to color (in)compatibilities. Familiar color incompatibilities include:

(1) No uniform thing is simultaneously blue and green.

Our focus is on colors from distinct spaces, something like:

(2) No uniform thing is simultaneously blue and shmeen.

One can generally reject color incompatibilities, in which case one rejects both (1) and (2). Alternatively, one might reject (2) while accepting (1). Given the above assumptions, there is merit in exploring this latter possibility: the assumptions do not conflict with (1); there are independent reasons for accepting (1); and *prima facie* one might be unsure how to approach (2) and thus remain open-minded about it.

Rejecting (2) while accepting (1) is a commitment of *Pluralist Selectionism* (hereafter Selectionism, its adherents being Selectionists). The view asserts Pluralism and Objectivism (hence rejects (2)), and holds that during color perception, a given species selects, from among the many colors that a sample uniform thing instantiates, colors from within the color space its vision system is attuned to (Kalderon 2007, Matthen 2005, Allen 2009; this is arguably a consequence of Byrne and Hilbert 2003). Thus, a uniform thing can simultaneously be both objectively blue and shmeen, but while human vision selects blue (resulting in us experiencing the thing's blue color), pigeon vision selects shmeen (resulting in pigeons experiencing the thing's shmeen color). A central goal of Selectionists is to nonetheless maintain (1), and they view the kind of incompatibility contained in (1) as not merely a feature of color experiences but as a feature of colors themselves. The aforementioned works achieve these aims by appeal to the determinable-determinate distinction. Colors within, say, human color space bear (in)compatibilities with one another by virtue of being determinates relative to the determinable human color space. But, it is argued, a given species' color space is not merely determinable but *super*-determinable, meaning that colors from different spaces avoid being mutually incompatible by being fundamentally *not comparable*. They are "just different" (Allen 2009: 208). The extent of non-comparability between families is a total, categorical, commitment:

> *Categorical Non-comparability between Color Spaces* (*Non-comparability*): colors from different spaces are categorically neither compatible nor incompatible with one another. They are non-comparable, disjoint sets of properties.[5]

Given Non-comparability, one has seeming grounds to reject (2) but is not pressured to reject (1). Non-comparability is an extreme position in regards to relations between different color spaces. An equally extreme position in the opposite direction is:

> *Categorical Incompatibility between Color Spaces* (*Incompatibility*): colors from different spaces are categorically incompatible with one another.

If Incompatibility is true, then (2) is true and there is a thorny relationship between Objectivism, Ecumenicism, and Disunity. I aim to defend an intermediary position, something between Non-comparability and Incompatibility. It is not clear to me that this is where we will end up, but I do believe that Selectionists cannot safely endorse Non-comparability, and a successful argument in favor of an intermediary position that still adheres to Objectivism secures this outcome.

2 Pure and applied Non-comparability

Debates about color (in)compatibilities are notoriously tricky. Evidential sources include experience, language, sensory physiology, optics, and so on. Arguments can appeal to color theory (e.g., opponent-process theory), abstract metaphysics (e.g., the determinable-determinate relation), analogies with relevant cases (e.g., between geometric and color spaces), et cetera. Each of these has at least some value and should contribute to a considered view. I must focus the discussion.

One thing that strikes me about using the determinable-determinate relation to defend Non-comparability is the abstractness of the reasoning. In my judgment, we can use this relation to argue that there is no incoherence in Non-comparability: each color space can be viewed as an internally consistent, self-contained "system of colors" that in principle does not invade or conflict with other systems. This is an argument for an *abstract* or *pure* kind of non-comparability. But Selectionists need something stronger. They defend a claim about *concrete* or *applied* non-comparability that, for example, a uniform thing *in our world* can simultaneously be blue and shmeen. This is a very different idea. Consider an analogy with geometric spaces (i.e., Euclidean and non-Euclidean spaces).

That there are numerous (in)compatibilities within a geometric space is adequately clear, as is the idea that each geometric space is self-contained and thus doesn't place constraints on other spaces. They are non-comparable in this rough sense.[6] The difference I wish to highlight is between pure and applied geometry, for *even if* we exclude (in)compatibilities between geometries in the abstract, it does not mean that they don't obtain in concrete realities. Indeed, one of the great achievements of Einstein's General Theory of Relativity was an argument to the effect that the universe has or obeys the rules of a fairly specific non-Euclidean geometric space. The other geometric spaces, though independent from this one *in the abstract*, are nonetheless inconsistent with this one *when applied to our world*.

This interpretation of general relativity is no doubt debatable, and the analogy between pure and applied geometric spaces and pure and applied color spaces deserves extended treatment. Regardless, the lesson is simple: non-comparability in the abstract need not translate into non-comparability in the concrete. In my judgment, the idea that there are distinct color spaces that are categorically not comparable (and hence avoid all incompatibilities), and motives for this idea drawn, for example, from the determinable-determinate distinction, are foremost about abstract color knowledge. When applied to concrete worlds, an entirely different set of considerations, notably *empirical* ones, come to the fore. In other words, the Selectionist argument for Non-comparability conflates two senses of "(in)compatibilities," one articulable in the abstract domain of inquiry, and the other articulable in the concrete domain. The determinable-determinate distinction can ground conclusions about the former, but not about the latter – and conclusions about the latter are what Selectionists seek to draw.

Primary sources of empirical evidence regarding concrete (in)compatibilities, including Non-comparability, are color experience, sensory physiology, and optics. By virtue of endorsing Objectivism, Selectionists cannot explain concrete (in)compatibilities in terms of sensory physiology, for colors are, by definition, independent of perceiver peculiarities. They may use sensory physiology to help uncover the empirical ground of concrete (in)compatibilities, but the ground must ultimately be in objective features. This is a nontrivial constraint.

Human color experience can be used to ground concrete (in)compatibilities within human color space, but at present not across human and nonhuman spaces, and so also for the indirect knowledge we have of the color experiences of other species. In theory, optics on its own might suffice, but we are not in a position to develop a robust theory of various objective color spaces merely through the study of interactions between light and substance. We need to coordinate the likes of optics, color experience, and sensory physiology to uncover objective concrete (in) compatibilities, and then the relevant parts of optics (/objective reality) to help ground them. Only then can we assess the status of Non-comparability in the applied domain of Objectivism. I will briefly sketch such an approach, one drawn from *color manipulation*[7] and designed to strictly work within Selectionist commitments. Even within these constraints, we should resist Non-comparability.

3 Color manipulation and Non-comparability

When we manipulate colors through objective processes such as painting, dying, and heating, we often witness color *replacement*, where the color at the end of the process is different from and has replaced the one at the beginning. For example, we turn a blue fabric into a green one via dyes and turn black into red coal via heat. Manipulations that do not result in replacement include ones that achieve color layering (both the original and new color are present, one before the other), failed attempts (e.g., the paint doesn't stick), and so on. Regardless of the exceptions, it is clear that manipulation routinely results in replacement.

Manipulation is a well-tested and tangible source for knowledge about color (in)compatibilities. When we dye the blue fabric green, we witness a kind of incompatibility between the two colors. By witnessing many such manipulations, we induce that there are numerous color incompatibilities, and that roughly, colors from the same level of determinacy are all mutually incompatible, that is: categorical colors like blue, green, and orange are all mutually incompatible; fine-grained colors like royal blue, aqua blue, and sky blue are all mutually incompatible. Colors across levels of determinacy can be compatible: blue and aqua blue are mutually compatible.[8]

At first pass, this source of information is confined only to the human color space: via manipulation, we only directly see human colors turn into human colors, and hence our resulting beliefs about (in)compatibilities are limited to that family. One might argue that because of this, it is impermissible to infer anything about animal colors from manipulation. Such arguments should be resisted. Our beliefs about animal colors (e.g., Disunity) derive from a decent understanding of the workings of the color visual systems and environments of various species and *not* from any direct observation of animal colors. If that source of information is available to justify Disunity or Pluralism, then surely it is available to critique it.

Beliefs about human color (in)compatibilities drawn from manipulation don't stem *only* from our color experiences, they also stem from robust knowledge of the impact manipulation has on the physical features of objects and how that is relevant to our color experiences and color perceptions more generally. This can be exploited to break into the debate over Non-comparability and Incompatibility precisely because the very same (or similar) physical features are equally (or similarly) relevant to the color perceptions of nonhumans. The result is that there are compatibilities and incompatibilities between human and animal colors within the broad Selectionist framework. Let me sketch the argument.

Manipulation changes human colors primarily because it changes the way objects reflect (transmit, produce[9]) light. The way objects reflect light is as critical an environmental factor for understanding animal color vision as it is for human color vision. If, like the Selectionist, one endorses Objectivism, then light reflectance is, if not definitive of color (e.g., Byrne and Hilbert 2003), at least something on which color supervenes (Allen 2009: 215). In saying that for Objectivism color supervenes on reflectance, I minimally mean that if one changes the color of something, then one changes its reflectance profile in some way, and that the reverse need not obtain, though often will. (Below, I consider an Objectivism that denies this supervenience.)

Suppose, with the Selectionist, that there is a uniform fabric that is blue and shmue, the former being the color human vision selects and the latter being the color pigeon vision selects. When we dye the fabric green, we change its reflectance properties, and as such there is every expectation that we might change it from shmue to (say) shmeen. Suppose we do not. Perhaps it is shmue because of a portion of its reflectance profile that was unchanged by the dye. Indeed, that portion may lie inside or outside the visible spectrum, since pigeon vision extends into both the ultraviolet and infrared ranges. In this case, we have *prima facie* evidence for a kind of compatibility between not only blue & shmue, but also between green & shmue. Suppose, for illustration, that all manipulations preserve the fabric's shmue, that is, that no manipulation in human color affects the fabric's shmue color: it is shmue no matter its human color. In this case, calling shmue "compatible" with blue, green, and the other human colors is strictly true, but seems too weak a conclusion. A more appropriate conclusion is that shmue is maximally compatible with, indeed independent from, human colors. This is the kind of outcome predicted by Non-comparability. Anything less would be an admission that shmue is incompatible with some human color, violating Non-comparability.

The problem with this picture should already be apparent. It stems from the implausibility of the idea that manipulating human colors will not impact animal ones, for the reverse will often, if not typically, obtain. Thus, suppose when we dye the blue fabric green, the fabric's shmue is replaced with shmeen. We now have *pima facie* evidence of compatibilities between blue & shmue and between green & shmeen, and evidence of *in*compatibilities between blue & green, and between shmue & shmeen. And even this does not exhaust what we've learned, for we *also* have *pima facie* evidence of an incompatibility between blue & shmeen and between green & shmue. This is nothing like the idea behind Non-comparability.

A fuller picture of this argument can be detailed with actual reflectance values and illuminants, and actual color visual states induced in pigeons, humans, and other species. We have working knowledge of how different reflectances interact with the color visual systems of different species, and of what various manipulations do to those reflectances, so we can figure out how various manipulations will and will not impact the color perceptions of different species – at least in partial, rough detail. These specifics I leave to scientists working in these fields. I predict that a complicated picture will emerge: some manipulations will not impact the color perceptions of some species but will impact those of others; some manipulations will similarly impact the color perceptions of two species and differently impact the perceptions of two other species; and so on. All of this is to say that, given the tools we have, and a set of assumptions that are friendly to Selectionism, we can develop an empirically informed model of various compatibilities and incompatibilities between colors across spaces, *pace* Non-comparability.

In reply, one might deny that color manipulation is an evidential source for color (in)compatibilities across color spaces. This is a bumpy road. As stated above, color manipulation is a very familiar and tangible source for knowledge about color (in)compatibilities within human color space, and we can work out (at least roughly) how manipulations will impact color perceptions across species. It is question-begging to assert that in principle, manipulations are irrelevant to assessing Non-comparability. We are owed an argument. Importantly, one means of mounting that argument is unavailable to adherents of Objectivism, namely, attempts to explain (in)-compatibilities across color spaces by appeal to sensory physiology. Another approach would be to free different color spaces from the physical underpinnings of human color. For example, one might think of pigeon colors as not only nonphysical features, but as features that do not supervene or in any important way correlate with reflectances. In this case, manipulating human colors will leave pigeon colors unaffected. Alas, this reply has numerous drawbacks: it is question-begging, makes colors rather mysterious, and stands in tension with the very evidence that underpins Selectionism (i.e., the well-studied relationships between reflectances and animal color vision). I thus submit that the above argument against Non-comparability has merit.

4 Conclusion: how bad is the problem?

In reply, the Selectionist might argue that the picture sketched in Section 3 admits that uniform objects can and often *do* have multiple colors (e.g., the uniform object is both blue and shmue at the outset, and both green and shmeen at the conclusion). In this sense, although it speaks against Non-comparability, it is consistent with *some* form of Objectivist Pluralism. That is, it certainly does not justify Incompatibility.

This misses the point. The argument wasn't intended to defeat Selectionism *simpliciter*, it was intended to undermine a common form of Selectionism, namely one that proposes Non-comparability to explain how Pluralism can obtain within Objectivism. That goal, I believe, the argument achieves. Beyond that, the above picture does feed into some well-known other challenges to Selectionism. In what remains, I sketch that impact.

Two central pressures against color Objectivism, including Selectionism, stem from the relativity of perception and the structure of color.[10] Regarding the former, the worry is that the color of a given objective thing can vary along dimensions that are extrinsic to that thing, such as the nature of the perceivers' perceptual apparati, and hence that the color at issue cannot be intrinsic to that thing. If that color in fact depends on perceptual apparati, then it is not only not intrinsic to the thing, it is at least somewhat subjective. The worry stemming from the structure of color typically proceeds by specifying various dimensions of colors (e.g., hues, saturations, and lightnesses) and various relations between colors (e.g., relations of composition, exclusion, similarity). The challenge to Objectivism advocates is to explain the resulting relations or overall structure between colors in terms of objective properties (e.g., in terms of reflectances and their features). This turns out to be a nontrival task, for various aspects of color structure seem to be well explained by appeal to perceivers' perceptual apparati, and less well explained solely by appeal to objective properties. While I am tempted by both arguments, I will not presume their soundness. Instead, I will conclude by remarking on how the above fits into them.

Since (in)compatibilities between colors are typically included within the structure of color, there is a natural connection between our topic and the argument from structure. Suppose there are (in)compatibilities between human and pigeon colors. Color ontologists must explain these in terms of their preferred ontology. Selectionists must therefore explain these in terms of relations between objective colors (or explain why they are not essential to the nature of human and pigeon colors – set this option aside). In one respect, we already have a hint of a solution. For illustration, suppose that something is blue because it reflects light from the short end of the visible electromagnetic spectrum and absorbs it from the long end, and something is shmeen because it reflects light from the long end and absorbs it from the short. We then have the roots of an explanation for why blue and shmeen are incompatible. In this regard, these considerations can *assist* Objectivism. This again illustrates that my target is not Objectivism so much as the Non-comparability explication of Selectionism. But the details matter, if for no other reason than that this "explanation" of color (in)compatibilities presumes the existence of a viable account of colors in terms of reflectances, and it is far from clear that there is one. Thus, even if some (in)compatibilities between color spaces can be given an objective explanation, it does not follow that all can. Nor does it follow that other aspects of the structures of color spaces fit into the ideals of Objectivism.

With regard to the relativity of color, Selectionism has been offered in part to undermine such arguments, which tend to rely on the premise that a uniform object cannot be one and another color at the same time (Kalderon 2007, Allen 2009). The Non-comparability approach can be used to resist that premise. However, given the above considerations, that approach should be resisted, for a more flexible view of the relations between applied color spaces seems more accurate. If such a "flexible" view can overcome the tension between Pluralism and Objectivism, then at least *this* challenge from the relativity of interspecies color perceptions would be contained. The challenges raised by other forms of relativity (see, e.g., Section 0) would remain unaddressed.[11]

Notes

1 Allen (forthcoming) provides a wonderful, accessible overview – one to which I am indebted.
2 See Matthen (1999) for an extended defense. "Exclusion ranges" is from Matthen (2005: 103–5) and "family" is from Kalderon (forthcoming). "Spaces" is used in various publications, but my main source is Allen (2009).
3 Kalderon (2007) contains a beautiful defense of a similar idea. Note that his preferred perceptual theory is relationalist as opposed to representationalist, and that his pluralism is specifically designed to preserve color objectivism, a matter to which I will turn below.

4 This conclusion may, but need not, be reached via dispositional color ontologies, views that assert that colors are powers of objects to produce color sensations in perceivers. The matter crucially depends on how "color dispositions" are fleshed out, something space prevents me from discussing.

5 This is a clear commitment of Matthen's exclusion ranges (Matthen 2005: 103–5), and arguably the Selectionist views of Kalderon (2007) and Allen (2009).

6 The matter is more complicated than this because we can articulate numerous mappings between geometries and discuss various ways in which items in one can be mapped into items in the other, and vice versa. Let us set aside whether or not these mappings can yield a relevant sense of (in)compatibilities between abstract geometries.

7 Campbell (2006) offers a great discussion of color manipulation, but doesn't consider its application to Pluralism.

8 There are numerous details about color (in)compatibilities within a color space that are worthy of exposition and analysis. Given length constraints, I must leave these details aside.

9 I suppress this qualification throughout.

10 Arguments from perceptual relativity against perceptual objectivity have well-known and ancient roots. A recent and influential use of this reasoning in color is Cohen (2009). Hardin (1988) is a well-known source for the argument from structure; another is Pautz (2006).

11 I am indebted to Jake Beck and Mohan Matthen for helpful comments on an earlier draft. Sincere thanks to Brandon University for granting the sabbatical leave during which this article was written, Clare Hall and The University of Cambridge for providing welcoming accommodations, and the Templeton Foundation and Tim Crane's *New Directions in the Study of Mind* project for financial assistance. This publication was made possible through the support of a grant from the John Templeton Foundation. The opinions expressed in this publication are those of the author and do not necessarily reflect the views of the John Templeton Foundation.

Further reading

Thompson, E., A. Palacios, and F. Varela (1992) "Ways of coloring: Comparative color vision as a case study for cognitive science," *Behavioural and Brain Sciences*, *15*: 1–74, was a ground-breaking work on comparative color vision. Hardin, C. L. (1992) "The virtues of illusion," *Philosophical Studies*, *68*(3): 371–82, argues that color vision evolved to help organisms engage with and think about their environments by creating colors for visual experience and thought. It is worth reading alongside Hilbert, D. (1992) "What is colour vision?" *Philosophical Studies*, *68*(3): 351–70, which argues that color constancy is central to color vision. Mollon, J. (1989) "'Tho' she kneel'd in that place where they grew...': The uses and origins of primate colour vision," *Journal of Experimental Biology*, *146*: 21–38, is an influential statement of the *frugivory hypothesis*, the idea that the purpose of color vision is to distinguish fruit from foliage.

References

Akins, K., and M. Hahn (2014) "More than mere colouring: The role of spectral information in human vision," *British Journal for the Philosophy of Science*, *65*: 125–171.

Allen, K. (2009) "Inter-species variation in colour perception," *Philosophical Studies*, *142*: 197–220.

——— (forthcoming) "Interspecies variations," in D. H. Brown and F. Macpherson, eds. *The Routledge Handbook on the Philosophy of Colour*, Milton: Routledge.

Broackes, J. (2010) "What do the color-blind see?" in J. Cohen and M. Matthen (eds.) *Color Ontology and Color Science*, Cambridge, MA: MIT Press.

Byrne, A., and D. Hilbert (2003) "Colour realism and colour science," *Behavioral and Brain Sciences*, *26*: 3–64.

Campbell, J. (2006) "Manipulating colour: Pounding an almond," in T. Gendler and J. Hawthorne (eds.) *Perceptual Experience*, pp. 31–49, Oxford: Oxford University Press.

Cohen, J. (2009) *The Red and the Real: An Essay on Colour Ontology*, Oxford: Oxford University Press.

Hardin, C. L. (1988) *Color for Philosophers*, Indianapolis, IN: Hackett.

Kalderon, M. (2007) "Color pluralism," *The Philosophical Review*, *116*: 563–601.

———— (forthcoming) "Monism and pluralism," in D. H. Brown and F. Macpherson, eds. *The Routledge Handbook on the Philosophy of Colour*, Milton: Routledge.

Matthen, M. (1999) "The disunity of color," *The Philosophical Review, 108*: 47–84.

———— (2005) *Seeing, Doing, and Knowing: A Philosophical Theory of Sense Perception*, Oxford: Oxford University Press.

———— "Novel colours in animal perception," Chapter 6 in this volume.

Pautz, A. (2006) "Can the physicalist explain colour structure in terms of colour experience?" *Australasian Journal of Philosophy, 84*(4): 535–564.

Tye, M. (2006) "The puzzle of true blue," *Analysis, 66*: 173–178.

PART II

Reasoning and metacognition

8

ANIMAL RATIONALITY AND BELIEF

Hans-Johann Glock

Moderate differentialists like Aristotle and Kant credited animals with "lower" mental/psychic phenomena like sentience, emotions, moods and perception, while denying the "higher" faculties of intellect and reason, including the capacity for genuine belief. In the same vein, Sellars (1957), Davidson (1985), Brandom (1994) and McDowell (1996) grant sentience or consciousness, while balking at intentional states like belief and desire. Against this stance, I shall rebut *a priori* philosophical objections against the idea of intentionality in animals, and present positive arguments in its favor.

Intentional verbs occur mainly in three sentential forms:

I	S	*V*s (thinks/believes/desires, etc.)	that *p*
II	S	*V*s (intends/wants/plans, etc.)	to *Φ*
III	S	*V*s (loves/desires/thinks about, etc.)	*X*

According to orthodoxy, the verbs that can replace "*V*" denote different types of *intentional attitudes*, and the substitution instances of "that *p*," "to *Φ*" or "*X*" their *contents*. *Prima facie*, sentences of type (I) state a *proposition*-oriented – or "that-ish" – *attitude*, those of type (II) an *action-oriented* – or "to-ish" – *attitude*, and those of type (III) an *object-oriented attitude*. Nonetheless, it is customary to subsume *all* forms of intentionality under the heading "propositional attitude," on the tacit assumption that *all* intentional verbs signify attitudes towards propositions. This by itself militates against the idea of animal intentionality, for the term "proposition" carries linguistic connotations. It begs fewer questions to speak of "intentional states" or "thinking." Furthermore, it is sheer dogmatism to insist that in order to desire a peanut or intend to play, animals must put themselves in relation to abstract propositions. Intelligent animals can devote their attention to, and hence think about objects or events (type III), and they can intend to do things (type II). What is controversial is whether the range of their thinking and intending is confined to the "here and now" or includes episodic memory and expectations concerning future eventualities (see Clayton et al. 2000; Mulcahy and Call 2006).

The lingualist master-argument

As regards animal intentionality of type I, a serious doubt arises out of the connection between contents, concepts and language. Donald Davidson illustrates it through an example of Malcolm's:

> Suppose our dog is chasing the neighbor's cat. The latter runs full tilt toward the oak tree, but suddenly swerves at the last moment and disappears up a nearby maple. The dog doesn't see this maneuver and on arriving at the oak tree he rears up on his hind feet, paws at the trunk as if trying to scale it, and barks excitedly into the branches above. We who observe this whole episode from a window say, "He thinks that the cat went up that oak tree."
>
> (Malcolm 1972–73: 13)

According to Davidson, however, Malcolm's dog cannot, strictly speaking, believe anything, because he lacks language (Davidson 1985: 474–8; 1984: 155). Davidson's stance is shaped by an influential line of reasoning, the "lingualist master-argument" (Glock 2010):

Concept thesis	Thinking (type I intentional states) requires concept-possession.
Language thesis	Concept-possession requires language.
Lingualist conclusion	Thinking requires language.
Dumbness thesis	Animals lack language.
Differentialist conclusion	Animals cannot think.

The argument is valid; whether it is sound depends on its three premises. My contribution brackets the dumbness thesis and tackles the other two premises in turn.

The representationalist picture of intentional states

The most potent argument for the concept thesis derives from representationalism, which regards intentional states as relations between a subject S and a propositional content. In the case of Malcolm's dog, it would have to be a relation of believing towards the propositional content that the cat is on the oak tree. But a propositional content is a mental or abstract entity; and that entity, according to mainstream representationalism, in turn consists of building blocks, concepts such as *cat*, *going up* and *oak tree*. By these lights, therefore, S cannot think that the cat went up the oak tree unless it possesses all of these component concepts.

One protective measure against the concept thesis postulates nonpropositional or "nonconceptual contents" (see Bermúdez and Cahen 2015). This response accepts that intentional verbs signify attitudes towards objects of a special kind, namely contents; it parts company by insisting that, in addition to propositional contents consisting of concepts (the contents of human thinking), there are "proto-propositional" contents consisting of nonconceptual components, notably sensory representations of a spatial kind (the contents of animal thinking and prereflective human perception). Unfortunately, it remains unclear how something can *both* be a content of a type I sentence, i.e. a signified by a that-clause, *and* proto-propositional, i.e. falling short of being a proposition. Furthermore, this rejection of the concept thesis creates a *congruity problem*. The distinction between different types of content counts against ascribing one and the same belief to humans and animals. It suggests that "Both Sarah and the dog believe that *p*" is not so much a falsehood as a zeugma – a potentially comical crossing of categories like "Both the exam and the chair were hard." For "Sarah believes that *p*" comes out as "Sarah stands in the relation of believing to the *thought* that *p*" while "The dog believes that *p*" comes out as "The dog stands in the relation of believing to the *protothought* that *p*." Some versions of nonconceptualism welcome this incongruity by insisting that animals represent in map-like, information-theoretic or analogue "formats" (respectively, Camp 2007; Allen 2013; Beck 2013), which resist faithful paraphrase in type I idiom. But this amounts to replacing the conceptual framework that laypeople and cognitive scientists successfully apply to animals. It remains to be shown that such novel characterizations of nonlinguistic cognition and conation are as illuminating as those couched in standard that-ish format. Indeed, the revisionist conceptual framework must ultimately allow explanation in terms of our established mental concepts, at least if they are to address our questions about the nature and extent of animal belief and rationality.

Another objection against the concept thesis reconceives rather than abandons the apparatus of intentional verbs and noun-clauses. It maintains that talk about "contents," whether conceptual or not, amounts to a misleading reification (Glock 2013). For one thing, the building-block model transposes the part/whole relation from the spatial and temporal sphere to a sphere – abstract entities – to which, *ex hypothesis*, neither spatial nor temporal notions apply. What is said or thought has genuine components only to the extent to which its linguistic expression has components.

For another, S's thinking that *p* is *not* a *bona fide* relation between S and an object *that p*, whether with or without components, whether abstract or mental. Admittedly, noun-clauses like "that the cat went up the oak tree" or "what Sarah believes" are, grammatically speaking, the objects of beliefs. Nevertheless, they no more refer to genuine objects than the quantifier in "Clare desires nothing." Properly analyzed, beliefs and desires are not genuine relations; instead they are, roughly speaking, dispositional properties of a creature. Although the sentences we use in ascribing thoughts to S include that-clauses with components, our ascriptions do not presuppose a prior ascription of the corresponding concepts. Instead, they are based on the subject manifesting certain perceptual capacities, attitudes and emotions. These manifestations include forms of behavior, postures and facial expressions which higher animals share with human beings.

Belief, truth and triangulation

This rebuttal of the concept thesis presupposes that animals can believe or know things; since they can be correct or mistaken as to how things are, they can have beliefs. Precisely that is contested by other considerations in favor of the concept thesis, which do not rely on representationalism. Starting out from the observation that a belief is something that "can be true or false" (1985: 479), Davidson in effect reasons along the following steps:

(i) S believes that *p* $\Rightarrow$ S can be *surpised* to find that ~*p*;
(ii) S can be *surprised* to find that ~*p* $\Rightarrow$ S can *recognize* that S was mistaken in believing that *p*;
(iii) S can *recognize* that S was mistaken in believing that *p* $\Rightarrow$ S has the *concept of belief*;
(iv) S has *the concept of belief* $\Rightarrow$ S is capable of *triangulation*, i.e. of linguistically communicating with another subject about the world, specifically about whether *p*.

Step (i) is contentious, however, since it bars a necessarily omniscient being (God) from believing things and rules out belief in necessary truths. Even if we set aside these exotic cases as irrelevant to the question of animal belief, objections remain. Step (ii) goes astray, insofar as it makes the possibility of believing dependent on *second-order* beliefs – beliefs about beliefs – to the effect that a previously held belief is mistaken. A simple change can lead S from the false belief that *p* to the true belief that not-*p*. S can recognize a mistake not just through thinking about its own prior belief, but also through correcting its behavior – notably through the deliverances of its senses – by pursuing a persistent goal in a more apposite manner. That S recognizes that things are other than S previously believed can be manifested in nonlinguistic reactions, such as surprise and disappointment. Findings suggesting that monkeys can recognize mistaken beliefs of their own in wager games (Kornell et al. 2007) put further pressure on Davidson's reasoning. If there is self-regarding metacognition in animals, either such cognition is nonconceptual – contrary to (iii) and the concept thesis – or nonlinguistic creatures can possess the concept of a mistake, contrary to the language thesis. Finally, concerning (iv), why shouldn't S be able to correct her beliefs by adopting a new perspective herself, rather than by conversing with another subject?

There is a possible response to this challenge. If S changes her perspective and subsequently alters her reactions to the objective situation, how can she distinguish correcting an objective error committed at time t_1 from the situation having changed by t_2? One option is the communication with another subject, who has held the situation fast in sight without altering her perspective. But couldn't S, while altering her perspective, keep the object in sight to a degree sufficient for ruling out pertinent changes? If so, triangular communication is *not necessary* for a grasp of the idea of objective truth. Indeed, unless S could trust her own individual ability to gauge the objective situation, how could she rely on the more presumptuous and precarious process of communication to undergird her judgment? Consequently, if triangular communication were necessary to assess the world objectively and hence for the idea of objective truth, as Davidson's argument assumes, it would *not be sufficient*, as he also contends.

Belief, knowledge and perception

Lingualist arguments against the possibility of animal belief are uncompelling. In addition, there are two reasons for positively accepting that some animals actually do have beliefs. The first arises from the connection between belief and knowledge. Intelligent animals command a sizable repository of "knowledge-how." They know, for example, how to crack nuts, hide provisions, entice a potential mate, etc. Such knowledge is not easily separated from *knowledge-that*. To know how to open a box is, among other things, to know that doing so requires lifting its lid. But now: S can only possess knowledge-that if it can also possess the corresponding beliefs. The pair knowledge/belief comes as a double-pack. To be more precise, the notion of believing must be available as a fallback option for characterizing the epistemic standing of a subject, if the latter exercises its cognitive abilities yet without acquiring knowledge. Even if not every case of knowing that *p* implies believing that *p* (as the tripartite conception of knowledge would vouchsafe), the *capacity* for knowledge presupposes the capacity for believing. To err is not just human! In animals, error manifests itself primarily in their behaving in ways that, though guided by their senses, are inadequate given the *de facto* situation (on the assumption of certain goals). Finally, the circumstances and causes of animal error are not just the stuff of anecdotes like that of Malcolm; they have been documented through ethology to the same extent as those of animal knowledge.

A second argument for animal belief revolves around the most basic cognitive ability. Higher animals are capable of perceiving their physical and social environment in various sense modalities. The crucial point is that they are capable not just of perceiving "things" (including organisms and events), but also of perceiving "facts" (cp. Dretske 2004). Animal perception does not just take the form

a)   S perceives X (the snake, the explosion, etc.).

It can also take the form

b)   S perceives that *p* (there is a snake ahead, there is an explosion, etc.).

This is demonstrated by the connection between perception and complex animal behavior.

Consider a dog that has learned not to grab anything when it is lying on the table but only when it is lying in his bowl. This dog now sees a bone on the table, but refrains from grabbing it and instead looks on, panting. Yet as soon as the bone is placed in the bowl, the dog goes for it. This mundane sequence is not explained by the dog simply perceiving discrete objects – the bone, the table and the bowl. It can only be explained in terms of the following opposition:

*   the dog sees at t_1 that the bone is on the table
*   the dog sees at t_2 that the bone is in the bowl.

Why? Because at both t_1 and t_2, the dog can see bone, table and bowl. So perception of the *conglomeration* formed by these three objects cannot explain the difference in its reactions at t_1 and t_2. One might respond that the problem vanishes if spatial relations like *x being on y* are among the objects that the dog can perceive. However, simply perceiving three distinct objects – bone, table, *x being on y* – does not explain the dog's behavior. Such an explanation is only in the offing if it can also perceive *that* the bone stands in the relation of *being on* to the table at one moment, to the floor at the next. And in that case, we are back with perceiving that *p*.

But, it might be objected, this behavior can be explained behavioristically. We only posit

*   stimulus at t_1: "bone on table" – reaction: "do not take"
*   stimulus at t_2: "bone in bowl" – reaction: "take."

Now, what sort of stimulus is this supposed to be? Is it purely proximal and physiological, like the pain stimuli to which even oysters react? This behaviorist fairy tale ignores the distinction between lower animals and higher ones like dogs, cetaceans and primates, which possess a range of different sense organs and corresponding sensory centers in the brain. Primates, at any rate, score well in the standard tests for object permanence and identification (Seed and Tomasello 2010: 409).

The alternative is to admit that the dog reacts not just to a proximal stimulus, but to perceived information. Yet how can this information be specified if not as a perceived *fact*? An apparent way out of this quandary might be as follows: what the dog perceives is not *that* the bone is on the table or in the bowl; what he perceives is "*bone on table*" or "*bone in bowl.*" However, if the determinants "on table" and "in bowl" are used *restrictively*, to indicate *which* bone the dog perceives, this does not explain the divergent behavior of the dog, which perceives the *same* bone at t_1 and t_2. Alternatively, if they are used as ellipses for "lying on the table" and "lying in the bowl," this explains the divergent behavior of the dog alright. Yet to perceive the bone *as* lying in the bowl is to perceive – albeit by another name – *that* the bone is lying in the bowl. One way or another, the dog's behavior can only be explained on the assumption of factual perception, perception *that*.

The second step in my argument simply pays due deference to the slogan *seeing is believing*. From "*S* sees *that p*" (the sun is shining, etc.), we may conclude either "*S* knows *that p*" (where "seeing" is used factively) or "*S* believes *that p*" (where it is not). But both "knowing *that p*" and "believing *that p*" are cases of "thinking *that p*" in the sense that is relevant here. One cannot resist this second step by rejecting these implications for the case of animals without a compelling argument to the effect that "sees *that p*" is systematically ambiguous as between humans and animals; and no such argument is in the offing. Consequently, the lingualist master-argument now faces a dilemma. *Either* the concept thesis is wrong, since we are compelled to ascribe thinking (perceptual beliefs) without imputing concepts. *Or* all animals capable of fact perception possess concepts, in which case the language thesis is wrong, since animals have many concepts.

Animal concepts

With respect to animal concepts, Kant and McDowell, among others, occupy the differentialist corner: animals can perceive, yet lack concepts of *any* kind. In the assimilationist corner are empiricists and many cognitive scientists, who have no qualms about ascribing complex concepts to animals. An intermediate position maintains that animals can possess some concepts, namely those that can be manifested in nonlinguistic behavior (e.g. Bekoff and Jamieson 1991: 19–20; DeGrazia 1996: 154–8). Their concepts may rarely be the ones we use in ascribing thoughts to them. For the discriminations which underlie animal behavior need not coincide with our verbal classifications, either extensionally – i.e. by grouping together the same objects – or intensionally – i.e. by grouping objects according to the same properties. A dog might group cats together with hamsters or distinguish black cats from all others; and even if it groups all and only cats together, it might recognize them by smell rather than visually. But this by itself is no obstacle to ascribing to animals concepts, albeit ones that *differ* from ours. Accordingly, what kind of concepts we should ascribe depends on empirical investigations into the parameters governing animal behavior.

Whether this alternative to the language thesis holds water naturally depends on what one makes of concepts and concept-possession. According to one account, concepts are principles of discrimination, and to possess a concept is to have the ability to recognize or discriminate different types of things (Price 1953: 355; Dupré 2002: 229). On this construal, some animals possess concepts. Both in the wild and in the laboratory, they distinguish between a host of different colors, tastes, sounds, shapes, stuffs, quantities, types of creatures, etc. Moreover, many of these discriminations are learned rather than innate.

Proponents of the language thesis protest that this account of concepts falls prey to a *reductio ad absurdum*.

> Unless we want to attribute concepts to butterflies and olive trees, we should not count the mere ability to discriminate between red and green or moist and dry as having a concept, not even if such selective behavior is learned.
>
> (Davidson 1997: 25)

Fortunately, however, these absurdities do not follow from treating concepts as powers of discrimination. Olive trees do not discriminate between moist and dry soil, since discrimination is a prerogative of *sentient* creatures. We must distinguish between mere differential reaction to causal inputs, which is a universal feature of physical phenomena, and discrimination, which is tied to perceptual capacities. Nevertheless, even proponents of animal concepts ought to accept that conceptualization requires more than discrimination. But what?

A common answer runs: S must not just be capable of "recognizing an F" but of "recognizing something *as* an F or recognizing it to be an F." This answer allows of different elaborations. According to Allen and Hauser, S must be able to recognize an F on the basis of several different properties, notably on the basis of properties which transcend perception. Preferably these properties should even be essential rather than accidental to F's (1996: 51).

This proposal explains why a subject that can recognize, e.g., a carburetor, only by its shape does not possess the concept of a carburetor. But an appeal to discrimination can also guarantee this result. For such a subject lacks the ability to discriminate between carburetors and things shaped like carburetors or between non-carburetors and carburetors of a novel design. Furthermore, the proposal rules out the possibility of distinguishing between perceptual and more abstract concepts, or between having more or less rich concepts of an F. Thus, the possession of everyday color concepts only requires mastery of one way of telling, and a purely perceptual one at that. It is even less plausible to suppose that one has the concept of an F only if one distinguishes F's by those features which we regard as essential to F's. To be sure, for a subject S capable of distinguishing between essential and nonessential properties, what concept of an F that S possesses may depend on what properties S regards as essential to being F. That capacity is clearly lacking in animals. However, distinguishing essential from accidental properties is prerequisite only to a theoretical understanding of concepts, not to their mere possession. We cannot exclude the possibility of baboons possessing the concept of an alpha male simply because they cannot regard some properties possessed by all alpha males – being the highest-ranking male – as essential, and others – e.g. being strong and aggressive – as inessential, i.e. as not required by the very concept of an alpha male.

A less-presumptuous explanation of "recognizing x as F" runs as follows: S does not just react differently, depending on whether or not x is F; rather, S *classifies* x as (non-)F. This, in turn, means S decides between distinct options: Is x F or not? Is x F or G? What is more, S is capable of doing this in a deliberate and considered manner (Glock 2010). These provisos add a *normative* dimension to the capacity to discriminate. By contrast to a purely mechanical disposition, classification can be correct or incorrect, since the sorting of things into F's and non-F's is to be measured against distinguishing features of F's that S herself regards as standards for treating something as F in her sorting behavior.

It might be objected that such classification amounts to what is traditionally known as "judgment," and thereby to an answering of *questions* of the form "Is x F or non-F?" and "Is x F or G?" Accordingly, classification would be tied to language after all; except that questions, though linguistic, are in the first instance the fallout from *problems*. Animals face problems of discrimination, and some of them can solve these by distinguishing things according to their properties in a deliberate and considered manner. Thus, chimpanzees can choose tools, e.g. for nut-cracking, in a way that is not just intelligent instead of mechanical, but also premeditated rather than simply based on trial and error.

Holism

There is an even more demanding conception, according to which S only possesses the concept of an F if S can draw inferences from the fact that x is F. At this juncture, the language thesis can be backed up by the "the intrinsically holistic character of the propositional attitudes," the alleged fact that "to have one is to have a full complement" (Davidson 1985: 473). Since at least some members of that complement are definitely beyond the ken for animals, they lack even the simple beliefs commonly ascribed to them. Malcolm's dog cannot believe of an object that it is a tree,

> unless we suppose the dog has many general beliefs about trees: that they are growing things, that they need soil and water, that they have leaves or needles, that they burn.

> There is no fixed list of things someone with the concept of a tree must believe, but
> without many general beliefs there would be no reason to identify a belief as a belief
> about a tree, much less an oak tree.
>
> (Davidson 1985: 475)

For one thing, Davidson contends that specific concepts that occur in our attributions even
of simple thoughts presuppose general beliefs, with which animals cannot be credited. But his
examples are far from compelling. He suggests that S can only believe that the cat went up the
oak or that the sun is behind clouds if S also knows that trees burn and that clouds consist of
water vapor. This would restrict the possession of many beliefs to moderately educated contemporaries. Furthermore, it implies that any alteration in general beliefs amounts to a conceptual
change, with the consequence that two scientific theories featuring incompatible empirical
claims cannot be talking about the same phenomena. As Davidson candidly admits, his holism
implies that the Ptolemeans could not believe that the earth is flat, since this would amount to
rejecting a belief that he treats as constitutive of our concept of the earth.

Like other proponents of the language thesis, Davidson has another string to his bow, namely
general holistic principles. But these are threatened by a *dilemma*: they are either too strong, since
they would also exclude plausible cases of human thought, or too weak, since they cannot rule
out all types of animal thought. The strongest holistic principle runs:

(A) (S believes that p & $p \Rightarrow q$) $\Rightarrow$ S also believes that q.

Principle (A) is excessively restrictive. Humans can believe the axioms of Euclidean geometry
without believing all the theorems entailed by them. According to a modally mitigated version,
S only needs to be *capable* of believing (learning, understanding) the consequences of its beliefs:

(B) (S believes that p & $p \Rightarrow q$) $\Rightarrow$ S is capable of also believing that q.

Even (B) is too demanding, however. For it is possible to believe the Euclidean axioms without
even being *capable of understanding* all of the theorems. It is more plausible to maintain that S need
be capable of appreciating only *some* rather than all of the things entailed by S's beliefs:

(C) S believes that $p \Rightarrow$ (there is at least one other belief that q such that $p \Rightarrow q$ and S is capable
     of believing that q).

According to (C), if a human being is incapable of even grasping *any* of the theorems entailed
by Euclid's axioms, he cannot believe the axioms either. However, (C) only offers moderate
support to the language thesis. There are animals capable of appreciating *some* consequences of
simple perceptual beliefs. That Malcolm's dog consistently barks up the oak tree by itself does
not manifest a belief that the cat is not in the maple tree; but if he continues to ignore the maple
tree, even when prompted by us to attend to it, that would begin to suggest that he has the belief.
Even nonlinguistic creatures can, in principle, be guided not just by what they perceive, but also
by what follows from what they perceive.

On the other hand, the failure of this linguist reasoning does not imply that a creature could
entertain just a single belief. Indeed, the complex and flexible demeanor required for conceptual
belief is incompatible with a behavioral repertoire capable of exhibiting just a single belief. Still,
the web of which any belief must be part need not extend as far as the web of sophisticated

human thought. What kind of network is required may depend on the belief and the creature concerned. From the fact that an animal lacks our web of beliefs and our concepts, it does not follow that it has no beliefs and no concepts.

As a last resort, a holistic defender of the language thesis can raise the bar for concept-possession even higher. It does not suffice for S to be capable of entertaining some consequences of a purported belief; S must also be able to *infer* these consequences.

(D) That S believes that p entails that there is at least one other belief that q such that $p \Rightarrow q$ and S is capable of inferring that q from S's belief that p.

Rationality, intelligence and inference

Whether animals can draw theoretical and/or practical inferences is connected to the issue of animal rationality. A venerable tradition conceives of reason as a capacity to justify one's beliefs and actions, paradigmatically by deriving them from less-contentious assumptions. Thinking (believing/desiring) that p is a precondition for drawing inferences and hence for the faculty of reason. In both theoretical and practical reasoning, one moves from one or more thoughts, the premises, to another thought, the conclusion. According to (D), the reverse also holds, since beliefs and desires are the prerogative of subjects capable of reasoning. Reasoning must be held apart from *intelligence*. Roughly speaking, intelligence is the ability to solve problems – notably novel ones – in a flexible way, one which is not predetermined genetically or epigenetically. It therefore presupposes a capacity for *learning*. Learning, for its part, ranges from routines of strict conditioning, as in the case of pigeons and rats in a Skinner box, through the "trial and error" procedure of capuchin monkeys in the trap-tube task, to the insight and foresight displayed by some great apes and corvids in the employment and production of tools. Even here, however, it is controversial whether it involves inferences from premises to conclusions. For it remains unclear how such ratiocination can be ascribed to subjects without language (see Glock 2009).

Recall, however, the ancient tale of the dog of Chrysippus (Sorabji 1993: 26). In chasing a prey of which it has lost the scent, this dog reaches a crossroad; it sniffs down the first path, then sniffs down the second path, then it immediately follows the third *without* sniffing. Empirical studies suggest that dogs can at best pull off such a feat with prior training. Nevertheless, it is an intelligible capacity for a nonlinguistic creature. And the most plausible explanation of that capacity is that it evinces a disjunctive inference ("p or q or r; neither p nor q; ergo r"). A recent alternative (Rescorla 2009) appeals to Bayesian probabilistic reasoning, yet the latter would appear to be more cognitively demanding than simple disjunctive inference. To be sure, a nonlinguistic creature cannot silently consult logical principles, whether deductive or probabilistic. But even our intelligent performances are rarely accompanied by conscious consultations of this kind.

This leaves one residual worry. Although humans need not actually verbalize their reasoning, even in the imagination, they are *capable* of doing so. In the absence of this option, the question arises of what in an animal's behavior could correspond to the "ergo" of linguistic reasoning. This point may be unanswerable in the case of dogs. But in apes, there *can* be an analogue to our "ergo." In the context of encountering and pondering a problem, certain gestures and grimaces, followed by renewed activity, can naturally be interpreted as marking the point when the penny dropped. Even if this is an anthropomorphic interpretation in the case of chimpanzees, there were not-yet-linguistic hominins – let's say *homo erectus* – whose facial expressions, demeanor and gestures are so close to ours as to make such a description inevitable. Consequently, there is no compelling reason for supposing that nonlinguistic subjects are in principle incapable of drawing inferences. To what extent some primates and marine mammals actually engage in disjunctive and transitive reasoning is the topic of ongoing research (see Andrews 2015: 96–105).

Further reading

Andrews, K. (2010) "Animal Cognition," in E. N. Zalta (ed.), *The Stanford Encyclopedia of Philosophy*, www.science.uva.nl/~seop/entries/cognition-animal/ offers a succinct, well-informed and up-to-date account. Lurz, R. (2009a) "Animal Minds," in *The Internet Encyclopedia of Philosophy*, www.iep.utm.edu/ani-mind/ is also recommended, discussing not just cognition but also consciousness. Lurz, R. (ed.) (2009b) *The Philosophy of Animal Minds*, Cambridge: Cambridge University Press assembles recent contributions on a similarly wide range of issues – including animal inference and methodological questions – and places them within the context of the emerging subdiscipline that provides its title.

References

Allen, C. (2013) "The Geometry of Partial Understanding," *American Philosophical Quarterly* 50: 249–62.

Allen, C., and Hauser, M. (1996) "Concept Attribution in Nonhuman Animals," in M. Bekoff and D. Jamieson (eds.), *Readings in Animal Cognition*, Cambridge, MA: MIT Press.

Andrews, K. (2015) *The Animal Mind*, Abingdon: Routledge.

Beck, J. (2013) "Why We Can't Say What Animals Think," *Philosophical Psychology* 26: 520–46.

Bekoff, M., and Jamieson, D. (1991) "Reflective Ethology, Applied Philosophy, and the Moral Status of Animals," *Perspectives in Ethology* 9: 1–47.

Bermúdez, J., and Cahen, A. (2015) "Nonconceptual Mental Content," in E. N. Zalta (ed.), *The Stanford Encyclopedia of Philosophy*, http://plato.stanford.edu/archives/fall2015/entries/content-nonconceptual/

Brandom, R. B. (1994) *Making It Explicit*, Cambridge, MA: Harvard University Press.

Camp, E. (2007) "Thinking With Maps," *Philosophical Perspectives* 21: 145–82.

Clayton, N. S., Griffiths, D., and Dickinson, A. (2000) "Declarative and Episodic-Like Memory in Animals," in C. M. Heyes and L. Huber (eds.), *The Evolution of Cognition*, Cambridge, MA: MIT Press.

Davidson, D. (1984) *Inquiries Into Truth and Interpretation*, Oxford: Oxford University Press.

——— (1985) "Rational Animals," in E. Lepore and B. P. McLaughlin (eds.), *Actions and Events*, Oxford: Blackwell.

——— (1997) "Seeing Through Language," in J. Preston (ed.), *Thought and Language*, Cambridge: Cambridge University Press.

DeGrazia, D. (1996) *Taking Animals Seriously*, Cambridge: Cambridge University Press.

Dretske, F. I. (2004) "Seeing, Believing and Knowing," in R. Schwartz (ed.), *Perception*, Malden, MA: Blackwell.

Dupré, J. (2002) *Humans and Other Animals*, Oxford: Oxford University Press.

Glock, H.-J. (2009) "Can Animals Act for Reasons?" *Inquiry* 52: 232–55.

——— (2010) "Can Animals Judge?" *Dialectica* 64: 11–34.

——— (2013) "Animal Minds: A Non-Representationalist Approach," *American Philosophical Quarterly* 50: 213–32.

Kornell, N., Son, L., and Terrace, H. S. (2007) "Transfer of Metacognitive Skills and Hint Seeking in Monkeys," *Psychological Science* 18: 682–5.

McDowell, J. (1996) *Mind and World*, Cambridge, MA: Harvard University Press.

Malcolm, N. (1972–73) "Thoughtless Brutes," *Proceedings and Addresses of the American Philosophical Society* 46: 5–20.

Mulcahy, N. J., and Call, J. (2006) "Apes Save Tools for Future Use," *Science* 312: 1038–40.

Price, H. H. (1953) *Thinking and Experience*, London: Hutchinson.

Rescorla, M. (2009) "Chrysippus Dog as a Case Study in Non-Linguistic Cognition", in R. W. Lurz (ed.), *The Philosophy of Animal Minds*, Cambridge: Cambridge University Press.

Seed, A., and Tomasello, M. (2010) "Primate Cognition," *Topics on Cognitive Science* 2: 407–19.

Sellars, W. (1957) "Intentionality and the Mental," in H. Feigl, M. Scriven, and G. Maxwell (eds.), *Minnesota Studies in the Philosophy of Science*, Vol. 2, Minneapolis, MN: University of Minnesota Press.

Sorabji, R. (1993) *Animal Minds and Human Morals*, London: Duckworth.

9

INSTRUMENTAL REASONING IN NONHUMAN ANIMALS[1]

Elisabeth Camp and Eli Shupe

1 Instrumental reasoning: What is it? Why should we care?

People engage in instrumental reasoning all the time, in fluid and complex ways. Thus: you're at the office and want to use your new headphones, currently encased in non-frustration-free packaging. You could ask your colleague for scissors, but that would entail a lengthy conversation about *Westworld*. You wonder: are your keys might be sharp enough to cut the plastic, if you could get a grip on the upper corner? Would an unfurled paper clip pierce it? Or: you're tired of looking for parking, and want a house with a garage. How much would a three-bedroom house in the closest town with good schools cost? To afford a down payment within two years, you'd need to save at least $1,000 a month. Should you cancel cable and forgo all restaurants? Sell your car and commute by train? Reconcile with your rich but racist uncle?

In these cases and endless others, people form the intention to achieve a goal, G, by identifying a state of affairs M, which is neither inherently desirable nor currently actual, as to-be-done because it will centrally contribute to actualizing G. The ability to reason instrumentally is enormously practical, of course. But it is also theoretically interesting: it stands as a landmark on a trajectory from simple stimulus-response association to purely theoretical deliberation. A creature who can reason instrumentally doesn't just respond directly to its immediate environment, as a mouse fleeing the scent of a cat does. Nor does it act directly to satisfy a need, like a hungry bird flying off to a cache of nuts. Instrumental reason severs the direct connection between representation and action by interposing a cognitive representation of a possible state.

By giving an agent a wider range of means to achieve its goals, instrumental reason also begins to connect an agent's thoughts in richer, more flexible ways. As an agent's goals become increasingly independent of particular means, and as its representations of the world become increasingly independent of particular responses, those cognitive states become more recognizable as desires and beliefs, as opposed to the mixed "pushmi-pullyu" representations – food-to-eat, predator-to-avoid – that are characteristic of simpler creatures (Millikan 1996; Papineau 2001).

Who can reason instrumentally? On the one hand, it seems that nonhuman animals (hereafter simply animals) sometimes solve problems in ways similar to the package-opening and house-buying deliberations above. Thus, Comins et al. (2011) observe that, from a troop of approximately 1,000 rhesus monkeys, one individual, '84J,' can open the abundant local coconuts: by carrying them to a concrete dock (the island's hardest, flattest surface) and performing a distinctive toss, 84J is able to enjoy a delicious, otherwise inaccessible food. On the other hand, since we lack the access to 84J's mind that we have to our own minds (via introspection) and to other people's minds (by verbal report), it's not obvious that the underlying cognitive process is relevantly similar – in particular, it might have arisen "through trial and error association without reinforcement" (Comins et al. 2011: 2). More fundamentally, it's not obvious what does need to be true of 84J's cognitive abilities and mechanisms for his behavior to be justifiedly described as a result of instrumental reasoning.

A venerable tradition holds that 84J *can't* be engaged in instrumental reasoning (henceforth IR), because it is a distinctively human capacity. One route to this conclusion identifies genuine reason as a flexible, open-ended capacity to connect thoughts, of which IR is the most obvious practical instance. Thus, Descartes (1637/1985: 140) describes reason as a "universal instrument," and defends the conclusion "not merely that the beasts have less reason than men, but . . . no reason at all" by appealing to the observation that even "madmen" and "the stupidest child," but no animals, spontaneously "invent their own signs" "to make themselves understood."

An alternative route focuses on reason's depth rather than its breadth. Thus, Kant holds that reason is constituted by its availability for self-reflection: "the very existence of reason," he claims, rests on "the freedom of critique" (1781/1999: A738f/B766f). Because only humans can interrogate the basis of and relations between their beliefs and desires, only they can take the responsibility required for genuine belief. By contrast, because animals merely respond to a world and a set of needs that are given to them, they lack the intellectual and moral status of rational agency.

Against such exclusionary views, Hume (1748/1999: 80) defends the continuity of reason by pointing out that animals also learn from experience to "infer some fact beyond what immediately strikes [their] senses"; by exploiting such inferences, he claims, they can "be taught any course of action, and most contrary to their natural instincts and propensities." In particular, Hume rejects the hypothesis that the way ordinary humans make such inferences is by appeal to general causal laws, since these "may well employ the utmost care and attention of a philosophic genius to discover and observe." Instead, he concludes, both humans and animals cognize entirely through associative habit (1748/1999: 80).

Contemporary philosophers and psychologists are less prone to treat reason as an all-or-nothing faculty, and more likely to identify clusters of distinct abilities and processes. But the debate between proponents of qualitative difference and continuity persists. And in that debate, instrumental reasoning serves as a central proving ground for distinguishing rational from merely associative cognitive processes, and for identifying the boundary of 'distinctively human thought.' Thus, Papineau (2001), Millikan (2006), and Korsgaard (2009) have all recently argued that animals' cognitive activities are tethered to perception in a way that rules out IR.

Defenders of the human distinctiveness of IR deploy two converging lines of argument. On the one hand, they argue that IR entails an interlocking package of complex capacities that are only found in humans; on the other, they argue that putative instances of nonhuman IR can be explained by simpler associative mechanisms. In Section 2, we argue that each of these complex capacities can be implemented in a way that some other animals do plausibly instantiate. In Section 3, we outline some constraints on the production of IR, and argue that the conditions for goal-directed action, and IR in particular, do outstrip the resources of purely associative explanation. We conclude in Section 4 by sketching some key further differences between human and animal reason.

2 Distinctively human?

The core of instrumental reasoning is the identification of a merely possible, not inherently valuable state M as helping to actualize a goal state G. But not just any transition from a represented actual state of affairs A to G via M counts: the agent must act to actualize M *because* they recognize that M is appropriately connected to G. Thus, we can identify an epistemological and a metaphysical dimension to IR: the transition from representing A to G via M must be justified rather than accidental, in virtue of a grasp of the connection between M and G.

A common defense of the human distinctiveness of IR argues that only language has the expressive power to represent the connection between M and G in the right way. To be justified rather than accidental, the thought goes, the agent's actualization of M must be motivated by a representation of a general connection between M and G, as in a causal law; thus, Papineau (2001: 153) holds that IR involves "the use of . . . explicit general information to guide action." We know how this works with language: via syllogistic reasoning with sentences containing an operator embedding M and G and a modal operator on M. How else, one might wonder, could it go? As Devitt (2005:147) puts it, "We understand inference in formal terms – in terms of rules that operate on representations in virtue of their structure. But we have no theory at all of formal inferential transitions between thoughts that do not have linguistic vehicles" (cf. also Bermúdez 2003).

An initial worry about a restriction of IR to formal inference over explicit representations of general information concerns the requirement of generality. For many cases of IR, the salient contingency which the agent recognizes is grounded in an intricate cluster of interacting forces; the generality of any represented causal 'law' would be highly gerrymandered, and the underlying physical mechanisms would indeed require "the utmost care and attention of a philosophic genius to discover" (Hume 1748/1999: 80). Instead of a general law, it seems that an agent merely needs to represent the presence of a token causal connection between M and G, such that M is a 'difference-maker' for G (Woodward 2003).

A more promising way to capture the requirement of generality holds that the agent must grasp the connection as one that obtains between two or more states in the world, independently of the agent. Just as an agent who represents space egocentrically (e.g. in a GPS navigator's 'first-person view' v. traditional 'aerial' mode) will be unable to represent spatial relations among locations not involving her – say, from the nest to the pond when she is at the tree – so will a "causally egocentric" creature be limited to representing contingencies that are directly grounded in its own past interventions and immediate possible actions (Papineau 2001; Gopnik et al. 2004). An agent who grasps relations as objective thus treats them as being generally accessible, independently of its own current position and needs, in a way that the egocentric representer misses.

However, language isn't the only format for encoding causal relations and transitions in an non-egocentric, inferentially valid way. For familiar reasons, not all transitions between representations can be validated 'explicitly,' in the sense of recurrence of symbols, on pain of regress (Carroll 1895). Different systems parse out the representational burden between syntactic vehicles and transformation rules differently (Anderson 1978); and a transition between representational states is valid just in case the application of those rules to those vehicles is reliably truth-preserving (Sloman 1978:116).[2]

For causation in particular, flow-chart-like directed graphs or 'Bayes nets' provide a plausible, rigorously defined format for implementing non-egocentric causal knowledge and inference in humans (Pearl 2000; Gopnik et al. 2004; Holyoak and Cheng 2011; Elwert 2013). Further, there is evidence for non-egocentric causal representation in animals (Seed et al. 2009): among other findings, Blaisdell et al. (2006) found that rats differentiate common-cause and causal-chain structures and infer appropriate instrumental action from passive observation; while Call (2013: 12) argues that apes distinguish "mere co-occurrence" of cues and rewards from causal connections, and encode information about "object-object interactions."

If we grant the possibility of non-egocentric but nonlinguistic causal inference from M to G, how should we understand an agent's representing M as being merely possible, as is also required for IR? Rather than positing a modal operator within the represented content as would be natural in language, we might invoke a distinct attitude: of entertaining M, as opposed to believing or desiring it. Thus, Suddendorf and Whiten (2001), following Perner (1991), distinguish secondary representation from both primary and meta- representation: secondary representation "decouples" a represented goal G from the perceived reality A, so that G is "held in mind" simultaneously with and distinct from A. In IR, they suggest, an agent "collates" A and G by "mentally working back" from G to A. One standard model for such "working back" is simulation; on a simple view, simulation is just the off-line activation of cognitive, motor, and imagery mechanisms, producing a form of "trial and error in thought ... quicker and safer than ... either operant conditioning or natural selection" (Millikan 2006: 118). However, the process of "collating" A and G by entertaining M (and possibly alternatives M', M'', . . .) also plausibly involves restructuring perceived and recalled information and relating distinct pieces of information (Call 2013: 15). Such simulation and structuring can plausibly be represented non-linguistically in graphic and imagistic formats.

Finally, in the absence of a capacity for explicit self-critique, how should we understand the epistemic norm that the transitions among these representations of A, M, and G be justified? We've already seen that they can be implemented in a rigorously valid non-sentential system. A minimal further constraint is that the agent be sufficiently sensitive to the actual relations among A, M, and G, such that if they were to get information indicating alterations among those relations, their behavior would alter accordingly. More robustly, we might add a capacity for metacognition – monitoring the quality of information available either to oneself or to others – which is again possible in the absence of metarepresentation (Proust 2006, and Chapter 13 in this volume). Here too, some animals appear to pass the bar (Smith et al. 2003): for instance, dolphins and rhesus monkeys opt out of a visual–discrimination task in favor of a less-demanding, less-rewarding task as their performance becomes unreliable, suggesting some awareness of their unreliability.

In sum, we should attribute a capacity for IR when we have evidence that an agent acts to actualize M even though M is not inherently desirable, because it represents M in a non-egocentric way as a potential 'difference-maker' in a causal network connecting A to G, where its so acting is sensitive to the quality of its information about the relations among A, M, and G. We've already seen some evidence that some animals possess each of these constituent capacities. What about the whole package?

Most discussions of instrumental cognition in animals focus on tool use, especially in primates and some bird species (see Shumaker et al. 2011 for review). The least-sophisticated cases of putative tool use involve direct interventions on the environment, as in Köhler (1925)'s classic case of a chimpanzee moving a box to climb up and reach bananas. Following Piaget (1952), many comparative psychologists employ tasks challenging animals to pull rewards that are attached to strings (Jacobs and Osvath 2015), or placed on a tray or cloth. More complex, less perceptually driven tests for tool use, which have been passed by rooks, crows, orangutans, and rhesus monkeys, among others, include the 'Aesop's fable' tube task, in which subjects retrieve food at the bottom of a tube by adding stones (or spit) to the tube in order to make the food float within reach; and the tube-trap task, in which they must insert a tool to retrieve a reward in one set of circumstances, when the trap is functional, but ignore the trap in other circumstances, as indicated by slight variations in the setup (Emery and Clayton 2009; Seed et al. 2009). At the most challenging end lies metatool use: employing one tool to construct or obtain a second, such as fracturing one stone with another to cut a piece of rope with a resulting shard, or using a short tool to dislodge a longer one. Such behavior has been observed in great apes (Toth et al. 2006; Mulcahy et al. 2005; Martin-Ordas et al. 2012), other primates (Mannu et al. 2009), New Caledonian crows (Taylor et al. 2007; Wimpenny et al. 2009), and rooks (Bird and Emery 2009). Finally, animals may also use conspecifics in a way suggestive of IR: for instance, orangutan mothers will coerce their offspring to retrieve food they cannot reach themselves (e.g., by pushing them through a narrow opening), which they then steal (Völter et al. 2015).

3 Constraints on production and implementation

In Section 2, we cleared the way for instrumental reasoning in animals by means of non-egocentric representations of causal contingency, and cited some evidence that some animals might engage in it. But as noted in Section 1, the same observable behavior can be produced by importantly different processes, ranging from trial and error to spontaneous insight. Which mechanisms for producing a representational connection from A to G via M count as underwriting IR?

The most obvious mechanisms to rule out are those that are largely innate and inflexible, like the greylag goose's habit of rolling stray eggs back to her nest. Although the behavior appears purposeful, it is infamously automatic: even if her egg is removed just after she begins to roll it, the goose will complete the entire maneuver (Lorenz and Tinbergen 1938/1970). It is also plausible to exclude actions produced by direct response to perceptual features. For instance, an instrumental reasoner in a string-pulling task must tug the string because it represents a connection between string-pulling and food, not because it perceives the string as a visual extension of the food itself. Likewise, perceptual 'affordances' can be learned and quite rich, but don't interpose an intermediate state represented in a secondary mode as a potential difference-maker for achieving a distinct goal. At the other extreme, IR needn't be wholly underwritten by individual innovation. Just as few, if any, behaviors are completely innate, but almost always a mixture of genetic potential and learning (Staddon 2016), so too are few, if any, behaviors completely innovative. Genetic predispositions and individual learning are key preconditions for instrumental reasoning and action, for animals and humans alike.

In cognitive psychology, genuine reasoning is typically contrasted with association. While one might think that sophisticated, multistage processes like metatool use require reasoning, virtually all putative cases of IR have been re-described by skeptics in associative terms. Thus, in many metatool-use studies, the accessible tool is positioned near the inaccessible one, opening up the possibility that a subject wielding the former simply dislodged and acquired the latter through chance manipulation. Further, because subjects are often trained to perform a complex metatool task in stages, they might successfully retrieve a reward as the result of automatic chaining, whereby behaviors are linked sequentially as secondary reinforcers of the positive outcome (Epstein et al. 1984; Wimpenny et al. 2009; Martin-Ordas et al. 2012).

The possibility that even these paradigmatically rational behaviors can be explained associatively raises the specter that it may never be possible to establish a given behavior as resulting from genuinely rational as opposed to merely associative processes. One general methodological response is that the dichotomy itself is misguided. Insofar as the complex associative explanations invoked above appeal to transitions between internal states that are characterized in representational terms, they are themselves susceptible to, or tantamount to, rationalist reinterpretation (Papineau and Heyes 2006); and insofar as a system's processing architecture imposes normatively appropriate functional constraints, associative mechanisms can themselves mimic, or implement, rational cognition (Dickinson 2012).

A more specific, ambitious response is that the conditions for IR identified in Section 2 do impose robust constraints that distinguish merely associative from rational processes, in ways that are susceptible to experimental test. IR involves an agent representing a goal state G independently of current circumstances. By contrast, because chaining utilizes associations between stimulus and response (A-M), but never between response and outcome (M-G), a blind 'chainer' will implement M in A regardless of whether G is currently a goal. The fact that rats trained to press a lever for food press less frequently when they find the food less desirable (due to pre-feeding) suggests both that their incentive values are modulated by their motivational states and that their actions are influenced by a sensitivity to action-outcome contingencies (Balleine and Dickinson 1998). Similarly, IR involves connecting M to G independently of association with a particular stimulus state A. The studies of non-egocentric causal learning through transfer from passive observation cited in Section 2 suggest that this condition is also met, insofar as the observed condition is of another animal performing an action which is structurally analogous to M in a situation structurally analogous to A, but where the test subject has not itself previously encountered A or performed M directly (Papineau and Heyes 2006; Dickinson 2012). Thus, putting aside the specific worries about appropriate controls on the purported demonstrations of metatool use as instances of IR above, it is plausible that at least some animals do act in goal-directed ways that are not amenable to standard associationist explanation.

4 Degrees and differences

We now have a better grip on what instrumental reasoning is and how it might be implemented. Instrumental reasoning interposes a representation of a non-valued state M between an agent's representation of their current circumstances A and a goal state G, because they represent M as an achievable difference-maker for producing G. IR can be implemented in the absence of an expressively rich language, for instance through simulation using Bayes nets. And there is substantial, if not incontrovertible, evidence for IR in a range of nonhuman animals, especially rodents, corvids, and primates.

Still, there is a considerable grain of truth in Descartes' assertion of a qualitative gap between humans and other animals. In its scope, flexibility, and frequency, humans' capacity for problem-solving does approximate a "universal instrument" much more closely than even the most sophisticated cases of spontaneous metatool use cited above. In application to IR in particular, humans appear to have a markedly more nuanced grasp of causal networks as interacting clusters of multiple distinct forces. They have a markedly richer ability to explore alternative paths from A to G. And they have a markedly more robust ability to critique and revise those representations. Even if it is not an absolute condition on the possibility of instrumental reasoning, language clearly facilitates each of these abilities individually and in combination, in virtue of its combinatorial generality, its syntactic and semantic abstractness, and its indefinite recursive capacity (Camp 2015).

Our focus on IR should also not lead us to neglect an arguably more profound difference between human and animal cognition: not just a greater flexibility of means, but of ends. Millikan (2006: 122) claims that other animals, while capable of highly complex cognition, are still fundamentally 'pushmi-pullyu' creatures in the sense that they "solve only problems posed by immediate perception . . . by deciding among possibilities currently presented in perception, or as known extensions from current perception." We have seen that some animals do exploit possibilities that are not, and have never been, directly presented in or extending from perception. But there is less evidence that they solve problems that are not immediately present to them.

One distinctively human tendency may be to create our own problems – in particular, to set multiple innovative long-term goals, and to adjust and adjudicate among them in flexible, ongoing ways. Korsgaard (2009: 38) argues that by "shattering" the "teleological conception of the world" as embodying a given, fixed set of distinctions and desires, Kantian self-conscious reflection "creates both the opportunity and the necessity for reconstruction." We have seen that other animals are agents who do more than blindly respond to circumstances as given. But humans may be closer to achieving uniqueness in actively constructing ourselves *as* distinctive agents or selves (Camp 2011).

Imagination clearly plays a key role in instrumental reasoning, by enabling an agent to step back from current circumstances and identify alternative conditions that would make a difference to achieving a goal. Call points to a correlation between exploratory play and flexible problem solving, and suggests that play "performs a crucial role in the acquisition and storage of information" (2013: 12), especially of information about causal contingencies. However, play also involves trying on goals in a merely 'as-if,' exploratory mode. In this way, for humans at least, it also potentially contributes to the reconstructive project of making a self. In these respects, imagination should not be opposed to reason, but rather treated as an integral component of it.

Notes

1 Thanks to Ben Bronner, Federico Castellano, and Simon Goldstein for discussion, and Jake Beck for comments.
2 Papineau himself appears to understand explicitness in terms of an overall "system which processes … items of general information to yield new such general information" (2001: 155–6). He finds an evolutionary explanation in terms of language "attractive" but allows the possibility that "our ancestors played out various scenarios in their 'mind's eye'" (2001: 177).

Further reading

S. Hurley and M. Nudds, *Rational Animals?* (Oxford: Oxford University Press, 2006) brings together a wide range of scientists and philosophers discussing what it means to be rational and what behaviors indicate rationality. R. Lurz, *The Philosophy of Animal Minds* (New York: Cambridge University Press, 2009) contains valuable essays by philosophers on animals' capacity to reason. R. Shumaker, K. Walkup and B. Beck, *Animal Tool Behavior: The Use and Manufacture of Tools by Animals* (Baltimore, MD: The Johns Hopkins University Press, 2011) offers a rich compendium of examples of tool use in animals, ranging from spiders to primates. C. Sanz, J. Call and C. Boesch, *Tool Use in Animals: Cognition and Ecology* (Cambridge: Cambridge University Press, 2013) contains analytical essays by leading cognitive ethologists and animal psychologists about animal tool use.

References

Anderson, JR 1978, 'Arguments concerning representations for mental imagery', *Psychological Review*, vol. 85, no. 4, p. 249.

Balleine, BW, and Dickinson, A 1998, 'Goal-directed instrumental action: Contingency and incentive learning and their cortical substrates', *Neuropharmacology*, vol. 37, no. 4, pp. 407–419.

Bermúdez, J 2003, *Thinking without words*, Oxford University Press, Oxford.

Bird, CD, and Emery, NJ 2009, 'Insightful problem solving and creative tool modification by captive non-tool-using rooks', *Proceedings of the National Academy of Sciences*, vol. 106, no. 25, pp. 10370–10375.

Blaisdell, AP, Sawa, K, Leising, KJ, and Waldmann, MR 2006, 'Causal reasoning in rats', *Science*, vol. 311, no. 5763, pp. 1020–1022.

Call, J 2013, 'Three ingredients for becoming a creative tool user', in CM Sanz, J Call and C Boesch (eds.), *Tool use in animals: Cognition and ecology*, Cambridge University Press, Cambridge.

Camp, E 2011, 'Wordsworth's *Prelude*, poetic autobiography, and narrative constructions of the self', *Nonsite.org* vol. 3, http://nonsite.org/article/wordsworth%E2%80%99s-prelude-poetic-autobiography-and-narrative-constructions-of-the-self

Camp, E 2015, 'Logical concepts and associative characterizations', in E Margolis and S Laurence (eds.), *The conceptual mind: New directions in the study of concepts*, MIT Press, Cambridge, MA.

Carroll, L 1895, 'What the tortoise said to Achilles', *Mind*, vol. 104, no. 416, pp. 691–693.

Comins, JA, Russ, BE, Humbert, KA, and Hauser, MD 2011, 'Innovative coconut-opening in a semi free-ranging rhesus monkey (*Macaca mulatta*): A case report on behavioral propensities', *Journal of Ethology*, vol. 29, no. 1, pp. 187–189.

Descartes, R 1637–1985, 'Discourse on method', in J Cottingham, R Stoothoff and D Murdoch (eds.), *The philosophical writings of Descartes*, vol. 1, Cambridge University Press, Cambridge.

Devitt, M 2005, *Ignorance of language*, Oxford University Press, Oxford.

Dickinson, A 2012, 'Associative learning and animal cognition', *Philosophical Transactions of the Royal Society B: Biological Sciences*, vol. 367, no. 1603, pp. 2733–2742.

Elwert, F 2013, 'Graphical causal models', in SL Morgan (ed.), *Handbook of causal analysis for social research*, Springer, New York.

Emery, NJ, and Clayton, NS 2009, 'Tool use and physical cognition in birds and mammals', *Current Opinion in Neurobiology*, vol. 1, pp. 27–33.

Epstein, R, Kirshnit, CE, Lanza, RP, and Rubin LC 1984 '"Insight" in the pigeon: Antecedents and determinants of an intelligent performance', *Nature*, vol. 308, pp. 61–62.

Gopnik, A, Glymour, C, Sobel, DM, Schulz, LE, Kushnir, T, and Danks, D 2004, 'A theory of causal learning in children: Causal maps and Bayes nets', *Psychological Review*, vol. 111, no. 1, p. 3.

Holyoak, KJ, and Cheng, PW 2011, 'Causal learning and inference as a rational process: The new synthesis', *Annual Review of Psychology*, vol. 62, pp. 135–163.

Hume, D 1748/1999, *An enquiry concerning human understanding*, T Beauchamp (ed.), Oxford University Press, Oxford.

Jacobs, IF, and Osvath, M 2015, 'The string-pulling paradigm in comparative psychology', *Journal of Comparative Psychology*, vol. 129, no. 2, p. 89.

Kant, I 1781/1999, *Critique of pure reason*, P Guyer and A Wood (eds.), Cambridge University Press, Cambridge.

Köhler, W 1925, 'Intelligence of apes', *The Journal of Genetic Psychology*, vol. 32, pp. 674–690.

Korsgaard, CM 2009, 'The activity of reason', *Proceedings and Addresses of the American Philosophical Association*, vol. 83, no. 2, pp. 23–43.

Lorenz, K, and Tinbergen, N 1938/1970, 'Taxis and instinctive behaviour pattern in egg-rolling by the Greylag goose', *Studies in animal and human behavior*, Vol. 1, Harvard University Press, Cambridge.

Mannu, M, and Ottoni, EB 2009, 'The enhanced tool-kit of two groups of wild bearded capuchin monkeys in the Caatinga: Tool making, associative use, and secondary tools', *American Journal of Primatology*, vol. 71, no. 3, pp. 242–251.

Martin-Ordas, G, Schumacher, L, and Call, J 2012, 'Sequential tool use in great apes', *PLoS ONE*, vol. 7, no. 12, p. E52074.

Millikan, R 1996, 'Pushmi-pullyu representations', *Philosophical Perspectives*, vol. 9, pp. 185–200.

Millikan, R 2006, 'Styles of rationality', in SL Hurley and M Nudds (eds.), *Rational animals?*, Oxford University Press, Oxford.

Mulcahy, NJ, Call, J, and Dunbar, RI 2005, 'Gorillas (Gorilla gorilla) and orangutans (Pongo pygmaeus) encode relevant problem features in a tool-using task', *Journal of Comparative Psychology*, vol. 119, no. 1, p. 23.

Papineau, D 2001, 'The evolution of means-end reasoning', *Royal Institute of Philosophy Supplement*, vol. 49, pp. 145–178.

Papineau, D, and Heyes, C 2006, 'Rational or associative? Imitation in Japanese quail', in SL Hurley and M Nudds (eds.), *Rational animals?* Oxford University Press, Oxford.

Pearl, J 2000, *Causality*, Cambridge University Press, Cambridge.

Perner, J 1991, *Understanding the representational mind*, MIT Press, Cambridge.

Piaget, J 1952, *The origins of intelligence in children*, Norton, New York.

Proust, J 2006, 'Rationality and metacognition in non-human animals', in SL Hurley and M Nudds (eds.), *Rational animals?* Oxford University Press, Oxford.

Seed, A, and Call, J 2009, 'Causal knowledge for events and objects in animals', in S Watanabe, AP Blaisdell, L Huber and A Young (eds.), *Rational animals, irrational humans*, Keio University Press, Tokyo.

Shumaker, RW, Walkup, KR, and Beck, BB 2011, *Animal tool behavior: The use and manufacture of tools by animals*, JHU Press, Baltimore, MD.

Sloman, A 1978, *The computer revolution in philosophy: Philosophy, science and models of mind*, Harvester Press, Brighton.

Smith JD, Shields WE, and Washburn DA 2003, 'The comparative psychology of uncertainty monitoring and metacognition', *Behavioral and Brain Sciences*, vol. 3, pp. 317–339.

Staddon, JE 2016, *Adaptive behavior and learning*, Cambridge University Press, Cambridge.

Suddendorf, T, and Whiten, A 2001, 'Mental evolution and development: Evidence for secondary representation in children, great apes, and other animals', *Psychological Bulletin*, vol. 127, no. 5, p. 629.

Taylor, AH, Hunt, GR, Holzhaider, JC, and Gray, RD 2007, 'Spontaneous metatool use by New Caledonian crows', *Current Biology*, vol. 17, no. 17, pp. 1504–1507.

Toth, N, Schick, K, and Semaw, S 2006, 'A comparative study of the stone tool-making skills of Pan, Australopithecus, and Homo sapiens,' in N Toth, K Schick and S Semaw, *The Oldowan: Case studies into the earliest Stone Age*, pp. 155–222, Stone Age Institute Press, Gosport.

Völter, CJ, Rossano, F, and Call, J 2015, 'From exploitation to cooperation: Social tool-use in orangutan mother-offspring dyads', *Animal Behaviour*, vol. 100, pp. 126–134.

Wimpenny, JH, Weir, AA, Clayton, L, Rutz, C, and Kacelnik, A 2009, 'Cognitive processes associated with sequential tool use in New Caledonian crows', *PLoS ONE*, vol. 4, no. 8, p. E6471.

Woodward, J 2003, *Making things happen: A causal theory of explanation*, Oxford University Press, Oxford.

10

A DIFFERENT KIND OF MIND?

Matthew Boyle

1 Introduction

Aristotle famously characterized human beings as animals whose soul contains a rational princi-ple, and Scholastic philosophers codified this idea in the classical definition of man as a rational animal.[1] It is clear that authors writing in this tradition meant to claim, not just that rationality is a characteristic trait of humankind, but that it sets us apart from other animals in a fundamen-tal way. This is indicated in the traditional way of representing Aristotle's picture of the natural order, the so-called "Porphyrian Tree" (Figure 10.1).

The fact that rational animals appear on a separate branch of this tree reflects the classical doctrine that we rational animals are not just another *species* of animal but a different *kind* of animal, one whose distinctiveness constitutes a new category of animality. Since the Aristote-lian tradition thought of animals in general as distinguished from other living things by their possessing what we would now call *mental* capacities (specifically, capacities for perception and voluntary movement), we may express the Aristotelian view – anachronistically but not inac-curately – by saying that we rational animals have a *different kind of mind* from other animals.

This view of human mentality was dominant for millennia, but these days it is the object of mounting skepticism. No one doubts, of course, that there are many significant differences between human minds and the minds of other animals, but a number of well-known results in comparative psychology and cognitive science appear to cast doubt on the idea of a single, categorical difference. For on the one hand, many animals traditionally classified as "nonrational" behave in ways that plainly reflect considerable intelligence and representational sophistica-tion. And on the other hand, we "rational animals" prove on examination to be a good deal less rational than we would like to think, exhibiting systematic tendencies to accept unsound inferences, make unreasonable choices, and give confabulated rationales for our own beliefs and actions.

Before taking sides in this dispute, however, we should ask what the classical doctrine means. In the first place, what is "rationality"? In spite of its familiarity, this notion is somewhat obscure. There are, of course, various well-known claims about the distinctive capacities of rational animals: that only they can speak a language, engage in conceptual thought, draw inferences, understand the difference between right and wrong, etc. But these allegedly distinctive attrib-utes are presumably meant to be consequences of a more basic cognitive difference, not parts of

Figure 10.1 *Porphyrian Tree* by B. Strahowsky (1750), National Library of Poland

the definition of rationality itself. And in any case, one's answer to the question of what counts as speaking a language, drawing inferences, etc. is liable to be affected by one's view about the nature of rationality. If the capacity for inference is taken to be distinctive of rational animals, for instance, then where one draws the line between genuine inferences and noninferential cognitive transitions will depend on one's view of what makes a transition between representations genuinely rational in character. So our problem is to understand what rationality itself is, and this is not immediately clear.

Moreover, whatever rationality is supposed to be, it is unclear what might be meant by the claim that rational minds differ "in kind" from the minds of other animals. After all, there are many significant differences among the cognitive capacities of animal species: some possess the capacity for pattern recognition, others for episodic memory, still others for metacognition, etc. If every difference in cognitive capacities entails a difference between kinds of minds, then kinds of minds are cheap, and the claim that rational minds differ in kind from nonrational ones loses its special interest. But if not just any such difference entails a difference between kinds of minds, then what is our criterion for a difference "in kind"? Again, the answer is not obvious.

It is common in the popular press, and also in some scientific and philosophical work, for discussions of whether rational minds differ in kind from nonrational ones to take a position in this dispute without giving much attention to these preliminary questions. My focus here, by contrast, will be exclusively on the preliminaries: what rationality is, and what could be meant by the claim that its presence gives rise to a different kind of animal mind. I aim to give a brief and opinionated sketch of what the claim that rational minds differ in kind from nonrational ones could mean, and how it could be motivated. In answering these questions, my primary concern will be, not to capture the views of any particular historical advocate of the difference-in-kind thesis, but to indicate what I take to be the most plausible and interesting understanding of this idea.

2 What is rationality?

What, then, does it mean to call an animal "rational"?

In one sense, the term "rational" is applied to things that meet a certain normative standard. To call an act rational in this sense is, roughly, to say that it is well-proportioned to available reasons, and to call an agent rational is to say that she is disposed to perform such acts. When Aristotelian philosophers defined human beings as rational animals, however, this normative sense of rationality was surely not the one they had in mind. They did not intend to claim that human beings are distinctively *successful* at acting in ways well-supported by reasons: they were well aware that humans pay heed to reasons only very imperfectly, and can easily be swayed by nonrational forces. They intended to claim, rather, that human beings are, in a distinctive way, *capable* of acting from an appreciation of reasons (where acting is understood to include not only moving one's body but performing cognitive acts such as judging, inferring, and so on). Thus, Aristotle thought of rational animals as possessing a distinctive kind of capacity (a *dunamis meta logou*: a capacity imbued with reason), and he distinguished between merely acting *in accordance with* the right reason (*kata ton orthon logon*) and acting *from* the right reason (*meta tou orthou logou*).[2] A rational capacity is a capacity to act, not just in ways that are in fact supported by reasons, but from an appreciation of reasons.

To say that human beings are rational animals in this capacity-oriented sense is to claim that our central animal capacities – those that guide and govern our particular kind of animal life when it goes well – have this character: that they enable us, not just to act in ways that are in fact supported by reasons, but to act *from an appreciation of* such reasons. It is not to claim that we exercise these capacities with any particular regularity, or that when we do exercise them, we generally do so well (i.e., in ways that are rational in the normative sense). So – contrary to what some critics assume – the claim that human beings are rational animals is not open to swift refutation by studies showing that humans are regularly or even systematically disposed to make judgments and draw inferences in ways that are not normatively rational.[3] Since the claim at issue concerns our cognitive capacities, not our cognitive dispositions or practices, there is no direct route from such observations to a disproof of the claim that human beings are rational animals.[4]

Can more be said to clarify the contrast between acting in ways that are supported by reasons and acting from an appreciation of reasons? A common way to introduce this contrast is to draw attention to the intuitive difference between engaging in an activity with understanding and engaging in it without understanding. Thus, a person who computes the result of 12×17 by consciously applying a rule for solving multiplication problems understands why she gives the answer she does, but a person who reaches her answer through sheer numerical intuition, without grasping a rule that requires the answer she gives, lacks such understanding. Similarly, a person who considers whether a certain bridge is safe and reaches a conclusion on the basis of observations she takes to support this conclusion understands why she draws this inference; but a person who simply becomes convinced that the bridge is safe without awareness of which facts persuade her does not draw a comprehending inference, even if her conviction in fact results from the very same observations. Rational capacities are capacities that enable their bearers to act with understanding in the way that conscious rule-following and comprehending inference exemplify.

In general, then, rational activities are characterized by a certain intelligibility from the subject's own perspective, an intelligibility that involves the subject's understanding *why* she acts as she does. The relevant sort of understanding, however, is not merely a collateral or *post facto* understanding. It is not merely that, if a subject S performs a rational activity A for reason R, S will *in consequence* be aware that R is her reason for A-ing. Rather, S's taking R to be a reason for A-ing must itself explain (in a characteristically rational way) S's A-ing.[5] It is the capacity for this kind of *directive* understanding – an understanding that is the ground of one's doing what one takes there to be reason to do – that distinguishes rational animals as such. In virtue of this capacity, they are intelligent in a special sense: their thoughts and actions can be guided by an assessment of reasons, and they can adjust their beliefs and actions by reflecting critically on such assessments.

To claim that only rational animals are intelligent in this sense is not to deny that nonrational animals may exhibit other very significant forms of intelligence. It is not to deny that they may show flexibility and creativity in finding means to their ends, draw on information acquired in one context when solving problems in another, different context, or make subtle adjustments in their beliefs in response to evidence. Though some advocates of the rational–nonrational distinction have made more ambitious claims, sensible defenders of this distinction should not maintain that only rational animals can exhibit these sorts of intelligence. They should claim, rather, that only rational animals can exhibit them *in virtue of being able to reflect on their own reasons for belief and action.* That rational animals can reflect on their own reasons for belief and action presumably explains why they show *greater* flexibility, creativity, and capacity for generalization than their nonrational brethren, but there is – to my knowledge, anyway – no sound argument for the claim that only beings who are capable of reflecting on their reasons in this sense are capable of forming beliefs and performing actions in a way that responds systematically to the rational significance of their perceptions, desires, etc. And indeed, there is strong evidence that many kinds of animals traditionally classified as "nonrational" can succeed at tasks that require the kinds of intelligence distinguished above.[6]

What it means to speak of an act as "guided by an appreciation of reasons" obviously needs further clarification. It is a main task of a theory of rationality to clarify this idea. Here it is only possible to note a few constraints on the needed clarification. In the first place, it is *not* a requirement on an act A's being guided by an appreciation of some reason R that the subject who does A should consciously think that R supports doing A. A person may do A because she takes R to support doing A without ever consciously considering whether R supports doing A, or whether she should do A for this reason. This reflects a general point about the relationship between taking P to be the case and consciously thinking that P: to take P to be the case is to be in a certain cognitive state, and such a state may obtain even if no conscious event of thinking that P ever occurs (though it may indeed be true that taking P to be the case disposes one to think that P if one considers the question whether P). Many rational activities (e.g., my just now reaching for my water glass because I was thirsty and believed there was water in it) occur without any conscious thought about what one is doing. The marks of my reaching's being a rational activity – one guided by an appreciation of reasons – are that I understand my reasons for reaching, and that I would not reach if I did not take these considerations to speak in favor of my so acting.

It is also not a requirement on an act A's being guided by an appreciation of some reason R that the subject who does A should have command of concepts such as *is a reason for, is evidence for*, etc. It seems clear that a child might do A from an appreciation of reasons for doing A, or believe P in virtue of taking there to be evidence that P, well before she possessed these sorts of sophisticated concepts. And even for those of us who have mastered such concepts, what is essential to our appreciation of reasons is not our ability to think thoughts involving such higher-order concepts, but our ability to understand and respond relevantly to certain kinds of "why?" questions about first-order propositions we believe and actions we perform. If my decision to do A is challenged by someone who asks "Really, why do A?", I can understand what kind of response is being demanded – namely, one that identifies considerations that speak in favor of A-ing – even if I lack sophisticated concepts of rational appraisal such as *is a reason for*. Likewise, if my belief that P is challenged by someone who asks "Why accept P?", I may be able to respond relevantly to this challenge without possessing concepts such as *is evidence for*. To have the capacity to believe and act in ways guided by an appreciation of reasons consists fundamentally in a capacity to understand such questions (which one may put to oneself even when they are not put by another person) and to govern one's beliefs and actions according to one's satisfaction with one's own answers to them.

3 Interpreting the Difference-in-Kind Thesis

With this preliminary characterization of rationality in place, we can turn to the Aristotelian definition of human beings as rational animals. It is worth distinguishing three claims implicit in this definition. First, there is the basic claim:

Classificatory Claim (CC): Human beings are rational animals.

In suggesting that (CC) can serve as a *definition* of human beings, Aristotelians also implied:

Uniqueness Thesis (UT): Human beings are the only (mortal) rational animals.

Finally, their views about the structure of definitions by genus and differentia implied:

Difference-in-Kind Thesis (DKT): Rational animals differ in kind from nonrational animals.

Critics of Aristotle's position often focus on (CC) or (UT), but it should be clear on reflection that (DKT) is the claim of greatest conceptual interest. (UT) seems to be a thesis that, if true, is merely a contingent fact: if there is such a thing as rationality, it should be possible for other animal species besides *homo sapiens* to exhibit it. As for (CC), if *homo sapiens* is a natural kind, and if being rational is an essential property of this kind, then (CC) may be a necessary truth; but if so, it is not a conceptual truth, but a substantive fact about the nature of this kind.[7]

(DKT), by contrast, is a claim, not about the cognitive capacities of any particular animal species, but about the conceptual relationship between two modes of being: being an animal and being a rational animal. (DKT) asserts that the difference between these modes must be understood in a certain way. What way is that? For the Aristotelian tradition, the notion of a "difference in kind" has a specific meaning: it means that the concept *animal* is a proper *genus* (i.e., a proper kind), and that the modifier *rational* is a proper *difference* within this genus. A proper genus must be something that would be an appropriate and fundamental answer to the question about what a given thing *is*, rather than an answer to the question what it *is like* in some respect or other.[8] Thus, "animal" is a proper genus term, whereas a descriptive term such as "two-footed" is not. As for what counts as a proper difference, Aristotle says:

> Not only must the common nature attach to the different things, e.g. not only must both be animals, but this very animality must also be different for each . . . For I give the name of 'difference in the genus' to an otherness that makes the genus itself other.[9]

That is, a proper difference in a genus G must be not merely a trait that some but not all G's possess, but a characteristic whose presence *transforms what it is to be a G*. So if being rational differentiates the genus *animal*, it must, as Aristotle says, make the very animality of rational animals different from that of nonrational animals. And given that the Aristotelian tradition understands animality as defined by capacities of perception and voluntary movement, it follows that these capacities must take a distinctive form in rational animals.

We can get some grip on this idea by relating it to a much-discussed topic in recent philosophy of perception: whether the content of perception is "conceptual" (i.e., whether, in order for our perception to present things as being a certain way, it is necessary for us to possess the concepts required to specify how our perception presents things to be). A common argument for the nonconceptualist position is that nonrational animals can surely acquire information about their environment through perception, though they presumably do not possess the concepts required to specify how their perception presents things to be. Hence, it seems, acquiring information through perception cannot require possessing concepts.

This argument assumes, however, that if a nonrational animal can perceive without possessing appropriately related concepts, then the same must hold true of a rational animal. It assumes, in effect, that there is no fundamental difference between rational and nonrational perceptual capacities. This assumption is disputed by some contemporary conceptualists, for instance, by John McDowell, who writes:

> If we share perception with mere animals, then of course we have something in common with them. Now there is a temptation to think it must be possible to isolate what we have in common with them by stripping off what is special about us, so as to arrive at a residue that we can recognize as what figures in the perceptual lives of mere animals . . . But it is not compulsory to attempt to accommodate the combination of something in common and a striking difference in this factorizing way . . . Instead we can say that we have what mere animals have, perceptual sensitivity to features of our environment, but we have it in a special form.
>
> (McDowell 1994: 64)

We could call the sort of view McDowell recommends a *transformative theory* of rationality, since it takes the nature of our perceptual capacities themselves to be affected by the presence of rationality, in a way that makes rational perception different in kind from its nonrational counterpart.[10]

Transformative theories of rationality contrast with *additive theories*, which hold that the capacities which make us rational can be added to capacities for perception and voluntary movement that remain essentially similar to those of nonrational animals.[11] Nonconceptualists about perceptual content typically hold just this sort of view. According to Gareth Evans, for instance, the content of perception itself is nonconceptual, but

> we arrive at conscious perceptual experience when sensory input is not only connected to behavioral dispositions. . . – perhaps in some phylogenetically more ancient part of the brain – but also serves as the input to a *thinking, concept-applying, and reasoning system*; so that the subject's thoughts, plans, and deliberations are also systematically dependent on the informational properties of the input.
>
> (Evans 1982: 158)

Evans reserves the term "conscious perceptual experience" for perception whose informational content is made available to a special rationality system that forms conceptual representations and reasons about their significance. He assumes, however, that the "sensory input" taken up by this system is itself stored in a "nonconceptual" format, which means (given Evans's usage) that the operations of the perceptual system do not themselves draw on the rationality system. Our perceptual system itself is supposed to be essentially similar to the perceptual systems of nonrational animals.

Versions of the dispute between additive and transformative theories of rationality can arise for any cognitive capacity shared by rational and nonrational animals. For any such capacity C, the additive position will hold that, even in rational animals, C is intrinsically independent of any distinctively rational capacities, so that its being "shared" with nonrational animals amounts to its being essentially similar to the corresponding nonrational capacity. The transformative position, by contrast, will maintain that rational animals possess C in a special form. What rational and nonrational animals "share", on this view, is not a separable *factor* that is present in both, but a generic *structure* that is realized in different ways in the two cases. So the explanatory commitments of the two approaches can be diagrammed as shown in Figure 10.2.

The real question at stake in disputes about whether the minds of rational animals differ "in kind" from those of nonrational animals, I would suggest, is whether the cognitive differences by which we distinguish "rational" from "nonrational" animals are to be theorized in the way indicated by the diagram on the left or the diagram on the right (in Figure 10.2). (DKT) amounts to the claim that the right-hand diagram is correct.[12]

If (DKT) is true, then the difference between rational and nonrational animals is more closely analogous to the difference between animals and plants than to, e.g., the difference between animals with the capacity for echolocation and animals without this capacity. Bats, who can echolocate, have a capacity that distinguishes them from other animals, but recognizing this

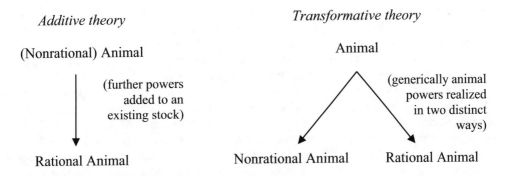

Figure 10.2 The structure of additive and transformative theories

distinctiveness does not require us to think of bats as characterized by a different kind of *animality* from non-echolating animals. But the difference between animal life and plant life does not merely consist in the presence of certain further capacities: what it is for an animal to be alive is – arguably – different from what it is for a plant to be alive. The difference here does not consist in an isolable capacity, but in a global transformation of the kind of living being that bears capacities. Advocates of (DKT) make a similar claim: that rationality does not merely add an isolable capacity to animal life, but globally transforms the nature of animal life itself. One might accept that human beings possess distinctively rational capacities, and that this sets them apart from other animal species, without accepting this claim of global transformation.

4 Motivating the rational-nonrational distinction

A full theory of rationality would need to say more about all these topics, but I will turn in closing to a different question: how we might argue for a basic distinction between rational and nonrational cognitive capacities.

It might seem that the motivation for this distinction must take the form of an "inference to the best explanation" of the observed differences between the cognitive abilities of humans and other animals. Such a motivation would emphasize, e.g., the striking differences between human symbolic communication and nonhuman communicative behaviors, the contrasts between the complex and evolving institutions of human society and the relatively simple and constant forms of behavior that characterize nonhuman animal societies, etc. It would argue that only the presence of capacities to reflect on reasons can explain these fundamental differences.

Advocates of the rational-nonrational distinction will certainly regard such contrasts as reflections of the difference between rational and nonrational cognition, but they need not rest their case on such contrasts. For if human beings *are* rational animals, then each of us is in a position to recognize our own capacities to believe and act for reasons, not by observing human behavior and comparing it with the behavior of other animal species, but simply by reflecting on our own cognition and action. A rational animal, we said, is one capable of acting from an appreciation of reasons for acting. Hence, if we are such beings, when we exercise this capacity, we will be aware of our own reasons for acting, and so will be in a position to recognize, on reflection, that we possess the capacity to act from an appreciation of reasons. We can then frame the idea of a nonrational animal by abstracting from this capacity in ourselves and considering which kinds of animal capacities could remain in its absence. When we turn to survey the natural world, we may discover species of animal life that exhibit this other kind of mentality, but our case for the rational-nonrational distinction need not rest on such a survey.

Indeed, the primary interest of the rational-nonrational distinction does not depend on any concern with making comparisons between humans and other animals. The distinction is important because it helps us to define the specific character of our own cognitive capacities. Having drawn the rational-nonrational distinction, we are in a position to consider what it is to form beliefs and perform actions, not just automatically, but on the basis of an appreciation of reasons, and to ask whether animals with the capacity to act in such ways must have correspondingly distinctive capacities for perception and voluntary movement (i.e., whether (DKT) is true). These are projects, not of self-aggrandizement, but of self-understanding. The thesis that human beings are rational animals is significant, then, not because it would vindicate human "specialness", but because it represents one of the most profound attempts to comprehend the basic character of our own capacities for thought and action, an attempt that enables us to formulate fundamental question about how perception can supply us with knowledge and how thought can govern our actions.[13]

Notes

1 For Aristotle's claim, see *Nicomachean Ethics* I.13 (1102a26–28), and cf. *De Anima* II.3 (415a8) and *Topics* II.5 (112a18–20). All quotations from Aristotle are from the translations in Aristotle 1984.
2 For the distinction between rational and nonrational capacities, see Aristotle, *Metaphysics* VIII.2. The distinction between acting in accordance with and acting from reason is drawn at *Nicomachean Ethics* VI.13 (1144b26–7).
3 See, for example, Stich 1985.
4 For further discussion, see Boyle 2012.
5 The phrase "in a characteristically rational way" is needed to rule out cases like Donald Davidson's imagined mountain climber, who wants to be rid of the weight and danger of the person she is belaying, suddenly thinks that she could simply let go of the rope, and is so shocked at having this thought that she loses her composure and lets go (Davidson 1980, p. 79). Here the climber takes the possibility of getting rid of the weight and danger to be a reason to let go of the rope, and this explains her letting go, but not in a characteristically rational way. How to characterize the normal way in which reasons explain action, and (relatedly) how to characterize the normal "basing relation" that connects belief with epistemic reasons for belief, are matters of controversy. For present purposes, however, what matters is simply that there are such characteristic forms of explanation.
6 For discussion of relevant evidence, see, for instance, the essays in Parts II–VI of Hurley and Nudds 2006 and many of the essays in this volume.
7 We shall see, however, that this substantive fact may have important implications for the epistemological basis of the rational-nonrational distinction.
8 Cf. Aristotle, *Topics*, I.4 (102a32–102b3).
9 Aristotle, *Metaphysics*, X.8 (1057b39–1058a7).
10 Note that one could accept this while rejecting many of the further claims that McDowell makes about perceptual content. One need not accept that the content of perception is restricted by the repertoire of concepts possessed by the perceiving subject, that it is propositional in structure, etc.
11 When I speak of a capacity C of a rational animal as "essentially similar" to the corresponding capacity of a nonrational animal, I mean that an account of how C functions need not itself appeal to distinctively rational powers, such as the power of conceptual representation or comprehending inference (supposing, as many authors do, that these powers are distinctive of rational creatures). Obviously there can be tremendous variation in how (e.g.) animal perceptual capacities function, but all such capacities will count as essentially similar in my sense so long as their functioning does not itself draw on any specifically rational abilities.
12 For further discussion, see Boyle 2016.
13 I'm grateful to Jake Beck for comment on an earlier draft.

Further reading

Aristotle's *De Anima* and *Nicomachean Ethics* (in Aristotle 1984) are classic expressions of the idea that human beings differ in kind from other animals in virtue of their rationality. For recent critical discussion of this idea from an empirically informed perspective, see the essays collected in S. Stich, *Knowledge, Rationality, and Morality* (Oxford: Oxford University Press, 2012). An influential defense of the rational-nonrational distinction is D. Davidson, "Rational Animals", *Dialectica*, 36:4 (1982), pp. 317–327. Hurley and Nudds 2006 is a collection of essays on the topic with contributions from philosophers and scientists.

References

Aristotle. (1984) *Complete Works*, 2 Vols. J. Barnes (ed.), Princeton, NJ: Princeton University Press.
Boyle, M. (2012) "Essentially Rational Animals" in *Rethinking Epistemology*, Vol. 2, G. Abel and J. Conant (eds.), Berlin: Walter de Gruyter.
———. (2016) "Additive Theories of Rationality: A Critique," *European Journal of Philosophy*, 24:3, pp. 527–555, doi:10.1111/ejop.12135

Davidson, D. (1980) "Freedom to Act" in his *Essays on Actions and Events*, Oxford: Oxford University Press.

Evans, G. (1982) *The Varieties of Reference*, Oxford: Oxford University Press.

Hurley, S., and Nudds, M. (eds.). (2006) *Rational Animals?* Oxford: Oxford University Press.

McDowell, J. (1994) *Mind and World*, Cambridge, MA: Harvard University Press.

Stich, S. (1985) "Could Man Be an Irrational Animal?" *Synthese*, 64:1, pp. 115–135.

11

CAN NONLINGUISTIC ANIMALS THINK ABOUT THINKING?

José Luis Bermúdez

1 Introduction

It is beyond serious doubt that nonlinguistic creatures are capable of thinking and reasoning about the physical environment in highly sophisticated ways. But can animals think about thinking? Alternatively put, are animals capable of metarepresentation? This question is at the heart of how we think about comparative psychology, animal cognition, and human cognitive development.

In Bermúdez 2003b and 2009, I proposed that certain types of thinking about thinking are only available to language-using creatures. My argument generated interesting debate and useful criticisms that helped me to refine and develop it. In this entry, I review the state of play, offering a revised version of the argument that addresses some of the principal objections.

2 Two important distinctions

As the entries to this companion amply attest, there is a rich experimental literature exploring the representational capacities of nonlinguistic creatures. A number of experimental paradigms directly address the question of whether animals can think about thinking. In order to get the issues clearly in view, it is important to make some basic distinctions between different types of thinking about thinking.

The first distinction has to do with whether the putative thinking about thinking is self-directed or other-directed. Discussions of metarepresentation in language-using humans typically distinguish between *metacognition*, on the one hand, and *mindreading*, on the other. Thinkers have metacognitive abilities to the extent that they are capable of monitoring and evaluating their own mental states. Mindreading, in contrast, is a matter of a creature's ability to think about another creature's mental states. We can ask, therefore, whether nonlinguistic creatures are capable of metacognition, of mindreading, or of both.

The second distinction has to do with the type of thinking that might be the object of metarepresentational thinking. Thinking about thinking might involve, on the one hand, thinking about another creature's perceptual states. So, for example, a primate might think that a conspecific can hear a predator or see a food source. Alternatively, the objects of thinking about thinking might be what philosophers typically call *propositional attitudes*, such as beliefs, hopes, fears, and so on. Perceptual states and propositional attitudes differ in important respects.

1   Perceptual states typically have direct implications for action – seeing a predator normally elicits a direct response (fight or flight). In contrast, there is generally no single way that a belief or desire will feed into action, because how one behaves depends upon all the other things that one believes or desires. For that reason, the path from propositional attitudes to behavior typically involves a process of reasoning – and, very relevant to the following, thinking about how another subject acts in virtue of their beliefs typically involves thinking about their reasoning.
2   Perceptions can be mistaken, of course, and often it makes very good sense to be prone to certain kinds of error (false positives are much better than false negatives when detecting predators, for example), but there are many more ways in which subjects can act in virtue of false beliefs. Moreover, understanding the possibility of false belief seems essential to grasping the concept of belief in a way that does not seem to hold for perception. This is the basic insight behind the Sally-Anne test, first proposed in Baron-Cohen, Leslie, and Frith 1985 and subsequently studied in many different forms (see Bermúdez 2014 Ch. 12 for details and references). The test is designed to assess young children's understanding of belief, the prototypical propositional attitude, through testing whether they grasp that another thinker might have a false belief about their environment.

Combining these two distinctions yields four distinct types of thinking about thinking, all of which are plainly available and widespread in language-using creatures. In the following, I will be focusing primarily on propositional attitude mindreading.

As will emerge in Section 4, thinking about propositional attitudes is a much richer and more demanding cognitive phenomenon than thinking about perceptual states. It is only for propositional attitudes that the question of language-dependence arises. Moreover, the most widely discussed evidence for metacognition in the animal kingdom comes from studies of animals' degrees of "uncertainty" about their perceptual judgments. In a typical metacognition experiment, for example, animals learn to perform a perceptual discrimination task and then are trained to use a "don't know" button in conditions of subjective uncertainty (see Smith 2005, for example). Even leaving aside the first-order (non-metarepresentational) interpretation of such experiments proposed by Carruthers 2008, the most that such experiments can show is the existence of perceptual metacognition (a nonlinguistic animal monitoring its own perceptual states). In contrast, psychologists, philosophers, and ethologists have made much stronger claims about nonlinguistic creatures being able to engage in propositional attitude mindreading.

My view of the extent of thinking about thinking in nonhuman animals is represented in Table 11.1.

Table 11.1 Varieties of mindreading in nonhuman animals

	Perceptual	*Propositional attitude*
Metacognition	Maybe	No
Mindreading	Yes	No

3 What is the role of *a priori* argument in thinking about empirical research programs?

There are some methodological issues to tackle before discussing my negative claims about propositional attitude mindreading. One response to the discussion so far would be to say that whether nonlinguistic animals can think about thinking is simply an empirical question, to be resolved by suitably designed experiments. There is no room for philosophical arguments or other theoretical speculations.

Robert Lurz has given eloquent expression to a view along these lines. After describing two important experimental paradigms in this area, he writes:

> The underlying assumption of the above research is that existence of nonlinguistic higher-order PAs [propositional attitudes] is an empirical question, not to be ruled out a priori but to be decided by running well-designed experiments and examining competing hypotheses against the data. If Bermúdez's theory is correct, however, this assumption is seriously mistaken: Whether nonlinguistic subjects can have higher-order PAs can be answered from the armchair, and the answer is, in principle, no. The point of mentioning the empirical research is not to make a positive empirical case for the existence of nonlinguistic higher-order PAs. I leave that to the researchers. It is to show that Bermúdez's theory denies an underlying assumption of a number of lines of current empirical research. The issue, to repeat, is whether we can know in advance of empirical investigation whether actual nonlinguistic subjects have or can have higher-order PAs, not whether the results of current empirical studies demonstrate the existence of nonlinguistic higher-order PAs. A significant consequence of Bermúdez's theory, then, is that continued empirical research into the existence of nonlinguistic higher-order PAs is known a priori to be misconceived and pointless.
>
> (Lurz 2007, p. 272)

I am sympathetic to Lurz's animadversions against the proverbial armchair. However, it seems to me that Lurz is setting up a false dichotomy. The significance of all experiments in this area depends upon how the crucial notions are operationalized, and that process of operationalization in turn depends upon a broader theoretical conception of the nature of thought and reasoning. One of the reasons this area is so exciting from an experimental point of view is that there is no standardly agreed conceptual framework for designing experiments and interpreting the results of those experiments.

The task of developing such a conceptual framework is one in which experimentalists are just as engaged as philosophers and theoretical cognitive scientists (see, for example, Heyes 1998 and Povinelli and Vonk 2006). Quine's well-known metaphorical description of science as a force field is particularly appropriate in this context. Most often Quine's metaphor is interpreted as showing the impossibility of purely *a priori* inquiry, which of course it does. But the very same picture of scientific inquiry shows also the naïveté of thinking that any interesting and theoretically loaded question has a straightforward empirical solution. As Quine puts it, "no particular experiences are linked with any particular statements in the interior of the field, except indirectly through considerations of equilibrium affecting the field as a whole" (Quine 1951, p. 40). The discussion in the remainder of this entry should be read as a contribution to the multidisciplinary task of determining just such an equilibrium between the different theoretical and practical pressures at play in this area (see Bermúdez 2011 for further discussion of Quine's force-field analogy in this context).

4 The basic argument

The distinction between propositional attitude mindreading and perceptual mindreading is important because they make very different cognitive demands. It is the additional demands imposed by propositional attitude mindreading that, I claim, require linguistic abilities. The difference can best be appreciated initially through diagrams.

Figure 11.1 shows a diagram illustrating perceptual mindreading. Subjects engaged in perceptual mindreading have to be able to represent three things. First, they need to be able to represent the perceiving agent. Second, they need to be able to represent the state of affairs that the other agent is perceiving. Third, they need to be able to represent the fact that the agent is perceiving that state of affairs. The first two do not introduce any additional representational demands, since any subject likely to be engaged in perceptual mindreading will already be perfectly capable of representing other agents (conspecifics and predators, for example). And, I claim, representing perception itself in this context need not be very demanding. It certainly involves being able to represent the other agent's sensitivity to the perceived state of affairs – that the agent is, or is about to, modify their behavior in response to information about their environment. Relatedly, it involves being able to represent that the agent is suitably placed to be sensitive to their environment – that its gaze is directed in the right direction, for example, or that the perceived state of affairs is in earshot.

Representing perception in this way certainly does not require language. It is beyond dispute that even cognitively unsophisticated nonlinguistic creatures are highly sensitive to contingencies between eye gaze and behavior (in conspecifics and in potential predators). Moreover, and most importantly, no metarepresentation is required. The perceptual mindreader does not need to be able to represent representations, in addition to representing objects and features of the world. Everything takes place at the same level as ordinary thought about the environment and

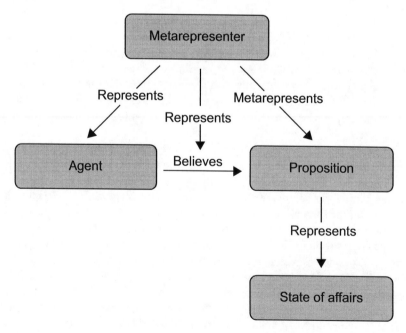

Figure 11.1 What goes on in representing perception. Note that representing perception does *not* require metarepresentation.

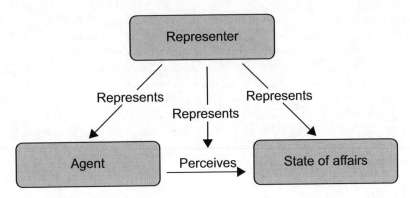

Figure 11.2 What goes on in representing belief. Note that representing belief requires metarepresentation.

what it contains. There is no need for what I have termed *intentional ascent* – the shift from think-ing about the world to thinking about thinking.

Propositional attitude mindreading is very different because it does require metarepresen-tation, as the diagram in Figure 11.2 brings out. The key point is that propositional attitude mindreading does not involve thinking about a *direct* relation between a subject and their environment in the way that perceptual mindreading does. That is the whole point of the Sally-Anne task and the various other false-belief tests. Beliefs can be false and false beliefs are just as powerful in bringing about behavior as true ones. It is what subjects believe about the world that explains and predicts their behavior. This means that representing another subject's belief state requires representing them as having representations of their environment – representations that can be either true or false. Philosophers typically analyze belief (and other propositional attitudes) as an attitude to a proposition or thought. The terminology is inessential, however. What matters is that understanding what another subject believes requires metarepresentation in a way that understanding what they are seeing or hearing does not.

So, any creature engaging in propositional attitude mindreading must be able to represent representations. In order to establish the language-dependence of propositional attitude mind-reading, we need to establish two things. The first is that belief-representations must be repre-sented linguistically (as opposed to being represented imagistically, for example). The second is that these representations must take place in a natural language (as opposed, for example, to a language of thought or some other subpersonal computational medium). In the remainder of this section, I sketch my case for these two claims. We will return to them in more detail below in the context of responding to objections.

To see why linguistic representation is required, we need to go back to the initial discussion of propositional attitudes. An important contrast with perception is that propositional attitudes such as belief do not typically impact upon behavior directly. How one behaves in virtue of what one believes depends upon what else one believes and what one wants to achieve. This means that propositional attitude mindreaders have to be able to represent propositions or thoughts in a way that allows them to work out how the relevant beliefs or other propositional attitudes will feed into action. Since the path from belief to action typically involves some sort of reasoning process, either implicit or explicit, a belief must be represented in a way that reveals its inferential relations to other beliefs and to other relevant mental states, such as desires.

Most of the logical/inferential relations between beliefs hold in virtue of structure. This is certainly true of the logical relations codified in the propositional and predicate calculus.

Take conditional beliefs, for example. A bird might have a conditional belief about its environment (if it rains, then there will be more insects on the leaves, for example), or about its own actions (e.g. if there are more insects on the leaves, then I should switch from foraging on the ground to foraging on the leaves). If the creature comes to believe that it is raining, then the combination of beliefs will lead it to switch from foraging on the ground to foraging on leaves. Another creature trying to predict the bird's behavior will need to recreate the obvious reasoning from the belief that it is raining via the two conditional beliefs to the decision to switch foraging strategies. That, in turn, requires representing the conditional beliefs as attitudes to a complex proposition that relates two other propositions, so that the entire reasoning process has the form

> If A then B
> If B then C
> A
> Therefore C

Only in language, I claim, can the structure of these beliefs be represented in the right way for their logical relations to emerge.

Language is a mechanism for creating complex representational structures from simple representations through combinatorial rules, in addition to possessing markers (such as logical connectives and quantifiers) that reveal the basic inferential connections between the propositions that sentences express. Because of this, linguistic representations have a canonical structure, which allows a conditional belief to be represented linguistically in the form "If A then B", for example. The only alternative to a language-like representational structure is a pictorial/imagistic structure. But pictorial/imagistic representations do not have a canonical structure and so cannot reveal inferential connections. We will return to the relation between language and inference in the next two sections.

Suppose, then, that beliefs and other propositional attitudes must be represented linguistically. It does not follow immediately that they must be represented in a natural (public) language. Many cognitive scientists and philosophers claim that there is a language of thought – a language-like computational medium for subpersonal information-processing. Why could the language of thought not do the job? My answer, in brief, is that propositional attitude mindreading is part of a creature's conscious mental life. This is because, for those creatures capable of it, propositional attitude mindreading is integrated with conscious practical decision-making. Creatures who understand and can think about the beliefs and desires of others typically do so in the context of working out what they themselves would do. We decide what to do in the light of what we predict others will do and the reasons that we can identify for their observed actions. This means that the representations exploited in propositional attitude mindreading must be consciously accessible elements of a creature's psychological life – and so cannot be sentences in the language of thought. More on this in Section 7.

5 Is there really a distinction between language-like and imagistic representations?

The argument in Section 4 plainly depends upon the cogency of the distinction between language-like and imagistic representation. That there is such a distinction has been denied by John Heil in a thoughtful and probing discussion of the relation between thought and language. According to Heil, "where cognition is concerned there is nothing special about language"

(Heil 2012, p. 263). His reason is that what I am calling language-like representations are really just images. Here are two illustrative passages.

> Just as you make use of sentences – written or spoken – to articulate ideas to others, you can use *inner* utterances in the articulation of ideas to yourself. You can talk through a problem, recall the details of an earlier conversation, or plan a course of action by listing steps to its completion in your head. In these cases, inner utterances are not manifestations or copies of thoughts; you are thinking with language just as you might open a can with a can-opener. . .
>
> Inner utterances (I say, siding with Bermúdez) are a species of mental imagery, where the images are images of what their audible, visual, or tactile counterparts sound, look, or feel like. There is no logical or conceptual gulf between linguistic ("propositional") imagery and imagery of other sorts, "pictorial" imagery. Conscious thought quite generally is imagistic.
>
> (Heil 2012, p. 265–6)

This is a very useful reminder. Heil is absolutely right to emphasize that language is a tool and that we think with or through language, rather than in language. We do not have "wordless" thoughts that we then translate into language.

I have no quarrel, moreover, with his claim that thinking through language is ultimately a matter of entertaining and manipulating linguistic imagery, so that in a sense, all thought comes out as imagistic/pictorial. I have no issues with reformulating my central claim in terms of linguistic imagery (as thinking about thoughts requiring linguistic imagery). I think that it will be very profitable to explore the mechanics of how we think through inner speech. This is a relatively unstudied area (see Vicente and Martinez-Manríque 2011 for a literature review and Bermúdez 2018 for further discussion of inner speech in the context of thinking about thinking). It promises to shed considerable light on cognition in general and metarepresentation in particular.

However, I cannot share Heil's confidence that "just as it seems unlikely that *any* tool is irreplaceable, so it seems unlikely that language is, for any particular task, irreplaceable" (2012, p. 265). As we saw in the previous section, the issue has to do with canonical structure and inference. My (reformulated) claim is that thinking about thoughts requires a special kind of imagery – linguistic imagery – to do a job that I claim nonlinguistic imagery cannot do, namely, represent the canonical structure of thinking in a way that will make inferential connections perspicuous. In order to defeat that claim, we need to have reasons for thinking that nonlinguistic imagery is an appropriate tool for that task. Heil does not provide such reasons, but in the next section we will look at an intriguing analysis of map-like representations that seems to be the most compelling proposal in this area.

6 Why can't maps do the job?

The contrast between language-like representational formats and imagistic ones is often mapped onto the distinction between digital and analog representations. There are two salient points of difference. The first has to do with how they respectively represent. Complex digital representations are built up in a rule-governed way from basic symbolic units that have a purely arbitrary connection with their objects, whereas analog representations represent through relations of similarity and/or isomorphism. The second has to do with their structure. Analog representations typically exploit continuously variable magnitudes (such as volume or color), while digital representations have a discrete structure.

Given the representational requirements laid out in Section 5, it seems highly plausible that purely analog representations will not suffice for propositional attitude mindreading, since that requires representing beliefs in a way that brings out their internal structure and inferential connections. However, in Bermúdez 2003a, I did not pay sufficient attention to the possibility of hybrid representational formats that might be sufficiently structured to meet the requirements of propositional attitude mindreading without being linguistic. The most promising candidates are cartographic (map-like) representations, which have been illuminatingly studied by Elisabeth Camp.

The following two passages give the flavor of Camp's rich discussion.

Cartographic systems are a little like pictures and a little like sentences. Like pictures, maps represent by exploiting isomorphisms between the physical properties of vehicle and content. But maps abstract away from much of the detail that encumbers pictorial systems. Where pictures are isomorphic to their represented contents along multiple dimensions, maps only exploit an isomorphism of spatial structure: on most maps, distance in the vehicle corresponds, up to a scaling factor, to distance in the world. Further, typically this spatial isomorphism itself only captures functionally salient features of the represented domain: for a road map, say, only streets and buildings and not trees and benches. Maps also depart from the direct replication of visual appearance by employing a disengaged, "God's eye" perspective instead of an embedded point of view.

(Camp 2007, p. 158–9)

In principle, it's not hard to extend maps to represent negative information. Most crudely, we could introduce a higher-order icon with the force of a "contrary operator": say, putting a slashed circle over the "Bob" icon to indicate that Bob is not at the represented location. Because we are already employing symbolic icons as constituents, this doesn't itself fundamentally change the sort of representational system we're employing. However, this technique would quickly lead to massive clutter. A more elegant solution would color icons and background regions to reflect positive and negative information. For instance, the default state could be a grey background, expressing neutrality about the presence and absence of every potentially representable object and property. A black (or other fully-saturated) icon would represent certainty that the relevant object/property is at that location, while a white (or anti-colored) icon would represent certainty of its absence; a white background could then represent certainty that there were no other, unrepresented objects or properties in that region besides those explicitly represented on the map.

(Camp 2007, p. 163)

The question, then, is why can't some sort of map-like representation be deployed nonlinguistically in propositional attitude mindreading?

The quick response, as Camp herself notes, would be to say that "diagrams and maps just are sentences written in a funny notation" (Camp 2007, p. 155). She responds, surely correctly, that maps and languages have very different combinatorial principles, so that thinking in maps is very different from thinking in words. As observed earlier, linguistic combinatorial principles are conventional and domain-general, whereas maps and pictures represent through isomorphism and similarity.

Nonetheless, in virtue of their hybrid nature, maps exploit representational devices much richer than direct isomorphism. This is central to Camp's argument that maps can function as nonlinguistic combinatorial representational systems. She analyzes what might be termed *structured maps*. Consider the following:

> In particular, because maps exploit discrete, recurrent syntactic constituents with stable, at least partly conventionalized, semantic properties, one can achieve something close to the effect of sentential structure within a cartographic system by manipulating the basic icons in ways that don't affect their spatial structure. In effect, we've introduced rules for generating syntactically complex icons which represent semantically complex objects and properties: not-Bob, past-Bob, etc. So long as these icons still function as labels placing objects and properties at locations, one might argue, and so long as their mode of combination sets up an isomorphism between their spatial structures and those of the analogous features in the world, we're still operating within a fundamentally cartographic system.
>
> (Camp 2007, p. 166)

Structured maps involve the addition of symbols, so that representation is not purely pictorial. This does not beg the question against the "sentences in funny notation" view, because of the very significant differences between symbol systems and languages proper. Researchers have successfully trained various different species of nonlinguistic animal to communicate through symbol systems (see the papers in Part V on Communication in this volume for more details), but none of these symbol systems have the properties of full-fledged languages – such as allowing recursive embedding and arbitrary combination, for example.

The real issue, I think, has to do with the ability to use maps as representational devices. Here we need to make a distinction between implicit and explicit mastery. Explicit mastery of a structured map would involve being able to spell out the representational conventions governing the synactically complex icons – being able to articulate, for example, how the "contrary operator" conveys the information that an object is not there. It would be hard to deny that such articulation requires language. But in order to think *with* a map (to echo John Heil's phrase), implicit mastery is all that is required. A competent map-user does not need to be able to articulate the conventions governing the map. They need simply to be guided by those conventions and to navigate in conformity with them.

For these reasons, I think that Camp is absolutely correct that maps can have more structure than I gave them credit for without being simply notationally different ways of writing down sentences. Her aim is to undermine standard arguments for the language of thought by showing that maps can function as combinatorial representational systems. However, the question that I am addressing in this chapter is somewhat different (and not one that she directly addresses). What I am interested in is whether thoughts can be represented nonlinguistically through structured maps, and here it is very unclear that structured maps can do the job.

Propositional attitude mindreading is metarepresentational because it involves spelling out how another agent represents the world. On almost all understandings of mindreading, this requires the mindreader to be able to think about the structured map as an articulation of how the other agent believes the world to be.[1] There is a fundamental difference between thinking with a structured map, on the one hand, and thinking about a structured map as a way of representing the world, on the other. We saw that implicit mastery of the map's representational conventions is all that's required for the first of these. But it is not sufficient for the second. Using a structured map to represent another agent's beliefs requires the mindreader to think directly about the map's representational properties. It is not enough just to be guided by them, or to act in accordance with them. Explicit rather than implicit mastery is required. But, as pointed out above, that sort of explicit mastery brings language back into the picture. Using a structured map to represent the world need not be a linguistic achievement. But thinking about how another creature might represent the world by means of a structured map requires a level of explicit grasp of how the map is functioning as a tool for representing the world. And that, I claim, is language-dependent in a way that simply using a structured map need not be.

7 Why can't the language of thought do the job?

It is essential to my argument for the language-dependence of thinking about thinking that the crucial metarepresentational work cannot be done by a subpersonal language of thought. As discussed in Section 4, my argument against the language of thought rested upon the claim that propositional attitude mindreading requires beliefs to be represented in a way that makes them consciously accessible. Robert Lurz has taken issue with that part of my argument. He writes:

> Bermúdez's reasoning here appears to rest upon the dubious assumption that if the vehicles of thought are subpersonal, the thoughts themselves (i.e. propositional contents) those vehicles represent are as well. But what needs to be at the personal level in bouts of second-order cognitive dynamics are thoughts (i.e. propositional contents), not their representational vehicles. It is thoughts, after all, that we hold in mind, and it is the relations among thoughts that we consider and evaluate during second-order cognitive dynamics. We needn't have any conscious accessibility to the representational vehicles of these thoughts in order to have conscious accessibility to the thoughts themselves.
>
> (Lurz 2007, p. 288)

Lurz's basic point is very valid, and I agree with him that a thought can be cognitively accessible without its vehicle being cognitively accessible. If that were not true, then there would not be any room for discussion and argument about how thoughts are in fact vehicled – we could just introspect the answer. Nonetheless, I am unconvinced by how he applies that point to my argument.

The problem is that "consciously accessible" is an equivocal expression. "Having a consciously accessible thought" can mean either "having a conscious thought" or "being conscious of a thought", and these are two very different things. Eliding them runs the risk of collapsing the basic distinction between first-order thought (which is about the world) and second-order thought (which is about thoughts).

It is certainly true that one can have a conscious thought without being conscious of the vehicle of that thought. This seems almost always to be the case. But that is because having a conscious thought does not involve being conscious of a thought at all. The consciousness of a conscious thought is, as it were, directed outwards. To have a conscious thought is to be conscious of whatever it is that one's thought is about. To have a conscious thought about the cat on the lawn is to be conscious of the cat on the lawn.[2] This is a paradigm case of first-order thought about the world – the cat is the object of one's thinking.

In contrast, being conscious of the thought that the cat is on the lawn is not an episode of first-order thought. Being conscious of a thought about the cat on the lawn is thinking about the thought, not thinking about the cat. The object of one's thinking is not the cat on the lawn, but rather the thought that the cat is on the lawn.

Lurz's point applies to first-order thought, but not (I claim) to second-order thought. We can think consciously about a cat without being conscious of the vehicle of our thinking. But we can only think consciously about the thought that the cat is on the lawn if the thought is vehicled in a certain way. A good analogy here is thinking about a sentence. We can only think about a sentence if it is written down or uttered. The sentence needs to be represented in a way that brings out its structure and composition. Thoughts are exactly the same. A thought is the thought that it is in virtue of its composition and structure. Thinking about a given thought, therefore, requires representing its composition and structure. So, the vehicle of second-order thought must make the structure and composition of the target thought perspicuous. But, by the argument of Sections 4 and 6, the vehicles of such second-order thinking must be linguistic.

8 Conclusion

In sum, objections to my argument in Bermúdez 2003a that thinking about thinking requires language have brought a number of interesting and important points into focus. These include a more nuanced picture of the relation between theory and experiment in discussing nonlinguistic cognition (Lurz); the role of linguistic imagery in thought (Heil); an insightful analysis of how cartographic representations can serve as vehicles for first-order thought (Camp); and the relation between content and vehicle in conscious thought (Lurz). These contributions have certainly helped me refine and develop the original argument. But, I submit, the basic claim that thinking about thinking requires language still stands.

Notes

1   The exception here is the radical version of simulationism initially proposed in Gordon 1986. On this view, mindreading simply requires deploying one's own propositional attitudes "off-line" in order to predict how others will behave, so that no metarepresentation is involved. If this is the correct model for propositional attitude mindreading, then that would undermine the distinction between implicit and explicit mastery that I am drawing. This is not the place to evaluate radical simulationism, but I have suggested elsewhere that off-line simulation is best viewed, not as a complete account of propositional attitude mindreading, but rather as one of a range of cognitive shortcuts that creatures employ to avoid the computational complexities of full-fledged metarepresentation (Bermúdez 2003b and 2006).
2   This only holds, of course, when there actually is a cat on the lawn. I am not familiar with a fully satisfying account of what goes on when one consciously thinks about the cat on the lawn and there is no cat on the lawn, but I see no plausibility in the thought that what one is conscious of in such cases is the thought that there is a cat on the lawn.

Further reading

The arguments explored in this chapter were first presented in Bermúdez 2003a, with critical commentary in Lurz 2007, Heil 2012, and Camp 2007. For further discussion of related issues in animal cognition and metarepresentation, see the papers in Hurley and Nudds 2006 and Lurz 2009.

References

Baron-Cohen, S., A. M. Leslie, and U. Frith. 1985. Does the autistic child have a 'theory of mind'? *Cognition* 21: 37–46.
Bermúdez, J. L. 2003a. *Thinking Without Words*. New York: Oxford University Press.

Bermúdez, J. L. 2003b. The domain of folk psychology. In A. O'Hear (Ed.), *Minds and Persons*. Cambridge: Cambridge University Press.

Bermúdez, J. L. 2006. A plausible eliminativism. In B. L. Keeley (Ed.), *Paul Churchland*. Cambridge: Cambridge University Press.

Bermúdez, J. L. 2009. Mindreading in the animal kingdom. In R. W. Lurz (Ed.), *The Philosophy of Animal Minds*. Cambridge: Cambridge University Press.

Bermúdez, J. L. 2011. The forcefield puzzle and mindreading in nonhuman primates. *Review of Philosophy and Psychology* 2: 397–410.

Bermúdez, J. L. 2014. *Cognitive Science: An Introduction to the Science of the Mind* (2nd edition). Cambridge: Cambridge University Press.

Bermúdez, J. L. 2018. Inner speech, determinacy, and thinking about thoughts. In P. Langland-Hassan and A. Vicente (Eds.), *Inner Speech: Nature, Functions, and Pathology*. Oxford: Oxford University Press.

Camp, E. 2007. Thinking with maps. *Philosophical Perspectives* 21: 145–82.

Carruthers, P. 2008. Meta-cognition in animals: A skeptical look. *Mind and Language* 23: 58–89.

Gordon, R. 1986. Folk psychology as simulation. *Mind and Language* 1: 158–71.

Heil, J. 2012. *The Universe as We Find It*. Oxford: Oxford University Press.

Heyes, C. M. 1998. Theory of mind in nonhuman primates. *Behavioral and Brain Sciences* 21: 101–34.

Hurley, S. L., and M. Nudds. 2006. *Rational Animals?* Oxford: Oxford University Press.

Lurz, R. W. 2007. In defense of wordless thoughts about thoughts. *Mind and Language* 22: 270–96.

Lurz, R. W. 2009. *The Philosophy of Animal Minds*. Cambridge: Cambridge University Press.

Povinelli, D., and J. Vonk. 2006. We don't need a microscope to explore the chimpanzee's mind. In S. Hurley and M. Nudds (Eds.), *Rational Animals?* Oxford: Oxford University Press.

Quine, W. V. O. 1951. Two dogmas of empiricism. *The Philosophical Review* 60: 20–43.

Smith, J. D., and D. A. Washburn. 2005. Uncertainty monitoring and metacognition by animals. *Current Directions in Psychological Science* 14: 19–24.

Vicente, A., and F. Martínez-Manrique. 2011. Inner speech: Nature and functions. *Philosophy Compass* 6: 209–19.

12

ON PSYCHOLOGICAL EXPLANATIONS AND SELF-CONCEPTS (IN SOME ANIMALS)

Eric Saidel

According to a recent study, prairie voles console one another when stressed. J. P. Burkett and his colleagues separated a pair of voles and subjected one of them (the "demonstrator") to light foot shocks.[1] The demonstrator was then reunited with the other vole (the "observer"), who had not witnessed the shocks. Burkett and colleagues found that the observer engaged in significantly longer grooming behavior directed toward the demonstrator than in the control situations in which the demonstrator was not shocked. The grooming, which Burkett and colleagues also call "consolation behavior," was limited to familiar voles; observers would not groom or console strangers. *The New York Times* reported on this experiment under the headline, "A Furry Shoulder to Cry On."[2] *The Times* report begins with the claim that "prairie voles console one another when distressed." There is a noticeable gap between the claims made by the scientists – that the observer grooms the stressed demonstrator – and those made by *The New York Times* – that the observer provides a shoulder for the distressed demonstrator to cry on. The claims made by *The Times* are evocative, suggesting a sympathetic response characterized by empathy and fellow feeling. The reader is practically invited to imagine the observer reaching out to the demonstrator, saying "I feel your pain." Such a scenario is clearly not experimentally supported. Any attribution of human-like experience to the prairie vole would be premature. Or would it? What warrants an attribution of human-like experience to a nonhuman animal? What evidence might we gather to support the claim that a nonhuman animal has thoughts and experiences similar to those that humans have?

In what follows, I suggest that the comparative evidence (gathered mostly from primate studies) suggests that even though some animals may have an active mental life that includes thoughts and goals, it is unlikely that the nonhuman animal's experience of its mental life is similar to human beings' experience of their mental life. Human mental experience relies on a concept of a self, which evidence suggests is missing in many nonhuman animals. To see why such a concept of the self is important, I start by looking some more at the ways in which prairie vole consolation behavior is similar to empathetic behavior found in human beings. Then I turn to remarkable planning behavior by a chimpanzee. Careful consideration of this behavior and the nature of the evidence it provides for the understanding of chimpanzee minds indicates the role a concept of the self plays in human mental life.

Burkett and colleagues uncover several details about prairie vole consolation behavior that suggest parallels to human empathic response. First, like a human being in an empathetic state, the prairie vole observers apparently experience a stressful state similar to the one the demonstrator is in, as indicated by their engaging in similar fear and stress-related behaviors, as well as by increases in hormones associated with stress. These hormone levels decreased if the observer was allowed to interact with and groom the demonstrator, but remained elevated if the observer was not allowed to groom the demonstrator. The observer voles also were more likely to groom demonstrators who were familiar to them, much like empathetic human beings, who are more likely to demonstrate empathy toward familiars. The voles also demonstrated an awareness of the distinction between self and other: even though both demonstrators and observers exhibited elevated levels of stress, only the demonstrator received comfort; demonstrators did not engage in increased grooming of the observers. Moreover, in human beings, empathetic behavior has been linked to the presence of oxytocin, so Burkett's team injected observers with an oxytocin antagonist in order to ascertain the effects of oxytocin on prairie vole empathetic behavior. Those prairie voles who had been injected with the oxytocin antagonist engaged in no consolation behavior subsequent to that injection.

In both human beings and prairie voles, consolation behavior is triggered by stress. Consolation behavior involves the empathetic increased sensation of stress in the consoling individual; involves a recognition that, of the two individuals experiencing stress, the originally stressed individual is the one who receives consoling; and is closely related to the presence of oxytocin in the system. Why not think that the prairie vole is experiencing a state much like that of a human being engaged in empathetic behavior?

We can ask a similar question about Santino, a chimpanzee at the Furuvik Zoo in Sweden. As reported by Osvath (2009),[3] Santino exhibited some remarkable aggressive behavior towards zoo visitors. Captive chimpanzees will often express themselves by throwing objects at visitors. Often these objects are whatever is at hand, including feces. However, Santino adopted a different strategy: he cached stones early in the day, before there were visitors at the zoo. Then, later, when visitors came to the zoo, he would recover the hidden stones and throw them at the visitors. Initially, his ammunition consisted of rocks found in the waterbed adjacent to his enclosure, cached along the shoreline closest to where the visitors would walk. Later, however, he added chunks of concrete to his ammunition, even going so far as finding where in his enclosure the concrete was likely to be weak and then breaking it off to use as ammunition. As zoo officials would remove his caches of stones, he took to manufacturing hiding places from hay that he found in his enclosure, and then concealing the stones and concrete under those new hiding places.[4] Santino was calm when he planted the ammunition in caches and angry later when he recovered the ammunition and threw it at the visitors. These details tempt one to conclude that Santino was engaging in advance planning. He knew that he would be angered by the presence of visitors, that he would want to demonstrate that anger, and that unless he prepared ahead of time, he would not be able to demonstrate that anger – and so he prepared ahead of time. This interpretation attributes to Santino several complex mental attitudes: a sense of self, knowledge about his current states of mind and how they may differ from his future states of mind, and an ability to take steps so that his future self will be satisfied, even at the cost of energy expenditure which is useless for his present self. Is this interpretation of Santino's behavior justified? Or is it an example of an unwarranted projection of human-like psychological attributes onto another animal?[5]

As these questions suggest, there are two obvious alternative accounts of Santino's behavior: the deflationary account that we can explain Santino's behavior in ways that don't involve attributing human-like psychological attributes to him (in the case of the prairie voles, this would amount to asserting that what they are experiencing is not compassion), and the inflationary account that Santino is truly engaged in planning for the future, that he is truly taking steps to ensure that his future self is able to achieve its goals (or, in the case of the prairie voles, that they are truly empathetic).[6] Several ethologists argue for the deflationary answer. For example, Roberts and Feeney (2010) argue that Santino's behavior does not demonstrate advanced planning. The fact that he does not stockpile ammunition during the off-season (during which the zoo is closed), but instead waits until visitors start arriving at the zoo in the spring to cache stones suggests that the first visitors "served as a contextual stimulus for storing rocks . . . without the anticipation of doing so at any specific time in the future" (Roberts and Feeney 2010: 53).[7] Suddendorf and Corballis (2010) argue that there are alternative explanations for Santino's behavior; the data collected by Osvath underdetermines the conclusion that Santino was planning for future dominance displays. Shettleworth (2010) repeats Suddendorf and Corballis's analysis, adding in her discussion that often apparently complex behavior can be explained by means of "elementary mechanisms." More generally, Balter (2012), reporting in *Science*, describes a general attitude among scientists that when there is a "simpler" explanation available (where cognitive explanations are viewed as more complex, and non-cognitive explanations are thought to be simpler), that simpler explanation is preferable to an explanation citing cognitive processes. Thus, the deflationary strategy: look for non-cognitive (or less cognitive) explanations of Santino's behavior and argue that because such explanations exist, the behavior does not merit a fully cognitive explanation.[8] We should not conclude on the basis of this evidence alone that Santino is planning for the future, nor that he is taking steps to ensure that his future self is able to achieve his goals, perhaps at the expense of his present goals.

This argument apparently relies on Morgan's Canon, the principle that we should avoid appealing to "higher" processes when we can explain behavior as a consequence of "lower" processes alone: "In no case is an animal activity to be interpreted in terms of higher psychological processes if it can be fairly interpreted in terms of processes which stand lower in the scale of psychological evolution and development."[9] However, Morgan's Canon has come under attack recently.[10] It relies on several questionable assumptions, for example, that there is a higher and a lower process when applied to psychology, and that evolution somehow makes a distinction between higher and lower.

Perhaps the deflationists need not rely on Morgan's Canon. Povinelli and Vonk (2003) argue that when it comes to attribution of a theory of mind (that is, thoughts that other individuals have minds), chimpanzee behavior can always be explained more simply. That is, when a chimpanzee's behavior is putatively caused by its representation of another animal's mental state, it must also be mediated by an abstract representation of the other animal's behavior. But, Povinelli and Vonk argue, the behavior we want to explain can be explained simply by reference to that mediating abstract representation of behavior. No further representation of the other animal's mental state is necessary. Rather than depending on a spurious distinction between higher and lower, Povinelli and Vonk are making an appeal to parsimony: the mindreading hypothesis requires chimpanzees to have representations of animals' mental states and of their behavior, while the behavior-reading hypothesis requires representations only of animals' behavior. Unless the evidence specifically requires both kinds of representation, we should prefer the explanation that postulates fewer intervening representations.[11]

Can this reasoning be applied to the debate about Santino? The key to Povinelli and Vonk's argument is that they find two structures that must be present for the mindreading explanation of the chimpanzee's behavior, but only one of those structures must be present for the behavior-reading explanation of the same behavior. The deflationists can argue that in order for the proper explanation for Santino's behavior to be that he is planning ahead, then that explanation must assert that he is both responding to cues in his current environment and engaging in mental states that involve projecting himself into the future. On the other hand, if the proper explanation for Santino's behavior does not involve advance planning, then the explanation need assert only that he is responding to cues in his current environment. Unless there is evidence that explaining Santino's behavior specifically requires both projecting himself into the future and responding to cues in the environment, we should prefer the deflationary view. This is the argument pattern that Roberts and Feeney (2010) seem to rely on when they argue that there is an explanation of Santino's behavior that relies only on contextual clues and not on any planning for the future.[12]

The problem with this argument pattern is that just as it could be easily generalized from issues having to do with theory of mind to issues having to do with advance planning, so too can it be easily generalized to any situation in which a cognitive explanation vies with a non-cognitive explanation. In each of these situations, the cognitive hypothesis will compete with a non-cognitive hypothesis that is largely the same, except that it does not postulate the existence of some extra mechanism. The problem is that every instance of behavior might have a non-cognitive explanation. That includes even paradigms of cognitive behavior such as speech; there are non-cognitive speech acts, e.g., parroting expressions without understanding them. If we follow Povinelli and Vonk's logic, no behavior requires us to adopt the cognitive explanation. Despite this, it seems apparent to us that some behavior is appropriately explained cognitively. Human beings engage in mindreading. Human beings plan for the future. Human beings engage in meaningful speech acts. But, of course, our mindreading behavior can also be explained by simply postulating behavior-reading mechanisms. Since any act of mindreading involves behavior-reading as well, doesn't Povinelli and Vonk's argument entail that we should never attribute mindreading to human beings? This suggests that something has gone wrong here; Povinelli and Vonk's conclusion is too strong.

I think Povinelli and Vonk go wrong by focusing on individual behaviors in isolation. (Morgan's Canon, at least as it is typically interpreted, makes this mistake as well.) When we look at patterns of behavior, and at different behaviors across different situations, we can observe evidence that supports (or fails to support) cognitive explanations. If Santino fails to engage in behavior suggestive of advance planning in other situations in which advance planning would be beneficial, then we might be justly hesitant to attribute advance planning to him in this situation. But if he engages in behaviors suggestive of advance planning in other situations, or in behaviors suggesting that he has a sense of a self who exists in the future, then the advance planning explanation of these behaviors looks much more plausible. We see the same in human behavior: you may be able to explain my reaction to a particular political candidate's name as a mere associative reaction, but when you observe other behaviors related to that candidate, each of which would require a different association, you may prefer to hypothesize that my behavior is better explained by citing my beliefs about that candidate.

The preceding argument is, at best, a strategy for a negative argument against the deflationary explanation of Santino's behavior. Is there positive reason to prefer the inflationary explanation? Several details of Santino's behavior are worth noting in this regard. First, while Santino initially hid his ammunition behind naturally occurring bodies (such as logs) that prevented the zoo visitors from seeing the piled rocks, he eventually manufactured hiding places from hay he found elsewhere in his enclosure, coming to prefer the manufactured hiding places.[13]

Second, Santino initially stockpiled stones that he found in the waterbed surrounding his enclosure. In addition to those stones, he would occasionally find bits of concrete that he also used as ammunition. The concrete bits were present as a consequence of cycles of freezing and thawing of the water that had seeped into the concrete structures of the zoo. Santino learned that when he knocked on the concrete rocks in his enclosure, he could determine by the sound which areas were damaged. He would then strike these areas more forcefully to detach more concrete to add to his stockpile.[14] Third, when Santino approached the zoo visitors aggressively, holding his ammunition and ready to throw it, the zoo guide would direct the visitors away from Santino, so that they would be out of his range. Consequently, Santino learned to approach without engaging in dominance behavior, with his ammunition hidden. In this way, he was more likely to be successful in throwing the stones at the visitors.[15] I have argued elsewhere that the ability to learn relative to a goal indicates that an organism's behavior (relative to that goal) is best explained by appeal to that organism's psychological states, such as beliefs and desires.[16] The reasoning supporting that conclusion is that an organism is only able to abandon an ineffective means of reaching a goal and adopt a different, perhaps more effective, means of reaching the goal if it has distinct representations of the means to the goal and the goal itself. Such distinct representations are necessitated by the structure of belief-desire explanations of behavior. Furthermore, if the organism is able to continue to learn relative to that goal, then there is evidence that the organism is not modifying its behavior according to what we might call "programming," prestructured by evolution. This suggests that the organism is actually sensitive to its goals and to the various means for reaching those goals that are at its disposal. Santino nicely fits this model. First he learns to collect and throw rocks, then he learns to collect the rocks ahead of time so that he is prepared to throw the rocks, then he learns to harvest concrete ammunition, and then, finally, he learns to better hide his ammunition. He continues to modify his behavior, all while maintaining the same goal, to throw rocks at the zoo visitors. This strongly suggests that Santino has the goal of throwing rocks at the zoo visitors and has representations of his environment that guide him in achieving that goal.

Does this argument indicate that Santino's stockpiling behavior is mediated by plans? Is he stockpiling ammunition because he recognizes that his future self will want to throw rocks and because he wants to make that future self happy? If so, Santino would have the ability to reflect on his current mental states, and his behavior would be guided by a self-concept. Do Santino's mental states include (1) representations of his mental states, and (2) beliefs (or other representations) about himself? Before addressing this question, let's pause and review how we got here. Often nonhuman animals exhibit behaviors that suggest that they have thoughts and feelings similar to those had by human beings. Examples of this occur in the consolation behavior of the prairie voles and in the planning behavior of Santino. There are two tempting responses to these behaviors. According to the deflationary response, careful scientific examination of the behavior reveals that it can be explained without recourse to concepts such as representation, empathy, goals, and distress; and that when the behavior is described as involving "consolation" and "planning," those descriptions should not be taken literally. However, according to the inflationary response, there is more to some nonhuman animal behaviors than a superficial similarity to human behavior. The prairie voles have an internal chemical response that is remarkably similar to the internal chemical response found in human beings when they demonstrate empathy. I have argued that Santino's behavior exhibits the plasticity that is concomitant with distinct representations of one's goals and one's means to achieve those goals. Thus, there is good reason to conclude that Santino does in fact have thoughts about what he wants to achieve and about how to achieve those goals. Does this mean that Santino is genuinely planning? Planning of this type – sacrificing in the present in order that one's future self is happier – requires more than distinct representations of one's goals and means to those goals. This sort of planning requires that one be able to represent one's own mental states, that one have a concept of one's self, inasmuch as one has a special relationship to the organism that benefits in the future as a consequence of one's present sacrifices. Thus, the question I am asking here: we have evidence that Santino has thoughts about how to best satisfy his goal of throwing rocks at the zoo's visitors, does he also have thoughts about how he will feel when he has satisfied this goal?

The data relevant to answering this question are equivocal at best. Several experiments seem to show that some primates (including chimpanzees) are capable of monitoring their internal mental states. In one paradigm, the subject is trained to respond to a forced-choice situation in which, if the subject makes the wrong choice, the reward is significantly worse than the reward for making the correct choice. For example, Smith et al. (1997) trained rhesus monkeys to respond differentially to a pixel display. When the display was dense (more dots), the monkeys learned to make one response; when it was sparse (fewer dots), the monkeys made a different response. Correct responses led to a reward, while incorrect responses led to a time-out, during which the monkey was unable to take the test and thus unable to secure the reward. The subjects became quite adept, except for displays that were near the border of sparse and dense. Once subjects learn the differentiation task, they are given an opt-out alternative. Choosing not to take the test guarantees a better reward than taking the test and failing, but not as good a reward as taking the test and passing. Thus, if the subjects were capable of monitoring their confidence level, we would expect them to opt out of taking the test when they are not confident that they will pass the test. In several experiments, this is exactly what happens.[17] Variations of this paradigm that involve betting (subjects bet more if they are more confident) or testing one's knowledge (subjects check the stimulus again if they are less confident) seem to show the same result: many primates are able to monitor their own confidence levels.[18] Of course, Santino's planning behavior does not involve monitoring his confidence levels, but these results do suggest that some animals, including chimpanzees, are able to think about their own states of mind and act on those thoughts.

Before we are swayed by these impressive results and we conclude that Santino does have thoughts about his state of mind, it is worth noting that these experiments have been subject to incisive critiques.[19] Both Peter Carruthers (2008) and Josef Perner (2012) argue that there are ways to interpret these experiments that do not require attributing metacognitive abilities to the subjects. Perner, for example, points out that the density test can be passed if the subjects merely create a third category of response for moderately dense displays. Rather than opting out, subjects are indicating that the display fits in this third category. Carruthers adopts a strategy that relies on Morgan's Canon. First, for each supposed metacognitive result, there is an explanation that postulates only the mediating factor of belief strength. If the subject has a weak belief that the pattern is strong and a strong belief that pressing the opt-out button will lead to a reward, the strong belief can overwhelm the weak belief; it can trigger action without the animal being self-aware. Since self-awareness is not necessary to explain the animal's behavior, Morgan's Canon suggests that we not appeal to self-awareness in our explanations of the results of the self-monitoring experiments.

The results of false-belief tasks also cast doubt on the conclusion that Santino has thoughts about his own states of mind. In these tasks, one of the standards for measuring metacognitive ability, subjects are asked to differentiate between their own knowledge of a situation and another's false belief about the same situation. Chimpanzees typically fail false-belief tasks.[20] For example, in a competition task in which a subdominant chimpanzee is asked to predict where a dominant will look for food, the subdominant fails to treat the case in which the dominant is ignorant of the location of the food as different than the case in which the dominant is wrong about the location of the food. (The consequence of failing to make this distinction is that the subdominant chimpanzees reap fewer rewards than they would otherwise.) This and other failures strongly suggest that chimpanzees do not have an understanding of false beliefs.

As I remarked above, the data are not univocal when it comes to chimpanzee self-concepts. Some data, such as the opt-out experiments, leave open the possibility that chimpanzees have internal representations of their own mental states. Other data, such as provided by the false-belief tasks, suggest that they do not have internal representations of the states of mind of other chimpanzees. How might we resolve this apparent impasse? I think two lines of argument suggest that chimpanzees are unable to represent their own states of mind. The first has to do with what we might call a meta-analysis of the experimental results. The second has to do with a careful consideration of what we are looking for when we look at these results.

First, recall that Carruthers explicitly appeals to Morgan's Canon in his deflationary arguments that opt-out tasks do not demonstrate that the animal subjects are relying on an introspective sense of self. His reasoning is that metacognition is more complex than first-order cognitive processes. Since we can explain the opt-out behavior by appeals only to first-order cognitive processes, we ought to prefer those explanations. I suggest above that there are good reasons to be suspicious of appeals to Morgan's Canon. However, I also suggest that when we broaden our scope of inquiry to look for patterns that appear in different domains, these patterns suggest what sort of cognitive processes can be legitimately appealed to in order to explain an organism's behavior. In this case, the fact that we can explain chimpanzee behavior on opt-out tasks without appealing to higher-order metacognitive states, coupled with poor chimpanzee performance on false-belief tasks, strongly suggests that chimpanzees do not have an understanding of belief states. These considerations indicate that we should prefer an explanation of Santino's behavior that does not rely on his beliefs about his mental states.

Second, we are looking for evidence that Santino is able to represent his own mental states. However, it is not enough that he represent his own mental states; the task facing Santino, if he is indeed legitimately planning for the future, is to represent future mental states, states that will differ from his present mental states, and to represent those future mental states as being of special interest to him (as opposed to the mental states had by some other chimpanzee or other organism). The first of these tasks is comparable to the task facing chimpanzees in the false-belief task: represent (and act on) mental states had by another organism, which are different than one's own. If chimpanzees are unable to do this, then Santino is likely to be unable to represent his own future mental states when they differ from his current mental states. Whether his current mental states are available to him or not, his future thoughts, when they differ from his current thoughts, are as opaque to him as are those thoughts of his conspecifics that differ from his own.

Nor is it clear that chimpanzees are capable of generating representations of their selves as being of special interest. The evidence relevant to chimpanzee self-representation comes from mirror self-recognition tests. In these tests, individuals first learn about mirrors (by interacting with them) and are later marked (with, for example, dye on the forehead) in a way that cannot be observed except by looking in the mirror. If the animal examines its mark in the mirror significantly more than it had examined that previously unmarked region, then experimenters conclude that it recognizes itself in the mirror. Such recognition involves a self-concept, according to the standard reasoning,[21] because in order to examine the mark, the animal must have both a stable self-image that is different than the image the animal now sees, and the animal must identify the image it now sees with itself. Without such identification, there would be no reason for the animal to examine its own forehead upon seeing the marked forehead in the mirror. No representation of the self; no mirror self-recognition. Mirror self-recognition thus implies a representation of the self. Since chimpanzees recognize themselves in the mirror, they must have a representation of themselves, right? Unfortunately these data are equivocal as well.[22] While the consensus seems to be that chimpanzees do recognize themselves in the mirror, and that such recognition is mediated by a self-concept, the data are not as clear as this consensus would suggest. A majority of chimpanzees tested actually fail the mark test for self-recognition; according to a review by Thornton and Lukas (2012), only 40% of the chimpanzees tested pass the mark test. Moreover, there have been few studies with the goal of illuminating the nature of this self-concept. Provocatively enough, one study (de Veer et al. 2002), the only study I know of which returned years later to reexamine the performance of chimpanzees who had passed the test, found that of nine chimpanzees that had passed the mark test in an earlier study, only six chimpanzees passed in the later study. It seems that whatever self-concept those chimpanzees relied on to pass the test was lost in the intervening time. At the very least, this suggests that any self-concept possessed by chimpanzees is not like the human self-concept; when chimpanzees and humans recognize themselves in the mirror, they seem to be doing different things.

We might think that Santino's behavior shows us that he has something of an understanding of his own current and future mental states, and that he is choosing to help satisfy the goals of his future self. But the studies I cite here point in a different direction. It seems unlikely that Santino is reflecting on his current mental states. These studies suggest that the sort of self-concept necessary for an understanding of one's own mental states is likely to be missing in the chimpanzee's mental economy. What, then, of the prairie voles, who not only console their familiars, but who also show many of the same physiological concomitants of consolation behavior as do human beings? Aren't the physiological data evidence that there is a strong similarity between the causes (and effects) of human and prairie vole consolation behavior? Yes, but our inclination to attribute to prairie voles an empathetic fellow feeling, a recognition that the observer is reaching out to the demonstrator as if to say "I feel your pain," may well be a symptom of something that is added on to our oxytocin-mediated empathetic response: human beings are capable of both empathetic behavior and the awareness that we are engaging in empathetic behavior (and that such behavior causes in us certain experiences). It may well be that a difference between us and Santino, and between us and the prairie voles, does not lie in the behavior, but in our awareness of the behavior.[23]

Notes

1 Burkett et al. (2016).
2 Bhanoo (2016).
3 See also Andrews (2015).
4 Osvath and Karvonen (2012).
5 My answer to these questions will be somewhere between these poles. I think Santino's behavior is evidence of human-like mental characteristics in some ways, but not in other ways. For this reason, I focus more on inflationary versus deflationary explanations than on the issues of anthropomorphic and anthropectic explanations.
6 There is another position one might adopt: Santino's behavior is unusual and not good fodder for induction to conclusions about the cognitive skills of typical, wild chimpanzees because it is an artifact of the training Santino may have received as a consequence of his prior interactions with his human caretakers. I am sympathetic to this response (see Saidel 2016), but I will not explore these issues here.
7 Roberts and Feeney's main focus is that Santino's planning, inasmuch as he is engaged in planning, involves semantic memory rather than episodic memory. That focus, while important, is not strictly relevant to the issues I am raising here.
8 What do "cognitive," "non-cognitive," and "fully cognitive" mean in this context? I'll admit that these are fuzzy terms, and, as will become apparent below, we should be suspicious of them in the context of Morgan's Canon. However, the intuitive idea is clear enough: don't give an explanation citing complex mental states when an explanation that does not cite complex mental states is available. My ultimate goal has to do with explanations that cite a concept of the self. So, a clearer version of a principle like Morgan's Canon is available to me: don't give explanations that rely on a concept of the self when explanations that do not rely on a concept of the self are available.
9 Morgan (1894).
10 See, for example, Sober (1998) and Fitzpatrick (2008), and see the essays in this volume by Buckner (2018, Chapter 39), Fitzpatrick (2018, Chapter 42), and Dacey (2018, Chapter 40).
11 On mindreading and Povinelli and Vonk, see the essays in this volume by Halina (2018, Chapter 22) and Lurz (2018, Chapter 21).

12 Again, the issues raised in the literature in which Santino figures have to do with different memory systems. Osvath believes that the best explanations of Santino's behavior appeal to episodic memory, while Suddendorf believes that the behavior may be explicable without appeal to episodic memory. Since both Osvath and Suddendorf agree on the other structures present in Santino's cognitive economy, if Suddendorf is correct, appeals to episodic memory would be unwarranted additions, doing no explanatory work that isn't already being done. Suddendorf can make this argument without appealing to Morgan's Canon.

13 Osvath and Karvonen (2012).

14 Osvath (2009).

15 Osvath and Karvonen (2012).

16 See, for example, Saidel (1998, 2009). In Saidel (1998), I argue that the only way an organism can exhibit the sort of goal-oriented plasticity Santino exhibits is if it has distinct representations of its goals and means to achieve those goals. I understand "beliefs and desires" relatively thinly here; a better description might be "representations of the environment" and "motivational or goal states."

17 For an overview of these experiments, see Terrace and Son (2009). There are many versions of these experiments. One might start with Hampton (2001) (rhesus monkeys) and Rosati and Hare (2011) (chimpanzees and bonobos). Even rats have been tested: Foote and Crystal (2007). For discussion, see Griffin (2001).

18 For betting, see Kornell, Son, and Terrace (2007); for knowledge testing, see Call (2010).

19 Proust (2018, Chapter 13 in this volume) discusses these experiments in much greater depth. She concludes that they provide evidential support for a kind of nonhuman animal metacognition, one that is based in evaluative, non-cognitive, sensing of affordances. This fits with the conclusion I draw here, that these experiments do not support claims that these animals have thoughts about their mental states. Proust's conclusion is also in line with my own; she argues that metacognitive nonhuman animals "probably don't think about themselves the way that we do."

20 See Call and Tomasello (1999); Kaminski, Call and Tomasello (2008); and Call and Tomasello (2008).

21 For the mark test for mirror self-recognition, see Gallup (1970). For arguments that a self-concept is involved in recognizing oneself in the mirror, see Boccia (1994) and Mitchell (1995).

22 See Saidel (2016) for a more in-depth discussion of these and other issues raised by the mirror self-recognition tests.

23 I am indebted to Mark Engelbert, Dan Hicks, Aleta Quinn, and, especially, Kristin Andrews for comments on a previous draft of this essay.

Further reading

I recommend starting with the chapters from this volume cited in the text. Sober (1998) and Fitzpatrick (2008) are excellent places to start for critiques of Morgan's Canon. Thornton and Lukas (2012) provide an indispensible overview of not just mirror self-recognition experiments, but also raise questions about the sorts of conclusions we are tempted to draw from limited experimentation. Also recommended reading are K. Andrews, *Do Apes Read Minds? Toward a New Folk Psychology* (Cambridge, MA: MIT Press 2012) and the papers collected in R. Lurz (ed.), *Animal Minds* (Cambridge: Cambridge University Press 2009).

References

Andrews, K. (2015) *The Animal Mind* New York: Routledge.

Balter, M. (2012) "'Killjoys' challenge claims of clever animals" *Science* 335(6072) pp. 1036–8.

Bhanoo, S. N. (2016) "A furry shoulder to cry on" *New York Times* January 26, 2016, p. D2.

Boccia, M. (1994) "Mirror behavior in macaques" in S. T. Parker, R. Mitchell, and M. L. Boccia (eds.) *Self-Awareness in Animals and Humans: Developmental Perspectives*. Cambridge: Cambridge University Press.

Buckner, C. (2018) "Understanding associative and cognitive explanations in comparative psychology" in K. Andrews and J. Beck (eds.) *Routledge Handbook of Philosophy of Animal Minds*. London and New York: Routledge.

Burkett, J. P., Andari, E., Johnson, Z. V., Curry, D. C., de Waal, F. B. M., and Young, L. J. (2016) "Oxytocin-dependent consolation behavior in rodents" *Science* 351:6271 pp. 375–8.

Call, J. (2010) "Do apes know they could be wrong?" *Animal Cognition* 13(5) pp. 689–700.

Call, J., and Tomasello, M. (1999) "A nonverbal false belief task: The performance of children and great apes" *Child Development* 70 pp. 381–95.

———— (2008) "Does the chimpanzee have a theory of mind? 30 years later" *Trends in Cognitive Sciences* 12(5) pp. 187–92.

Carruthers, P. (2008) "Meta-cognition in animals: A skeptical look" *Mind & Language* 23(1) pp. 58–89.

Dacey, M. (2018) "A new view of association and associative models" in K. Andrews and J. Beck (eds.) *Routledge Handbook of Philosophy of Animal Minds*. London and New York: Routledge.

de Veer, M., Gallup, G., Theall, L., van den Bos, R., Povinelli, D. (2002) "An 8-year longitudinal study of mirror self-recognition in chimpanzees (Pan troglodytes)" *Neuropsychologia* 1493 pp. 1–6.

Fitzpatrick, S. (2008) "Doing away with Morgan's Canon" *Mind & Language* 23(2) pp. 224–46.

———— (2018) "Against Morgan's Canon" in K. Andrews and J. Beck (eds.) *Routledge Handbook of Philosophy of Animal Minds*. London and New York: Routledge.

Foote, A. L., and Crystal, J. D. (2007) "Metacognition in the rat" *Current Biology* 17(6) pp. 551–5.

Gallup, G. (1970) "Chimpanzees: Self-recognition" *Science*, New Series 167(3914) pp. 86–87.

Griffin, D. R. (2001) "Animals know more than we used to think" *Proceedings of the National Academy of Sciences* 98(9) pp. 4833–34.

Halina, M. (2018) "What apes know about seeing" in K. Andrews and J. Beck (eds.) *Routledge Handbook of Philosophy of Animal Minds*. London and New York: Routledge.

Hampton, R. R. (2001) "Rhesus monkeys know when they remember" *Proceedings of the National Academy of Sciences* 98(9) pp. 5359–62.

Kaminski, J., Call, J., and Tomasello, M. (2008) "Chimpanzees know what others know, but not what they believe" *Cognition* 109(2) pp. 224–34.

Kornell, N., Son, L. K., and Terrace, H. S. (2007) "Transfer of metacognitive skills and hint seeking in monkeys" *Psychological Science* 18 pp. 64–71.

Lurz, R. (2018) "Animal mindreading: The problem and how it can be solved" in K. Andrews and J. Beck (eds.) *Routledge Handbook of Philosophy of Animal Minds*. London and New York: Routledge.

Mitchell, R. (1995) "Evidence of dolphin self-recognition and the difficulties of interpretation" *Consciousness and Cognition* 4 pp. 229–34.

Morgan, C. L. (1894) *An Introduction to Comparative Psychology* London: Walter Scott.

Osvath, M. (2009) "Spontaneous planning for future stone throwing by a male chimpanzee" *Current Biology* 19(5) pp. R190–1.

Osvath, K., and Karvonen, E. (2012) "Spontaneous innovation for future deception in a male chimpanzee" *PLoS ONE* 7(5) p. e367782.

Perner, J. (2012) "Minimeta: In search of minimal criteria for metacognition" in M. J. Beran, J. L. Brandl, J. Perner, and J. Proust (eds.) *Foundations of Metacognition* Oxford: Oxford University Press.

Povinelli, D. J., and Vonk, J. (2003) "Chimpanzee minds: Suspiciously human?" *Trends in Cognitive Sciences* 7(4) pp. 157–60.

Proust, J. (2018) "Metacognition and self-awareness in nonhumans" in K. Andrews and J. Beck (eds.) *Routledge Handbook of Philosophy of Animal Minds*. London and New York: Routledge.

Roberts, W. A., and Feeney, M. C. (2010) "Temporal sequencing is essential to future planning: Response to Osvath, Raby and Clayton" *Trends in Cognitive Sciences* 14(2) pp. 52–53.

Rosati, A. G., and Hare, B. (2011) "Chimpanzees and bonobos distinguish between risk and ambiguity" *Biology Letters*, 7 pp. 15–18.

Saidel, E. (1998) "Beliefs, desires, and the ability to learn" *American Philosophical Quarterly* January, 1998 pp. 21–37.

———— (2009) "Animal thoughts," in R. Lurz (ed.) *Animal Minds* Cambridge: Cambridge University Press.

———— (2016) "Through the looking glass, and what we (don't) find there" *Biology and Philosophy* 31(3) pp. 335–52.

Shettleworth, S. J. (2010) "Clever animals and killjoy explanations in comparative psychology" *Trends in Cognitive Sciences* 14(11) pp. 477–81.

Smith, J. D., Shields, W. E., Schull, J., and Washburn, D. A. (1997) "The uncertain response in humans and animals" *Cognition* 62(1) pp. 75–97.

Sober, E. (1998) "Morgan's canon" in D. D. Cummins and C. Allen (eds.) *The Evolution of Mind* New York: Oxford University Press.

Suddendorf, T., and Corballis, M. C. (2010) "Behavioural evidence for mental time travel in nonhuman animals" *Behavioural Brain Research* 215 pp. 292–98.

Terrace, H. S., and Son, L. K. (2009) "Comparative metacognition" *Current Opinion in Neurobiology* 19 pp. 67–74.

Thornton, A., and Lukas, D. (2012) "Individual variation in cognitive performance: Developmental and evolutionary perspectives" *Philosophical Transactions of the Royal Society B* 367 pp. 2773–83.

13

NONHUMAN METACOGNITION

Joëlle Proust

Introduction

There is evidence that nonhuman animals that have not evolved a mindreading capacity, such as macaques and rodents, are nevertheless able to appropriately evaluate their self-confidence level in perceptual and memory tasks. This creates a puzzle, because self-knowledge seems to require embedding a representation into another, i.e. *metarepresenting* one's own states, as exemplified in mindreading. Part of the puzzle has to do with disunified terminology. "Meta", it is often claimed, means "being about". "Metacognition", then, is taken to refer to cognition *about* one's own cognition, "thinking about one's own thinking", or, in short, to meta-knowledge. This terminology owes its influence to the early models of the relations between the control and monitoring aspects of metamemory. To philosophers, this acception of metacognition is consonant with deeply entrenched views about the exclusively human character of rationality. Caution, however, is needed to disentangle the terminological from the empirical issues: terminology should follow, rather than preempt, research. Section 1 will present the evidence. Section 2 will discuss the view that metacognition is self-directed metarepresentation. Section 3 will discuss the "no-metacognition" view, which claims that animals merely rely on observable stimuli – such as an oscillating behavior – or on anticipated reward to decide what to do. Section 4 will present the "experience-based" accounts, in which metacognition is neither a mere matter of first-order cognition, nor of metarepresentation. It will be proposed that animal metacognition depends on a non-propositional evaluative attitude called affordance-sensing, which is common to human and some nonhuman cognitive systems.

1 Experimental evidence for nonhuman metacognition

There is now ample comparative evidence that many nonhumans, although unable to read minds, manifest the ability to evaluate what they can perceive or remember as humans do. The experimental paradigms used to elicit metacognitive evaluations include three main tasks:

1   Tasks requiring the animals to seek information before acting (Call 2010), or obtain it from a helper, at a cost.

2   Tasks allowing the animals to choose to perform or reject cognitive tasks as a function of their difficulty: for example, categorizing perceived densities as low or sparse (Smith et al. 2008), or retrieving paired items presented earlier (Hampton 2001).

3   Tasks requiring the animals to wager on their own cognitive decision right after having made it.

Rhesus monkeys (Smith et al. 2010) and rats (Foote and Crystal 2007) were found to be able to evaluate their own perceptual access to stimuli. Rhesus monkeys (Hampton 2001), pigeons (Adams and Santi 2011), chimpanzees and orangutans (Suda-King 2008) have been shown to flexibly search for needed information and to reliably monitor their memory; rhesus monkeys have shown an ability to express their retrospective confidence in a response by wagering (Kornell et al. 2007). Crucially, the response patterns in each case are similar to those of humans in the same task (see discussion in Couchman et al. 2012; Beran and Smith 2014). Other animal species, however, have been found to fail on the tasks above, for example capuchin monkeys (Basile et al. 2015; Beran and Smith 2011). The tasks 2 and 3 listed above have been used in behavioral and in neuroscientific studies, where the activation of neural assemblies involved in metacognitive decisions by rhesus monkeys or rodents was tracked over time (Fleming and Dolan 2012; Kepecs et al. 2008). Computational modeling has been made possible by precise quantitative data being collected with either behavioral (Smith et al. 2014) or neuroscientific methods (Kepecs and Mainen, 2012). How can the evidence of animal success in the tasks above be explained?

2 Metacognition as meta-knowledge (MK)

2.1 Stronger version

MK-strong is a class of views that take metacognition to involve some form or other of metarepresentation. On the richer MK view, metacognitive animals have a disposition to *know that* they themselves are in a given mental state, for example, that they are trying to remember whether they have perceived a given stimulus in a prior occasion. "Knowing that", by definition, has propositional content. As a consequence, embedded contents should include concepts of mental states and of oneself as the target knower. Evaluation, in other words, cannot occur without metarepresentation of one's own mental states. Asking oneself whether one remembers something presupposes that one possesses the concept of memory, of remembering (and cognate notions), and, furthermore, the capacity to represent one's own self as endowed with various states and attitudes, each having a specific cognitive content.

    Three main arguments have been provided in favor of metacognitive judgments being metarepresentational. First, flexible prospective assessments of uncertainty, in the absence of the primary test stimuli, express a declarative, i.e. an explicit representation of knowledge in a nonhuman (Hampton 2003; Smith et al. 2003). Second, the evidence for easy transfer of retrospective assessments of confidence across tasks suggests that monkeys express their declarative knowledge about their first-order epistemic states (Son and Kornell 2005). Finally, the similarity of pattern in uncertainty responses in humans and in rhesus monkeys indicates that a metarepresentational account is justified in both cases (Son and Kornell 2005).

Discussion

With the benefit of hindsight, the arguments offered by MK-strong fail to be convincing. Flexibility in self-evaluation clearly shows that animals rely on a context to decide how to act – independently of the stimulus presented in the first-order task; they are not merely conditioned to act. But it is premature to conclude that metarepresentation explains flexibility. Second, the "reportlikeness" of the response is merely a paradigm effect; animals do not report or declare what they know, they decide how to act. Finally, the similarity of performances between nonhuman and human primates does not entail that metarepresentations underly these performances, but merely that a similar kind of information is available in both cases.

A major weakness of the MK-strong view is that, granting that rodents and pigeons cannot represent second-order attitudes through concepts such as "believing", "knowing", "being uncertain", etc., they should not be able to evaluate *to what extent* they themselves can remember or perceive, which they were found able to do. They cannot attribute beliefs to others or to themselves, and hence, the MK view predicts that they cannot evaluate their own perception or their own memory. Against this objection, it has been claimed that metacognitive ability is a matter of degree (Smith et al. 2009). It has also been proposed that success in metacognitive tasks constitute evidence for an animal's ability to form mental concepts *about its own states*, although not about mental states in general. Such a defense, however, is unparsimonious and ad hoc. The proposal that nonhumans might represent "only in their own case" that they believe, perceive, and so on, infringes the Generality Constraint as applied to what it is to possess the concept of a mental state (Evans 1982). The MK definition of metacognition, in its strong form, is therefore difficult to reconcile with current evidence. If non-mindreaders such as rhesus monkeys can evaluate their memory, then their metamemory can be exercised with no concept of memory. Unless, obviously, the studies reported above have conflated metacognition and mere cognition (see Section 3).

2.2 MK as introspection

An alternative MK view has been proposed: even though the animals successfully tested for metacognition cannot read their own minds the way humans do, they might *still have conscious self-reflective access to their uncertainty, and hence qualify as genuinely metacognitive* (Son and Kornell 2005; Metcalfe and Kober 2005). Self-reflectiveness is a particular way of being conscious: not merely having conscious experiences of the world (such as seeming to perceive red objects), but having conscious experiences of oneself as having these experiences (such as feeling uncertain of being able to discriminate red objects).

This view, however, still retains the gist of MK: a metacognitive ability is constituted by a meta-level reflecting on the representational content of an object-level. Metacognition is a form of introspection – a mechanism akin to sensory perception, but directed inward. For example, animals might know what they know (or don't know) by glancing at the content of their memory, as hypothesized in the human case by Josef T. Hart (Hart 1965). In contrast with the preceding view, however, awareness of a *nonconceptual thought content* (an animal, for example, being aware of its "memory strength") is seen as sufficient to adaptively guide behavior. You no more need to know what memory is to gain access to its content than you need to know what hunger is to feel hungry. Metacognition could, then, qualify as a primary form of self-awareness (Metcalfe and Kober 2005).

Discussion

First, note the conceptual difficulty of this view. Reflective self-consciousness is supposed to embed a first-order thought (for example: a memory state "glanced at") in a second-order thought ("I have this memory state"). The view implies that the animals, lacking the appropriate concepts, can still non-conceptually metarepresent their own internal impressions and feelings. But what can it mean to metarepresent a thought, when the state so metarepresented is non-propositional and when the metarepresentation includes no concepts for categorizing its relation with the embedded content? (For an extensive discussion, see Proust 2013: 142–144).

A second problem for the view is that, in humans, introspection can, at best, be claimed to access one's own sensory states and emotions. The propositional contents of one's own attitudes, in contrast, are not directly perceivable by an inner eye (Carruthers 2011). On this view, inferring the contents of one's attitudes requires conceptual interpretations of what one believes, desires or intends to do, as well as the directing of mindreading towards oneself, in order to know what type of attitude is activated. Hence, nonhumans cannot infer what they believe or are uncertain about.

Another objection to the intermediate MK model, however, points to an alternative account of the informational source of metacognition, which will be discussed in Section 4. Human agents cannot know what they remember (or don't remember) by introspecting the content of their memory, as was first hypothesized by Hart (Koriat and Goldsmith 1996). They rather use heuristic strategies based on predictive, activity-dependent cues, in order to predict their ability to perceive or remember. These heuristics elicit noetic feelings that guide cognitive decisions (Koriat 1993). On this view, introspection to inner thought contents is no longer required, while the notion that nonconceptual cues may be used to monitor epistemic success is fully endorsed.

Some comparative psychologists, however, have attempted to exercise parsimony by reducing metacognition to cognition. They claimed that the information that animals use when performing tasks qualified as "metacognitive" are of a behavioral nature, and that the corresponding abilities actually reflected reinforcement and sensitivity to payoff rather than a sensitivity to subjective uncertainty. We now turn to this family of accounts, the "no-metacognition" views.

3 The no-metacognition views

3.1 Associative accounts (AA)

In stark contrast with the MK views, some theorists have claimed that the relevant information, in tasks 1–3, is exclusively behavioral: opting out, and the other tasks reviewed, can be solved on the basis of operant conditioning.[1] (Crystal and Foote 2009; Le Pelley 2014). An animal's willingness to opt out from a cognitive task, from this viewpoint, *depends on a state of the world represented as worth producing*, rather than on an internal evaluation of the agent's own uncertainty or on an emotional appraisal. This interpretation has motivated computer simulations able to model relevant correlations between animals' decisions and low-level cues, where the latter should only consist in observable properties, such as time elapsed, oscillatory behavior and associated reward. A major objection that AA has raised to non-parsimonious accounts is that opt-out experiments do not allow a clear distinction to be made between the animal's decision – performing the task or opting out – and the confidence report. It has also been noted that confidence is indistinguishable from variables such as attention and vigilance, which can be conditioned and influence performance. One may summarize AA in terms of the following four claims:

1   The information involved in cognitive monitoring by animals is behavioral.
2   Opting out is a cognitive (rather than metacognitive) decision based on stimulus features and payoff.
3   Payoff is what motivates decisions.
4   The form of learning involved is operant conditioning through past trials.

In response to AA claim 3, experimenters suppressed direct reinforcement from the opt-out task paradigm; in spite of lacking information about reward, animals maintained their ability to opt out reliably (Smith et al. 2006). Another way of circumventing an associative account was to compare free-choice with forced-choice decisions for the same stimuli: a systematic increase in successful freely chosen trials versus forced ones suggests that endogenous cues were involved in guiding decisions (Hampton 2001). A third tack consisted in showing that computer simulations based on AA claim 2 were actually unable to track animals' monitoring-based response patterns (Smith et al. 2008, 2014).

Another way of addressing AA, however, is to directly question its first clause by combining a computational method with an analysis of the brain correlates of perceptual decisions under uncertainty in animals. The most compelling study uses a post-decision report of confidence, which allows the collecting, in contrast with an opt-out paradigm, of both an answer to the first-order cognitive task *and* a confidence evaluation in each trial (Kepecs and Mainen, 2012). The authors are able to demonstrate that confidence level plays a role in decision-making that is independent of reward. Correct and erroneous choices for the same stimulus are found to systematically vary in their confidence levels. Single-cell recordings in other studies make it clear that the kind of cues that rats are using to evaluate their own uncertainty include late onset, intensity (firing rates are higher at chance performance) and the coherence of the neural activity currently triggered by a first-order cognitive task (Kiani and Shadlen, 2009). These cues, however, *are not related to stimulus information, nor to recent reward history*: they are generated by the current first-order neurocognitive activity. Disclaiming 1 and 3, in turn, disposes of AA as articulated above.

3.2 The executive account (EA)

Another version of the no-metacognition view relies on a contrast between action guidance and self-attribution. The tasks 1–3 above do not qualify as "*meta*cognitive", because they are not about one's own cognition at all. A key issue is the status of noetic feelings. "What is it that one feels bad about, when one feels uncertain?" Carruthers and Ritchie (2012) ask. Is it about the likelihood of a cognitive perceptual or memory task being correct/incorrect? Is it not, rather, about the likelihood of a reward being missed/obtained? Carruthers and Ritchie find the second hypothesis both more plausible and more parsimonious. Monkeys' epistemic decisions are embedded in a rewarded task, where the monkeys rely on their emotions to select a reward-conducive decision. There are in the same situation as human subjects completing the Iowa Gambling Task, where subjects have to select cards from four decks with different probabilities for winning or losing various amounts of money (Bechara et al. 1994). The point is that selecting the right deck requires extracting a subpersonal heuristic for selecting the "good" decks of cards, that produces steady gains in the long run. Similarly, the authors claim, feelings of uncertainty are directed at the primary actions open to them, rather than at their own mental states. "It is the performance of the action that seems bad, not the fact that one is thinking about it" (Carruthers and Ritchie, 2012: 82). There is nothing specifically metacognitive about the feelings that guide animals' decisions in the tasks described above.

Discussion

EA contains a grain of truth: given that metacognition includes a control dimension, it partly depends on executive capacities – i.e. the abilities involved in selecting a behavior as a function of one's goal, in inhibiting it, shifting it, and updating it. But it also includes a monitoring dimension, whose function is not to select, but to predict epistemic outcome. Concentrating on the monitoring part reveals that there is more to animal and human metacognition than appetitive control. In metacognition, incentive gradient (expected reward or penalty) affects the amount of effort expended, hence the success of the outcome. Agents, accordingly, tend to scale up their confidence level as a function of their own invested effort (Koriat et al. 2014). This "goal–driven" dimension of metacognitive evaluation, however, is complemented by a "data–driven" dimension, namely the feedback from the task being performed. This dimension is reflected in the remarkable *comparative* stability of evaluations across incentives: agents assess similarly their *relative* confidence across stakes. In other words, even though confidence is enhanced by added time and effort, relative uncertainty across trials remains similarly influenced by subjectively felt difficulty at each incentive level.

This behavioral finding in humans is compatible with the view that animals use two separate subsystems for evaluating, respectively, subjective uncertainty and reward (see also Kornell et al. 2007). In an experiment by Zakrzewski et al. (2014), monkeys have proved able to avoid risky trials (where, if there is failure, all the accumulated food tokens can be lost) *only when* they feel unsure that they will correctly carry them out. Higher accumulated numbers of tokens make the monkeys more conservative about performing the primary task. Hence, conservativeness of the response criterion (knowing when to perform) is modulated *both* by the payoff schedule and by the confidence level. Behavioral evidence from comparative studies, then, confirm the neural–computational argument offered at the end of the last section. EA, as a result, is not the most parsimonious hypothesis for explaining animal evidence: it does not account for the combination of epistemic sensitivity and reward appetence in animals.

4 Evaluative-associative accounts of animal metacognition

An alternative theory hypothesizes that the information that is crucial for metacognition lies in the vehicle of thought rather than its content, and that this information is meant to guide cognitive actions rather than world–directed action. This insight is at the core of a set of views that we will call "evaluative–associative accounts" (EAA). Four claims are common to these accounts:

1 The information involved in cognitive monitoring by animals is endogenous rather than behavioral: it consists in activity-dependent information generated in a current cognitive task.
2 The information that predicts success/failure in a cognitive task is carried by the vehicle of mental activity (e.g. the dynamic features of the firing rates), not by its content.
3 A noetic feeling associated with the subpersonal heuristics motivates an epistemic decision to act.
4 Learning consists in a) extracting implicit decisional cues, and b) calibrating decision thresholds over time through reinforcement.

4.1 Experience-based (EB) metacognition

An analysis involving these four claims can be extracted from Asher Koriat's characterization of human metacognition and applied to animal performances. In "experience-based" (EB) metacognition, agents form metacognitive predictions on the basis of a variety of associative cues elicited by the current cognitive activity and assembled in subpersonal heuristics [claim 1]. These cues are "structural" in the sense that they belong to the activity elicited by a task, not to its content [claim 2]. Recognizing the role of nonconceptual information in epistemic decision-making is a remarkable step, first established through behavioral experiments, and now supported by neuroscientific evidence. A conscious noetic feeling is generated by the discrepancy between stored and observed values of the heuristic standard (Koriat 2000). This conscious feeling in turn motivates and flexibly controls the decision to act [claim 3]. The expression of "epistemic decision" is justified, to the extent that the cues used in prediction are those that, in the past, have had "diagnostic" value (namely, those that carried accurate information about future success or failure) (Koriat 2012: 227) [claims 2 and 4]. The valence and intensity of noetic feelings is the most parsimonious way of explaining why agents so readily and flexibly rely on subpersonal heuristics to guide their decisions. Feelings, however, are "noetic" in the sense that their valence is not reducible to their reward value.

In Koriat's model, humans additionally enjoy "concept-based" metacognition, through which, for example, they apply to their performances what they believe to be the case concerning their own cognitive abilities. Experience-based metacognition, however, does not depend on such beliefs, and can thus be operational in agents that do not have the conceptual equipment for reading minds, such as animals and young children.

In summary: a prominent feature of EB models is that they are *evaluative* rather than declarative. An evaluative attitude represents a gradient, which adjusts epistemic decision to the evidence accumulated in its favor. This feature suggests a continuity between nonhumans and humans through a nonlinguistic, nonconceptual informational route based on the heuristics cum feelings elicited by a cognitive task. An additional argument in favor of this continuity is that the cues assembled in the evaluative heuristics cannot be reported by human agents,[2] which suggests that they have been acquired through *implicit* learning, rather than by self-description (by "know-how" rather than by "know-that"). Animal and human implicit learning systems, then, use Bayesian predictive processing to extract heuristics from the associations between prior cues and decision feedback.[3]

4.2 Animal metacognition relies on cognitive affordance-sensings (AS)

This section presents a philosophical conception of the representational format of metacognition compatible with the evidence reviewed above. It is based on an architecture of the mind in which nonconceptual, emotional information plays a crucial evaluative role. The type of evaluative attitude – called "affordance-sensing" (AS) – that will now be defended fulfils the four functional characterizations listed above, which, taken together, constitute experience-based metacognition. Its semantics, its scope, its structure, its functions will be briefly described.

The semantics of affordance sensings

The predictive function of interest for animal metacognition is exercised in a non-propositional attitude, associated with cognitive actions – actions whose goal is to acquire or retrieve information – called "affordance-sensing" (AS). AS applies in other domains beyond metacognition whenever an opportunity (either positive or negative) is detected, estimated, and used or rejected in taking action. Under a variety of names,[4] affordance-sensings have been claimed by philosophers to form a specific set of mental states with an associative structure, available to humans as well as nonhumans. Affordance-sensings can be described as "pushmi-pullyu" attitudes, as defined by Ruth Millikan (Millikan 1995). Granting, however, that the conditions of correctness for belief and desire are incompatible, the semantics of AS is not constituted by subject-predicate propositions, but by properties assessed from a subjective viewpoint, and endowed with a gradient of valence and intensity. As the following examples illustrate, world-directed and cognitive affordance-sensings have a similar relational structure; they engage a subjective experience and a motivation to act on it; they depend both on subjective needs and perceived opportunities, rather than on objective (subject-independent) world properties:

1   When hungry, an animal perceives *this* food (or this food smell) as an affordance of a given valence and intensity.
2   When trying to jump between two somewhat distant rocks, an animal must evaluate the valence and intensity of this jumping affordance (whether it feels safe to jump that far), given its present motivation and effort readiness.
3   When trying to categorize this display (as dense or sparse), or to remember whether this icon was perceived earlier, an animal must evaluate its present perceptual or memorial affordance (does this task look achievable to me?).

Feelings, i.e. AS, optimally represent these pairings because they make a property salient from a specific subjective viewpoint (e.g., [food for me to eat]). In addition, they provide relevant directional information about how to act.

Structure

Having an essential relation to an occurrent event or affordance, the semantic structure of AS is indexical: [Here is this substance for me!] The content so indexed is an *occurrent* (relational) affordance, rather than an individual event or object. Here is how this indexical meaning decomposes:

{Affordance$_a$ [Place=here], [Time= Now/soon], [Valence$_{a=+}$], [Intensity$_{a=.8}$ (comparatively specified on a scale 0 to 1)], [motivation to act of degree$_d$ according to action program$_a$]}

The subscript "$_a$" is meant to indicate that all the elements having this subscript characterize the type of affordance as what it contextually appears to be.

The scope of affordance sensings

Similarity of structure in AS does not entail that affordances are equally detected and relied upon across domains of interest. Sensing affordances is a matter of the opportunities that a lifestyle makes salient to agents. Based on the dual system discussed in Section 3, it is justified to distinguish *appetitive* AS, which are elicited by bodily needs and opportunities, from *metacognitive* AS, which are elicited by cognitive needs and opportunities. In contrast to appetitive AS, metacognitive AS do not involve a specification of place. They are elicited by the activity, but they neither coincide with the appetitive experience driving the cognitive motivation itself (such as a food affordance when trying to remember where the food is), nor metarepresent the mental states associated with it.

Function: the role of gradiency

As a graded detector of affordance intensity, affordance-sensings depend on metacognitive emotions for providing an *immediate* evaluation of the *degree* of subjective likelihood of a cognitive opportunity, and for immediately activating the selection and execution of an appropriate and timely action (Barrett and Bar 2009; Griffiths and Scarantino, 2009; Proust 2015a, 2015b). Reactivity in detection and guidance explains why emotions have been recruited in forming evaluative representations. This also explains why cognitive affordance-sensings are involved in monitoring fluency, informativeness and relevance of signals and messages in nonhuman and human communication (Proust 2016).

Function: prediction vs. explanation

An association between cues is learned through reinforcement learning; it allows a form of restricted Bayesian reasoning, i.e. prediction of task success. When monitoring their own cognitive actions, animals can transfer their ability to form evaluations to new tasks of the same type, but cannot generalize their findings beyond present opportunities (inference, in contrast, through concept use, enables theory building and hypothetical reasoning). Contrary to propositional thought, AS has no combinatorial semantics and no truth conditions. It has conditions of appropriateness, however, related to the actual predictive power that it makes available to an organism. Appropriateness requires integration of affordances, which AS is tailored to do. In particular, a cognitive affordance can be combined with a reward affordance of the distal goal on the basis of their respective weighted gradients of valence and intensity (De Martino et al., 2013). Affordance-sensings are a common currency for decision-making in a world of conflicting opportunities.

Conclusion

The evaluation-based view explains how metacognitive awareness develops in rhesus monkeys, in rodents, and in human infants in the absence of a mindreading ability. Evaluating a cognitive task as feasible, or a cognitive outcome as satisfactory, depends on an associative, comparative process of affordance-sensing. Affordance-sensings allow agents to assess and exploit what appears to them as opportunities when deciding how to act.

Acknowledgements

I am grateful to Richard Carter and to Nicole Hall for their linguistic help, to Mike Beran for personal communication about his recent experiments, and to Kristin Andrews and Reinaldo Bernal for their critical remarks and useful suggestions.

This chapter was prepared thanks to an advanced grant of the European Research Council #269616.

Notes

1 In operant conditioning, an action that turns out to have positive consequences for the agent tends to be reinforced, i.e. reproduced.
2 See Koriat and Ackerman (2010).
3 Such learning ability does not build up metacognitive heuristics in every animal species. While some species, such as rhesus monkeys, have high predictive needs associated with non-cooperative foraging, others, such as capuchin monkeys, do not, because for them food is plentiful and foraging is cooperative.
4 Bermúdez's frames (2009), Cussins' NASAS [for representations including Normative feedback, Affective element, Attention soliciting, Subjective valence] (2012), Dreyfus and Kelly's affordance-sensings (2007), Gendler's aliefs (2008), Griffiths and Scarantino's emotional representations (2009), and Nanay's pragmatic representations (2013).

Further reading

Articles in a 2014 issue of the *Journal of Comparative Psychology* by N. Kornell offer interesting critical views about animal metacognition (*128*(2), 143–149 and 160–162, http://dx.doi.org/10.1037/a0033444–a0036194). For a presentation of the neuroscientific correlates of metacognition in nonhumans and humans, see S. M. Fleming and C. D. Frith (eds.), *The Cognitive Neuroscience of Metacognition* (Berlin and Heidelberg: Springer-Verlag, 2016). *Foundations of Metacognition* offers an interdisciplinary discussion of the emergence of metacognition, of its criteria and of its functions (M. J. Beran, J. L. Brandl, J. Perner and J. Proust, eds., Oxford: Oxford University Press)

References

Adams, A., and Santi, A. (2011). Pigeons exhibit higher accuracy for chosen memory tests than for forced memory tests in duration matching-to-sample. *Learning and Behavior, 39*(1), 1–11. doi:10.1007/s13420-010-0001-7

Barrett, L. F., and Bar, M. (2009). See it with feeling: Affective predictions during object perception. *Philosophical Transactions of the Royal Society of London B: Biological Sciences, 364*(1521), 1325–1334. doi:10.1098/rstb.2008.0312

Basile, B. M., Schroeder, G. R., Brown, E. K., Templer, V. L., and Hampton, R. R. (2015). Evaluation of seven hypotheses for metamemory performance in rhesus monkeys. *Journal of Experimental Psychology: General, 144*(1), 85–102. doi:10.1037/xge0000031

Bechara, A., Damasio, A. R., Damasio, H., and Anderson, S. W. (1994). Insensitivity to future consequences following damage to human prefrontal cortex. *Cognition, 50*(1), 7–15. http://dx.doi.org/10.1016/0010-0277(94)90018-3

Beran, M. J., and Smith, J. D. (2011). Information seeking by rhesus monkeys (Macaca mulatta) and capuchin monkeys (Cebus apella). *Cognition, 120*(1), 90–105.

Beran, M. J., and Smith, J. D. (2014). The uncertainty response in animal-metacognition researchers. *Journal of Comparative Psychology, 128*(2), 155–159. http://dx.doi.org/10.1037/a0036564

Bermúdez, J. L. (2009). Mindreading in the animal kingdom. In R. W. Lurz (ed.), *The Philosophy of Animal Minds*. Cambridge: Cambridge University Press, 145–164.

Call, J. (2010). Do apes know that they could be wrong? *Animal Cognition, 13*(5), 689–700. doi:10.1007/s10071-010-0317-x

Carruthers, P. (2011). *The Opacity of Mind: An Integrative Theory of Self-Knowledge*. Oxford: Oxford University Press.

Carruthers, P., and Ritchie, J. B. (2012). The emergence of metacognition: Affect and uncertainty in animals. In M. J. Beran, J. Brandl, J. Perner and J. Proust (eds.), *Foundations of Metacognition*. Oxford: Oxford University Press, 76–93.

Couchman, J. J., Beran, M. J., Coutinho, M. V. C., Boomer, J., and Smith, J. D. (2012). Evidence for animal metaminds. In M. J. Beran, J. Brandl, J. Perner and J. Proust (eds.), *Foundations Metacognition*. Oxford: Oxford University Press, 21–35.

Crystal, J. D., and Foote, A. L. (2009). Metacognition in animals: Trends and challenges. *Comparative Cognition and Behavior Reviews, 4*, 54–55. doi:10.3819/ccbr.2009.40001

Cussins, A. (2012). Environmental representation of the body. *Review of Philosophy and Psychology, 3*(1), 15–32. doi:10.1007/s13164-012-0086-3

De Martino, B., Fleming, S. M., Garrett, N., and Dolan, R. J. (2013). Confidence in value-based choice. *Nature Neuroscience, 16*(1), 105–110. doi:10.1038/nn.3279

Dreyfus, H., and Kelly, S. D. (2007). Heterophenomenology: Heavy-handed sleight-of-hand. *Phenomenology and the Cognitive Sciences, 6*(1–2), 45–55. doi:10.1007/s11097-006-9042-y

Evans, G. (1982). *The Varieties of Reference*. Oxford: Oxford University Press.

Fleming, S. M., and Dolan, R. J. (2012). The neural basis of metacognitive ability. *Philosophical Transactions of the Royal Society B, 367*(1594), 1338–1349. doi: 0.1098/rstb.2011.0417

Foote, A. L., and Crystal, J. D. (2007). Metacognition in the rat. *Current Biology, 17*(6), 551–555. doi:10.1016/j.cub.2007.01.061

Gendler, T. S. (2008). Alief and belief. *The Journal of Philosophy, 105*(10), 634–663.

Griffiths, P. E., and Scarantino, A. (2009). Emotions in the wild: The situated perspective on emotion. In M. Aydede and P. Robbins (eds.), *The Cambridge Handbook of Situated Cognition*. New York: Cambridge University Press, 437–453.

Hampton, R. R. (2001). Rhesus monkeys know when they remember. *Proceedings of the National Academy of Sciences, 98*(9), 5359–5362. doi:10.1073/pnas.071600998

Hampton, R. R. (2003). Metacognition as evidence for explicit representation in nonhumans. *Behavioral and Brain Sciences, 26*(3), 346–347. http://dx.doi.org/10.1017/S0140525X03300081

Hart, J. T. (1965). Memory and the feeling-of-knowing experience. *Journal of Educational Psychology, 56*(4), 208–216. http://dx.doi.org/10.1037/h0022263

Kepecs, A., and Mainen, Z. F. (2012). A computational framework for the study of confidence in humans and animals. *Philosophical Transactions of the Royal Society of London B: Biological Sciences, 367*(1594), 1322–1337. doi: 10.1098/rstb.2012.0037.

Kepecs, A., Uchida, N., Zariwala, H. A., and Mainen, Z. F. (2008). Neural correlates, computation and behavioural impact of decision confidence. *Nature, 455*(7210), 227–231. doi:10.1038/nature07200

Kiani, R., and Shadlen, M. N. (2009). Representation of confidence associated with a decision by neurons in the parietal cortex. *Science, 324*(5928), 759–764. doi:10.1126/science.1169405

Koriat, A. (1993). How do we know that we know? The accessibility model of the feeling of knowing. *Psychological Review, 100*(4), 609–639. doi:10.1037/0033-295X.100.4.609

Koriat, A. (2000). The feeling of knowing: Some metatheoretical implications for consciousness and control. *Consciousness and Cognition, 9*(2), 149–171. http://dx.doi.org/10.1006/ccog.2000.0433

Koriat, A. (2012). The subjective confidence in one's knowledge and judgments: Some methatheoretical considerations. In M. J. Beran, J. Brandl, J. Perner and J. Proust (eds.), *Foundations of Metacognition*. Oxford: Oxford University Press, 215–233.

Koriat, A., and Ackerman, R. (2010). Metacognition and mindreading: Judgments of learning for self and other during self-paced study. *Consciousness and Cognition, 19*(1), 251–264. http://dx.doi.org/10.1016/j.concog.2009.12.010

Koriat, A., and Goldsmith, M. (1996). Memory metaphors and the real-life/laboratory controversy: Correspondence versus storehouse conceptions of memory. *Behavioral and Brain Sciences, 19*(2), 167–188. doi:10.1017/S0140525X00042114

Koriat, A., and Levy-Sadot, R. (2000). Conscious and unconscious metacognition: A rejoinder. *Consciousness and Cognition, 9*(2), 193–202. doi:10.1006/ccog.2000.0436

Koriat, A., Nussinson, R., and Ackerman, R. (2014). Judgments of learning depend on how learners interpret study effort. *Journal of Experimental Psychology: Learning, Memory, and Cognition, 40*(6), 1624–1637. doi:10.1037/xlm0000009

Kornell, N., Son, L. K., and Terrace, H. S. (2007). Transfer of metacognitive skills and hint seeking in monkeys. *Psychological Science, 18*(1), 64–71. doi:10.1111/j.1467-9280.2007.01850.x

Le Pelley, M. E. (2014). Primate polemic: Commentary on Smith, Couchman, and Beran. *Journal of Comparative Psychology, 128*(2), 132–134. http://dx.doi.org/10.1037/a0034227

Metcalfe, J., and Kober, H. (2005). Self-reflective consciousness and the projectable self. In H. S. Terrace and J. Metcalfe (eds.), *The Missing Link in Cognition: Origins of Self-Reflective Consciousness*. Oxford: Oxford University Press, 57–83.

Millikan, R. (1995) Pushmi-Pullyu representations. *Philosophical Perspectives, 9*, 185–200.

Nanay, B. (2013). *Between Perception and Action*. Oxford: Oxford University Press.

Proust, J. (2013). *The Philosophy of Metacognition: Mental Agency and Self-Awareness*. Oxford: Oxford University Press.

Proust, J. (2015a). The representational structure of feelings. In T. Metzinger and J. M. Windt (eds.), *Open Mind*. www.open-mind.net. doi:10.15502/9783958571044

Proust, J. (2015b) Time and action: Impulsivity, habit, strategy? *The Review of Philosophy and Psychology, 6*(4), 717–743. doi:10.1007/s13164-014-0224-1

Proust, J. (2016). The evolution of primate communication and metacommunication. *Mind & language*, *31*(2), 177–203. doi:10.1111/mila.12100

Smith, J. D., Beran, M. J., Couchman, J. J., and Coutinho, M. V. (2008). The comparative study of metacognition: Sharper paradigms, safer inferences. *Psychonomic Bulletin & Review*, *15*(4), 679–691. doi:10.3758/PBR.15.4.679

Smith, J. D., Beran, M. J., Redford, J. S., and Washburn, D. A. (2006). Dissociating uncertainty responses and reinforcement signals in the comparative study of uncertainty monitoring. *Journal of Experimental Psychology: General*, *135*(2), 282–297. http://dx.doi.org/10.1037/0096-3445.135.2.282

Smith, J. D., Couchman, J. J., and Beran, M. J. (2014). Animal metacognition: A tale of two comparative psychologies. *Journal of Comparative Psychology*, *128*(2), 115–131. http://dx.doi.org/10.1037/a0033105

Smith, J. D., Redford, J. S., Beran, M. J., and Washburn, D. A. (2010). Rhesus monkeys (Macaca mulatta) adaptively monitor uncertainty while multi-tasking. *Animal Cognition*, *13*(1), 93–101. doi:10.1007/s10071-009-0249-5

Smith, J. D., Shields, W. E., and Washburn, D. A. (2003). The comparative psychology of uncertainty monitoring and metacognition. *Behavioural and Brain Sciences*, *26*, 317–373.

Son, L. K., and Kornell, N. (2005). Meta-confidence judgments in rhesus macaques: Explicit versus implicit mechanisms. In H. S. Terrace and J. Metcalfe (eds.), *The Missing Link in Cognition: Origins of Self-Reflective Consciousness*, 296–320.

Suda-King, C. (2008). Do orangutans (Pongo pygmaeus) know when they do not remember? *Animal Cognition*, *11*(1), 21–42. doi:10.1007/s10071-007-0082-7

Zakrzewski, A. C., Perdue, B. M., Beran, M. J., Church, B. A., and Smith, J. D. (2014). Cashing out: The decisional flexibility of uncertainty responses in rhesus macaques (*Macaca mulatta*) and humans (*Homo sapiens*). *Journal of Experimental Psychology: Animal Learning and Cognition*, *40*(4), 490–501. doi.org/10.1037/xan0000041

PART III

Consciousness

14

SO THAT'S WHAT IT'S LIKE!

Sean Allen-Hermanson

Introduction

The example of bat echolocation is commonly used to set up discussions of the explanatory gap, the subjective-objective distinction, and the ultimate nature of consciousness. Many philosophers have held that we cannot say what it is like to be a bat since it presents a fundamentally *alien* form of life (Nagel, 1974/1998). Another view held by some philosophers, bat scientists, and even many laypersons is that echolocation is somehow, at least in part, a kind of visual experience. Either way, bat echolocation is taken to be something very mysterious and exotic. However, I contend that we can say something about what it is like to be a bat. Though highly plausible, this view has mostly been overlooked by philosophers of mind. That they might be so mistaken about something often taken as obvious and certain is rather curious! If many or most philosophers are in error about what it is like to echolocate, this calls for reflection on philosophies dependent on immediate knowledge of our ongoing conscious states.

I begin by saying something about the distribution of animal consciousness. Concerning whether bats are conscious, I set aside the notion that it isn't like anything, as argued by "across the board" eliminativists, who do away with consciousness altogether, and "species-specific" eliminativists, who argue for skepticism for individual cases – as Akins does concerning bats (Akins, 1996). For myself, I am a species-specific eliminativist only when it comes to very simple-minded organisms, or "natural zombies," such as insects (Allen-Hermanson, 2008). The argument is that if we assume a broadly functionalist and representationalist framework (e.g. in terms of global accessibility or a cognitive "workspace"), then many animals, especially mammals and birds, and certainly bats, are most likely conscious.[1] Meanwhile, there are prima facie doubts about consciousness in "simple-minded" organisms, which act more like blindsight subjects. In short, the behavior of, e.g. honeybees, doesn't seem best explained in terms of guidance by inner representations that are globally accessible. In any case, here I take the distribution question as, more or less, settled in order to turn to the phenomenology of bat echolocation. Any attempt to actually characterize what it is like to be a bat might strike you as a crazy notion, but bear with me.

Echolocatory experience probably just has an auditory character. It's the experience of hearing rapid squeaks and shrieks, and their echoes, and though a bit unusual to consider, it is easily within one's imaginative grasp.[2] To the complaint that knowing what it is like *for a bat* to hear echoes isn't the same as knowing what it is like for a human, or *for me*, one need only point out that it should at least be no more mysterious than asking what it is like for a dog to see something.[3] Presumably, it is like seeing something. Notice people tend to concur about what vision is like, but not echolocation.

If echolocation is sound experience, and yet we fail to notice this, perhaps it is because conscious introspection is unreliable. Having a poor grasp on the phenomenological character of our own echolocatory experiences would explain why we find it difficult to cope with imagining what echolocation is like for other species. So is disarray and uncertainty about bats best explained by the fact that conscious introspection is untrustworthy? The remainder of this chapter considers this challenge and how it might be answered.

What philosophers have said

"The man born blind cannot grasp the concept of a visual experience of red, and human beings cannot conceive of the echolocatory experiences of bats." So says McGinn (1991, p. 9), who maintains there is *cognitive closure* of first-person subjective experience from impersonal objective descriptions of behavior and brain states. Our failure to form a conception of echolocatory experience illustrates the poverty of our conceptual resources when they are deprived of the right type of first-person experience. The problem is supposed to be intractable. Even those who deny conclusions about the irreducibility of subjectivity and phenomenal appearances often take up Nagel's premise that the experiential character of echolocation is, at least for now, closed to us. Biro (1991), for instance, allows that a bat can perceive what I do though things would "look very different to it" (p. 124) in virtue of a different type of "perceptual apparatus." Certainly, Biro and others may simply be granting a "vast difference between the character of their experience and ours" (p. 126) merely for the sake of argument, though consider how awkward it would be if the example had been about, say, a cat looking at a bird. Many seem to agree with Nagel that bats are *alien*, such as Russow (1982, p. 57), who finds the "qualitative differences . . . especially striking" as we perceive and experience "by means of different senses." Alter (2002) mentions Lewis (1988/1990, p. 500), who writes that we'd need far-fetched neuroscience or "magic" to be able to know what it is like. Also consider Maloney (1985), who supposes without argument that bat consciousness must "radically differ" from our own, attributing this to features of their "unique" system of representation, which is dubbed "Batese," in contrast with our own Fodorian Mentalese (p. 43). Representational tokens in Batese differ as "physical kinds" from ours, resulting in a "unique phenomenological realm." And yet, since Maloney recognizes that Batese representational tokens likely consist in transformations of sound waves within auditory systems (p. 44), the reader wonders why this does not at least raise the possibility that they fall under our physical type after all. Perhaps it is just a bad example, as surely there are some types of experience inaccessible to any particular human being. But there is considerable irony if, perhaps, *the* paradigmatic example of an intractably foreign experience turned out to be all too familiar to us.

Other intuitions about bats

Another view, held by ordinary people and some philosophers and scientists, is that echolocation has, at least in part, a visual quality. I've asked audiences ranging from freshmen to professional philosophers variations on this question over the years:

What is it like for a bat to echolocate?

Even when asked what it is like for a bat echolocating *in the darkness*, I have found people rate visual experience almost as prominently as auditory experience – a typical set of responses from a survey of 39 undergraduates is summarized in Table 14.1 (see Appendix). Respondents were allowed to pick more than one modality, thus accommodating those who thought echolocatory experience combines sight and sound. Only 68% mentioned audition *at all*, with a measly 15% saying echolocation is exhausted by auditory experience. Meanwhile, a little more than half mentioned vision. You might expect that people would be uncertain or reluctant about committing themselves to judgment about seemingly alien phenomenology, yet this seems hardly ever to be the case. In this instance, literally nobody thought there was nothing that it was like to echolocate, and hardly any said it is like something, though we cannot say what. The remaining modalities received little support. So again, most people I've encountered (of those who think we can know what it is like) fall under one of three groups: it is like audition, or vision, or, somehow, a combination of the two. Assuming these results really are typical (perhaps they are not), what does this say about the phenomenological judgments of human beings? One's first reaction is to think, "Somebody must be wrong!" But let us proceed more carefully.

One possibility is that the question is misleading, and some people are confusing the character of echolocatory experience with associated visual imagery. Perhaps most people actually think, qua echolocation, that bats are just hearing sounds, though this is accompanied by visual ideas. Such a view is inspired by everyday experience, as when one tries to visualize a room while groping around in the dark. Another possibility is that respondents are confusing echolocatory with other types of experience a bat might simultaneously undergo while flying around eating bugs. With these points in mind, I consulted another group of 53 undergraduates who were allowed to select only one modality in response (results are summarized in Table 14.2 in the Appendix). This time, audition scored much more strongly, though about a third refused to agree that it was the best choice, with 11% opting for vision, again despite the question explicitly stating that the bat was echolocating in the darkness! I also used a five-point scale to measure responses to "How confident are you about your answer?" with the result that there was no significant difference between those who chose audition (3.87) versus vision (3.83). I found these results surprising. Significant minorities seem committed to the view that echolocatory experience is either somehow visual, or perhaps something beyond the usual five senses, though when pressed most people acknowledge the primacy of audition.

Some philosophers and scientists have also been drawn to the view that echolocation is comparable to vision, including Dawkins (1986, p. 33ff.), and more recently Macpherson (2011) and Godfrey-Smith (2013). In a *Nature Podcast* episode, philosopher David Papineau and echolocation expert Jim Simmons are asked about what it might be like for bats.[4] Papineau says he isn't sure if it is sight or sound, as "we don't have the physical goings on," though we might be able to figure it out by learning more about echolocation. On the other hand, Simmons' research has convinced him "the bats are clearly seeing things . . . they're not hearing sounds, they're seeing objects."

Occasionally philosophers offer explicit arguments, such as Macpherson (2011), who contends that it is unclear whether or not echolocation is a kind of hearing. This is because no matter which criterion we choose for individuating the senses, echolocation shares some features with seeing, others with hearing, and still others with neither. She notes that echolocation consists in representing three-dimensional objects moving through space, a proprietary feature of sight (p. 30). But since bats represent through sound, and not paradigmatic visual contents, such as colors, we are pulled in two directions (p. 30). In addition, she argues that since the bat's ears, sonar inputs, and auditory system are somewhat different from our own, maybe they aren't "ears" at all. Perhaps echolocation is better compared to vision, some combination of seeing and hearing, or perhaps even something weird and altogether different. But I suspect these points exaggerate the differences.

As noted by Aristotle,[5] other senses also provide information about shape, number, and movement, so why should the presentation of objects in egoistic space be assumed to be propriety of vision rather than a "common sensible"? It is question-begging to say that a feature shared between vision and some other sense ought to be assumed to belong to the former. Meanwhile, bat ears and auditory cortex are not *that* different from our own – they are mammals, their "ears" process sound waves, etc. . . . and there is no confusing these structures with parts of the bat resembling parts of the human visual system. I side with Akins in rejecting the idea that echolocation has a "strangely 'visual' quality" (1996, p. 349).

Another possibility is that Macpherson and others are drawn to a comparison with vision because it provides such a *highly detailed* representation of the spatial environment. In noticing that it is difficult to imagine highly detailed auditory representations of space, but easy to imagine highly detailed visual representations, we might infer the function and character of auditory experience in humans and bats differs. This is an interesting suggestion, but I am doubtful. First, bat echolocation is not that detailed (Akins, 1996); meanwhile, we get some sense of space from sound. Second, in general there is little to no expectation that an amplification of detail would tend to shift a sensory experience from one type to another. Although it is hard for us to imagine the detailed olfactory experiences of a dog, this is not a reason to think they are not undergoing smells.

Echolocation is just auditory experience

Assuming bats are conscious, can we go further and say something about what echolocation might be like? Nagel's argument assumed not. On his view, bat sonar is "not similar in operation to any sense that we possess" (1974/1998, p. 520), and so we are limited to, at most, "a schematic conception" which leaves out the essential character of consciousness as it is experienced in the first person (p. 521). Knowing what it is like requires taking up the perspective of another being, and for entities with radically different sense modalities, this seems impossible. But perhaps we can be reasonably confidant about the character of subjective experiences for those we do share. Although this sounds straightforward, some cases might require a certain amount of introspection and reflection to make this clear. Other cases might be indeterminate. What of bat echolocation? I can think of four reasons why echolocatory experience is auditory:

1   Ears are for hearing sound waves, and bats have ears.
2   Hearing an echo sounds like something.
3   Echolocation is processed in auditory cortex in neurotypical human subjects.
4   Processing differs in congenitally blind expert echolocators; nevertheless, they describe their experiences exclusively in terms of sound.

As I've already said something about the first point, I'll confine my remarks to the remainder. First, I'll reiterate that, phenomenologically, echolocation is just a form of hearing. It's not uncanny to use sound to identify objects and locate them in space relative to one's own body, or hear one's way through the spatial environment. This is commonplace, though thinking of sound experience in this way is perhaps a little unfamiliar. Yet we know what it is like to "see" an insect flying nearby with our ears. It isn't seeing, but hearing, when I identify a mosquito buzzing within a few centimeters to the right and towards the back of my head, moving horizontally and counterclockwise. True, these judgments are crude compared to what bats do, but there's nothing mysterious about knowing what it is like to recognize an insect by sound alone and form an awareness of its rough position and trajectory. Genuine echolocation is also a feature of ordinary human hearing. Some even refine this ability to the point that they can make very subtle discriminations.

In his pioneering work, Griffin (1958, p. 324) notes:

> echolocation has long been used by sailors under conditions of fog or darkness when shore or rocks are suspected to be near at hand . . . Sometimes a shout suffices . . . and it is sometimes quite easy to hear a distinct echo a second or two after the emission of such a signal.

Localization can be achieved through careful listening at intervals, and Griffin remarks that the primitive technique has been employed "probably since the days of the Phoenicians" (pp. 324–5). Some blind persons achieve more impressive results by utilizing taps with a cane or stick, or by making clicking noises with the tongue and carefully attending to the reflected sounds (Stroffregen and Pittenger, 1995). Though human echolocation has occasionally been confused with tactile experiences felt on the face, sometimes known as "facial vision" (Ammons et al. 1953), it is clearly a form of hearing. Human echolocation can be developed to staggering accuracy, enabling identifications of everyday objects such as trees, walls, garbage bins, and cars. One expert echolocator, Daniel Kish, goes hiking, rides a bike, and plays basketball despite his lifelong blindness (Thaler et al., 2011). Acuity studies are suggesting that the precision of human echolocation is comparable to the abilities of bats and human peripheral vision (Teng and Whitney, 2012). Expert echolocators attend to stimuli average people could notice, but ordinarily don't. It improves with practice, even for those who start late in life. Though they normally have no reason to develop it, those with sight can rapidly acquire proficiency (Ammons et al., 1953; Teng and Whitney, 2012). Perhaps echolocation is easier to develop in the absence of vision because the various senses compete for the use of attention or other neural resources. Or perhaps this has something to do with the primacy of vision as a source for our intuitions and metaphors about perception and everyday spatial representation. It is not clear.

Then again, just because echolocation in sighted subjects is auditory, could blind echolocators be experiencing it differently? It could be argued that human echolocation is only somewhat like ordinary hearing, though the difference seems more a matter of degree than kind – just as we don't think of colorblind persons as lacking vision just because they don't access the same frequencies as others. There are, however, some special considerations in play when it comes to persons such as Kish. The area known as calcarine cortex or V1, associated with visual perception in sighted persons, is responsible for processing auditory inputs in blind echolocators (Thaler et al., 2011), perhaps suggesting that it is experienced as sight, not sound (their auditory cortex still processes other kinds of sounds). Yet it is also reasonable to expect Kish's brain to be somewhat unusual given a lifetime of blindness, and so perhaps for him, V1 has been "recruited" by the auditory system. Another possibility is that V1 has been misidentified as "visual" cortex and is dedicated to processing spatial representations regardless of their sensory origins, as suggested by Pascual-Leone and Hamilton (2001, p. 15). If so, V1 is better thought of as *spatial* cortex: though it normally handles inputs from multiple modalities (again in keeping with the ancient observation that other senses convey spatial information), this has been overlooked because inputs arising from these other sources are normally masked by the massive contribution from vision. We can also note that while tactile inputs for congenitally blind persons reading Braille are processed in "visual" cortex, the resulting phenomenology is, nevertheless, tactile (Hurley and Noë, 2003, p. 139). If sensory cortex "defers" to auditory inputs, then Kish is experiencing echoes as sounds.

This interpretation is backed up by the way Kish talks and writes about what it is like. For example, in an instructional document subtitled "Learning a new way to see," Kish uses both visual and auditory descriptors for his "flash sonar."[6] Yet despite the seemingly radical implications of the title, auditory descriptors like "hear," "sound," or "listen" predominate, and are only used with reference to echolocation, whereas visual descriptors are often used metaphorically as cognates for non-perceptual judgment, as in "we see this process as interactive." In addition, although he often uses quotation marks to hedge the description of echolocation as "seeing," Kish never implies non-literal meaning for auditory descriptors like "hear," "sound," or "listen." Despite Kish's occasional references to generic "images," echolocation is never characterized as "vision," "visual," or "sight." Meanwhile, he pays close attention to the specific character of sounds, which can be "broad and sparse," "hollow," or "scattery." While other alternatives cannot be completely ruled out, the balance of experimental evidence, Kish's self-reports, and plain commonsense suggests that echolocation is a type of auditory experience.

So blind humans who echolocate report sounds, not visual images, and although they utilize "visual" cortex, perhaps the brain is deferring to auditory input and their cortical regions function differently. Meanwhile, ordinary humans also echolocate, and though it often functions unconsciously, it sometimes takes the form of auditory experience and is never experienced visually.

The threat to naïve introspection

People are often confused about all sorts of things, so why not about what it is like to echolocate? Perhaps the problem is that naïve introspection about here-and-now conscious appearances is simply unreliable. This view finds support with those such as Schwitzgebel, who contends:

> We have no reliable means of learning about our own ongoing conscious experience, our current imagery, our inward sensation – we are as in the dark about that as about anything else, perhaps even more in the dark . . . [w]e are both ignorant and prone to error . . . and we make gross, enduring mistakes about even the most basic features of our currently ongoing conscious experience.
>
> (2008, pp. 246–247)

If this is correct, then it is not at all surprising people will falter when it comes to judgments about the inner lives of another species! Indeed, although we echolocate frequently, Schwitzgebel claims we often confuse this with fictitious haptic experiences or "facial vision." These errors are so serious that he is led to provocatively conclude, "we hardly even know what it is like to be ourselves" (Schwitzgebel and Gordon 2000, p. 244). The implications are several. Whether conscious introspection is in general trustworthy matters, because it is commonly taken to be an important source of self-knowledge. In addition, it is critical to foundationalist theories of knowledge and challenges the view of neurophilosophers that the natural sciences take a privileged place epistemically. Finally, this issue bears on disagreement about how first-person reports should be utilized in cognitive science (Peels 2016). I would add that the unreliability of introspection bears on the stock we should place in claims about what is or isn't conceivable. If I am in the dark about what it is like, *for me, right now*, then why would I expect that my "intuitions" (my nonreflective, nondiscursive, and immediate beliefs) about immediate sensory awareness are any guide to what is or isn't the case when it comes to bats? Though I agree that most people, even many philosophers, seem to be mixed up about this, there's nothing wrong with naïve introspective judgment.

Certainly if ordinary people confused sounds with tactile experiences felt on the face, this would be a stunning failure of first-person epistemic authority. But I think this worry is overblown. Some human echolocators are accurately reporting diverse experiences from other sense modalities, especially those that are haptic. Some do hear sounds, though this is complicated by the fact that echolocation is often confused with a related phenomenon known as "spatial hearing."[7] Meanwhile, those who report not hearing sounds are probably echolocating unconsciously. Genuine tactile feelings on the face might be caused by "tensing up" in anticipation of a collision, air currents, drafts, and gusts of wind; the latter are especially likely concerning reports made outdoors. When considered carefully, the example of human echolocation rather strongly supports the presumption of introspective privilege after all (Allen-Hermanson, 2015).

Assessing the threat

What do judgments about what it is like to be a bat suggest about introspection – about whether it is reliable and trustworthy? Despite the fact that I want to assert both that echolocatory experience is auditory, and that philosophers and non-philosophers often get this wrong, these errors do not pose a serious threat to the reliability of naïve introspection. I propose that the reason is because these are only performance errors. When people are attending carefully, they will tend to get things right. There are some scientists who appear to agree – de Waal, for one, has called the claim that we can't imagine what it is like to be a bat "overly pessimistic" in light of human echolocators (de Waal 2001, p. 76). Surely a few philosophers over the past 40 years have noticed that the flagship example of cognitive closure is not cognitively closed. And indeed, several have.

Alter (2002, p. 145) realizes "bat sonar involves hearing. Thus, perhaps the bat's experiences are less alien to us than Nagel supposes," though Alter doesn't seem to realize that humans literally echolocate; it is assumed to be a "modality we lack" and an imaginative difference in kind, not degree (p. 146). However, he adds that bats are "only an example" and play no essential role in the argument, as there "could be such creatures" (p. 145)."[8] Flanagan goes further (1996, p. 447), even declaring it "patently false" that humans cannot know what it is like to be a bat. Of course, we never experience the world exactly as another being does (including each other), but we certainly do grasp what it is like to have echolocatory experiences as a type, since "All humans make use of echolocation in getting about. If anything will help to form 'a schematic conception' of what it is like to be a bat, practicing echolocation will" (Flanagan, 1996, p. 447). There's also Lopes, who states that echolocatory experiences have the "phenomenal character of hearing" (2000, pp. 449–50). Thus, some "experts" (insofar as philosophers can be trusted!) really do see things more or less clearly, and when they seem not to, it's beside the point of their argument. Still, why should there be confusion at all, and why should it tend to involve vision?

Part of the explanation may be that some philosophers and others are misled by popular culture. Movies, educational materials, comic books, and other media sometimes portray echolocation using the bright greens and sharp lines characteristic of the display screens of submarines or what transpires in the mind's eye of superhumans like *Daredevil*. Educational films and nature programs often explicitly present bat echolocation in visual motifs inspired by sonar or radar, and the audience might even be told echolocation is literally "seeing with sound." But this explanation only puts off the problem, for why does popular culture have this tendency? The likely answer is that most people haven't put much thought into it, and as we are visual creatures, we instinctively think in these terms when it comes to spatial awareness with fine detail. However, the surveys I conducted (tentatively) suggest that when attending more carefully, people converge on the idea that it is just sound, after all.

Conclusion

So, does confusion and disarray about what it is like to echolocate mean we are poor introspectors? Perhaps not, though we are often unreflective introspectors. Indeed, instead of saying that introspection is untrustworthy, we might instead call into question the claims of those who say that the problems of consciousness are intractable.

APPENDIX

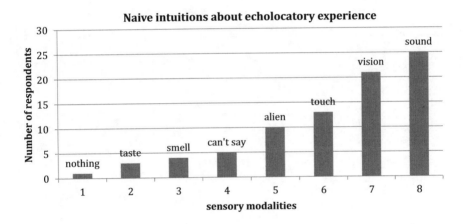

Naive intuitions about echolocatory experience

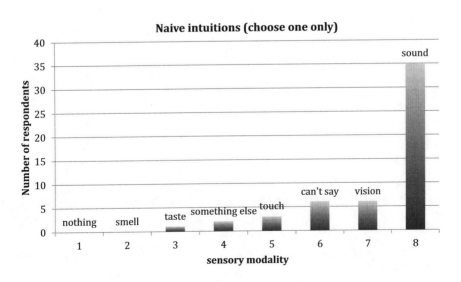

Naive intuitions (choose one only)

Sample questionnaire

What kind of experience best describes what it is like to be a bat echolocating in the darkness? (Choose one only):

a) vision
b) audition
c) taste
d) smell
e) touch
f) something else
g) can't say
h) nothing

How confident are you about your answer?
     (circle one):

not confident at all		*somewhat confident*		*Very confident*
1	2	3	4	5

Notes

1 Here I also set aside "new Mysterian" concerns about a potential gap between consciousness construed in terms of information-processing functions (e.g. what Block 1995 calls "access" consciousness) and phenomenal awareness.
2 Or click here, then close your eyes: www.werc.usgs.gov/OLDsitedata/bats/sounds/california-myotis-search.wav
3 Biro (1991, p. 123) notes Nagel's ambiguity between the problem of "ineliminable individual subjectivity" and "types of points of view."

4 "What is it like to be a bat?" January 12, 2015, www.nature.com/nature/podcast/index-audio-file-2015-01-12.html
5 "Common sensibles are movement, rest, number, figure, magnitude; these are not special to any one sense, but are common to all" (*De Anima*, Book II, Ch. 6).
6 Daniel Kish, "Learning a new way to see," www.worldaccessfortheblind.org/sites/default/files/snr-pgm2011.htm (retrieved on January 11, 2013).
7 This refers to the use of any acoustical information (even if nonechoic) to localize the directions of sound sources or form judgments about the spatial environment.
8 Nagel (1974/1998, p. 526 n.8) himself briefly entertains the idea that echolocation is a form of audition, but sets it aside as it is not relevant to his central point about the gap between subjectivity and objectivity. Though his example is poorly chosen, presumably there are many types of experiences inaccessible to humans, such as "bee purple" perceived only by insects and birds sensitive to ultraviolet light, or electroreception in certain fish.

Further reading

For a reply to Akins on bats, see S. Allen-Hermanson (2015), "Strong neurophilosophy and the matter of bat consciousness: A case study," *Erkenntnis* 80 (1): 57–76. D. C. Dennett's (1995), "Animal consciousness: What matters and why," *Social Research* 3: 691–710, is insightful and got me interested in this topic. B. L. Keeley (2002/2011), "Making sense of the senses: Individuating modalities in humans and other animals," in F. Macpherson (ed.) *The Senses: Classic and Contemporary Philosophical Perspectives*, pp. 220–40 (Oxford: Oxford University Press), discusses sensory individuation by way of the "star-nosed mole problem." A. Surlykke, J. A. Simmons and C. F. Moss (2016), "Perceiving the world through echolocation and vision," in M. B. Fenton, A. D. Grinnell, A. N. Popper and R. R. Fay (eds.) *Bat Bioacoustics*, pp. 265–88 (New York: Springer,), offer a fascinating summary of recent research on bat echolocation. For recent findings on human echolocation, see A. J. Kolarik, S. Cirstea, S. Pardhan and B. C. Moore (2014), "A summary of research investigating echolocation abilities of blind and sighted humans," *Hearing Research* 310: 60–8.

References

Akins, K. (1996). "A bat without qualities," in M. Bekoff and D. Jamieson (eds.) *Readings in Animal Cognition* (pp. 345–58). Cambridge, MA: The MIT Press.

Allen-Hermanson, S. (2008). "Insects and the problem of simple minds: Are bees natural zombies?" *The Journal of Philosophy* 105(8): 389–415.

Allen-Hermanson, S. (2015). "Introspection, Anton's syndrome, and human echolocation," *Pacific Philosophical Quarterly* (published online November 10, 2015).

Alter, T. (2002). "Nagel on imagination and physicalism," *Journal of Philosophical Research* 27: 143–58.

Ammons, C. H., Worchel, P., and Dallenbach, K. M. (1953). "Facial vision: The perception of obstacles out of doors by blindfolded and blindfolded-deafened subjects," *The American Journal of Psychology* 66(4): 519–53.

Aristotle (1984). "De Anima," in J. Barnes (ed.) *The Complete Works of Aristotle: The Revised Oxford Translation*. Princeton, NJ: Princeton University Press.

Biro, J. I. (1991). "Consciousness and subjectivity," *Philosophical Issues* 1: 113–33.

Block, N. (1995). "On a confusion about a function of consciousness," *Behavioral and Brain Sciences* 18: 227–47.

Dawkins, R. (1986). *The Blind Watchmaker*. New York: Norton.

de Waal, F. B. (2001). *The Ape and the Sushi Master: Cultural Reflections of a Primatologist*. New York: Basic Books.

Flanagan, O. (1996). "Recent problems," in P. A. Morton (ed.) *A Historical Introduction to the Philosophy of Mind: Readings With Commentary* (pp. 369–450). Peterborough, ON: Broadview Press.

Godfrey-Smith, P. (2013). "On being an octopus," *Boston Review*, June 3, pp. 46–50.

Griffin, D. (1958). *Listening in the Dark*. New Haven, CT: Yale University Press.

Hurley, S., and Noë, A. (2003). "Neural plasticity and consciousness," *Biology and Philosophy* 18: 131–68.

Lewis, D. (1988/1990). "What experience teaches," In *Proceedings of the Russellian Society*. Reprinted in W. Lycan (ed.) *Mind and Cognition* (pp. 499–518). Cambridge: Basil Blackwell.

Lopes, D. M. (2000). "What is it like to see with your ears?" *Philosophy and Phenomenological Research* 60(2): 439–53.

Mcginn, C. (1991). *The Problem of Consciousness*. Oxford: Blackwell.

Macpherson, F. (ed.). (2011). *The Senses: Classic and Contemporary Philosophical Perspectives*. Oxford: Oxford University Press.

Maloney, C. J. (1985). "About being a bat," *Australasian Journal of Philosophy* 63(1): 26–49.

Nagel, T. (1974/1998). "What is it like to be a bat?" in *Philosophical Review*. Reprinted in N. Block, O. Flanagan, and G. Güzeldere (eds.) *The Nature of Consciousness: Philosophical Debates* (pp. 519–27). Cambridge, MA: The MIT Press.

Pascual-Leone, A., and Hamilton, R. (2001). "The metamodal organization of the brain," in C. Casanova and M. Ptito (eds.) *Progress in Brain Research* 154 (1–19). Elsevier B.V.

Peels, R. (2016). "The empirical case against introspection," *Philosophical Studies* 173(9): 2461–485.

Russow, L. M. (1982). "It's not like that to be a bat," *Behaviorism* 10(1): 55–63.

Schwitzgebel, E. (2008). "The unreliability of naïve introspection," *Philosophical Review* 117(2): 245–73.

Schwitzgebel, E., and Gordon, M. S. (2000). "How well do we know our own conscious experience?" *Philosophical Topics* 28(2): 235–46.

Stroffregen, T. A., and Pittenger, J. B. (1995). "Human echolocation as a basic form of perception and action," *Ecological Psychology* 7(3): 181–216.

Teng, S., and Whitney, D. (2012). "Ultrafine spatial acuity of blind expert human echolocators," *Experimental Brain Research* 216(4): 48.

Thaler, L., Arnott, S. R., and Goodale, M. A. (2011). "Neural correlates of natural human echolocation in early and late blind echolocation experts," *PLoS ONE* 6(5): e20162. doi:10.1371/journal.pone.0020162

15

DO FISH HAVE FEELINGS?

Michael Tye

It is obvious that some things in nature are conscious, for example, human beings. It is equally obvious that some things in nature are not, for example, blades of grass. What is not obvious is where to draw the line. The conscious/nonconscious division patently does not coincide with the living/nonliving one. So where does it lie? And how are we to decide? In this essay, I shall focus on the case of fish and one conscious state in particular, that of pain.

I want to begin by making some general remarks about how to proceed with respect to the question of animal consciousness. Consider the case of other human beings. What makes it rational for me to believe that you have similar experiences to me? Not the old argument from analogy, I suggest, but rather an inference to the best available explanation of your behavior. This is an application of a rule formulated by Sir Isaac Newton in his *Principia* to the effect that we are entitled to infer like cause from like effect unless there is defeating evidence. This rule is best seen, in my view, as providing the basis for rational preference instead of rational belief, but I shall pass over that for present purposes.

What is a defeater here? Well, suppose I find out that your head is empty and that you have only an organic exterior. Your movements are controlled by Martians. You are a Martian marionette. This new evidence defeats my entitlement to prefer the view that you have experiences and feelings like me, even though you behave in very similar ways.

Alternatively, suppose I find out that you have only a silicon chip in your head with a vast look-up table inscribed on it, a table that controls your every move. Again, I have a defeater.

These points can be applied to the case of fish. The idea that it is fine to eat fish is pretty commonly held. Kurt Cobain of Nirvana fame wrote "It's okay to eat fish 'cos fish don't have feelings" in a well-known song. This view is also presumably held by Kevin Kline in the famous British movie, *A Fish Called Wanda*. Kline wants to discover the location of some stolen jewels and so, in an effort to get Michael Palin to talk, he takes Palin's beloved tropical fish out of their tank one by one and slowly eats them, as Palin is forced to watch. It is obvious that Palin thinks of the fish as creatures with feelings. He desperately wants them not to experience pain or fear or anxiety. But Kline couldn't care less. For him, they are zombies (or at least they should be treated as if they are). Who is right?

Some philosophers and scientists think that a fruitful way to proceed on the question of animal consciousness is via an investigation of their metacognition. If animals behave in ways that indicate that they have a cognitive grasp on how things appear to them, and not just on how they are, then the obvious conclusion is that things really do appear to them in various ways. And if things *appear* to them, then the animals must be conscious of those things – they must *experience* them. This is a strategy proposed by Shea and Heyes (2010) and also by Allen and Bekoff (1997). What would count as evidence that an animal has a cognitive grasp on how things appear to it? A complex form of behavior providing such evidence would be using appearances to deceive other animals. A simpler form of behavior would be recognizing how something visually appears color-wise (where that appearance is different from the customary and real color of the thing) and matching the appearance to the real color of something else in order to get a reward.

This seems to me a worthwhile and important field of research. However, we should be clear on what it shows. If a positive result is obtained, then that is evidence that the animal is indeed conscious. But if a negative result ensues, what follows is only that higher-order consciousness has not been found (that is, awareness of how things appear – a second-order mental state). And that is perfectly compatible with the existence of first-order consciousness – feelings such as pain, experiences such as the visual experience of red, etc. As already noted, no one wants to claim that a one-year-old child cannot feel pain because it is incapable of cognizing its state *as* painful.[1] That sophistication does not come until later. I return to the topic of higher-order consciousness below.

So, how should we proceed? Given my earlier remarks in connection with Newton's Rule, here is my suggestion. Take the case of pain. Humans, upon encountering a noxious stimulus S, feel pain. The feeling of pain in humans causes a certain pattern of behavior B very roughly as follows.

Protecting/guarding part of body damaged by S

Withdrawing from stimulus S unless there is a strong need/desire for something else that requires enduring S (trade-off behavior)

Decreased feeding

Irritable and aggressive behavior (increasing with severity of noxious stimulus S); physical signs of stress

Avoiding (or behaving warily towards) other stimuli that have become associated with S

Suppose we find that in fish, there is the same pattern of behavior B in response to noxious stimuli. Then it is rational for us to prefer the hypothesis that the feeling of pain causes B in fish to the hypothesis that some other cause is operative, unless we have further evidence that defeats that preference. Additional confirmation that the feeling of pain causes B in fish is the cessation or reduction in B, given morphine or other opiates, as is the case with us – again, unless there is defeating evidence.

Let us then take a quick look at the behavior of fish. First, though, it is worth pointing out that on the input side, teleost fish (that is, fish with bony skeletons) have nociceptors just as we do. Under a microscope, they look just like our nociceptors. These receptors in their skin respond to the same noxious stimuli as ours. Interestingly, shark lack nociceptors, as do other elasmobranchs (fish such as sharks that have cartilaginous skeletons). One consequence of this is that shark are able to feed on prey that would otherwise be noxious. For example, hammerhead shark prey on stingrays. These sharks have been found with as many as 96 stingray barbs embedded in their mouths (Rose 2002)! Yet sharks react in the same way as telelost fish to being caught on a hook. They struggle and try to get away. What seems to trigger their escape response is interference with free movement. For elasmobranchs, so far as I am aware, there is *no* behavior, the best explanation of which is that they feel pain.[2] Let us then put the case of sharks (and stingrays) to one side.

Fish exhibit trade-off behavior. In one experiment, trout were trained to feed in a part of the aquarium where they subsequently got a shock to the flank. It was found that the number of feeding attempts decreased with increased shock intensity. However, with increased food deprivation, the number and duration of feeding attempts increased, as did escape responses as the zone was entered. A plausible hypothesis is that fish balance their need for food against the avoidance of acute noxious stimuli. We do this too. Think about the case of picking up a very hot plate, in the one case when it is full of food and you are very hungry, and in the other when the plate is empty. You are much more likely to hold on to the plate in the former instance even though doing so is causing you pain. Fish, it seems, are like us. Similar behavior is found in hermit crabs, I might add.

In another experiment, Elizabeth Sneddon, a British scientist, injected bee venom and also acetic acid (the latter being the main ingredient in the vinegar used in the United Kingdom with fish and chips) into the lips of trout while they were under anesthetic. Sneddon chose the lips since trout lips have polymodal receptors very like those found in human lips. When the trout came to, they rubbed their lips against the sides of the tank and the gravel on the bottom. They also sat on the bottom and rocked from side to side. Primates in a poor welfare state display rocking behavior too – as a sign of their having been in acute discomfort.

This suggests that the trout have been through an aversive experience. It is also interesting to note that trout take about three hours to start feeding again after they have been injected with acetic acid – roughly the amount of time human beings whose lips have been injected with acid take to stop feeling pain.

Sneddon also found a greatly increased beat rate of the opercula (the bony flaps covering the gills) in the trout injected with bee venom or acetic acid as compared to the others. This is usually taken as an indicator of stress, and Sneddon takes it to add further support to her hypothesis that the trout injected with bee venom and acetic acid feel pain. In general, the overall pattern of behavior fish produce is indeed similar to that we produce in response to the feeling of pain, as is their reaction to opiates. So, we should prefer the hypothesis that they feel pain too.

But is there defeating evidence here? In human beings generally, the experience of pain is generated by activity in regions of the neocortex (specifically, the somatosensory cortex and the anterior cingulate cortex). Fish, however, lack a neocortex. This neurophysiological difference makes a difference, so some say: fish cannot feel pain. What are we to say about this?

The claim that in humans, pain and other experiences require a neocortex, is widely accepted. For example, the American Academy of Neurology (AAN) asserts (1989):

> Neurologically, being awake but unaware is the result of a functioning brainstem and the total loss of cerebral cortical functioning . . . Pain and suffering are attributes of consciousness requiring cerebral cortical functioning.

This does not seem to sit very well with the facts. It certainly seems to be true that adult humans who, later in life, come to lack a functioning cerebral cortex, are then in a vegetative state. But this is not always true for children born without a cerebral cortex. Recently, Bjorn Merker (2007), who spent several weeks with decorticate children and their families, said the following:

> These children are not only awake and often alert, but show responsiveness to their surroundings in the form of emotional or orienting reactions to environmental events . . . ,

most readily to sounds but also to salient visual stimuli. . . . They express pleasure by smiling and laughter, and aversion by "fussing", arching of the back and crying (in many gradations), their faces being animated by these emotional states. A familiar adult can employ this responsiveness to build up play sequences predictably progressing from smiling, over giggling to laughter and great excitement on the part of the child.

(p. 79)

There can be no doubt that these children are very impaired behaviorally. But in addition to apparently showing pleasure, they also sometimes apparently feel pain, by rubbing an area that has been banged or pinched. This is shown by facial expressions such as wincing, grimacing and flinching in 14% of the children; vocally in ways such as crying, screaming and yelling in 78% of the children; and body use such as wriggling, pulling away and startling in 4% of the children. Certainly, their behavior is nothing like that of the few children who have congenital pain insensitivity. These children ignore noxious stimuli and feel no pain from them, with the result that they behave as if nothing bad has happened, sometimes with dire consequences. One such child, Gabby Gingrass, poked out an eye and bit her gums down to the bone when she was teething. She also dislocated her jaw with no one being any the wiser, and an infection resulted.

So, at a minimum, it is not even clearly true that *in humans* a neocortex is needed for consciousness and pain in particular. What about other species? Well, here it is worth noting the case of birds. Birds lack a neocortex. Yet they engage in some very complex behavior similar in various ways to ours. So, what is going on in birds at a neurophysiological level? It has recently been proposed that there are homologous cells in bird and human brains (cells, that is, that share a common evolutionary origin) that mediate the behavioral similarities. But how can this be, if humans have a neocortex and birds lack one? This question becomes even more puzzling if we think of the neocortex in the way it is often described as a unique component of mammalian brains, something without a prior history.

The solution to the puzzle lies with the realization that the neocortex did *not* suddenly appear by magic in mammals. What happened with mammals was that certain sorts of cells present in non-mammalian brains and around for hundreds of millions of years were grouped together into layers to form the laminar structure of the cortex. This is what is genuinely new. But the constituent neuron types and the microcircuitry aren't new – or so at least it has recently been hypothesized, dating back to earlier speculation by Karten in the 1960s (Karten and Hodos 1967; also Karten 1997).

The relevant cells for birds are preserved in a structure of a vastly different shape from the neocortex, known as the dorsal ventricular ridge (DVR). The cells in the DVR share the same physiological properties as the cortical cells (Dugas-Ford et al. 2012). It has recently been hypothesized that a similar structure of cells is to be found in the forebrain of fish, too (Ito and Yamamoto 2009).

The upshot: the fact that fish lack a neocortex does not, in and of itself, defeat preference for the simplest hypothesis, namely that fish, like us, feel pain or something very like it. What defeats this potential defeater is the following: a) the case of birds shows that cells homologous to those in the neocortex can be present without a neocortex, and at least according to some scientists, fish have such cells and similar microcircuitry in their forebrains; and b) it isn't clear that such a structure in the brain is needed anyway, even in the case of human beings, given the example of some decorticate children – indeed, it seems not to be the case.

So, I think that it is rational for us to prefer the view that fish have feelings to the view that fish do not. Of course, the feeling I have focused on, that of pain, is phylogenetically fixed. This is not true of so-called "secondary emotional experiences", for example, feeling insulted or feeling remorseful. No claim is being made that fish are capable of undergoing these experiences.

There is one further line of resistance I want to mention to the claim that fish have feelings. It goes as follows.

Concepts are required to have feelings

Fish don't have concepts

So,

Fish don't have feelings.

Were this argument sound, it would provide a defeater to the inference from fish behavior to the existence of fish feelings and pain in particular (in the case of *B*).

The argument is unpersuasive, however. It is not at all obvious that fish lack concepts, even if they lack *our* concepts. After all, they engage in some pretty intelligent behavior. And there is evidence that they can reason transitively (Grosenick et al. 2007).

The first premise is also highly dubious. As noted above, the feeling of pain (and many other feelings) are fixed in human beings by their biological makeup. They are naturally taken to be phylogenetic states, liability to which does not require learning. So, for many feelings, it doesn't seem that concepts are required.

There is one well-known theory of the nature of the subjective character of experience that forges a direct link between feelings and concepts, namely the higher-order thought theory (Rosenthal 1986). On this view (the HOT view), for a creature to *feel* pain, its pain state must be accompanied by a higher-order thought to the effect that it is in pain, where this thought is arrived at non-inferentially. Some versions of the higher-order thought theory make more modest claims. But this version is wildly implausible. As noted earlier, small babies feel pain, yet they are not capable of thinking to themselves that they are in pain; for they lack psychological concepts generally, and the concept PAIN in particular.

Another problem is that the HOT view is committed to there being pains that do not feel any way, namely pains that do not have accompanying higher-order thoughts. On the face of it, this erroneously supposes that if a pain is unconscious – if, that is, it is a pain of which its subject is not conscious (and so not thinking about non-inferentially) – then it is a pain without any felt character. But surely pain is a feeling; and a feeling must have a felt character, even if it is a feeling of which its subject is not conscious (and in that sense, an unconscious feeling).

In conclusion, it is interesting to compare and contrast the case of fish with that of insects. Eisemann et al. (1984) comment in a review of biological evidence for pain in insects:

No example is known to us of an insect showing protective behavior towards injured parts, such as by limping after leg injury or declining to feed or mate because of general abdominal injuries. On the contrary, our experience has been that insects will continue with normal activities even after severe injury or removal of body parts. An insect walking with a crushed tarsus, for example, will continue applying it to the substrate with undiminished force. Among our other observations are those on a locust which continued to feed while itself being eaten by a mantis; aphids continuing to feed whilst being eaten by coccinellids; a tse-tse fly which flew in to feed although half-dissected; caterpillars which continue to feed whilst taccinid larvae bore into them; many insects which go about their normal life whilst being eaten by large internal parasitoids; and male mantids which continue to mate as they are eaten by their partners.

(p. 166)

Eisemann et al. (1984) also point out that insects do not respond to pain by ceasing to move or protecting injured parts in the way that mammals do. In general, they do not react to treatment that would undoubtedly cause severe pain in mammals. In these respects, insects are unlike fish.[3]

Notes

1 Well, almost no one. Carruthers (2000) says that consciousness goes with the capacity to make the appearance-reality distinction. On one reading of this claim (a cognitive one), his view has bad consequences for newborn babies!
2 There are reports from whalemen of sharks that they have split in two continuing to feed – likewise for sharks that have been disemboweled by other sharks attacking them. Apparently their fatal wounds do not cause them to feel pain.
3 The issue of insect pain is not quite as clear-cut as Eisemann et al. suggest. For more on this and on the question of animal consciousness generally, see Tye 2016.

References

Allen, C., and Bekoff, M. 1997 *Species of Mind: The Philosophy and Biology of Cognitive Ethology*. Cambridge, MA: MIT Press.

American Academy of Neurology. 1989 "Position of the American Academy of Neurology on certain aspects of the care and management of the persistent vegetative state patient," *Neurology* 39: 125–126.

Bateson, M., Desire, S., Gartside, S., and Wright, G. 2011 "Agitated honeybees exhibit pessimistic cognitive biases," *Current Biology* June 21; 21(12): 1070–1073.

Carruthers, P. 2000 *Phenomenal Consciousness: A Naturalistic Theory*. Cambridge: Cambridge University Press.

Dugas-Ford, J., Rowell, J., and Ragsdale, C. 2012 "Cell-type homologies and the origins of the neocortex," *Proceedings of the National Academy of Sciences* 109(42): 16974–16979.

Eisemann, C. H., Jorgensen, W. K., Merritt, D. J., Rice, M. J., Cribb, B. W., Webb, P. D., and Zalucki, M. P. 1984 "Do insects feel pain? A biological view," *Experientia* 40: 164–167.

Fields, H. 1999 "Pain: An unpleasant topic," *Pain Supplement* 6: S61–S69.

Grosenick, L., Clement, T., and Fernald, R. 2007 "Fish can infer social rank by observation alone," *Nature* 445: 429–432.

Ito, H., and Yamamoto, N. 2009 "Non-laminar cerebral cortex in teleost fish?" *Biological Letters* 5: 117–121.

Karten, K. 1997 "Evolutionary developmental biology meets the brain: The origins of mammalian cortex," *Proceedings of the National Academy of Sciences* 94, 2800–2804.

Karten, H. J., and Hodos, W. 1967 *A Stereotaxic Atlas of the Brain of the Pigeon (Columba livia)*. Baltimore: Johns Hopkins University Press.

Merker, B. 2007 "Consciousness without a cerebral cortex: A challenge for neuroscience and medicine," with commentaries, *The Behavioral and Brain Sciences* 30: 63–134

Newton, I. 1687 *Principia Mathematica*.

Rose, J. D. 2002 "The neurobehavioral nature of fishes and the question of awareness of pain," *Reviews in Fisheries Sciences* 10(1): 1–38.

Rosenthal, D. 1986 "Two concepts of consciousness," *Philosophical Studies* 49: 329–359.

Shea, N., and Heyes, C. 2010 "Metamemory as evidence of animal consciousness: The type that does the trick," *Biology and Philosophy* 25: 95–110.

Shewmon, A., Holmes, G., and Byrne, P. 1999 "Consciousness in congenitally decorticate children: 'Developmental Vegetative State' as self-fulfilling prophecy," *Developmental Medicine and Child Neurology* 41(6): 364–374.

Sneddon, L. U. 2003 "The evidence for pain in fish: The use of morphine as an analgesic," *Applied Animal Behaviour Science* 83(2): 153–162.

Sneddon, L. 2012 "Pain perception in fish: Evidence and implications for the use of fish," *Journal of Consciousness Studies* 18: 209–229.

Sneddon, L. U., Braithwaite, V. A., and Gentle, M. J. 2003 "Do fishes have nociceptors? Evidence for the evolution of a vertebrate sensory system," *Proceedings: Biological Sciences* 270: 1115–1121.

Tye, M. 2016 *Tense Bees and Shell-Shocked Crabs: Are Animals Conscious?* Oxford: Oxford University Press.

16

THE UNPLEASANTNESS OF PAIN FOR NONHUMAN ANIMALS

Adam Shriver

Introduction

Most people agree that, in general, pain is bad and should be avoided when the pain is not necessary for the achievement of some future benefit. Moreover, the badness of the pain seems to be directly related to the experience of pain; pains are bad, at least in part, because they feel bad. Yet for roughly the past fifty years, philosophers have been puzzled by reports of people who claimed that they were "feeling pain" but not "bothered by it." These reports are surprising because on one common interpretation, pain is essentially bothersome; one cannot have a pain without having an experience that is unpleasant or aversive in some way.

One well-supported explanation of these reports is that the experience of pain has at least two distinct components: a sensory component and an affective component (Melzack and Casey 1968). Many experiments have shown that these two dimensions can be influenced independently of one another. As such, we can view reports of feeling pain but not minding it as instances where the affective dimension of pain is selectively impaired, but the sensory dimension is operating normally.

In this essay, after reviewing the importance of understanding the affective dimension of pain, I will describe what is known about this dimension of pain in other species. Ultimately, I will argue, the main impediment to progress in understanding the unpleasantness of pain is the lack of a sufficiently detailed investigation of cases where humans report feeling pains without finding them unpleasant. In reviewing the literature on pain in animals, I do not intend to suggest that current invasive and/or painful research is justified; indeed, it may be the case that what we learn from such research is enough in itself to provide an indictment of certain research practices. However, I do think we should use the information we currently have to improve our understanding of how pain relates to important philosophical issues.

The unpleasantness of pain and why it matters for animal ethics

It is generally thought that intentionally causing pain to others is morally problematic, and most people extend this reasoning to our treatment of nonhuman animals. This is not to say that any action that causes pain is automatically wrong, but rather that pains considered by themselves are a bad thing and causing pain to others, without having some reason that outweighs the harm

176

caused by the pain, is therefore bad. For example, taking a dog to the vet to get a blood sample might cause some momentary pain, but because that pain is in the service of improving future quality of life, we can see that the overall action is good for the dog. So we can amend the above statement to the suggestion that most people would agree that causing *unnecessary* pains to others is morally wrong.

The idea that causing unnecessary pains is wrong has been at the heart of many debates about our treatment of animals. Critiques of factory farming and animal experimentation have referenced the pain caused to animals as primary reasons why those practices are wrong (Singer 1975, Regan 1983). And defenders of the practices typically do not say that causing pain doesn't matter, but rather suggest either that the pain is minimal or that the pains are balanced out by other considerations.

However, the reports of people who feel pains but are not bothered by them suggest that the situation is even more complicated. It is not *pain* that is always bad, but rather a specific component of the experience of pain: the unpleasantness of pain. Pains that are not unpleasant, or that are not bothersome, are not bad in the same way as the typical pains we are familiar with.

In what follows, I describe the relevance of the affective/sensory dissociation in pain for our treatment of animals. Before highlighting the intersection with philosophical issues, however, I have to say a little more about our current understanding of the different dimensions of painful experience.

The sensory dimension of pain is generally described as consisting of three elements: the, "quality, intensity, and spatio-temporal characteristics," of the pain sensation (Rainville et al. 1999, p. 159). When we experience a typical acute pain, we experience it as occurring in a particular part of our body and having certain temporal properties (for example, a "throbbing" pain rapidly fluctuates in intensity); this is the spatio-temporal aspect referred to by Rainville. Our experience also typically represents pains as being of a certain type: a "cutting pain" or a "burning pain" or a "pinching pain," for example. These different types of pains typically result from the activation of nerve fibers in the skin, called nociceptors, that respond to different forms of potentially damaging events, such as extreme temperatures, chemical substances, or tissue damage. The representation of these *types* of pain is the "quality" of the pain referenced in the quote above. Finally, pains vary in degrees of intensity. Some pains, of course, are stronger than others.

Somewhat surprisingly, however, these three sensory characteristics do not fully determine the immediate experienced unpleasantness of the pain. Under the right conditions, more intense pains can be less unpleasant, and less intense pains can be more unpleasant. If a person is expecting a pain, this can influence the perceived unpleasantness of a pain, even as the ratings of pain intensity stay the same (Sawamoto et al. 2000). Likewise, increased anxiety causes pains to feel more unpleasant even when the ratings of intensity stay the same (Ploghaus et al. 2001). Moreover, certain drugs appear to selectively influence the stated unpleasantness (Keats and Beecher 1950). And lesions to particular brain areas have resulted in patients who claim that they feel pains but no longer find the pains unpleasant (Foltz and White 1962, Grahek 2001, Aydede 2006). Indeed, the affective dimensions of pain can be manipulated independently of the sensory dimension, and two distinct activation patterns during brain imaging correspond to the different dimensions (Rainville et al. 1997, Rainville et al. 1999).

Because people's reports of pain intensity can diverge from their reports of unpleasantness, we should acknowledge that the two dimensions come apart. Nevertheless, there still are many questions remaining about the nature of unpleasantness. What role does unpleasantness, as opposed to other aspects of pain experience, play in our behavior? How was it useful from an evolutionary standpoint? Is there some other psychological capacity or behavioral indicator that could help us to understand what unpleasantness is actually doing?

Many pain researchers use the term "affective-motivational" to describe the pathway involved in unpleasantness, which implies that this pathway also underlies the motivational urge associated with pain. Some have suggested the unpleasantness of pain can be linked with the motivational force of pain; that is, if we find a pain unpleasant, we necessarily have some motivational urge to escape the pain. However, the science relevant to this claim is currently inconclusive, and thus it remains an open possibility that the affective and motivational aspects of pain are two separate components.

Beyond motivation, there are a host of other features that may or may not be correlated with the affective dimension of pain. Austen Clark has listed all of the following conceptually distinct variables as possible features linked to the affective dimension of pain: the desire to end the pain, the feeling of urgency to do something about it, the degree to which pain grabs one's attention, the extent to which pain alters one's preferences, the degree to which the reduction of pain can serve as a reward, and the degree to which the pain reduces the probability of future behaviors (2005, p. 185). All of these are potential correlates of pain's unpleasantness that could potentially be used in third-person assessments of suffering, and therefore could be important for determining which nonhuman animals have the capacity to experience the unpleasantness of pain.

Making this determination has a number of important ethical implications. Consider animal agriculture, where there are a large number of practices that are extremely morally problematic if, as the animals' behavior indicates, the animals involved are capable of suffering (see Rossi and Garner 2014 for a useful review). Undercover footage reveals that insufficient stunning prior to slaughter occurs frequently, leading to animals who are conscious as their throats are slit. Techniques such as the dehorning and branding of calves, the castration of boars, and the debeaking of chickens are frequently done without painkillers. Many animals are kept in cramped conditions where they are unable to engage in natural movements, which results in joint and bone damage. And animals are often fed extremely unnatural diets, which leads to digestive problems known to be extremely painful in humans. This is just a small sample of likely painful events in animal agriculture; but even from this limited set, it should be clear that if these animals feel the unpleasantness of pain in a manner similar to humans, it becomes extremely difficult to provide moral justification for an industrial agriculture system that is not necessary for human health or survival.

In the context of research on nonhuman animals, millions of animals in laboratory settings are reported to experience moderate to severe pain each year (Rowan 2012, p. 207). This includes many invasive procedures that fall under what is classified as "Category E" research in the United States, where animals known to be in distress are not given painkillers because it is believed they might interfere with the validity of the study's findings. Even in cases where animals are given painkillers, it is often standard practice to, for example, give primates post-surgical analgesia for a period of one to two days after a procedure that would call for several weeks of painkillers in humans (Balcombe 2014). It should be clear that in animal agriculture and animal research, as well as many other practices such as hunting, trapping, and the use of animals for entertainment, determining which animals have the capacity to suffer will have enormous moral significance. But how do we go about determining which animals are capable of suffering? Our ability to determine this will depend, at least in part, on our understanding of the neural mechanisms underlying suffering.

For example, fish scientist James Rose (2002) has suggested that the fact that fish lack the brain areas involved in mammalian pain affect excludes them from moral consideration. Rose put his arguments in terms of consciousness in general; however, the areas he cited as crucial were specifically those that are associated with unpleasantness in humans. Craig (2009) has suggested that the insula (a structure involved in the affective dimension of pain) integrates bodily information (including information about pain) into a conscious representation of the body, and argues that only humans and possibly great apes have the relevant brain structures to support conscious awareness. And Allen et al. (2005) and Shriver (2006) have noted that all mammals appear to have many of the relevant brain areas underlying the affective dimension of pain in humans. On the other end of the spectrum, Klein and Barron (2016) recently argued that insects possess the relevant neural hardware required for sentience. Clearly, a better understanding of pain's unpleasantness and the underlying neural activity will have extremely important implications for our moral obligations to other animals.

Searching for the unpleasantness of pain in other species

Since pain research on nonhuman animals has been a large target of research, one might hope that there would be a great deal of research to draw upon to learn about the unpleasantness of pain. Unfortunately, due to an emphasis on easily reproducible measurements, much of the research has focused on measurements that tell us very little about the affective dimension of pain. Several researchers (Vierck et al. 2008, Roughan et al. 2014, Gregory et al. 2013) have highlighted the fact that many preclinical studies involving animals rely on reflexive responses to pain controlled by neurons in the spinal cord rather than the brain, and as such have done a very poor job predicting the efficacy of various treatments on humans' experiences of pain, and particularly the affective dimension of pain.

Relatedly, many ethicists and advocates have referenced the fact that many animals, when encountering noxious stimulation, display a similar behavioral repertoire to humans', and infer from this fact that the animals are in pain. Though the observation of behavioral similarities combined with a principle of erring on the side of caution gives us strong reasons to treat animals as moral subjects, skeptics can object, and with some reason. Common examples of behavioral indicators of pain such as crying, moaning, wincing, and withdrawing from the source of the stimulation are not necessarily connected with the painful experience. For example, humans in vegetative states will sometimes cry out, withdraw, and/or exhibit facial contortions after noxious simulation (Laureys 2007), but these reactions are known to be reflexive. Similarly, many of the behavioral measures of pain in tests on animals, such as tail flicks and paw withdrawal, are known to be mediated by neurons in the spinal cord and don't require the involvement of the brain, which is typically involved in affective pain. If we can understand the mechanisms that explain pain behavior in the absence of affect, and if we have information about the processes in the brain that are involved in conscious pain processing, we can shift our attention away from those behaviors that do not require unpleasantness and towards other activity that may depend on the conscious experience of unpleasantness to try to determine the essential mechanisms of affective processing.

In humans, the two brain areas that are most consistently activated during a wide variety of pains in imaging scans are the anterior cingulate cortex (ACC) and the insula cortex (along with the adjacent parietal operculum, which appears to be functionally continuous with parts of the posterior insula). Single-unit recordings in humans performed during surgeries, which measure the activity of individual neurons, have demonstrated that the anterior cingulate contains neurons that selectively respond to painful stimuli but not other forms of somatosensory stimulation (Hutchison1999). EEG recordings have also found that the posterior insula responds to painful stimulation (Garcia-Larrea 2012), and direct stimulation of regions of the insula results in pain reactions in humans (Ostrowsky et al. 2002). Research has also shown that selectively enhancing or diminishing the unpleasantness of pain also enhances or diminishes activity in these areas (Rainville et al. 1997, 1999). Moreover, patients with lesions in the ACC or insula have reported feeling pains but no longer being bothered by them (Foltz and White 1962, Berthier et al. 1988). Thus, there is good prima facie evidence that both of these regions play a role in the unpleasantness of pain, or at least of some pains.

It should be noted that for the ACC and for the insula, there are complications with any claims that the area is a "center of pain's unpleasantness." For one thing, both areas are involved in a huge number of other processes and emotions, and there are a number of competing hypotheses about what their precise role in cognition is. This worry can be diminished somewhat as the localization claims are made a bit more precise; for example "sadness" is often suggested to be localized in the ACC, but actually tends to occur in an area in front of and below (anterior and inferior in neuroscience speak) the area involved in pain (Vogt 2005). Similarly, the pain processing area of the insula can be kept distinct from other areas of the insula, including those that process gustatory information (Nieuwenhuys 2011). Nevertheless, at the level of precision detectable by our current best brain-imaging techniques, there are no voxels of neural tissue exclusively activated by pain or by unpleasantness.

Since there is good evidence that parts of the insula and ACC are playing some important role related to the unpleasantness of pain in humans, how could it be assessed whether these brain areas, or analogous areas, are playing a similar role in other animals? Given the problem of other minds (Hyslop 2016) and the specific difficulties of assessing mental states in nonlinguistic animals, there is no perfect answer to this question. However, by combining behavioral measures with knowledge of neural similarities and responsiveness to known human analgesics, we can generate plausible answers.

A converging set of evidence has suggested that the anterior cingulate cortex is involved in some affective aspects of pain perception in other mammals. As noted above, studies relying on spinally mediated behaviors have tended to be very poor predictors of the clinical efficacy of pain drugs. However, several authors have presented data arguing that a more successful method can be used based on measurements of escape and avoidance.

Sufka (1994) developed one of the earliest avoidance-based operant conditioning models of the effectiveness of analgesics. On his model, animals exposed to repeated noxious stimuli are confined to one location while under the influence of a particular drug and are confined to a different area, still exposed to the same noxious stimulation, while not under the influence of the drug. The animals are then offered a series of choices between the two locations, and the outcomes of the choices are measured. The rationale is that if animals experience more pain when not under the influence of the analgesic, they will form a negative association with the location, and as such will be more likely to choose the location paired with drugs that are effective analgesics than the other location. Of course, one worry is that because many analgesics also have positive reward properties independent of any pain relief, these tests might simply be measuring the rewarding effects of the drugs, rather than pain relief. However, Sufka later cites a number of studies demonstrating that the conditioned place-aversion effects of pain relief can be dissociated from the place preference caused by the reward value of the drugs, suggesting that a separate mechanism is involved in learning to avoid aversive stimuli (Roughan et al. 2014).

The efficacy of conditioned place preference tasks, however, depends on a crucial assumption, namely that there is a link between the unpleasantness of pain and learning to avoid the pain in the future. Unquestionably, these are conceptually distinct from one another, whether or not they are reliably correlated. As such, it is difficult to evaluate how successful this approach is at indicating the existence of the unpleasantness of pain in other animals.

For this reason, several authors have expanded upon the conditioned place-preference task by also adding an escape component that more closely captures the immediate feeling of unpleasantness (as opposed to a future motivation to avoid cues that were previously paired with noxious stimuli). On these models (Vierk et al. 2008, Morgan et al. 2008, Gregory et al. 2013), animals are offered an opportunity to escape from a potentially noxious environment by moving to a new location. In contrast to reflexive behaviors such as crying out, tail flicks, immediate paw withdrawal, etc., the assumption in these studies is that the animal has to recognize the negative stimulus and then use this information to make a decision to move to a new location. Again, of course, this behavior does not prove the existence of unpleasantness or even conscious pain, since it's possible that the animals have unconscious mechanisms for motivating behavior (even complicated behavior) away from threatening features of the environment.

Interestingly, however, the effects of opiates and targeted lesions in the ACC on escape and conditioned place preference in nonhuman mammals mirror the dissociation observed in humans. Lesioning the anterior cingulate results in mice who still withdraw from painful stimuli, but no longer choose to escape from areas where the pain should be greater nor learn to avoid these areas (LaGraize et al. 2004). Similarly, giving the rats opioids produces the same dissociation (LaGraize et al. 2006). Thus, there's at least a prima facie argument by analogy that in most mammals, the affective pain pathways are operating very similarly to how they operate in humans, since damage and activation of similar brain regions results in similar behavioral profiles (Shriver 2006).

Connecting nonhuman and human studies of pain

Nevertheless, important questions remain. In particular, it's not clear what brain activity is really necessary for pain affect. One interpretation of the available data is that activity in the network formed by the cingulate and insula, or perhaps one of those brain areas individually, appears to mediate the unpleasantness of pain. One could then claim that only animals who have these brain areas feel the unpleasantness of pain in a manner similar to humans. This, however, would lead to the counterintuitive result that only mammals truly have the affective component of pain, since these brain areas have not been found in other species.

Alternatively, one might instead suggest that there are analogous areas that operate in a similar enough manner to the cingulate and/or insula in other species to generate unpleasantness (Shriver 2016). On this interpretation, the human cingulate and insula have specialized to perform additional operations in humans, but still play a role in the experience of pain that is played by other brain regions in other species. This is plausible, since it appears the insula involves a specialization of pain-perception processes that also exist in a number of other species (Garcia-Larrea 2012, Nieuwenhuys 2011). Moreover, many other species, including birds, fish, reptiles, and possibly even crabs, have been shown to demonstrate conditioned place-preference behaviors.

Nevertheless, we are faced with the problem that neither any one particular measure of behavior, including conditioned place-preference tasks, nor the involvement of any particular brain region, such as the insula, has been shown to reliably indicate the presence or absence of the affective dimension of pain. Only by learning more about the specific way neural activity underlies behaviors associated with pain affect can we hope to abstract the processes involved in causing pain's unpleasantness. And this, in turn, will require far more research aimed at conceptually understanding the nature of pain affect in humans. For example, though there have been a number of reports of people who "feel pain but don't mind it," most notably in cases of pain asymbolia, there has ultimately been very little investigation of what the full behavioral profile of such patients is, and how reliably this profile is linked to damage of specific brain areas. If we could discover that pain affect, but not sensory pain, was necessarily linked to a particular type of learning, or to a certain form of attentional process, this could give us a better target for understanding what precisely needs to be sought out in other species. In particular, if it was demonstrated clearly in humans that the unpleasantness of pain is reliably correlated to escape impulses or conditioning, this would make an important difference in how confidently we could interpret the results from other mammals.

It is only after we have detailed knowledge of the correlations that the real questions of philosophy of mind come in. For example, let's say we discover that self-reports of unpleasantness in humans turn out to be perfectly correlated with a particular type of neural activity and with a particular behavioral profile. Even then, we can question how we should view the central processes involved. Does the particular type of neuron involved in the activity matter, or does it only matter that certain information was transmitted? Can aspects of the phenomenal character be explained by describing the activity of the neurons, or are we left with only a correlation that is not fully understood? These questions, I believe, can only be fully addressed *after* a detailed scientific investigation that narrows down the true nature of unpleasantness by precisely determining the neural and behavioral features that reliably correlate with human reports of unpleasantness.

As such, though I think philosophers can usefully discuss these issues in the philosophy of mind and in ethics, the conclusions that can be reached are currently limited by the absence of crucial information from the sciences. My belief is that philosophers' most useful role in this context at the present, aside from producing arguments about how we ought to interpret limited and uncertain information, is to help think of experiments conceptually clarifying the nature of pain's unpleasantness, with an eye towards addressing issues of pressing philosophical and social significance.

I envision philosophers and scientists working together as follows: philosophers can be helpful in keeping the focus on important theoretical questions about the nature of experience and the nature of (dis)value, and on how the findings of empirical research can inform a number of practical ethics questions. However, the theorizing of philosophers is limited in at least two significant ways that require contributions from the sciences. First, we don't yet know how important psychological concepts are related to one another, and how they should best be "lumped" and "split." For example: is the unpleasantness of pain always accompanied by a motivational signal, or by some other relevant psychological feature? And second, we don't know how the absence of various features would influence people's assessments of their own pains: if we were to selectively inhibit the motivational system of a person, how would that influence her interpretation of pain? Thus, I see progress in understanding the unpleasantness of pain as depending upon an ongoing conversation between cognitive scientists and philosophers.

Conclusion

Understanding pain is important for a number of philosophical projects. And the unpleasantness of pain is of particular importance. Though the science of pain has helped us to learn quite a bit about the unpleasant dimension of pain, we still lack crucial information needed to provide complete answers to questions in value theory, applied ethics, and the philosophy of mind.

Given these limitations, the most important role philosophers can be playing is to be collaborating with scientists to help nudge research towards answering some of these questions. Neither a pain science devoted exclusively to chasing clinically relevant results nor philosophers working primarily from intuitions can answer the most important questions about pain on their own. It is only through a collaboration that progress on the most important issues surrounding the unpleasantness of pain will occur.[1]

Note

1 Thanks to David Bain, Michael Brady, Jennifer Corns, Kristin Andrews, and audiences at the University of Glasgow, York University, the University of Michigan-Flint, Penn State University, and the University of Pennsylvania for helpful comments on this essay.

Further reading

See Colin Allen's "Animal Pain" (2004); Chapter 5 of Gary Varner's *Personhood, Ethics, and Animal Cognition* (2012); and Victoria Braithwaite's *Do Fish Feel Pain* (2010) for interesting discussions of these issues.

References

Allen, C. (2004). Animal pain. *Nous, 38*(4), 617–643.

Allen, C., Fuchs, P., Shriver, A., and Wilson, H. (2005). Deciphering Animal Pain. In M. Aydede (ed.), *Pain: New Essays on the Nature of Pain and the Methodology of Its Study* (pp. 352–366). Cambridge, MA: MIT Press.

Aydede M. (2006) *Pain: New Essays on Its Nature and the Methodology of Its Study.* Cambridge, MA: MIT Press.

Balcombe, J. (2014). *White Paper: A Longitudinal View of Primate Life in Two American Laboratories.* http://animalstudiesrepository.org/acwp_arte/5/

Berthier, M., Starkstein, S., and Leiguarda, R. (1988). Asymbolia for pain: A sensory-limbic disconnection syndrome. *Annals of Neurology, 24,* 41–49. www.ncbi.nlm.nih.gov/pubmed/3415199

Braithwaite, V. (2010). *Do Fish Feel Pain.* New York: Oxford University Press.

Clark, A. (2005). Painfulness Is Not a Quale. In Aydede (ed.), *Pain: New Essays on Its Nature and the Methodology of Its Study.* (pp. 177–198). Cambridge, MA: MIT Press.

Craig, A. D. (2009). How do you feel-now? The anterior insula and human awareness. *Nature Reviews Neuroscience, 10,* 59–70.

Foltz, E. L., and White, L. E. (1962). Pain "relief" by frontal cingulotomy. *Journal of Neurosurgery, 19,* 89–100.

Garcia-Larrea, L. (2012). The posterior insular-opercular region and the search of a primary cortex for pain. *Neurophysiologie Clinique, 42*(5), 299–313.

Grahek, N. (2001). *Feeling Pain and Being in Pain.* Cambridge, MA: MIT Press.

Gregory, N. S., Harris, A. L., Robinson, C. R., Dougherty, P. M., Fuchs, P. N., and Sluka, K. A. (2013). An overview of animal models of pain: Disease models and outcome measures. *The Journal of Pain, 14*(11), 1255–1269.

Hyslop, A. (2016). Other Minds. In Edward N. Zalta (ed.), *The Stanford Encyclopedia of Philosophy* (Spring 2016 Edition). http://plato.stanford.edu/archives/spr2016/entries/other-minds/

Keats, A., and Beecher, H. (1950). Pain relief with hypnotic doses of barbiturates and a hypothesis. *Journal of Pharmacology and Experimental Therapeutics, 100*(1), 1–13.

Klein, C., and Barron, A. B. (2016). Insects have the capacity for subjective experience. *Animal Sentience,*100. http://animalstudiesrepository.org/animsent/vol1/iss9/1/

LaGraize, S., Borzan, J., Peng, Y. B., and Fuchs, P. (2006). Selective regulation of pain affect following activation of the opioid anterior cingulate cortex system. *Experimental Neurology, 197,* 22–30.

LaGraize, S., Labuda, C., Rutledge, R., Jackson, R., and Fuchs, P. (2004). Differential effect of anterior cingulated cortex lesion on mechanical hypersensitivity and escape/avoidance behavior in an animal model of neuropathic pain. *Experimental Neurology, 188,* 139–148, 740.

Laureys, S. (2007). Eyes open, brain shut. *Scientific American, 296,* 84–9.

Melzack, R. and Casey, K. L. (1968). Sensory, Motivational, and Central Control Determinants of Pain: A New Conceptual Model. In D. Kenshalo (ed.), *The Skin Sense* (pp. 223–243). Springfield, IL: Thomas.

Morgan, D., Carter, C. S., DuPree, J. P., Yezierski, R. P., and Vierck Jr, C. J. (2008). Evaluation of prescription opioids using operant-based pain measures in rats. *Experimental and Clinical Osychopharmacology, 16*(5), 367.

Nieuwenhuys, R. (2011). The insular cortex: A review. *Progress in Brain Research, 195,* 123–163.

Ostrowsky, K., Magnin, M., Ryvlin, P., Isnard, J., Guenot, M., and Mauguière, F. (2002). Representation of pain and somatic sensation in the human insula: A study of responses to direct electrical cortical stimulation. *Cerebral Cortex, 12*(4), 376–385.

Ploghaus, A., Narain, C., Beckmann, C. F., Clare, S., Bantick, S., Wise, R., Matthews, P. M., Rawlins, J. N., and Tracey, I. (2001). Exacerbation of pain by anxiety is associated with activity in a hippocampal network. *The Journal of Neuroscience, 21*(24), 9896–9903.

Rainville, P., Carrier, B., Hofbauer, R. K., Bushnell, M. C., and Duncan, G. H. (1999). Dissociation of sensory and affective dimensions of pain using hypnotic modulation. *Pain, 82,* 159–171.

Rainville, P., Duncan, G. H., Price, D. D., Carrier, B., and Bushnell, M. C. (1997). Pain affect encoded in human anterior cingulate but not somatosensory cortex. *Science, 277,* 968–971.

Regan, T. (1983). *The Case For Animal Rights.* Berkeley: University of California Press.

Rose, J. D. (2002). The neurobehavioral nature of fishes and the question of awareness and pain. *Reviews in Fisheries Science, 10,* 1–38.

Rossi, J., and Garner, S. (2014). Industrial farm animal production: A comprehensive moral critique. *Journal of Agricultural and Environmental Ethics, 27,* 479–522.

Roughan, J. V., Coulter, C. A., Flecknell, P. A., Thomas, H. D., and Sufka, K. J. (2014). The conditioned place preference test for assessing welfare consequences and potential refinements in a mouse bladder cancer model. *PLoS ONE, 9*(8), e103362. doi:10.1371/journal.pone.0103362

Rowan, A. (2012). Debating the Value of Animal Research. In J. Garrett (ed.), *The Ethics of Animal Research: Exploring the Controversy.* Cambridge, MA: MIT Press.

Sawamoto, N., Honda, M., Okada, T., Hanakawa, T., Kanda, M., Fukuyama, H., Konishi, J., and Shibasaki, H. (2000). Expectation of pain enhances responses to nonpainful somatosensory stimulation in the anterior cingulate cortex and parietal operculum/posterior insula: An event-related functional magnetic resonance imaging study. *The Journal of Neuroscience, 20*(19), 7438–7448.

Shriver, A. (2006). Minding mammals. *Philosophical Psychology, 19,* 433–442.

Shriver, A. (2016). Cortex necessary for pain – but not in sense that matters. *Animal Sentience* 2016.034. Shriver Commentary on Key on Fish Pain.

Singer, P. (1975). *Animal Liberation.* New York: Random House.

Sufka, K. J. (1994). Conditioned place preference paradigm: A novel approach for analgesic drug assessment against chronic pain. *Pain, 58,* 355–366.

Varner, G. (2012). *Personhood, Ethics, and Animal Cognition: Situating Animals in Hare's Two Level Utilitarianism.* New York: Oxford University Press.

Vierck, C. J., Hansson, P. T., and Yezierski, R. P. (2008). Clinical and pre-clinical pain assessment: Are we measuring the same thing? *Pain, 135,* 7–10.

Vogt, B. (2005). Pain and emotion interactions in subregions of the cingulate gyrus. *Nature Reviews Neuroscience, 6*(7), 533–544.

17

ATTENTION, WORKING MEMORY, AND ANIMAL CONSCIOUSNESS

Jesse Prinz

Introducing the AIR theory

In order to decide whether nonhuman animals are conscious, it is helpful to begin with an empirically motivated account of the precise conditions under which consciousness arises in human beings. Reliance on behavior alone can lead to shaky inferences. Many animals behave very differently from humans, and behaviors associated with consciousness can be carried out without a central nervous system; for example, an excised octopus leg will avoid noxious stimuli (Alupay et al., 2014), and scratching behavior in sea turtles can be controlled by the spine (Stein, et al. 1995). In humans, much of what can be done consciously can also be done unconsciously (e.g., Prinz, 2017). Confidence about other animals will increase if we can identify mechanisms that match the correlates of consciousness in us. Here I will briefly summarize an account of those mechanisms, defended at great length elsewhere, and I will suggest that a surprising number of taxa may satisfy its fairly demanding conditions.

The account of consciousness that I favor is called the AIR theory, which stands for Attended Intermediate-Level Representations (Prinz, 2012). Drawing on a large body of empirical evidence, the theory makes two main claims. First, consciousness arises only at an intermediate-level of abstraction in hierarchical sensory systems. The senses move from very local feature detectors, corresponding to cellular transduction mechanisms, on up to categorical representations that are invariant across a wide range of stimulus conditions; in human beings, all consciousness seems to arise between these extremes. Second, consciousness seems to arise when and only when sensory states are modulated by attention. There have been some empirical challenges to this later claim, but I think they are largely terminological. "Attention" can refer to several different processes. In the AIR theory, it refers to just one: a change in processing that allows information in sensory systems to activate working memory. In a slogan: consciousness is the categorical basis of availability to working memory. The AIR theory also advances a hypothesis about this categorical basis, stated in neurocomputational terms: cellular activity in intermediate-level sensory systems becomes available to working memory when and only when assemblies of sensory neurons fire in phase-synched oscillations in the gamma frequency (about 25–100 Hz).

Each component of the AIR theory has been defended on its own by others. There are those who locate consciousness in the intermediate level (Jackendoff, 1987), those who identify consciousness with attention (Mack and Rock, 1998), those who relate consciousness to working-memory access (Baars, 2002), and those who suggest that gamma oscillations are the neural correlates of consciousness (Singer and Gray, 1995; Crick and Koch, 1990; Engel et al., 1999; Gaillard et al., 2009). The AIR theory integrates all of these proposals. It is therefore a synthesis of the theories that enjoy most empirical support. If it can be shown that a nonhuman animal satisfies all of these conditions, that would be powerful evidence for the attribution of consciousness, since such a creature would satisfy a number of different theories. Of course, there might be creatures that satisfy some of these conditions and not others. Here, the AIR theory would deliver a negative verdict. There could also be creatures that have mechanisms that are similar, but not identical to those specified in the AIR theory; for example, different oscillation frequencies underlying working-memory access. Such cases would be very difficult to settle empirically, unless future work can establish such variation in human correlates of consciousness. One might worry, then, that the AIR theory is too stringent or too difficult to apply to creatures very different from us. It turns out, however, that a surprising number of taxa satisfy the conditions of the AIR theory. Therefore, even if we make the conservative assumption that consciousness requires neurofunctional correlates like those found in us, a strong case can be made for the conclusion that consciousness is widespread in nature.

Mechanisms of consciousness in nonhuman taxa

With the AIR theory of consciousness in hand, we can look at evidence for consciousness in nonhuman animals. In this brief review, I will try to indicate that indicators of consciousness have been measured in a wide range of taxa. I will not attempt to cover the biological work exhaustively, and I will rely on some folk categories (such as fish) that include much more diversity than represented here. Still, a modest sample will reveal that evidence for consciousness is impressive. Though much empirical work remains to be done, the available evidence suggests that consciousness may be more widespread than many people would be antecedently disposed to believe. I will begin with some brief remarks on the intermediate-level hypothesis, and then I will turn in greater detail to attention and working memory.

The intermediate level: knowns and unknowns

I am not aware of any research that attempts to locate consciousness at the intermediate level of sensory processing in nonhuman animals. That said, human visual neuroscience often uses animal models (cats were used in Hubel and Wiesel's discovery of edge detectors, and macaques have been sacrificed in countless studies of visual processing, including those that led to Weiskrantz's discovery of blindsight). There are many homologies between mammalian brains. All mammals have a laminar neocortex and hierarchically organized sensory areas. Mammals also face the same challenge as humans when it comes to perception: converting local cells at the sensory periphery into representations of complex properties and objects. This gives some reason for thinking that mammals, at least, have brain organization capable of supporting intermediate-level sensory representations. There is even evidence in monkeys that intermediate-level vision is the first and primary locus of attention modulation (Mehta et al., 2000). This does not prove that the intermediate level is the locus of consciousness in mammals, but it is certainly suggestive that there is a sensory hierarchy that interacts with attention in ways that parallel observations in humans.

What if we move beyond mammals? A surprising range of taxa show evidence for hierarchically organized senses. This is true of cephalopods, birds, and insects. Feinberg and Mallat (2016: 176: Table 9.2) provide what may be the most complete review of this issue in the literature. They argue that multi-level hierarchies can be found in the sensory systems of most multi–cellular taxa. Exceptions include gastropods, such as snails, as well as flatworms, round-worms, and other simple protozomes. Feiberg and Mallat suggest that their hierarchies may be too simple to support consciousness (p. 187).

The picture that emerges from this work is consistent with the conjecture that animals with greater sensory complexity than snails might perceive the world consciously. In what follows, I will restrict myself to these more complex creatures and I will assume they meet the basic condition of organization within their sensory system. This assumption must be treated as both speculative and tentative. For while sensory hierarchies abound, they differ in a variety of ways. Whether these differences make a difference is an open empirical question.

To illustrate, consider some of the variety in mammals (Northcutt and Kaas, 1995). Despite widespread homology, there are also interesting differences. For example, one of the layers in squirrel visual pathways has three sublayers, and these seem to have evolved independently from sibling species. Similarly, cats and monkeys both have layers in their lateral geniculate nuclei (a hub for sensory processing), but these appear to have evolved independently. There are variations in complexity as well. Rodents have five to eight visual areas, whereas we have dozens.

There are even differences among primates. Primates have many subregions in their visual pathways, but they differ in number across species (20–40), and not all are homologous. Functional differences in visual systems of humans and monkeys have been observed using neuroimaging (Orban et al., 2004), and there are also structural differences distinguishing humans and great apes (Preuss, 2007). We simply don't know whether these differences make a difference with respect to consciousness.

Attention and working memory in nonhuman taxa

Mammals

Let's turn now from the intermediate level to attention and working memory. Here, evidence is clearer. Beginning with mammals, there is overwhelming behavioral evidence for both attention and working memory, and there is also some evidence implicating related brain systems.

Mammalian attention shows a broadly consistent functional profile. When an object of interest is presented to a mammal, it will process it in ways that indicate enhanced encoding. In monkeys, attention is known to increase the sensitivity of intermediate-level visual neurons and to reshape receptive field sizes. Monkey attention also has a similar time course as measured by "inhibition of return," which is interpreted as the rate of endogenous attentional resetting in visual search tasks (Torbaghan et al., 2012). Inhibition of return has not been observed in rats (Wagner et al., 2014), but rats' parietal cortex is known to regulate attention, much as it does in humans (Bucci, 2012). Parietal cortex also gates activity to frontal working-memory structures in monkeys and rats. Such findings indicate similar circuits of attention across mammals.

Mammals also show similar capacities for working memory. All mammals can retain information for brief intervals, after a stimulus has been removed. This is frequently measured by delayed match-to-sample tasks. After a stimulus is removed, an animal must select it from options. The delay period between cue and test provides a measure of working-memory duration. Lind et al. (2015) report similar durations for chimpanzees, monkeys, dolphins, rats, and other mammals. Primates do not stand out here from other mammals (p. 55). In direct comparisons between monkeys and humans, our species shows stronger working-memory performance, as we mature, but monkey performance rivals human four-year-olds (Chelonis et al., 2014).

Anatomically, working memory is associated with prefrontal cortex in both rats (Kesner et al., 1996) and monkeys (Goldman-Rakic, 1990). Homologies are close enough that animal research on working memory is often conducted to draw conclusions about humans. That said, there are some differences in prefrontal areas that should be taken into account. Croxson et al. (2005) report a number of differences in the connectional anatomy of human and macaque prefrontal cortex, though they note similarities in connections to parietal areas that have been implicated in working memory. Pruess (1995) reports that rats lack an anatomical homologue of dorsolateral prefrontal cortex, which is a locus of visual working memory in humans, but others have shown that rats have frontal brain areas that function in analogous ways (Birrell and Brown, 2000; Dalley et al., 2004).

In addition, there is evidence that gamma-band oscillations contribute to attention in mammalian species. This is well demonstrated using cellular recordings in monkeys (Fries et al., 2001). Gamma has also been associated with visual stimulus presentation in mice (Nase et al., 2003).

Despite some cross-species differences mentioned here, the overall picture suggests that the psychological and neural correlates of human consciousness can be found in other mammals. If the AIR theory is right, I think we can be relatively confident about attribution in these cases.

Birds

Let's move now to animals whose brains are quite different from our own. I will begin with birds. Mammalian brains have many parts with no homologues in the brains of birds, but there are functional similarities that have emerged through convergent evolution. Therefore, they are a good test case for the applicability of AIR to creatures that differ from us anatomically and evolutionarily.

Bird working memory has been studied using some of the same tasks that are used in mammals, including delayed matching to samples. This task has been tested in a number of species, including various jays, crows, chickadees, chickens, pigeons, and juncos. Performance measures favorably to mammals, with similar psychometric profiles (Lind et al., 2015). There is also evidence for a similar anatomic implementation. Milmine et al. (2008) trained pigeons on a selective forgetting version of the delayed match-to-sample task. To succeed, the birds needed to retain a memory of a previous cue during a delay period. In this interval, the researchers measured activity in the nidopallium caudolaterale, a structure that has been called the avian prefrontal cortex, because it is a highly integrative area implicated in executive functions. They found evidence for temporary memory encoding, akin to what has been observed in mammals. Similar results are reported by Rose and Colombo (2005). They find that delay-period activity in the nidopallium caudolaterale is present on experimental trials when pigeons must hold information in working memory, and absent on trials where retention is not called for.

Attention has been studied in birds in a variety of different ways. The most impressive results adapt a paradigm that is frequently used in human and monkey research. Sridharan et al. (2014a) presented chickens with a spatial cue followed by a target. Target detection improved with cueing, the effect of distractors reduced, response times shortened, and confidence increased (as measured by choice behavior). Birds do not have a parietal cortex for controlling attention, but they do have a homologue of the mammalian superior colliculus, which is a subcortical structure that can control attention. This structure is called the optic tectum. Research in pigeons suggests that it controls attention (Marín et al., 2005). Strikingly, it appears to do so by modulating gamma activity (Neuenschwander et al., 1996; Sridharan et al., 2014b).

Reptiles and amphibians

Turning to (nonavian) reptiles and amphibians, evidence is both harder to come by and harder to interpret. Most standard tests for working memory and attention have not been applied to frogs, lizards, snakes, toads, or turtles, much less crocodiles. There is, however, some research that lends itself to speculative inference. It should be noted at the outset that although the categories of reptiles and amphibians are philogenetically close, there may be significant psychological differences between them. Cabanac et al. (2009) argue that reptiles show a greater capacity for play and reward learning, and they take this to suggest that they are more likely than amphibians to be conscious. I share this assessment, for slightly different reasons, but I also think there are some grounds for doubting consciousness in both classes of animals.

Evidence for attention in reptiles and amphibians is inconclusive. There are various findings that indicate selective *orienting* responses. For example, Schwartz and Gerhardt (1989) presented green tree frogs with aggression calls set against a background of noise. They find that the frogs were able to detect the calls and orient towards them. They compare this behavior to the cocktail party effect, where we hear our own names against the clatter of a crowded room. Strictly speaking, however, they show only that frogs orient towards a meaningful stimulus, not that they attend. In primates, orienting and attending are correlated by dissociable responses. Orienting is a matter of changing bodily position to improve stimulus processing, whereas attention is a change in processing itself. For example, when we shift gaze direction, that is an orienting response, but we can look one way while attending the other way. Orienting may predate attending phylogenetically, so results like this do not decisively establish attention in frogs. Similarly, there are studies that use increased tongue flicking and postural changes in lizards as an indicator of attention (e.g., Greenberg, 2002), but these behaviors constitute orienting, rather than attending, since they are ways to more effectively sample the environment, rather than changes in how a sample, once perceived, gets processed. More direct measures of attention would be helpful.

Herpetological research on working memory also tends to be somewhat indirect. For example, Wilkinson et al. (2007) investigate tortoise performance in radial mazes, and mention that success depends on something akin to working memory, since information about successful routes must be retained. But success could also reflect another kind of short-term (or even long-term) memory. Amphibians are less successful than reptiles in radial mazes, which may indicate a lack of working memory, but more research is needed to confirm this conclusion (Bilbo et al., 2000).

There is evidence that reptiles' and amphibians' brains make use of synchronized oscillations in perception. Prechtl (1994) reports neural synchrony in the turtle visual system, averaging around 20 Hz, and Hall and Delaney (2001) report synchrony between 7 and 12 Hz in the frog olfactory bulb. Notice that these oscillations are appreciably slower than gamma. In fact, gamma reduces during visual perception in turtles. This indicates that the temporal neurodynamics of perception differs from what has been found in mammals and birds.

It is difficult to deliver a decisive verdict about reptiles and amphibians, given findings such as these. It may be that their information-processing systems are similar to ours in certain respects, but also different in ways that reduce confidence when attributing consciousness. Without a fixed metric for similarity, and with a need for more research, a decisive conclusion would be premature, but I am tentatively inclined to say that we lack solid grounds for believing that reptiles and amphibians have the psychological and neural processes required for consciousness.

Fish

Let's move on to fish. It must first be stressed that this folk category is highly heterogeneous, so generalization may be impossible (Allen, 2013). With that caveat, I think we can say that there is intriguing but inconsistent and incomplete evidence regarding consciousness in various species.

There is some indirect evidence for attention in fish. For example, Piffer et al. (2012) show that guppies can differentiate small quantities. This indicates attention, they argue, since some models of such numerical behavior in mammals make reference to attention; the limits in competence with exact numerosities is said to correspond to the capacity of multi-object attention (Hyde and Wood, 2011). In another study, Jun et al. (2016) argue for attention in electric fish. They investigate active sensing and novelty responses in a dark environment, and conclude that the fish are showing signs of selection and intensive processing, which are signature features of attention. On its own, active sensing behavior might just indicate orienting, but the presence of novelty response and evidence of learning indicates that something more may be going on here. Perhaps the fish are attending and information is being retained in working memory to guide ongoing behavior.

There have been various efforts to investigate working memory in fish more directly. In one unsuccessful effort, Newport et al. (2014) administered a delayed match-to-sample task to archerfish. This species could not learn the task. Other species may work differently. For example, Guttridge and Brown (2014) show that Port Jackson sharks are susceptible to trace conditioning. In this paradigm, there is a 10-second delay between the unconditioned and conditioned stimuli, indicating brief retention in memory.

In addition, there is intriguing evidence for neural synchrony. For example, Friedrich et al. (2004) recorded synchronous gamma-band oscillations in zebrafish during an odor discrimination task. In another study, Ramcharitar et al. (2006) investigated the "jamming avoiding response" (JAR) in electric fish. JAR is used to block out electric signals from conspecifics that might prevent a fish from obtaining accurate sensory information. As the authors point out, JAR is, in that sense, like a filter for attention. They find that JAR is associated with gamma-band synchronization.

The fish findings reviewed here are intended to illustrate lines of research that indicate that some kinds of fish may have the kinds of psychological and neurophysiological resources posited by the AIR theory of consciousness. The evidence is far from conclusive, but sufficient, I hope, to suggest that we cannot rule out consciousness in fish.

Cephalopods

Sticking with sea creatures, I want to turn to cephalopods – the class that includes squids, cuttlefish, and octopuses. Some of the animals, especially octopuses, are known for their impressive cognitive abilities, such as strategic hunting, but what shall we say about their consciousness?

Evidence that bears on the AIR theory is hard to come by. There is a lot of research on orienting responses in cephalopods, but little that tries to differentiate orienting and attending. For example, when cuttlefish see a prey animal, they change gaze direction toward it, erect their first pair of harms, and alter their body pattern. Hanlon and Messenger (1996: 51) call this attention, but it is an orienting task. There are not, to my knowledge, studies that use methods that are common in mammal attention research, such as tests of discrimination accuracy in cued locations (these tests are most convincing when they control for orienting, which may be difficult with cephalopods). More suggestive are studies indicating selection processes. For example, Alves et al. (2007) trained cuttlefish to navigate using different spatial cues. They found that the animals could flexibly adapt to new cues and choose between cues when more than one was present, using cue salience and other factors. This may be explained by selective attention, but it could also be achieved by learned associations between cues and motor planning centers.

This brings us to the issue of working memory. To my knowledge, cephalopods have not been shown to succeed at standard tests such as delayed match-to-sample or trace conditioning. They do show the ability to learn in mazes, but the learning lasts for days, suggesting that they may not require working memory for this. Admittedly, maze performance requires a brief store of where the animal has been. Mather (1991) argues that this requires working memory, but this can be achieved using a specialized spatial memory that operates independently of working memory, as with the hippocampal place system in rodents. Graindorge et al. (2006) has obtained evidence based on lesion studies that the vertical lobe in the cephalopod brain works similarly to the hippocampus.

There is other evidence for brief memory in cephalopods. For example, Dickel et al. (1998) measure cuttlefish capacity to remember that prey are inedible when trapped in a glass tube. This is true just for the duration of the task, so it does not require long-term memory. The effect does last many minutes after training, however, so it is not necessarily evidence for working memory.

Mather (2008) argues that octopuses have working memory. She points out that the animals do no react immediately to prey, but rather engage in strategic planning once prey are identified. They also show flexibility, learning multiple responses and cues and choosing between them. This suggests that sensory information is passed on to brief storage for executive processing. On the whole, I find such evidence convincing, but more direct tests would be welcome.

What about gamma in cephalopods? Here, evidence is scant, but there are studies indicating that synchronized neural activity is used by the octopus nervous system and that such synchrony is sometimes in the gamma range (Bullock and Budelmann, 1991). There is no evidence as yet that gamma synchrony is linked to attention, but it does seem to reflect transient states in these animals, rather than standing waveforms, which indicates that it could serve such a function.

Putting this altogether, I think we can conclude that cephalopods may indeed have the necessary substrates for consciousness, though further investigation is needed. The mere possibility is intriguing, given how different they are from mammals. As with birds, cephalopods could establish that the mechanisms of consciousness can emerge through convergent evolution.

Insects

Let's turn, finally, to insects. Here, again, there is much variety, but also impressive similarities across taxa, and impressive signs of conservation, linking insects to each other, and to many more remotely related species, spanning the range from tardigrades to humans.

In recent years, there has been a flurry of impressive work on insect attention (see de Bivort and van Swinderen, 2016, for a review). Much of it takes advantage of an apparatus in which a flying insect can be tethered in a harness and surrounded by a controlled environment that contains visual information. Sareen et al. (2011) used such a setting to show that flies respond to cues. After cuing in one of two locations, two stumuli were concurrently presented. Torque responses indicated preferential processing of the cued location. Measurements from the insect nervous system indicate that such attention effects do not operate at the earliest stages of visual processing, but on secondary stages (Seelig and Jayaraman, 2015). This might indicate an analogue of the intermediate level.

There is also research indicating that insects have working memory. Pahl et al. (2013) report numerical cognition in various insects, which may suggest both attention and brief storage. In a more direct investigation of working memory, Giurfa et al. (2001) show that honeybees perform well in a delayed match-to-sample task. Interestingly, attention and working memory may be genetically linked in insects (van Swinderen, 2007), suggesting that, as with mammals, these processes are closely related.

There is even evidence that these processes involve gamma oscillations. Van Swinderen and Greenspan (2003) found that salience modulates 20–30 Hz brain activity in fruit fly brains, which pushes into gamma. Gamma frequencies have also been implicated in locust brains during sensory discrimination (Stopfer, et al. 1997).

Strikingly, then, insects do seem to have the basic ingredients of consciousness as postulated by the AIR theory.

Conclusions

In searching for consciousness in other creatures, we cannot rely on the presence of mere behavior, such as pain avoidance. We should look instead for the psychological and neural mechanisms that underlie consciousness in us. This may seem chauvinistic, but, given the enormous behavioral complexity that we ourselves can exhibit without consciousness, coarse behavioral measures run the risk of being too permissive. To find a more principled test, I introduced the AIR theory, which integrates some of the leading empirically based approaches to consciousness. According to that theory, consciousness requires hierarchical sensory processing, attention, and working memory, along with high-frequency, phase-locked neural oscillations. There is very strong evidence for these components in mammals, but also in a range of creatures whose brains are very different from our own. The case is especially strong in avian species, but also surprisingly strong in insects. Gastropods probably lack consciousness, given the simplicity of their nervous systems, but cephalopods are good candidates. The case for fish is less clear at this point, and the evidence for consciousness in reptiles and, especially, amphibians, is compatatively low.

Many questions remain. How much similarity to us is required? For example, must neural oscillations fall in a specific range, or just any range adequate for flow to working memory? Here, I have treated working memory as a system for ephemeral retention of perceptual information, but working memory can also encompass processes that allow for executive control. It may turn out that consciousness involves sophisticated forms of working memory. This would add further constraints to our search. The proposals advanced here must therefore be regarded as provisional. Still, they give us an empirical basis for attribution of consciousness that can be applied on the basis of extant data, and the conclusions reached, however tentative, provided principled answers rather than mere speculation based on gross behavior and phylogenetic similarity.

Acknowledgements

I am grateful for helpful feedback from Kristin Andrews, Jake Beck, and Peter Godfrey-Smith.

References

Allen, C. (2013). Fish cognition and consciousness. *Journal of Agricultural and Environmental Ethics, 26,* 25–39.

Alupay, J. S., Hadjisolomou, S. P., and Crook, R. J. (2014). Arm injury produces long-term behavioral and neural hypersensitivity in octopus. *Neuroscience Letters, 558,* 137–142.

Alves, C., Chichery, R., Boal, J. G., and Dickel, L. (2007). Orientation in the cuttlefish *Sepia officinalis*: Response versus place learning. *Animal Cognition, 10,* 29–36.

Baars, B. (2002). The conscious access hypothesis: Origins and recent evidence. *Trends in Cognitive Science, 6,* 47–52.

Bilbo, S. D., Day, L. B., and Wilczynski, W. (2000). Anticholinergic effects in frogs in a Morris water maze analog. *Physiology & Behavior, 69,* 351–357.

Birrell, J. M., and Brown, V. J. (2000). Medial frontal cortex mediates perceptual attentional set shifting in the rat. *Journal of Neuroscience, 20,* 4320–4324.

Bucci, D. J. (2012). Posterior parietal cortex: An interface between attention and learning? *Neurobiology of Learning and Memory, 91,* 114–120.

Bullock, T. H., and Budelmann, B. (1991). Sensory evoked potentials in unanesthetized unrestrained cuttlefish: A new preparation for brain physiology in cephalopods. *Journal of Comparative Physiology, 168,* 141–150.

Cabanac, M., Cabanac, A. J., and Parent, A. (2009). The emergence of consciousness in phylogeny. *Behavioural Brain Research, 198,* 267–272.

Chelonis, J. J., Cox, A. R., Karr, M. J., Prunty, P. K., Baldwin, R. L., and Paule, M. G. (2014). Comparison of delayed matching-to-sample performance in monkeys and children. *Behavioral Processes, 103*, 261–268.

Crick, F., and Koch, C. (1990). Towards a neurobiological theory of consciousness. *Seminars in Neuroscience, 2*, 263–275.

Croxson, P. L., Johansen-Berg, H., Behrens, T. E. J., Robson, M. D., Pinsk, M. A., Gross, C. G., Richter, W., Richter, M. C., Kastner, S., and Rushworth, M. F. (2005). Quantitative investigation of connections of the prefrontal cortex in the human and macaque using probabilistic diffusion tractography. *Journal of Neuroscience, 25*, 8854–8866.

Dalley, J. W., Cardinal, R. N., and Robbins, T. W. (2004). Prefrontal executive and cognitive functions in rodents: Neural and neurochemical substrates. *Neuroscience and Biobehavioral Reviews, 28*, 771–784.

de Bivort, B. L., and van Swinderen, B. (2016). Evidence for selective attention in the insect brain. *Current Opinion in Insect Science, 15*, 9–15.

Dickel, L., Chichery, M.-P., and Chichery, R. (1998). Time differences in the emergence of short- and long-term memory during post-embryonic development in the cuttlefish, *Sepia. Behavioral Processes, 44*, 81–86.

Engel, A. K., Fries, P., Brecht, M., and Singer, W. (1999). Temporal binding, binocular rivalry and consciousness. *Consciousness and Cognition, 8*, 128–151.

Feinberg, T. E., and Mallatt, J. M. (2016). *The ancient origins of consciousness: How the brain created experience.* Cambridge, MA: MIT Press.

Friedrich, R. W., Habermann, C. J., and Laurent, G. (2004). Multiplexing using synchrony in the zebrafish olfactory bulb. *Nature Neuroscience, 7*, 862–871.

Fries, P., Reynolds, J. H., Rorie, A. E., and Desimone, R. (2001). Modulation of oscillatory neuronal synchronization by selective visual attention. *Science, 291*, 1560–1563.

Gaillard, R., Dehaene, S., Adam, C., Clemenceau, S., Hasboun, D., Baulac, M., Cohen, L., and Naccache, L. (2009). Converging intracranial markers of conscious access. *PLoS Biology, 7*, e61.

Giurfa, M., Zhang, S., Jenett, A., Menzel, R., and Srinivasan, M. V. (2001). The concepts of "sameness" and "difference" in an insect. *Nature, 410*, 930–933.

Goldman-Rakic, P. S. (1990). Cellular and circuit basis of working memory in prefrontal cortex of nonhuman primates. *Progress in Brain Research, 85*, 325–335.

Graindorge, N., Alves, C., Darmaillacq, A.-S., Chichery, R., Dickel, L., and Bellanger, C. (2006). Effects of dorsal and ventral vertical lobe electrolytic lesions on spatial learning and locomotor activity in *Sepia officinalis. Behavioral Neuroscience, 5*, 1151–1158.

Greenberg, N. (2002). Ethological aspects of stress in a model lizard, *Anolis carolinensis. Integrative and Comparative Biology, 42*, 526–540.

Guttridge, T. L., and Brown, C. (2014). Learning and memory in the Port Jackson Shark, *Heterodontus portusjacksoni. Animal Cognition, 7*, 415–425.

Hall, B., and Delaney, K. (2001). Cholinergic modulation of odor-evoked oscillations in the frog olfactory bulb. *Biological Bulletin, 201*, 276–277.

Hanlon, R. T., and Messenger, J. B. (1996). *Cephalopod behaviour.* Cambridge: Cambridge University Press.

Hyde, D. C., and Wood, J. N. (2011). Spatial attention determines the nature of non-verbal numerical cognition. *Journal of Cognitive Neuroscience, 23*, 2336–2351.

Jun, J. J., Longtin, A., and Maler, L. (2016). Active sensing associated with spatial learning reveals memory-based attention in an electric fish. *Journal of Neurophysiology, 115*, 2577–2592.

Kesner, R. P., Hunt, M. E., Williams, J. M., and Long, J. M. (1996). Prefrontal cortex and working memory for spatial response, spatial location, and visual object information in the rat. *Cerebral Cortex, 6*, 311–318.

Lewis, D. K. (1980). Mad pain and Martian pain. In N. Block (Ed.), *Readings in philosophy of psychology, Vol. 1* (pp. 216–222). Cambridge, MA: MIT Press.

Lind, J., Enquist, M., and Ghirlanda, S. (2015). Animal memory: A review of delayed matching-to-sample data. *Behavioural Processes, 117*, 52–58.

Marín, G., Mpodozis, J., Sentis, E., Ossandon, T., and Letelier, J. C. (2005). Oscillatory bursts in the optic tectum of birds represent re-entrant signals from the nucleus isthmi pars parvocellularis. *Journal of Neuroscience, 25*, 7081–7089.

Mather, J. A. (1991). Navigation by spatial memory and use of visual landmarks in octopuses. *Journal of Comparative Physiology A, 168*, 491–497.

Mather, J.A. (2008). Cephalopod consciousness: Behavioral evidence. *Consciousness and Cognition, 17*, 37–48.

Mehta, A. D., Ulbert, I., and Schroeder, C. E. (2000). Intermodal selective attention in monkeys. I: Distribution and timing of effects across visual areas. *Cereb Cortex, 10*, 343–358.

Milmine, M., Rose, J., and Colombo, M. (2008). Sustained activation and executive control in the avian prefrontal cortex. *Brain Research Bulletin, 76*, 317–323.

Nase, G., Singer, W., Monyer, H., and Engel, A. K. (2003). Features of neuronal synchrony in mouse visual cortex. *Journal of Neurophysiology, 90*, 1115–1123.

Neuenschwander, S., Engel, A. K., König, P., Singer, W., and Varela, F. J. (1996). Synchronization of neuronal responses in the optic tectum of awake pigeons. *Visual Neuroscience, 13*, 575–584.

Newport, C., Wallis, G., and Siebeck, U. E. (2014). Concept learning and the use of three common psychophysical paradigms in the archerfish (*Toxotes chatareus*). *Frontiers in Neural Circuits, 8*, 39.

Northcutt, R. G., and Kaas, J. H. (1995). The emergence and evolution of mammalian neocortex. *Trends in Neurosciences, 18*, 373–379.

Orban, G. A., Van Essen, D., and Vanduffel, W. (2004). Comparative mapping of higher visual areas in monkeys and humans. *Trends in Cognitive Science, 8*, 315–324.

Pahl, M., Si, A., and Zhang, S. (2013). Numerical cognition in bees and other insects. *Frontiers in Psychology, 4*, 162.

Piffer, L., Agrillo, C., and Hyde, D. C. (2012). Small and large number discrimination in guppies. *Animal Cognition, 15*, 215–221.

Prechtl, J. C. (1994). Visual motion induces synchronous oscillations in turtle visual cortex. *Proceedings of the National Academy of Science USA, 91*, 12467–12471.

Preuss, T. M. (2007). Evolutionary specializations of primate brain systems. In M. J. Ravosa and M. Dagasto (Eds.), *Primate origins: Adaptations and evolution* (pp. 625–675). New York: Springer.

Prinz, J. J. (2012). *The conscious brain*. New York: Oxford University Press.

Prinz, J. J. (2017). Unconscious vision and the function of consciousness. In Z. Radman (Ed.), *Before consciousness: In search of the fundamentals of mind*. Exeter: Imprint Academic.

Pruess, T. M. (1995). Do rats have prefrontal cortex? The Rose-Woolsey-Akert program reconsidered. *Journal of Cognitive Neuroscience, 7*, 1–24.

Ramcharitar, J. U., Tan, E. W., and Fortune, E. S. (2006). Global electrosensory oscillations enhance directional responses of midbrain neurons in *Eigenmannia*. *Journal of Neurophysiology, 96*, 2319–2326.

Rose, J., and Colombo, M. (2005). Neural correlates of executive control in the Avian brain. *PLoS Biology, 3*, e190.

Sareen, P., Wolf, R., and Heisenberg, M. (2011). Attracting the attention of a fly. *Proceedings of the National Academy of Sciences USA, 108*, 7230–7235.

Schwartz, J. J., and Gerhardt, H. C. (1989). Spatially-mediated release from masking in an anuran amphibian. *Journal of Comparative Physiology A, 166*, 37–41.

Seelig, J. D., and Jayaraman, V. (2015). Neural dynamics for landmark orientation and angular path integration. *Nature, 521*, 186–191.

Singer, W., and Gray, C. M. (1995). Visual feature integration and the temporal correlation hypothesis. *Annual Review of Neuroscience, 18*, 555–586.

Sridharan, D., Ramamurthy, D. L., Schwarz, J. S., and Knudsen, E. I. (2014a). Visuospatial selective attention in chickens. *Proceedings of the National Academy of Science USA, 111*, E2056–E2065.

Sridharan, D., Schwarz, J. S., and Knudsen, E. I. (2014b). Selective attention in birds. *Current Biology, 24*, R510–R513.

Stein, P. S. G., Victor, J. C., Field, E. C., and Currie, S. N. (1995). Bilateral control of hindlimb scratching in the spinal turtle: Contralateral spinal circuitry contributes to the normal ipsilateral motor pattern of fictive rostral scratching. *Journal of Neuroscience, 15*, 4343–4355.

Stopfer, M., Bhagavan, S., Smith, B. H., and Laurent, G. (1997). Impaired odour discrimination on desynchronization of odour-encoding neural assemblies. *Nature, 390*, 70–74.

Torbaghan, S., Yazdi, D., Mirpour, K., and Bisley, J. W. (2012). Inhibition of return in a visual foraging task in non-human subjects. *Vision Research, 74*, 2–9.

van Swinderen, B. (2007). Attention-like processes in *Drosophila* require short-term memory genes. *Science, 315*, 1590–1593.

van Swinderen, B., and Greenspan, R. J. (2003). Salience modulates 20–30 Hz brain activity in *Drosophila*. *Nature Neuroscience, 6*, 579–586.

Wagner, U., Baker, L., and Rostron, C. (2014). Searching for inhibition of return in the rat using the covert orienting of attention task. *Animal Cognition, 17*, 1121–1135.

Wilkinson, A., Chan, H. M., and Hall, G. (2007). A study of spatial learning and memory in the tortoise (*Geochelone carbonaria*). *Journal of Comparative Psychology, 121*, 412–418.

18

ANIMAL CONSCIOUSNESS AND HIGHER-ORDER THOUGHTS

Rocco J. Gennaro

Representational theories of consciousness attempt to reduce consciousness to "mental representations" rather than directly to neural states. Examples include first-order representationalism (FOR), which attempts to explain conscious experience primarily in terms of world-directed (or first-order) intentional states (Tye 1995); and higher-order representationalism (HOR), which holds that what makes a mental state M conscious is that it is the object of some kind of higher-order mental state directed at M (Rosenthal 2005, Gennaro 2012). The primary focus of this chapter is on HOR and animal consciousness.

In Section 1, I introduce the more general problem of other minds with respect to animals. In Section 2, I provide a brief sketch of representationalism, which is the theory of consciousness that the higher-order thought (HOT) theory falls under in the standard taxonomy. Section 3 motivates HOT theory and presents some of its details. In Section 4, I present evidence in favor of the view that HOT theory is consistent with animal consciousness. In Section 5, I briefly consider the potentially damaging claim that HOT theory requires neural activity in the prefrontal cortex in order for one to have conscious states.

Perhaps the most commonly used notion of 'conscious' is captured by Thomas Nagel's "what it is like" sense (Nagel 1974). When I am in a conscious mental state, there is "something it is like" for me to be in *that state* from the first-person point of view. When I smell a rose or have a conscious visual experience, there is something it "seems like" from my perspective. This is primarily the sense of 'conscious state' that I use throughout this chapter.

1 Introduction to the problem of other (animal) minds

We have come a long way from Descartes' view that animals are mere "automata" and do not have conscious experience. In addition to the obvious behavioral similarities between humans and many other animals, much more is known today about physiological similarities such as brain and DNA structures. To be sure, there are also important differences and some genuinely difficult grey areas where one might legitimately doubt an animal's consciousness. Nonetheless, the vast majority of philosophers today accept that a significant portion of the animal kingdom has conscious mental states. This is obviously not to say that most animals can have *all* of the sophisticated conscious states enjoyed by human beings, such as reflecting on philosophical problems, enjoying artworks, thinking about the vast universe or distant past, and so on. However, it seems reasonable to believe that most animals have some conscious states from rudimentary pains to perceptual states.

One way to approach this topic has been via the traditional "problem of other minds," that is, how can one know that others have conscious mental states, given the comparatively indirect access we have to another's mind? Although virtually everyone is willing to take for granted that other human beings have conscious states similar to our own, knowledge of animal minds does present some difficulties. Nonhuman animals cannot describe their mental states using our public language. Although there have been attempts to teach human-like languages to members of other species, none can do so in a way that would easily solve this problem. Nonetheless, a strong inductive rationale for animal consciousness seems sufficient to establish a reasonable belief that (most) animals have conscious mental states. This has traditionally taken the form of an argument by analogy such that we know how we feel when we exhibit the behavior of someone in fear or in pain, and so it seems reasonable to think that the same conscious states are present when a dog or lion displays the similar behavior. This is presumably because we think of such behavior as *caused by* the relevant conscious state.

Although many different criteria might be put forth (Baars 2005), most evidence of other minds falls under at least one of the following:

1   Non-verbal or non-vocal behavioral evidence.
2   Ability to use language and/or to communicate.
3   Ability to learn, solve problems, and be creative.[1]
4   Similarity of brain structure (including evidence of shared evolutionary history).

Tables and rocks display none of the above criteria, and so we don't think they are conscious. Trees and plants are alive but also do not meet any of the above criteria. For example, they don't jump away or scream when approached with a chainsaw or lawnmower. At the other extreme, humans normally seem to meet all four criteria. However, when we look at the animal kingdom, we find evidence that can be somewhat mixed. Some animals may meet only two or three criteria, whereas others might meet only one. At the least, we might suppose that the more criteria met, the more likely an animal is conscious, and there seems to be a major difference between, say, a house fly and a chimp or dolphin. The matter can also be complicated by the fact that it may depend upon the *degree* to which a given animal meets a particular criterion.

2 Representationalism

Some theories attempt to reduce consciousness in *mentalistic* terms, such as 'thoughts' and 'awareness,' rather than directly in neurophysiological terms. One popular approach is to reduce consciousness to mental representations. The notion of a "representation" is, of course, very general and can be applied to pictures and various natural objects, such as the rings inside a tree. Much of what goes on in the brain might also be understood in a representational way. For example, mental events represent outer objects partly because they are caused by such objects in cases of veridical visual perception. Philosophers often call such mental states 'intentional states' which have representational content, that is, mental states are "directed at" something, such as a thought about a horse or a perception of a tree. Although intentional states, such as beliefs and thoughts, are sometimes contrasted with 'phenomenal states,' such as pains and color experiences, it is clear that many conscious states, such as visual perceptions, have both phenomenal and intentional properties.

The general view that we can explain conscious mental states in terms of representational states is called 'representationalism.' Most representationalists believe that there is room for a second-step reduction to be filled in later by neuroscience. The idea, then, is that if consciousness can be explained in representational terms and representation can be understood in purely physical terms, then there is the promise of a naturalistic theory of consciousness. Most generally, however, representationalism can be defined as the view that the phenomenal properties of conscious experience (that is, the 'qualia') can be explained in terms of the experiences' representational properties.

3 Higher-order thought (HOT) theory

One question that should be answered by any theory of consciousness is: what makes a mental state a *conscious* mental state? There is a long tradition that has attempted to understand consciousness in terms of higher-order awareness, but this view has been vigorously defended by several contemporary philosophers (Rosenthal 1986, 1997, 2005, Lycan 1996, 2001, Gennaro 1996, 2012). The basic idea is that what makes a mental state M conscious is a higher-order representation (HOR) of M. A HOR is a "metapsychological" or "metacognitive" state, that is, a mental state directed at another mental state ("I am in mental state M"). So, for example, my desire to write a good chapter becomes conscious when I am (non-inferentially) "aware" of the desire. Intuitively, conscious states, as opposed to unconscious ones, are mental states that I am "aware of" being in. This overall idea is sometimes referred to as the Transitivity Principle (TP):

(TP) A conscious state is a state whose subject is, in some way, aware of being in it.

Conversely, the idea that I could be having a conscious state while totally *unaware* of being in that state seems like a contradiction. A mental state of which the subject is completely unaware is clearly an *un*conscious state. For example, I would not be aware of having a subliminal perception, and so it is unconscious.

There are various kinds of HOR theory, with the most common division between higher-order thought (HOT) theories and higher-order perception (HOP) theories. HOT theorists, such as Rosenthal (2004, 2005) and Gennaro (2012), think it is better to understand the HOR as a thought containing concepts. HOTs are treated as cognitive states involving some kind of conceptual component. HOP theorists urge that the HOR is a perceptual state which does not require the conceptual content invoked by HOT theorists (Lycan 1996, 2004). One can also find something like TP in premise 1 of Lycan's (2001) more general argument for HOR:

(1)   A conscious state is a mental state whose subject is aware of being in it.
(2)   The "of" in (1) is the "of" of intentionality; what one is aware of is an intentional object of the awareness.
(3)   Intentionality is representational; a state has a thing as its intentional object only if it represents that thing.
       Therefore, (4) Awareness of a mental state is a representation of that state. (From 2, 3) *Therefore,* (5) A conscious state is a state that is itself represented by another of the subject's mental states. (1, 4)

The intuitive appeal of the first premise leads to the final conclusion – (5) – which is really just another way of stating HOR.

It might seem that HOT theory results in circularity by defining consciousness in terms of HOTs (since HOTs can be thought of as a kind of higher-order "awareness" of mental states, as in TP). It also might seem that an infinite regress results because a conscious mental state must be accompanied by a HOT which, in turn, must be accompanied by another HOT *ad infinitum.*

However, the standard and widely accepted reply is that when a conscious mental state is a first-order world-directed conscious state, the higher-order thought (HOT) is *not* itself conscious. But when the HOT is itself conscious, there is a yet higher-order (or third-order) thought directed at the second-order state. In this case, we have *introspection*, which involves a conscious HOT directed at an inner mental state. When one introspects, one's attention is directed back into one's mind. For example, what makes my desire to write a good chapter a conscious first-order desire is that there is an *unconscious* HOT directed at the desire. In this case, my conscious focus is directed outward at the paper or computer screen, and so I am not consciously aware of having the HOT from the first-person point of view. When I *introspect* that desire, however, I then have a *conscious* HOT (accompanied by a yet higher, third-order, HOT) directed at the desire itself. It is thus crucial to distinguish first-order conscious states (with unconscious HOTs) from introspective states (with conscious HOTs). HOT theory can be illustrated by Figure 18.1 below.

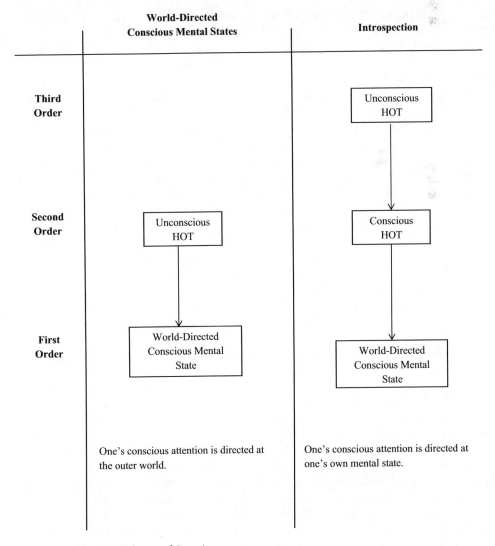

Figure 18.1 The HOT Theory of Consciousness

4 HOT theory and animal consciousness

A number of objections to higher-order theories (and counter-replies) can be found in the literature. One of these says that animals (and even infants) are not likely to have the conceptual sophistication required for HOTs, which would then render animal (and infant) consciousness very unlikely (e.g. Seager 2004). Are cats and pigs capable of having complex higher-order thoughts, such as "I am in mental state M"? Although most who raise this issue are not HOT theorists, Carruthers (1989, 2000) is one HOT theorist who actually embraces the normally unwelcome conclusion that (most) animals do not have phenomenal consciousness. I initially replied that HOTs need not be as sophisticated as they might initially appear, and there is ample comparative neurophysiological evidence, such as the presence of certain shared cortical and even *neo*cortical structures, supporting the conclusion that animals have conscious mental states and HOTs (Gennaro 1996).

In my view, numerous recent experiments also show that animals have "metacognitive" states which provide further evidence for HOTs. A number of key areas are under continuing investigation, including animal memory and uncertainty monitoring. The term 'I-thoughts' is also often used in the literature to mean "thoughts about one's own mental states or oneself." Thus, they are very similar to HOTs and closely linked to what psychologists call 'metacognition,' that is, mental states about mental states, or 'cognitions' about other mental representations (Koriat 2007). Although some reject the notion that most nonhuman animals have I-thoughts, the evidence seems to be growing that many animals do in fact have them, and may even be able to understand the mental states of others (Terrace and Metcalfe 2005, Hurley and Nudds 2006).

One area of inquiry has to do with episodic memory (EM), which is an explicitly conscious kind of remembering involving "mental time travel" (Tulving 1983, 2005). It is often contrasted with *semantic* memory, which need only involve knowing that a given fact is true or what a particular object is, and *procedural* memory, whereby memory of various learned skills is retained. Some notion of "I" or self-concept seems necessary to have a genuine EM. I recognize an EM *as mine* and as representing an event in *my* past. To give an example from animal cognition research, Clayton and Dickinson and their colleagues report convincing demonstrations of memory for time in scrub jays (Clayton, Bussey, and Dickinson 2003: 37). Scrub jays are food-caching birds, and when they have food they cannot eat, they hide it and recover it later. Because some of the food is preferred but perishable (such as crickets), it must be eaten within a few days, while other food (such as nuts) is less preferred but does not perish as quickly. In cleverly designed experiments using these facts, scrub jays are shown, even days after caching, to know not only *what* kind of food was *where*, but also *when* they had cached it (see also Clayton, Emery, and Dickinson 2006). Although still somewhat controversial, these experimental results at least seem to show that scrub jays have some episodic memory which involves a sense of self over time. This strongly suggests that the birds have some degree of metacognition with a self-concept (or "I-concept") which can figure into HOTs. Further, many crows and scrub jays return alone to caches they had hidden in the presence of others and recache them in new places (Emery and Clayton 2001). This suggests that they know that *others* know where the food is cached, and thus, to avoid having their food stolen, they recache the food. This strongly suggests that these birds can even have some mental concepts directed at other minds, which is sometimes called 'mindreading.' Of course, there are many different experiments aimed at determining the metacognitive abilities of various animals, so it can sometimes be difficult to generalize across species.

There is also the much-discussed work on uncertainty monitoring with animals such as monkeys and dolphins (Smith, Shields, and Washburn 2003, Smith 2005). For example, a dolphin is trained in a perceptual discrimination task, first learning to identify a particular sound at a fixed frequency (the "sample" sound). The dolphin later learns to match other sounds to the sample sound. When presented with a sound that is either the same or different in pitch as the sample sound, he has to respond in one way if it is the same pitch (such as by pressing one paddle) and another way if it is a different pitch (pressing another paddle). Eventually the dolphin is introduced into a test environment and forced to make extremely difficult discriminations. To test for the capacity to take advantage of his own uncertainty, the dolphin is presented with a third "uncertain" response, the Escape paddle, which yields a greater reward than an incorrect response but a lesser reward than a correct response. The dolphin chooses the Escape paddle with a similar response pattern to humans and rhesus monkeys, which suggests that the dolphin is aware of his state of uncertainty; that is, he has some knowledge of his own mental state. This is clearly a metacognitive state: the dolphin is aware that he doesn't know something, in this case, whether or not a sound matches (or is very close to) the sample sound.[2]

Some authors (e.g. Carruthers 2000, 2005, 2009), however, have cited experimental work suggesting that even chimps lack the ability to attribute mental states *to others* (Povinelli 2000). These experiments are designed to determine if chimps take notice of when an experimenter is looking at something (say, food) or is unable to see something (for example, due to blind-folding). Chimps were just as likely to ask for food from an experimenter with a bucket over her head as from one who could see, which seems to indicate a lack of the mental concept 'seeing' or 'visual perception.' Carruthers further argues that animals with HOTs should also be able to have thoughts about the mental states of *other creatures*. However, it is not at all clear that having I-thoughts requires being able to read *other* minds. And in any case, the evidence seems to be growing that many animals can mind-read. For example, Laurie Santos and colleagues show that rhesus monkeys attribute visual and auditory perceptions to others in competitive paradigms (Flombaum and Santos 2005, Santos, Nissen, and Ferrugia 2006). Rhesus monkeys preferentially attempt to obtain food silently only in those conditions where silence was relevant to obtaining the food undetected. While a human competitor was looking away, monkeys would take grapes from a silent container, thus apparently understanding that hearing leads to knowing on the part of human competitors. Subjects reliably picked the container that did not alert the experimenter that a grape was being removed. This suggests that monkeys take into account how auditory information can change the knowledge state of the experimenter.[3]

5 HOT theory, animals, and the prefrontal cortex

One interesting development in recent years has been on attempts to identify how HOT theory might be realized in the brain. The issue is sometimes framed in terms of the question: How global is HOT theory? That is, do conscious mental states require widespread brain activation, or can at least some of them be fairly localized in narrower areas of the brain? Perhaps most interesting is whether or not the prefrontal cortex (PFC) is required for having conscious states (Gennaro 2012: chapter nine). I disagree with those who think that, according to HOT theory and related views, the PFC is required for most conscious states (Kriegel 2009, Block 2007, Lau and Rosenthal 2011). It may very well be that the PFC is required for the more sophisticated *introspective* states, but this isn't a problem for HOT theory because it does not require introspection to have first-order conscious states.

There seems to be significant evidence for conscious states without PFC activity. For example, Rafael Malach and colleagues show that when subjects are engaged in a perceptual task or absorbed in watching a movie, there is widespread neural activation but little PFC activity (Grill-Spector and Malach 2004, Goldberg, Harel, and Malach 2006). Although some other studies do show PFC activation, this is mainly because of the need for subjects to *report* their experiences. Zeki (2007) also cites evidence that the "frontal cortex is engaged only when reportability is part of the conscious experience" (2007: 587), and "all human color [brain] imaging experiments have been unanimous in not showing any particular activation of the frontal lobes" (2007: 582). Similar results are found for other sensory modalities, such as auditory perception (Baars and Gage 2010: chapter seven). Also, basic conscious experience is certainly not eliminated entirely even when there is extensive bilateral PFC damage or lobotomies (Pollen 2008). It seems to me that this line of argument would be an advantage for HOT theory with regard to animal and infant consciousness. If HOT theory does not *require* PFC activity for *all* conscious states, then it is in a better position to account for animal and infant consciousness since it is doubtful that infants and most animals have the requisite PFC activity.

One might still ask: why think that unconscious HOTs can occur outside the PFC? If we grant that unconscious HOTs can be regarded as a kind of "pre-reflective" self-consciousness, we can, for example, look to Newen and Vogeley (2003) for some answers. They distinguish five levels of self-consciousness ranging from "phenomenal self-acquaintance" and "conceptual self-consciousness" up to "iterative meta-representational self-consciousness." The majority of their paper is explicitly about the neural correlates of what they call the "first-person perspective" (1PP) and the "egocentric reference frame." Citing numerous experiments, they point to various neural signatures of self-consciousness. The PFC is rarely mentioned, and then usually only with regard to more sophisticated forms of self-consciousness. Other brain areas are much more prominently identified, such as the medial and inferior parietal cortices, the temporoparietal cortex, the posterior cingulate cortex, and the anterior cingulate cortex (ACC). Even when considering the neural signatures of "theory of mind" and "mindreading," Newen and Vogeley have replicated experiments indicating that such meta-representation is best located in the ACC. In addition, "the capacity for taking 1PP in such [theory of mind] contexts showed differential activation in the right temporo-parietal junction and the medial aspects of the superior parietal lobe" (Newen and Vogeley 2003: 538). Once again, even if the PFC is essential for having *some* HOTs and conscious states, this poses no threat to HOT theory provided that the HOTs in question are of the more sophisticated introspective variety.

This neurophysiological issue is certainly not yet fully settled, but I think it is a mistake to hold that HOT theory should treat first-order conscious states as essentially including PFC activity. I would make the following concession, however: if I ever became convinced that animal consciousness is really inconsistent with HOT theory, then I would be much more inclined to give up HOT theory rather than the view that most animals have conscious states.

Kozuch (2014) presents a nice overall discussion of the PFC in relation to higher-order theories, but he argues that the lack of dramatic deficits in visual consciousness in patients with PFC lesions presents a compelling case against higher-order theories. I agree with much of Kozuch's analysis, especially with respect to the notion that some (visual) conscious states do not require PFC activity (sometimes focused more on the dorsolateral PFC, or dlPFC). However, Kozuch rightly notes that my view is left undamaged, at least to some extent, since I do not require that the PFC is where HOTs must be neutrally realized. I would add that we must also keep in mind the distinction between unconscious HOTs and conscious HOTs (= introspection). Perhaps the latter require PFC activity, given the more sophisticated executive functions associated with introspection, but having first-order conscious states does not require introspection.

In closing, then, HOT theory is a viable theory of consciousness which is consistent with the presence of consciousness in at least most animals. Evidence from studies on animal memory, uncertainty monitoring, and competitive paradigms support the notion that most animals are capable of having some HOTs. Further, there is little reason to suppose that HOTs must essentially involve activity in the PFC.

Notes

1 I list this separately because some of this evidence may be more sophisticated than the more basic behavioral or communicative evidence in the first two criteria.

2 Nonetheless, some authors (Carruthers 2008) argue that these and other experiments do not *force us* to infer the presence of metacognition. But see Gennaro 2012, chapter eight (especially section 8.3), for further counter-reply on this point.

3 I lack the space here to delve further into this massive literature, but see, for example, the essays in Part IV, Mindreading, of this volume and in Terrace and Metcalfe 2005. For much more on the overall issue of mindreading and metacognition in animals and infants, see Carruthers 2009 (and the peer commentary which follows), as well as Nichols and Stich (2003), Goldman (2006), and Gennaro (2009, 2012, chapters seven and eight). For further defense of the view that self-attribution of mental states (metacognition) is prior to our capacity to attribute mental states to others (mindreading), see Goldman (2006). A more modest view, offered by Nichols and Stich (2003), is that the two capacities are independent and dissociable. Carruthers (2009) argues that mindreading is actually *prior to* metacognition. I am not convinced that the evidence supports his view better, say, than Nichols and Stich's position. Two often-discussed views are simulation theory (ST) and theory-theory (TT). ST holds that mindreading involves the ability to imaginatively take the perspective of another. TT holds that metacognition results from one's "theory of mind" being directed at oneself.

Further reading

For more on metacognition, see D. DeGrazia, "Self-Awareness in Animals," in R. Lurz (ed.), *The Philosophy of Animal Minds* (New York: Cambridge University Press, 2009); J. Proust, *The Philosophy of Metacognition* (New York: Oxford University Press, 2013); and M. Beran, J. Brandl, J. Perner, and J. Proust (eds.), *The Foundations of Metacognition* (New York: Oxford University Press, 2012). For more on mindreading, see R. Lurz, *Mindreading Animals* (Cambridge, MA: MIT Press, 2011). For a nice overview of some of the themes in this chapter and related topics, see K. Andrews, "Animal Cognition", in Edward N. Zalta (ed.), *The Stanford Encyclopedia of Philosophy* (Summer 2016 Edition), http://plato.stanford.edu/archives/sum2016/entries/cognition-animal/.

References

Baars, B. (2005) "Subjective Experience Is Probably Not Limited to Humans: The Evidence From Neurobiology and Behavior," *Consciousness and Cognition* 14, pp. 7–21.

Baars, B., and Gage, N. (2010) *Cognition, Brain, and Consciousness: Introduction to Cognitive Neuroscience*, second edition, Oxford: Elsevier.

Block, N. (2007) "Consciousness, Accessibility, and the Mesh Between Psychology and Neuroscience," *Behavioral and Brain Sciences* 30, pp. 481–499.

Carruthers, P. (1989) "Brute Experience," *Journal of Philosophy* 86, pp. 258–269.

Carruthers, P. (2000) *Phenomenal Consciousness*, Cambridge: Cambridge University Press.

Carruthers, P. (2005) *Consciousness: Essays From a Higher-Order Perspective*, New York: Oxford University Press.

Carruthers, P. (2008) "Meta-Cognition in Animals: A Skeptical Look," *Mind and Language* 23, pp. 58–89.

Carruthers, P. (2009) "How We Know Our Own Minds: The Relationship Between Mindreading and Metacognition," *Behavioral and Brain Sciences* 32, pp. 121–138.

Clayton, N., Bussey, T., and Dickinson, A. (2003) "Can Animals Recall the Past and Plan for the Future?" *Nature Reviews Neuroscience* 4, pp. 685–691.

Clayton, N., Emery, N., and Dickinson, A. (2006) "The Rationality of Animal Memory: Complex Caching Strategies of Western Scrub Jays," In Hurley and Nudds (2006).

Emery, N., and Clayton, N. (2001) "Effects of Experience and Social Context on Prospective Caching Strategies in Scrub Jays," *Nature* 414, pp. 443–446.

Flombaum, J., and Santos, L. (2005) "Rhesus Monkeys Attribute Perceptions to Others," *Current Biology* 15, pp. 447–452.

Gennaro, R. (1996) *Consciousness and Self-Consciousness: A Defense of the Higher-Order Thought Theory of Consciousness*, Amsterdam and Philadelphia: John Benjamins.

Gennaro, R. (2004) "Higher-Order Thoughts, Animal Consciousness, and Misrepresentation: A Reply to Carruthers and Levine," In R. Gennaro (ed.) *Higher-Order Theories of Consciousness: An Anthology*, Amsterdam and Philadelphia: John Benjamins.

Gennaro, R. (2009) "Animals, Consciousness, and I-thoughts," In R. Lurz (ed.) *Philosophy of Animal Minds*, New York: Cambridge University Press.

Gennaro, R. (2012) *The Consciousness Paradox: Consciousness, Concepts, and Higher-Order Thoughts*, Cambridge, MA: The MIT Press.

Goldberg, I., Harel, M., and Malach, R. (2006) "When the Brain Loses its Self: Prefrontal Inactivation During Sensorimotor Processing," *Neuron* 50, pp. 329–339.

Goldman, A. (2006) *Simulating Minds*, New York: Oxford University Press.

Grill-Spector, K., and Malach, R. (2004) "The Human Visual Cortex," *Annual Review of Neuroscience* 7, pp. 649–677.

Hurley, S., and Nudds, M. eds. (2006) *Rational Animals?* New York: Oxford University Press.

Koriat, A. (2007) "Metacognition and Consciousness," In P. Zelazo, M. Moscovitch, and E. Thomson (eds.) *The Cambridge Handbook of Consciousness*, Cambridge, MA: Cambridge University Press.

Kozuch, B. (2014) "Prefrontal Lesion Evidence Against Higher-Order Theories of Consciousness," *Philosophical Studies* 167, pp. 721–746.

Kriegel, U. (2009) *Subjective Consciousness*, New York: Oxford University Press.

Lau, H., and Rosenthal, D. (2011) "Empirical Support for Higher-Order Theories of Conscious Awareness," *Trends in Cognitive Sciences* 15, pp. 365–373.

Lurz, R. ed. (2009) *The Philosophy of Animal Minds*, Cambridge, MA: Cambridge University Press.

Lycan, W. (1996) *Consciousness and Experience*, Cambridge, MA: MIT Press.

Lycan, W. (2001) "A Simple Argument for a Higher-Order Representation Theory of Consciousness," *Analysis* 61, pp. 3–4.

Lycan, W. (2004) "The Superiority of HOP to HOT," In R. Gennaro (ed.) *Higher-Order Theories of Consciousness: An Anthology*, Amsterdam: John Benjamins.

Nagel, T. (1974) "What Is It Like to Be a Bat?" *Philosophical Review* 83, pp. 435–456.

Newen, A., and Vogeley, K. (2003) "Self-Representation: Searching for a Neural Signature of Self-Consciousness," *Consciousness and Cognition* 12, pp. 529–543.

Nichols, S., and Stich, S. (2003) *Mindreading*, New York: Oxford University Press.

Pollen, D. (2008) "Fundamental Requirements for Primary Visual Perception," *Cerebral Cortex* 18, pp. 1991–1998.

Povinelli, D. (2000) *Folk Physics for Apes*, New York: Oxford University Press.

Rosenthal, D. M. (1986) "Two Concepts of Consciousness," *Philosophical Studies* 49, pp. 329–359.

Rosenthal, D. M. (1997) "A Theory of Consciousness," In N. Block, O. Flanagan, and G. Güzeldere (eds.) *The Nature of Consciousness*, Cambridge, MA: MIT Press.

Rosenthal, D. M. (2004) "Varieties of Higher-Order Theory," In R. Gennaro (ed.) *Higher-Order Theories of Consciousness: An Anthology*, Philadelphia and Amsterdam: John Benjamins.

Rosenthal, D. M. (2005) *Consciousness and Mind*, New York: Oxford University Press.

Santos, L., Nissen, A., and Ferrugia, J. (2006) "Rhesus monkeys, *Macaca mulatta*, Know What Others Can and Cannot Hear," *Animal Behaviour* 71, pp. 1175–1181.

Seager, W. (2004) "A Cold Look at HOT Theory," In R. Gennaro (ed.) *Higher-Order Theories of Consciousness: An Anthology*, Amsterdam: John Benjamins.

Smith, J. D. (2005) "Studies of Uncertainty Monitoring and Metacognition in Animals," In Terrace and Metcalfe (2005).

Smith, J. D., Shields, W., and Washburn, D. (2003) "The Comparative Psychology of Uncertainty Monitoring and Metacognition," *Behavioral and Brain Sciences* 26, pp. 317–373.

Terrace, H., and Metcalfe, J. eds. (2005) *The Missing Link in Cognition: Origins of Self-Reflective Consciousness*, New York: Oxford University Press.

Tulving, E. (1983) *Elements of Episodic Memory*, Oxford: Oxford University Press.

Tulving, E. (2005) "Episodic Memory and Autonoesis: Uniquely Human?" In Terrace and Metcalfe (2005).

Tye, M. (1995) *Ten Problems of Consciousness*, Cambridge, MA: MIT Press.

Zeki, S. (2007) "A Theory of Micro-Consciousness," In M. Velmans and S. Schneider (eds.) *The Blackwell Companion to Consciousness*, Malden, MA: Blackwell.

19

MINDS AND BODIES IN ANIMAL EVOLUTION

Michael Trestman

Introduction

Consciousness is a notoriously elusive notion, in part because it points to a cluster of related phenomena (see Van Gulick, 2014, for a broad overview; see Godfrey-Smith, 2016, and Trestman and Allen, 2015, for discussions of this issue in the context of the evolution and phylogenetic distribution of consciousness). My target notion is subjective experience – having any experience at all. This is sometimes called the 'phenomenal' or 'phenomenological' notion of consciousness. When I am aware of anything at all, I have an experience, and I am the subject of that experience. That experience is what it is like to be me in that given situation, the 'experiential quality' of my existence in that moment. If there is something it is like to be a given creature, that creature is conscious. Which animals are conscious in the sense of experiencing their presence in the world? How can we tell?

The strategy I employ here is to use insight from phenomenological analysis of consciousness to generate differentiating empirical predictions about the behavior of animals that have consciousness and those that don't. This 'Structural-Functional' approach (Trestman and Allen 2015, part 5) relies heavily on the assumption that the intentional structure of consciousness as revealed through phenomenological analysis of consciousness can be mapped meaningfully to the computational structure of cognition, as considered from the perspective of the behavioral sciences such as behavioral psychology, ecological psychology, ethology, and functional neuroscience (Varela 1996). This assumption is rooted in the naturalistic stance that consciousness is an aspect of our biology, that it is grounded in the interaction of our body with our environment. We are (more or less) our bodies; the experiential dimension of consciousness (subjective experience) just is what it is like to be a certain kind of body.

Cognition, intentionality, and information processing are abstractions for describing the processes that mediate sensation and behavior. We use this level of abstraction to understand our own experience as we make sense out of the world, extracting meaning from what we see and hear, and how it provokes us to feel and respond. We also use it to understand how others do the same. Because it is an abstraction, it inevitably loses detail and directness – an abstraction never fully captures what it is an abstraction of, and in that sense we can never *fully* know the experience of any other sentient being (human or otherwise). Nonetheless, this abstraction layer allows for meaningful contact between the 'first-person' perspective of phenomenology and the 'third-person' perspective of the behavioral and brain sciences, allowing us to ground our reasoning about others' experiences in empirical evidence.

I present here a model of the cognitive structure of consciousness that was developed to answer the question:

(Q1) What is the cognitive substructure of consciousness that makes possible its temporal dimension?

I believe it also answers a very different question:

(Q2) What is the core information-processing structure required for an adaptive control-system for complex, active animal bodies?

That the model answers both Q1 and Q2 suggests that the cognitive structure described by the model – consciousness – was a key evolutionary novelty that contributed to the diversification of animals with complex active bodies. This implies that the emergence of consciousness has a detectable signature in evolution: adaptive radiation driven by diversification of complex, active bodies.

The structure of consciousness

As a conscious subject, one is immersed in a changing flow of sensation, perception, thought, and feeling. Normally, one's attention is occupied not by low-level sensations (pixels, color patches, edges, tones, pressure or stretch on the skin) but *objects*, things in the world like trees and dogs and humans and cups of coffee, and the features and conditions of these that are most salient to one's preferences and intentions. Typical experience situates us in a world with a coherent spatial structure – objects are located *out there*, and we are aware of their relation to our body (itself a kind of special object with a spatial structure) and in particular to the cyclopean hole in the center of our face that we experience as the locus of our visual perspective (Merker 2013). We perceive a scene of worldly objects *through* a changing array of sensations. How does this interpretation work? How does worldly, situated experience emerge from sensory flux?

Intentionality – 'aboutness' in the sense that a perception or thought is *about* an object – implies experiencing a sensory image as an appearance *of* an object that transcends – exists apart from – the appearance (Husserl 1963; Zahavi 1999). If you see a cup sitting on a table, you implicitly understand that the cup can appear differently. Its appearance will change slightly in one way if you move your head to the left, in another if you move your head to the right. If you reach out and touch it, the cup will feel a certain way in your hand. These are all appearances *of* the same cup, the *object*, which therefore transcends the constantly changing ways in which it appears. Intentionality implies identity in multiplicity – high-level patterns persist as sensations change.

Perception is fundamentally dynamic, temporal. Understanding the scene before you is a matter of understanding *what is happening*. If a ball is in the middle of a table, you cannot tell from a snapshot whether it is sitting still or rolling, but perceiving a ball roll is different than perceiving a ball sitting still. Perceiving an object involves an awareness of its trajectory – where it has been and where it is going, how it has appeared and how it will appear.

One's sense of what is happening, of one's situation in the world, is extended in time. James (1890/1950) observed that the sense of the present has an extension of about 3 to 10 seconds. Within this range, we are aware of the fine-grained temporal structure of events – properties like duration and rhythm. Longer into the past than that, we can remember or figure out how things were in terms of their temporal properties, but our judgments over these extended timescales have the character of inference rather than perception, relying on background information about events with known durations or labeled time coordinates (dates and times). A wide variety of subsequent research has confirmed that the timescale of about 3 seconds seems to have a special status as a 'window of temporal integration' for perception, judgment, and action (Poppel 2009; Wackerman 2007). We experience a rich sensory array that persists for a few seconds, allowing us to notice details and recognize objects; afterwards, what we remember is very selective and depends heavily on what we were paying attention to and how we interpreted the scene (Block 2011; Pinto et al. 2013).

Consciousness has a tripartite structure: our *impression* of the sensory present is accompanied by a *retention* of the previous impression, as well as an open-ended anticipation or *protention* of upcoming impressions, to use Husserl's terminology (Husserl 1963; Zahavi 1999). Further, this *retention-impression-protention (R-I-P)* structure is *iterated*: the retention associated with the current impression itself has an R-I-P structure. What we retain from the previous moment of awareness isn't just the sensory impression, but that moment's full sense of past-present-future. This is implied by the experience of surprise, an awareness of mismatch between prior expectations and actuality (Trestman 2014).

The *iterated R-I-P (ItRIP)* structure is essential for capturing the structural property of 'flow' exhibited by consciousness. Our sense of time is not a static linear series, but a series with an internal motion defined in relation to a perspective – the now – which we, as subject, occupy. Future events approach, and past events recede.

Crucially, a given event (e.g. a book falling to the floor, taking a sip of wine) maintains an identity as it traverses the different 'zones' of future, present, and past: the sound-of-the-book-hitting-the-floor that I hear now is then, a moment later, the very same sound-of-the-book-hitting-the-floor that I am aware of as having just occurred. The sip I anticipate is the same sip I take, and the same sip I then remember – even if my expectations were slightly off, they were slightly-off-expectations of *that* sip, how it would appear to my senses in the moment.

The structure of iterated retention allows moments of experienced time to emerge as invariants across the series of retained moments. A single point of time – a moment – is first anticipated, then experienced as present, then experienced as past. This cross-time identity of moments supports identity of events over time, since events are happenings that are temporally bound. In turn, this supports objects as things that can persist across time – I can understand that the cup that I saw sitting on the table a moment before is the same cup that I'm now holding.

Our experience of time is not only extended across time – 'temporally thick'; it is also extended across alternate possibilities – it is 'modally broad'. We experience time as having a *branching* structure in the future direction – hence the name *BItRIP (branched, iterative retention-impression-protention)* for the full model (Trestman 2014).

This is fundamental to our experience of agency in its most basic form: body ownership. I experience my body as the medium of my actions, and the medium of my perceptions. What I do, I do with my body; what I perceive, I perceive through my body. This is what distinguishes my body from other objects; my hand is an object that I can see, but I can also feel with it, and do with it (Husserl 1963; Carman 1999). My body is under my control in a direct, immediate way that nothing else is. But to experience control of my body is to experience a plurality of future possibilities – to protend multiple branching sequences. Ultimately your divided intent resolves or collapses – *I can do [x, y, z]* becomes *I do x*. We retain a sense of what we could have done, choices we made and did not make slipping into the past. This implies that the branched structure of protention is retained within R-I-P elements in the retentional sequence.

Bodily agency is a ubiquitous feature of conscious experience, especially when we consider its role in perception of objects and the spatial structure of the environment (Trestman

2014). Space is experienced in relation to the body's axes of orientation and capcities for action. Egocentric spatial positions are invariants relative to the body's dynamics (Mossio and Taraborelli 2008; Merker 2005, 2013), so positions in space relative to the body must be defined in terms of positions in time. To experience a stable, spatially coherent world depends on an animal's ability to predict and compensate for sensory change due to saccades, postural shifts, and any other bodily actions that influence the optic array exposed to the eye (Merker 2013).

The branching nature of our experience of time is also fundamental to another core feature of consciousness – affective valence. There are a variety of theories of hedonic experience, but a broadly shared theme is that it involves both anticipation and comparison – specifically, comparison of alternate ways one's situation could change (see Aydede 2013 for a review of theories of pain). Roughly, experiencing something as aversive is wanting it to cease/not happen, and experiencing something as pleasurable or desirable is wanting it to continue/happen.

Human judgments of temporal properties such as order and simultaneity have a limit at short timescales. Fusion intervals for stimuli are generally on the order of about 30–40 ms, suggesting a cyclical process of general perceptual integration operates on this timescale (Poppel 2009; Wackerman 2007). This timescale corresponds approximately to the ~40-hz oscillations of thalamocortical reentrant neural activity by which low-level perceptual features are bound into higher-level object-oriented perceptual contents (Baldauf and Desimone 2014), and which has been advanced as the neural correlate of consciousness in vertebrates (Tononi and Edelman 1998; Crick and Koch 2003; Singer and Gray 1995).

If, as I have argued, consciousness is constituted by an iterated sequence of sensory impressions, retentions, and protentions, the 30–40ms timescale suggests the rate of iteration. If 3 seconds represents a typical window of the experienced present, and this experienced present is constituted by an iterated series of R-I-P elements retained at a rate of ~1/30 ms, then the experienced present is typically composed of on the order of 100 R-I-P iterations.

The cognitive prerequisites to controlling a body

A complex active body (CAB) is one equipped for perceptually guided, powered motion: swimming, crawling, climbing, leaping, flying, burrowing; and object manipulation (grabbing, carrying, turning, crushing, tearing, separating, etc.). Such a body has the following attributes (Trestman 2013):

- many degrees of freedom of controlled motion;
- senses that can quickly gather distal information (vision, hearing);
- anatomical capability for active, distal-sense-guided mobility (fins, legs, jet propulsion, etc.);
- anatomical capability for active object manipulation (e.g., chelipeds, hands, tentacles, sensitive mouth-parts).

Millions of living animal species display an astonishing diversity of CABs, but they exist in only three out of roughly 35 animal phyla: *arthropods* (e.g. insects, spiders, crustaceans); *chordates* (e.g. humans, salmon, pterodactyls); and *mollusks*, within the cephalopod lineage (squids, octopus, cuttlefish). Other lineages include animals that are diverse in many ways, including size and shape; metabolic and ecological specializations such as symbioses and parasitisms; chemical, visual, or mechanical defenses and signaling systems; complex multi-stage life cycles; and elaborate modes of reproductive. But brains, sensory organs, skeletomusculature and behavioral repertoires remained relatively simple outside of these three taxa.

In the evolution of each lineage, the appearance of CABs precipitated prolific radiation – if a lineage can produce one kind of CAB, it can produce others. Morphological diversification corresponded to behavioral and ecological diversification, with animals in these lineages rapidly exploring the space of possibilities for crucial types of behavior, including foraging, anti-predator defense, and selecting and/or constructing favorable habitats. This macroevolutionary pattern strongly suggests that complex active bodies evolve only together with an adaptable cognitive tool-kit for controlling those bodies (Trestman 2013). It also points to a general and open-ended developmental tool-kit for producing complex active bodies and the brains that control them, rather than a brittle or 'one off' solution. There are no animals with CABs surrounded phylogenetically by animals without CABs.

I use the term basic cognitive embodiment (BCE) to refer to the suite of cognitive phenotypes required for control of a CAB (Trestman 2013). These are capacities without which CABs could not evolve, since the reliable development of ecologically valid repertoires of coherent goal-direct behavior with a CAB would be all but impossible without them. Not every item on the lists below is strictly necessary; some are more complex than others and build on the more fundamental. Cognitive embodiment comes in a spectrum of complexity as well as a wild diversity of forms.

BCE has three main categories or dimensions: spatiality, object-orientation, and action-orientation.

Spatiality

Adaptive control of a CAB requires animals to flexibly track and coordinate behavior to the following sorts of spatial invariants in the body-environment system.

- *Orientation* of an animal's body toward external targets is fundamental to much of behavior. For animals with CABs, orientation is a complex problem requiring coherent activity throughout the body that is specific to the target orientation (Merker 2005, 2103). Orientation is relative to an animal's bodily structure and capacities for action. A single body may have many different ways to orient itself toward a target, such as orienting whole-body posture, head, eyes, ears. Actions often need to be readied by orienting special parts of the body to grab, reach, or otherwise move toward a target. Many animals with CABs can orient simultaneously to multiple targets in different respects, for example, turning the head to track a suspected threat while readying the body to dash back toward the safety of a burrow. Maintaining orientation to a target that is out of direct perceptual contact through a series of bodily movements requires *path integration*.
- Many targets of interest in an animal's environment move, as does the animal itself, so rather than a static relative position, orientation will often be toward the *trajectory* of a target.
- *Distances* and *sizes* must be judged in a myriad of ways. Usually what is relevant to an animal is not size or distance in objective terms, but in terms of invariants that relate the animal's body and behavior to an object. For example, animals must often judge if they can grab something, if they can fit through an opening, or how quickly they can reach a spot. One example of a generally useful invariant is *tau of a gap* – the size of a gap divided by its current rate of closure. This invariant affords powerful control heuristics for guiding behavior: if the animal decelerates its approach such that tau is maintained at exactly 1/2, the motion will stop just as the gap closes; keeping tau lower stops the motion before the gap closes; the higher tau is (above 1/2), the more energetic the collision will be. David Lee and colleagues have demonstrated apparent use of tau to control behavior in a number of

vertebrates. Examples include: humans performing familiar behaviors such as parking a car or catching a ball, as well as unfamiliar experimental tasks; bats landing on a perch using echolation; pigeons landing on a perch using visual control; hummingbirds inserting their bill into a feeder; gannets closing their wings as they dive into water (reviewed in Lee 2009). In principle, tau-based heuristics apply not only to the spatial gap between an animal and a target toward which it is moving, but also to any gap between a target state and its current state along a continuous dimension.

- *Objects* will be discussed below, but much of what defines an object is spatial binding – an object is a cluster of features that travels together through space.
- *Places* are occupiable regions of space with certain predictable properties, and can be considered a sort of object. Places differ in food availability, safety, and many other important respects. Making best use of a CAB implies evaluating places in terms of these qualities and moving the body so as to spend the most time in the most advantageous places. Creating a burrow or nest, forraying out into the environment, and then returning is a common behavioral pattern across many arthropods, vertebrates, and cephalopods, but no other animals (as far as I know), but it requires the ability to find the location again.
- *Paths* are ways of moving through an environment from one location to another target location through intermediate, less intrinsically desirable locations. Animals with BCE use a variety of tactics to track paths, such as computing path integrations, recognizing landmarks, and scaffolding the environment with trail markers.
- *Detours* are novel, indirect, multi-part paths to a target in situations where a direct or familiar path is unavailable. Detour use has been demonstrated in a wide variety of vertebrates and in spiders (reviewed in Jackson and Cross 2011). Experiments have failed to document detouring in cephalopods, although this is likely due to experimental limitations, as wild cephalopods probably use detours in their natural behavior (Alves et al., 2007).

Object-orientation

The environment contains repeatable, predictable chunks – objects – that can be good (food, friendly conspecifics, mates, safe places) or bad (predators, environmental hazards, social conflicts) for an animal. These features are structural invariants of the environment – they are there regardless of how or whether they are detected, and they are there regardless of what the animal is doing.

Objects as such have distinctive spatial properties invariants. They:

- have a single *location* at a time. Location changes smoothly (no teleportation);
- have persistent state;
- have *dispositions* (they will change or respond depending on what happens), including *affordances* – potentials for the animal to interact with the object;
- can have spatial *parts* with distinct properties and affordances. These:

  - usually move together through space; they predict each other's location;
  - often have predictable spatial relations (e.g. the shell has food inside it).

- fit into *categories* – clusters of strongly associated properties, features, and affordances.

A *search image* is a set of perceptual features an animal uses to detect a specific type of target object (or unique target object) in its environment (Tinbergen 1960; Ishii and Shimada 2010; Jackson and Cross 2011). Possessing or using a search image makes an animal more likely to detect the target object and less likely to detect others, particularly in a noisy or hostile environment where objects are disguised or hidden. Search images have been described in many vertebrates, and more recently in some invertebrate species, including parasitoid wasps (Ishii and Shimad 2010) and jumping spiders (Jackson and Cross 2011).

For most animals with CABs, many salient objects in the environment are *other animals*, affording predator/prey interactions, sexuality, resource competition, cooperative sociality, communication, social learning, etc. Animals with CABs, and therefore BCE, have distinctive invariants that can be tracked for effective interaction:

- *orientation*

    - *gaze*
    - *heading*
    - *action trajectories*

- *states of awareness* (e.g. has this predator noticed you?)
- *action capacities* and *dispositions to respond* to environmental conditions, and the perceiving animal's own behavior (including *communication*)
- *goals* as dynamic invariants toward which the animal's behavior is directed (Trestman 2010, 2012).

Action-orientation

Nearly everything that an animal needs to know must be in relation to its own body's requirements and capacities for action.

To behave in a coherent, goal-directed way, an animal must compose complex actions from simpler units of behavior (Trestman 2010, 2012). At every level of this compositional hierarchy, there exist structural invariants in the environment and sensorimotor-dynamic invariants in the interaction between the animal's body and the environment. These invariants must be discovered and continuously calibrated as body and environment change.

From an associative learning perspective, the problem is to select the correct behavior for the right situation. Complex behaviors must be formed through chaining and shaping (Skinner, 1981). From an ecological perspective, an animal's core cognitive/perceptual problem is to track invariants that allow for recognition and exploitation of affordances – opportunities for interaction (Gibson 1979). Affordances are relational – they are about the coupled dynamics of animal and environment, about what possibilities are offered by a situation given the body's capacities. In addition to the associative clusters that correspond to *objects*, the most important associations to be built are between affordances and behaviors that exploit them. Simple associative learning – classical conditioning and operant conditioning for atomic behaviors – is ubiquitous among even the simplest animals, and appears to be widespread in single-celled organisms, including bacteria. More complex kinds of learning, those that build associations between objects and actions in the senses I've developed here, are found only in arthropods, vertebrates, and cephalopods.

Social learning processes such as *local enhancement, stimulus enhancement, vicarious conditioning, emulation,* and *imitation* have differing cognitive prerequisites related to the elements of BCE described here. Other than the simplest, local enhancement, these forms of learning are found only in the three taxa with BCE. For the most part, they have only been demonstrated in vertebrates and bees (Avargues-Weber et al., 2014), but research on complex and social learning has been sadly lacking in invertebrates (but see Perry et al., 2016; Hollis and Guillette, 2015).

BItRIP as scaffolding for basic cognitive embodiment

Consciousness is a stream of sensory and motor information, consumed by the process of extracting intentional objects (objects, properties, events, space, and the body) in order to guide action with motivationally valenced anticipations of consequences. This shares the structure of the information-processing problem facing a brain in a complex, active body: extracting spatial, object-oriented, and action-oriented invariants from a stream of sensorimotor data. Just as the BItRIP structure described above is required to explain the phenomenology of experience, it is also required to account for the extraction of invariants crucial for perception and behavior.

As conscious animals, sensory impressions inform our understanding of the world around us, and our understanding of the world lets us predict our incoming sensory impressions. This ability to predict allows us to move our bodies to effectively gather information and reduce the uncertainty in our understanding of our world. We iteratively refine our understanding of the world by gathering information, making predictions, moving our bodies, and comparing our previous expectations to new sensations. Subjective experience is the highest-level integration of this flow from gathered information into expectation and intention to act. The *things* that we perceive in the world – affordances, people, places, features, properties, etc., are invariants that emerge in this flow.

The ability to predict the next few seconds based on the last few seconds is essential to experience, perceptual control of behavior, and also the learning that makes complex cognition, perception, and action possible. This is especially clear in Rescorla-Wagner learning, wherein degree of learning depends on degree of surprise, and in operant conditioning with negative reinforcement, wherein the *absence* of an inhibiting stimulus reinforces a behavior. The same sequence of environmental conditions can serve as a reward or a punishment, depending on the salient alternative possibility. Affective valence is at the core of our experience, and it is also a crucial driver of adaptive behavior (Ginsburg and Jablonka 2007, 2015). It binds our past, through learning, to our present actions, which shape the future. It drives our attention, our motivation, and our learning, and determines what we value, seek, and avoid.

Consciousness, the predictive extraction of intentional content from a temporalized stream of perception- and action-data, provides the cognitive structure crucial for control of a CAB. Therefore, it is a good bet that consciousness emerged in evolution together with complex active bodies; the cognitive structures essential to consciousness are crucial prerequisites to having a CAB as well. Consciousness and CABs may also have been lost together in evolution, for example, in taxa with parasitic lifestyles and extreme reduction in size and bodily complexity (e.g. some mites). The strength of my argument relies on the strength of association between the cognitive and bodily traits I've identified. How well do the cluster of cognitive and bodily traits hold together in evolution within the three taxa I've identified? Are there peaks of bodily or cognitive complexity of the relevant sort in other taxa? These are open questions. My argument also relies on the analysis of what cognitive structure is essential to consciousness. There is more work to be done on all fronts, but I hope to have outlined a promising approach to the phylogenetic question of consciousness.

Michael Trestman

References

Alves, C., Boal, J., and Dickel, L. 2007. Short-distance navigation in cephalopods: A review and synthesis. *Cognitive Processing, 9*(4), 239.

Avargues-Weber, A., and Chittka, L. 2014. Local enhancement or stimulus enhancement? Bumblebee social learning results in a specific pattern of flower preference. *Animal Behavior, 97*, 185–191.

Aydede, M. 2013. "Pain", in Edward N. Zalta (ed.), *The Stanford Encyclopedia of Philosophy* (Spring 2013 Edition), http://plato.stanford.edu/archives/spr2013/entries/pain/.

Baldauf, D., and Desimone, R. 2014. Neural mechanisms of object-based attention. *Science, 344*(6182), 424–427.

Block, N. 2011. Perceptual consciousness overflows cognitive access. *Trends in Cognitive Sciences, 15*(12), 567–575.

Carman, T. 1999. The body in Husserl and Merleau-Ponty. *Philosophical Topics, 27*(2), 205–226.

Crick, F., and Koch, C. 2003. A framework for consciousness. *Nature Neuroscience, 6*(2), 119–126.

Gibson, J. J. 1979. *The Ecological Approach to Visual Perception*. Boston: Houghton Mifflin.

Ginsburg, S., and Jablonka, E. 2007. The transition to experiencing: II. The evolution of associative learning based on feelings. *Biological Theory, 2*(3), 231–243.

Ginsburg, S., and Jablonka, E. 2015. The teleological transitions in evolution: A Gántian view. *Journal of Theoretical Biology, 381*, 55–60.

Godfrey-Smith, P. 2016. "Animal evolution and the origins of experience", in David Livingstone Smith (ed.), *How Biology Shapes Philosophy: New Foundations for Naturalism*. Cambridge: Cambridge University Press.

Gutnick, T., Byrne, R. A., and Hochner, B. Octopus vulgaris uses visual information to determine the location of its arm. *Current Biology, 21*(6), 460–462.

Hollis, K. L., and Guillette, L. M. 2015. What associative learning in insects tells us about the evolution of learned and fixed behavior. *International Journal of Comparative Psychology, 28*(1).

Husserl, E. 1963. *Cartesianische Meditationen und Pariser Vorträge, Husserliana* I, 2nd ed., ed. S. Strasser (Dordrecht: Kluwer Academic Publishers, 1963), §44: 128. Translated as *Cartesian Meditations: An Introduction to Phenomenology*, trans. D. Cairns (The Hague: Martinus Nijhoff Publishers, 1960), 97.

Ishii, Y., and Shimada, M. 2010. The effect of learning and search images on predator – prey interactions. *Population Ecology, 52*(1), 27–35.

Jackson, R. R., and Cross, F. R. 2011. Spider cognition. *Advances in Insect Physiology, 41*, 115.

James, W. (1890/1950) *The Principles of Psychology*. New York, Dover Publications.

Lee, D. N. 2009. General Tau theory: Evolution to date. *Perception, 38*(6), 837.

Merker, B. 2005. The liabilities of mobility: A selection pressure for the transition to consciousness in animal evolution. *Consciousness and Cognition, 14*, 89–114.

Merker, B. 2013. The efference cascade, consciousness, and its self: Naturalizing the first person pivot of action control. *Frontiers in Psychology*. http://journal.frontiersin.org/article/10.3389/fpsyg.2013.00501.

Mossio, M. and Taraborelli, D. 2008. Action-dependent perceptual invariants: From ecological to sensorimotor approaches. *Consciousness and Cognition, 17*(4), 1324–1340.

Perry, B., and Cheng, K. 2016. Invertebrate learning and cognition: Relating phenomena to neural substrate. *Wiley Interdisciplinary Reviews: Cognitive Science, 4*(5), 561–582.

Pinto, Y., Sligte, I. G., Shapiro, K. L., and Lamme, V. A. 2013. Fragile visual short-term memory is an object-based and location-specific store. *Psychonomic Bulletin & Review, 20*(4), 732–739. doi:10.3758/s13423-013-0393-4.

Pöppel, E. 2009. Pre-semantically defined temporal windows for cognitive processing. *Philosophical Transactions of the Royal Society of London B: Biological Sciences, 364*(1525), 1887–1896.

Singer, W., and Gray, C. M. 1995. Visual feature integration and the temporal correlation hypothesis. *Annual Review of Neuroscience, 18*(1), 555–586.

Skinner, B. F. 1981. Selection by consequences. *Science, 213*(4507), 501–504.

Tinbergen, L. 1960. The natural control of insects in pine woods. I. Factors influencing the intensity of predation by songbirds. *Archives Néerlandaises de Zoologie, 13*, 265–343.

Tononi, G., and Edelman, G. M. 1998. Consciousness and complexity. *Science, 282*(5395), 1846–1851.

Trestman, M. 2010. *Goal-Directedness, Behavior and Evolution: A Philosophical Investigation.* Davis: University of California.

Trestman, M. 2012. Implicit and explicit goal-directedness. *Erkenntnis,* 77(2), 207–236.

Trestman, M. 2013. The Cambrian explosion and the origins of embodied cognition. *Biological Theory, 8*(1), 80–92.

Trestman, M. 2014. The modal breadth of consciousness. *Philosophical Psychology, 27*(6), 843–861.

Trestman, M., and Allen, C. 2015. "Animal Consciousness", in Edward N. Zalta (ed.), *The Stanford Encyclopedia of Philosophy* (Summer 2015 Edition). http://plato.stanford.edu/archives/sum2015/entries/consciousness-animal/.

Van Gulick, R. 2014. "Consciousness", in Edward N. Zalta (ed.), *The Stanford Encyclopedia of Philosophy* (Spring 2014 Edition). http://plato.stanford.edu/archives/spr2014/entries/consciousness/.

Varela, F. J. 1996. Neurophenomenology: A methodological remedy for the hard problem. *Journal of Consciousness Studies, 3*(4), 330–349.

Wackerman, J. 2007. Inner and outer horizons of time experience. *Spanish Journal of Psychology, 10,* 20–32.

Zahavi, D. 1999. *Self-awareness and alterity: A phenomenological investigation.* Evanston, IL: Northwestern University Press.

20

THE EVOLUTION OF CONSCIOUSNESS IN PHYLOGENETIC CONTEXT

Peter Godfrey-Smith

Introduction

The aim of this chapter is to chart a number of options for the evolution of consciousness (in a broad sense of that term) with particular attention to how consciousness fits into the genealogical relations between animals represented in the "tree of life." The evolution of consciousness has been an area of rampant speculation. That speculative quality will remain for some time, but progress in various parts of biology is beginning to give us a more constrained sense of the likely shape of the history, or at least a range of possible shapes. The treatment in this chapter is preliminary and exploratory, though, and often written in a conditional mode: *if* biological feature *X* matters to consciousness, then the history of consciousness may have gone like this . . .

I focus especially on the following questions: Was there one path through which consciousness arose, or more than one? That is, was a single origin followed by radiation down various lines, or were there several independent origins? If there were multiple paths, is this a matter of a single *type* of path, and several instances or tokens of that type, or was there more than one type?

A second question is related: did consciousness arise in a gradual way, or was there more of a jump or threshold effect? In philosophy, people often talk as if consciousness is either present or absent; there's something it's like to be this creature, or there is not. But this may be a matter of degree, either with or without an "absolute zero."

The issues of gradualism and path number interact. The greater the role for gradual change, the deeper the evolution of consciousness probably goes (the further back a non-zero value probably goes), and hence the greater likelihood of one origin and subsequent radiation.

These questions would have simple answers if only humans, or only primates, were conscious. Then there would probably be a single origin, and radiation down just a few lines. I assume this restriction of the trait is unlikely. Other background assumptions made include materialism, and the assumption that a great many entities have no scrap of consciousness at all – there is an "absolute zero," and this is a common value. I also assume a mainstream neo-Darwinian form of evolutionary theory. The term "phylogenetic" in my title refers to large-scale historical patterns, especially the genealogical relationships between different kinds of organisms.

My title uses the term "consciousness" in a broad sense now common in the literature. In this sense, if there is "something it's like" to be an animal, then that animal is conscious (Nagel 1974, Chalmers 1996). I think this is not a helpful terminology. Historically, the term "consciousness" has usually suggested a rich form of experience, not the simple presence of feelings. Confusion arises from the terminological shift, as talk of consciousness in animals inevitably suggests a sophisticated "here I am" state of mind, not just a wash of feeling. Aside from the history of ideas, I expect the eventual shape of a good theory to be one that recognizes a broad category of *sentience*, something present in many animals, and treats consciousness as a narrower category. That broad-versus-narrow distinction could be marked in various ways, though, and terminology *per se* does not matter much. So especially when discussing other people's views, I will use "consciousness" in a broad manner here, only occasionally being more careful with the term.

The next section discusses the evolutionary history of animals. I then lay out some biological and cognitive features that have a *prima facie* relationship to consciousness, and look at their different evolutionary paths.

Evolutionary background

The history of life on earth is often said to form the shape of a tree. What is meant is that from a single origin, a series of branching events gave rise to the different forms of life present at later times. The tree model does not fit all forms of life well (bacteria, for example, form a network with a different shape), but this chapter focuses on animals, and the genealogical relationships among animals are indeed tree-like.

Animals originated something like 700–900 million years ago, and comprise a single tree-shaped branch within the total genealogical structure. It is still common, mostly outside of biology, to talk of "higher" and "lower" animals, and of a phylogenetic "scale." (A person might ask: "where in the phylogenetic scale does consciousness begin?") This does not make much sense as a way of describing the evolutionary relationships. In a tree, there is "higher and lower" in the sense of *earlier* and *later*. But there are lateral relationships as well, and much of what people have in mind when they talk of a phylogenetic scale is not a matter of temporal order. They might intend a distinction between simple and complex, but there are many varieties of complexity (is a bee less complex than an eel?).

Jellyfish, for example, might be called "lower animals," but present-day jellyfish are the products of as much evolution as we are. There were jellyfish-*like* animals well before there were human-like animals; present-day jellyfish have relatives much lower (earlier) on the tree who look a fair bit like them, most likely, whereas all our relatives from that time look very different from us. Some of our ancestors might have looked something like jellyfish. But simple animals living now need not resemble ancestors, either of them or of us, and complex earlier forms can have simpler descendents.

So within a tree-based picture of animal life, there is earlier versus later, closer versus further (from us, or someone else), and there are various senses of simple versus complex. None of these match up well with "higher versus lower."

Any two animals alive now have various common ancestors, including a *most recent* common ancestor, the last one before the evolutionary lines leading to each present-day animal diverged. The shape of the history of animals is shown in Figure 20.1. Among the groups left out of the figure are two problematic ones: ctenophores and placozoans. Ctenophores are also known as "comb jellies," though they are not really jellyfish. Placozoans are mysterious creeping animals without nervous systems. Nervous systems appear to have evolved early (perhaps 700 million years ago) and are seen in nearly all animals. It is contentious whether nervous systems evolved once or more than once, due especially to uncertainty over the location of ctenophores, which have nervous systems, in relation to sponges and placozoans, which do not. I'll set those questions aside and look just at the large branch of animals who have nervous systems and are on

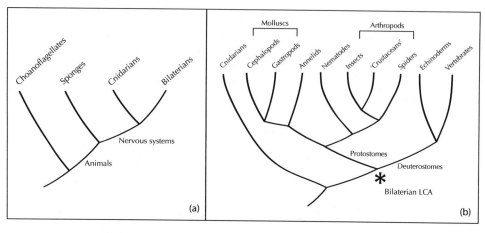

Figure 20.1 Genealogical relationships between some animal groups. Present-day organisms are along the top and the past extends down the page. Figure 20.1(a) shows the branching of animals from their nearest non-animal relatives, the choanoflagellates, and the relationships between sponges, cnidarians, and all bilaterian (bilaterally symmetrical) animals. Two controversial groups are not shown, ctenophores and placozoans. As ctenophores may have branched from the line leading to bilaterians before sponges did, and ctenophores have nervous systems, it is possible that nervous systems originated twice, and only one origin is shown here. Figure 20.1(b) is a finer-grained representation of the relationships between bilaterian groups discussed in the text, with cnidarians to their left as in Figure 20.1(a). The "bilaterian LCA" is the last common ancestor of bilaterian animals. The traditional category "crustacean" is probably non-monophyletic (does not pick out a single branch of the tree); the crustaceans relevant here are all Malacostraca. Branch lengths are not to scale, taxonomic ranks are mixed, and many groups are omitted.

the right of sponges on Figure 20.1(a). Those are the cnidarians, which include jellyfish, corals, and anemones, and *bilaterians* – bilaterally symmetrical animals – which include us, fish, birds, octopuses, ants, crabs, and others.

The last common ancestor of bilaterian animals (hereafter, "bilaterian LCA") lived perhaps 600 million years ago. It was very possibly a small flattened worm, but no fossil record exists of this animal. If the figure of 600 million years ago is right, then the setting for the evolution of this animal is the *Ediacaran* period (635–540 million years ago), a time when all animals were soft-bodied and marine, probably with very limited behavioral capacities (Peterson et al. 2008, Budd and Jensen 2015). Genetic evidence places many significant branchings in this period. Then, in the *Cambrian* period (540–485 million years ago), bodies with hard parts appeared – shells, legs, and claws – along with image-forming eyes. Most of the familiar groups of present-day animals have a recognizable fossil record from this time, including arthropods, molluscs, and vertebrates. Predation is also evident from the fossils. Animal life was still entirely marine, though some animals began to move onto land from about 430 million years ago. In a few groups, significant neural and behavioral complexity also arose, especially in vertebrates, arthropods, and one group of molluscs, the cephalopods.

A first rough count might then recognize three independent origins for conspicuously complex nervous systems and behavior. Those origins are independent – in this first count – because the most recent common ancestor of those three groups was probably a simple worm-like animal. In addition, cephalopods acquired their large nervous systems in a process that stemmed from a simple shelled mollusc. Figure 20.1(b) shows the relationships between these groups in more detail (see also Trestman 2013, Farris 2015, Feinberg and Mallatt 2016).

That first count of three origins for complex behavior will be contentious for many reasons. Animals differ in cognitive and behavioral styles, showing many kinds of complexity. There are also lumping-versus-splitting issues. I counted one origin for vertebrates, but mammals and birds are more neurally complex than other vertebrates, including their common ancestor, so you can count two origins within the vertebrates for complex behavior in one reasonable sense. Within the arthropods are several groups with complexity of their own particular kind, not all clustered together. Behaviorally complex spiders, for example, are some distance from behaviorally complex insects such as bees. Still, there is some sense in that first count of three evolutionary lines producing significant neural and behavioral complexity.

Complexity and integration

Which biological features are relevant to the evolution of subjective experience? There is no consensus on what matters – on what makes the difference between there being, or not being, "something it's like" to be an animal. This chapter aims at a compromise between covering ideas that have been influential in the literature, exploring directions I think are promising, and discussing options that illuminate evolutionary possibilities. (For a more opinionated treatment, see Godfrey-Smith forthcoming). I'll begin by looking at a view based on a kind of overall cognitive complexity in animals, and then move to views that posit more specific innovations.

The first option can be motivated by the idea that perhaps what we call "consciousness" is just cognition, the information-processing side of the mind, as seen "from the inside," though perhaps only cognition that has a certain degree of complexity suffices. As emphasized above, there are different kinds of complexity. But it might be possible to pick out a common element, and a common currency, that get us some purchase on the situation. Many kinds of complexity in how animals handle sensory information and control action can be understood in terms of *integration*. In some, but not all, animals, the deliverances of many senses are integrated when working out what to do, and this integration might amount to building a kind of "model" of the world. Present experience may also be integrated with earlier experience, by means of memory. Choice of action may be conditioned by motivational tradeoffs – an integrated handling of competing goals. These are all moves away from simple patterns in which a sensed event gives rise to a fixed response.

The idea that integration is pivotal to consciousness figures in several other literatures. An extreme development of the idea is the "Integrated Information Theory" of Tononi and Koch (2015), in which *any* sort of integration of processing in a system counts – whether or not the system is alive, and whether or not it has senses and controls action. I don't think that near-panpsychist view is well motivated (2015), but integration might be important in other ways. "Global workspace" theories of consciousness treat the integration of sensory information, and sensory information with memory, as a feature of brain processes associated with consciousness (Baars 1988, Dehaene 2014). Some versions of this view associate integration and the creation of a "workspace" with particular vertebrate-specific brain structures. A more liberal version would see integration of information as achievable in various ways. Far from the usual territory of workspace views, Klein and Barron (2016) argue for the likely presence of consciousness in insects, based on the integrated way they handle sensory information and determine behavior: "Centralization in the service of action selection is ... the advance that allowed for the evolution of subjective experience."

If an approach along these lines were right, it would suggest a gradualist view of the evolution of consciousness. Cognitive complexity of a kind measured by integration shades off into low values, and does so in a way that extends well outside animals. Even some bacteria have a sensorimotor arc that works through a comparison of what is sensed in the present and in the immediate past (Baker et al. 2006).

Dramatic changes occurred in this feature, however, in animal evolution. The invention of the nervous system – with the branching dendrites of neurons ideal for integrating inputs – was a landmark, as was the invention of the bilaterian body plan, which led to the evolution of centralized nervous systems. (Cnidarians have nervous systems but not the centralization associated with a brain.)

In Figure 20.1(b), the bilaterian LCA is marked with an asterisk. The traditional picture of this animal has been that it was small and simple, probably flatworm-like, with little or no neural centralization. The brains of arthropods and vertebrates were seen as independent inventions, without a common design or a mapping from part to part based on common ancestry. Some recent work, though, has posited a richer endowment at this crucial stage. Wolff and Strausfeld (2016) argue that commonalities in layout between arthropod and vertebrate brains show that an "executive brain" was present in their common ancestor. What is meant by "executive brain" is less tendentious than it might sound; the suggestion is that there was some centralization, featuring two circuits that achieve integration in the sense introduced above. One circuit integrates different sensory inputs, and the other enables comparison of present input with the recent past (Strausfeld, personal communication). The quiet years of the Ediacaran may then have seen the origin of a new kind of control device in animals.

Within the view positing an executive brain in early bilaterians, cephalopods become a very special case. The argument for complexity in the bilaterian LCA by Wolff and Strausfeld is based on a comparison of vertebrates and arthropods. Cephalopod brains, they note, are different from both. The resulting picture would be one in which the bilaterian LCA had an executive brain carried forward through arthropod and vertebrate lines, but early molluscs threw this brain away. Cephalopods eventually evolved a new one with a different organization. There would then be two origins for an integrating executive brain, one for cephalopods and one for everyone else who has one.

Sensing and perceptual representation

The first option, which suggested a gradualist view, supposed that consciousness is just the information-processing side of the mind as seen "from the inside," and the evolution of consciousness tracks the general evolution of cognitive complexity. This has not been the approach generally taken in recent discussions. Instead, the usual aim has been to find one or more specific innovations that are the basis for consciousness. Most researchers accept that even quite complex perception, cognition, and control of action can go on entirely "in the dark" (Milner and Goodale 2005, Dehaene 2014). If "much of what can be done consciously can also be done unconsciously" in the human case (Prinz, Chapter 17 in this volume), it makes it unlikely that the division between conscious and non-conscious across animals is a simple matter of complexity of the nervous system.

Though much work has been guided by this perceived dissociation between cognitive complexity and consciousness, such a view can be challenged even for the human cases that provide the data. Morten Overgaard, for example, argues that a close look at "blindsight," and related phenomena, shows a tighter relationship between what is experienced and what can be done (Overgaard et al. 2006). I won't take sides on this debate, and in the rest of the chapter I'll look at views that isolate specific traits as crucial to consciousness.

The first is a family of views that focus on sensing and perceptual representation. Perhaps what matters to consciousness is a particular kind of processing along a sensory path. Certainly it seems that, for us, subjective experience is brimful of sensory encounter with the world.

A theory of consciousness might then be a theory of a specific kind of processing of sensory information – Prinz (Chapter 17 in this volume) defends a view of this kind.

Sensing itself is ubiquitous; it is seen in unicellular organisms and plants as well as animals. If you think sophistication in sensory systems holds the key to consciousness, you could opt for a gradualist view that extended some degree of consciousness outside animals. But there are landmarks in the evolution of sensing that might have special importance. Looking first at sense organs themselves, the Cambrian sees the evolution of image-forming eyes of two kinds, the compound eyes of arthropods and camera eyes of vertebrates. Cephalopods later evolved camera eyes independently. This is the beginning of the sensory presentation of objects in space. Dan-Eric Nilsson's survey of animal eyes (2013) recognizes just three groups with "Class IV" eyes, high-resolution image-forming eyes: arthropods, vertebrates, and cephalopods, the same three groups picked out at the end of the previous section.

Feinberg and Mallatt (2016) link the evolution of consciousness to the invention of brains that *map* what is sensed, with spatially organized neural structures. Some animals, and not all, engage in neural processing that is isomorphic to the structure of sensory stimulation. The presence of spatially organized processing of sensory information may indeed be a landmark, though the way Feinberg and Mallatt bring this feature to bear on consciousness has some problems. They say that spatially organized neural structures give rise to mental *images*. The idea of a mental image is experiential, but the "images" that Feinberg and Mallatt describe neurobiologically are map-like internal structures. Citing the presence of neural "images" in this sense does not itself establish a link to consciousness.

Prinz argues that the special feature distinguishing conscious from unconscious sensing involves how the senses connect to the next stages downstream, through *attention* and *working memory*. Attention is a gateway to working memory, and for sensory information to be in attention is for it to be conscious.[1] Prinz, in Chapter 17 in this volume, discusses how these traits might be distributed among animals. They are not restricted to mammals. Both are present in birds, and fish can also achieve "trace conditioning," which involves holding a stimulus "in mind" over a delay. Trace conditioning is both a test for working memory and a form of conditioning with an empirical connection to conscious reportability in humans (Allen, Chapter 38 in this volume). Even some insects have attention and working memory. Cephalopods, for Prinz, are a "maybe." Put into the phylogenetic structure of Figure 20.1(b), this suggests a view with multiple path *tokens* and one path *type*. Consciousness for Prinz has a unified basis – the same package of features have to be present in every case – but the package probably evolved more than once. If cephalopods are included, three path tokens is again a plausible number, unless there was more than one origination event within one or more of those large groups.

Prinz sees attention and working memory as definite inventions, which are either present or not. But both might be seen as shading off into minimal forms (recurrent neural network structures in the case of working memory; any kind of flexible allocation of resources in the case of attention). Then the story would be more gradualist and might push deeper, yielding fewer distinct origins.

I'll discuss one more view that emphasizes the sensory side, drawing on Merker (2005). If an organism has rich senses and can also move freely, this introduces ambiguity into the origins of sensory stimulation. Was that sensory event due to what I did, or to a change out in the world? In invertebrates, Merker says, this problem tends to be handled peripherally, with a neural patch of some sort, but in vertebrates it motivates the construction of a centralized "model" of the world, with the self as part of the model. Barron and Klein (2016) argue that insects do construct such models in a relevantly similar way to vertebrates, and this feature is indicative of consciousness in both cases.

Either tied to the notion of "world model" or in a more general way, the transition to a form of sensing that includes internalization of a distinction between self and other may be particularly relevant to the evolution of consciousness. Once again, this begins early and in simple forms (Crapse and Sommer 2008); circuitry that handles self/other issues in this way is found even in nematodes, which have only a few hundred neurons. Animals can have this capacity while not having image-forming eyes or similarly sophisticated senses. A version may have been present even in the bilaterian LCA, though this is also a plausible candidate for several independent inventions.

Evaluation and feelings

Another candidate for a basic, old form of subjective experience is *feelings* of the kind that figure in evaluation – feelings marking a distinction between good and bad, welcome and unwelcome. Perhaps the first kind of subjective experience was affective or evaluative? This is a form of experience with a plausible evolutionary rationale (Denton et al. 2009, Damasio and Carvalho 2013).

If we start with the general idea of valuation – treating events as welcome or unwelcome – then we again face the fact that this capacity goes back far in history and reaches far away on the tree. Bacteria and plants are valuers in a broad sense, discriminating welcome from unwelcome events. But as with sensing, there might be some landmark introducing a kind of evaluative processing with plausible links to consciousness.

One way to develop such a view looks at the role of evaluation in learning. This view can be introduced through recent work on pain. "Nociception" – detecting damage and producing an immediate response, such as withdrawal – is very common in animals. Pain as a *feeling*, with its distinctive aversive quality, is thought to involve something extra. Perhaps the organisms that experience aversive feelings are the ones that can put the detection of unwelcome events to work in rewiring their behavior for later occasions (Allen et al. 2005, Elwood 2012). Pain, on this view, is a teacher for the long term.

This view might be generalized to feelings other than pain. Indeed, pain is a special case, as it has a sensory side that is concerned with (putting it briefly) facts as well as values. "Classical" theories of pain distinguish two neural paths, one tracking locations and varieties of damage (that's a sting, in my toe . . .), and another concerned with the unpleasantness of pain (. . . and it feels very bad). There is "pain affect" as well as "sensory pain experience." Here we are especially concerned with the affective side. Perhaps the felt side of valuation and reward systems in animals has a general involvement with learning. Animals that cannot learn by tracking aversive and positive experiences would then lack (this kind of) subjective experience.

I don't know of a theory that makes that claim in a simple and direct way, though some are close. Ginsburg and Jablonka (2007) see associative learning as crucial to the evolution of consciousness, but they have in mind a subset of reward-based learning together with some other kinds, unified by their "open-ended" character (see below). Similarly, Allen et al. (2005) do not argue that all instrumental learning comprises evidence for pain affect, only kinds powerful enough to establish novel behaviors in an individual's repertoire. I think the claim that learning is *the* key to consciousness is unlikely to be right. But let's follow this path some distance, and then look at reasons to modify it.

I'll use the term "instrumental learning" for learning by tracking the good and bad consequences of actions. This is one of two main kinds of "associative" learning. The other, "classical" conditioning, as seen in Pavlov's dog, is essentially predictive and need not involve (much) evaluation. One event (a bell) is used as a predictor of another (food). Classical conditioning is very common in bilaterian animals and has been reported (once) in an anemone. (I use here a survey of invertebrate learning by Perry et al. 2013.) The first credible report of classical conditioning in a plant has also just been published (Gagliano et al. 2016). Instrumental learning appears to be rarer. It is scattered through the tree of animals in a way that suggests it may have evolved a number of times. It is seen in vertebrates, in some molluscs (gastropods and cephalopods), and some arthropods. Various insects, especially bees, are good at it, but in some others it has not been seen. The Perry et al. review I rely on here reports cases where the trait has been shown *present*, and does not make claims about what is absent (which would be harder to do). But the review does list it as unreported in an interesting range of groups, including wasps (which are insects), spiders, myriapods such as millipedes, and starfish.

This sets up an interesting relation between the family of traits discussed in the previous section, concerned with sensing, and those discussed here. Animals can have one while lacking the other, it seems. I'll discuss that relationship below. First I will look more closely at valuation and learning.

The boundary between instrumental and other kinds of learning does not appear to be sharp, and the boundary between instrumental *learning* and reward-based behavior of other kinds is not sharp either. Beginning with the second relationship, moment-to-moment guidance of behavior with reward systems is more common than learning through reward. Moment-to-moment guidance of this kind is seen in an animal's tendency to stay in the area of a rewarding stimulus, or continuing to approach it, in a way that need have no long-term consequences. A wide range of these reward-based behaviors across animals have a common neurochemical basis, in dopamine systems (Barron et al. 2010). Reward-responsive behavior is mediated by dopamine in nematodes, molluscs, and vertebrates – animals whose most recent common ancestor was again the bilaterian LCA. That suggests that dopamine-based reward-guided behavior might have evolved before the Cambrian. Barron et al. (2010) raise this possibility but think it unlikely. Instead, they think that an old role for dopamine, and/or related compounds, in modulating behavior in response to environmental stimuli made them natural raw materials for use in the evolution of genuine reward-based control systems, when they arose in various animals later on.

The view tying feelings to learning is one way of finding an evolutionary landmark distinguishing simple from complex evaluation. But some of the best behavioral evidence for pain in invertebrates involves moment-to-moment reward-based behavior, not long-term change (Elwood 2012). These behaviors show trade-offs between competing goals – hermit crabs will leave shells to avoid electric shock, but better shells will only be relinquished after stronger shocks. Those trade-offs, which need not involve lasting behavioral change, seem powerful evidence for affect in their own right. In reply, it might be noted that these animals *can* also learn instrumentally. Still, is there reason to think that learning *per se* is what counts? An alternative view is that learning is standing in here for a general sophistication in the handling of valence in experience, or is one variety of this sophistication among several. Perhaps instrumental learning (or a subset of it) is sufficient but not necessary for the kind of evaluative cognition associated with subjective experience.[2] Something that does seem to make sense at this point, though, is the general idea of an *evaluative path* to consciousness.

Divergences

Evaluative feelings are plausible early forms of subjective experience. Perceptual states of some kinds are another plausible form. Both have been used in single-factor theories. People also often write as if they go together – as if once you are "conscious," you are aware of the world *and* experience things as good or bad. But these two features might come apart; the presence of one does not imply other, and each might have their own role in evolution.

First, it seems possible in principle to have a rich form of evaluation present in an animal that is quite unsophisticated on the sensory side. Such an animal would not be entirely cut off from the world; no animal is. But assuming some distinction between genuine perception and mere sensitivity (Burge 2010), it seems there could be an animal that was richly involved with evaluation and affect, but not in a way that included a sophisticated referral of sensed events to objects in the environment. The organism might lack the ability to track exactly what is going on around it, but have a stronger registration of whether whatever is going on is welcome or unwelcome.

The other separation seems possible as well. There could apparently be an animal that tracked the world with its senses in acute and complex ways, handling the self/other divide in a sophisticated manner, but was much simpler on the evaluative side – an animal more "robotic" in that sense.

In vertebrates, we have both sides – complex sensing and evaluation. The same is seen in octopuses. But other cases might probe the relationship between the two. For example, some land-dwelling arthropods might be examples of perceptually complex animals with much simpler evaluation.

All the cases are uncertain. Some spiders show complex behavior (Jackson and Cross 2011). In Perry et al. (2013), spiders are absent from the list of instrumental learners. Sometimes jumping spiders *are* reported as instrumental learners, but at best they are an interesting borderline case, given what is known. What has been shown is that during an attempt to catch an individual prey item, a trial-and-error process is used to find a way of deceiving the prey with signals. Successful signals are not (as far as is known) carried over from day to day, and there is no reason why they should be. I said above that I doubt that learning is *the* crucial element on an evaluative path to consciousness, so I don't think the absence of learning here need be especially significant, but spiders remain animals where there is an apparently limited role for integrated, non-routine guidance of behavior by evaluative experiences.

Wasps are also listed as classical but not instrumental learners in the Perry et al. review (though I have seen one positive report: Huigens et al. 2009). The category "wasp" does not pick out a definite branch of the phylogenetic tree, as ants and bees are embedded within the same branch, surrounded by various animals with a wasp-like lifestyle.

These sorts of cases give us at least a sense of what to look for, and *if* arthropods of this kind had rather simple evaluative capacities, that would make ecological sense. Terrestrial arthropods such as wasps often have short lives dominated by routine – by a specific series of behaviors that have to be performed. But these animals can face substantial sensorimotor demands, especially those that can fly.

What about the other side? In the Perry et al. review, gastropods (slugs and snails) are the least mobile animals reported to have shown instrumental learning. What has been found is, as far as I know, very simple forms of this learning, not the discovery and entrenchment of novel behaviors. But they seem a possible case. They have fairly simple eyes (though some do have low-resolution image-forming eyes – Nilsson's "Class III" eyes) and simple ways of moving (no flight, though some can swim). They may be simple on the sensory side and stronger on the evaluative side: they might have a fairly rich sense of good and bad, but a weaker grip on what exactly is going *on* in the world.

So there are two traits here that have plausible connections to subjective experience, but they do not look like *different paths to the same thing*. They lead to different things. Both of them can be summarized with the idea that there is "something it's like to be" one of those animals, but the evaluative and perceptual forms of this feeling-like-something are different. Animals might gain both features, either one first and then the other, or both at once. They might also stop having gained one, if the second is of little use or precluded for some reason. Are all the sequences equally plausible in principle? Speculatively, I suggest that the evaluation-only and evaluation → perception paths might be less straightforward. Animals may need to have fairly complex behavioral capacities in order for complex evaluation to do them much good, and if they have those complex behavioral capacities, they might need fairly complex sensing as well. The converse does not hold; if your life is short and routinized, then evaluation may remain simple, even if you have complex sensorimotor tasks to deal with. This would make it hard to start with the evaluative form of consciousness and move to the perceptual form, easier to move in the other direction. I raise this asymmetry tentatively, and I may also be short-changing the gastropods (Gelperin 2013).

Earlier I discussed Feinberg and Mallatt's view of sensing and consciousness (2016). In their full treatment, they distinguish several kinds of consciousness: *exteroceptive*, *interoceptive*, and *affective* (sometimes collapsing these into *sensory* and *affective* consciousness). They see instrumental learning as important on the affective side, and note the possible role of gastropods as richer on the affective than sensory side. But they group arthropods together as a single case, one probably showing all their varieties of consciousness. I think, instead, that arthropods might diverge in notable ways. Some marine crustaceans are long-lived and may have more "open" lives than arthropods on land. Adamo (2016), commenting on Klein and Barron's claims for insect consciousness, also notes that insects tend to face selective pressure to reduce the size of their brains. A short-lived animal with little scope for flexible, open-ended behavior that is also under pressure to keep its brain small might keep its evaluative machinery simple – too simple for consciousness. Elwood's work (discussed above) shows that evidence for pain is quite strong in some crustaceans – stronger than it is for insects, who have not, to my knowledge, been found to engage in behavioral trade-offs or wound-tending of the kind seen in crustaceans (Eisemann et al. 1984, Sneddon et al. 2014). On the other hand, instrumental learning has been found in insects of several kinds, including learning based on aversive stimuli (heat).

So at least in principle, we see several different path *types* that animals may have taken in the evolution of consciousness, as well as a significant chance of multiple path instances. A single path instance is only plausible if consciousness is very evolutionarily shallow, restricted to animals like us, or very deep, creeping into existence early in animal life, or even before.

Notes

1 Prinz also thinks that a kind of synchronized neural pattern, gamma waves, have special importance to consciousness – I won't discuss that part of his view here.
2 I am indebted to Tyler Wilson for pressing this argument about learning to me. See also Shevlin (forthcoming) on the significance of motivational trade-offs.

References

Adamo SA (2016). Consciousness explained or consciousness redefined? *Proceedings of the National Academy of Sciences USA* 113(27): E3812.

Allen C (Chapter 38 in this volume). Associative learning.

Allen C, Fuchs P, Shriver A, and Wilson H (2005). Deciphering animal pain. In M Aydede (ed.), *Pain: New Essays on Its Nature and the Methodology of Its Study*. Cambridge, MA: MIT Press, pp. 351–366.

Baars B (1988). *A Cognitive Theory of Consciousness*. Cambridge: Cambridge University Press.

Baker M, Wolanin P, and Stock J (2006). Signal transduction in bacterial chemotaxis. *Bioessays* 28: 9–22.

Barron AB, Søvik E, and Cornish JL (2010). The roles of dopamine and related compounds in reward-seeking behavior across animal phyla. *Frontiers in Behavioral Neuroscience* 4: 1–9.

Budd G, and Jensen S (2015). The origin of the animals and a 'Savannah' hypothesis for early bilaterian evolution. *Biological Reviews* 92(1): 446–473, epub ahead of print. doi:10.1111/brv.12239

Burge T (2010). *Origins of Objectivity*. Oxford: Oxford University Press.

Chalmers D. (1996). *The Conscious Mind: In Search of a Fundamental Theory*. Oxford: Oxford University Press.

Crapse P, and Sommer M (2008). Corollary discharge across the animal kingdom. *Nature Reviews Neuroscience* 9: 587–600.

Damasio A, and Carvalho G (2013). The nature of feelings: Evolutionary and neurobiological origins. *Nature Reviews Neuroscience* 14: 143–152.

Dehaene D. (2014). *Consciousness and the Brain: Deciphering How the Brain Codes Our Thoughts*. New York: Penguin Random House.

Denton D., McKinley MJ, Farrell M, and Egan DF (2009). The role of primordial emotions in the evolutionary origin of consciousness. *Consciousness and Cognition* 18: 500–514.

Eisemann, CH, Jorgensen WK, Merritt DJ, Rice MJ, Cribb BW, Webb PD, and Zalucki MP (1984). Do insects feel pain? – a biological view. *Experientia* 40: 164–167.

Elwood RW (2012). Evidence for pain in decapod crustaceans. *Animal Welfare* 21: 23–27.

Farris SM (2015). Evolution of brain elaboration. *Philosophical Transactions of the Royal Society of London B* 370: 20150054.

Feinberg T, and Mallatt J (2016). *The Ancient Origins of Consciousness*. Cambridge, MA: MIT Press.

Gagliano M, Vyazovskiy V, Borbély A, Grimonprez M, and Depczynski M (2016). Learning by association in plants. *Scientific Reports* 6: 38427.

Gelperin A (2013). Associative memory mechanisms in terrestrial slugs and snails. In R Menzel and P Benjamin (eds.), *Invertebrate Learning and Memory*. London: Elsevier, pp. 280–290.

Ginsburg S, and Jablonka E (2007). The transition to experiencing: II. The evolution of associative learning based on feelings. *Biological Theory* 2: 231–243.

Godfrey-Smith P (2015). *Integrated information*. http://metazoan.net/27-integrated-information/

Godfrey-Smith P (forthcoming). Evolving across the explanatory gap.

Huigens ME, Pashalidou FG, Qian M-H, Bukovinszky T, Smid HM, van Loon JJA, Dicke M, and Fatouros NE (2009). Hitch-hiking parasitic wasp learns to exploit butterfly antiaphrodisiac. *Proceedings of the National Academy of Sciences USA* 106: 820–825.

Jackson R, and Cross F (2011). Spider cognition. *Advances in Insect Physiology* 41: 115–174

Klein C, and Barron AB (2016). Insects have the capacity for subjective experience. *Animal Sentience* 9(1).

Merker B (2005). The liabilities of mobility: A selection pressure for the transition to consciousness in animal evolution. *Consciousness and Cognition* 14: 89–114.

Milner D, and Goodale M (2005). *Sight Unseen: An Exploration of Conscious and Unconscious Vision*. Oxford: Oxford University Press.

Overgaard M, Rote J, Mouridsen K, and Ramsøy TZ (2006). Is conscious perception gradual or dichotomous? A comparison of report methodologies during a visual task. *Consciousness and Cognition* 15: 700–708.

Nagel T (1974). What is it like to be a bat? *Philosophical Review* 83: 435–450.

Nilsson D-E (2013). Eye evolution and its functional basis. *Visual Neuroscience* 30: 5–20.

Perry C, Barron A, and Cheng K (2013). Invertebrate learning and cognition: Relating phenomena to neural substrate. *WIREs Cognitive Science* 4: 561–582. doi:10.1002/wcs.1248

Peterson K, Cotton J, Gehling J, and Pisani D (2008). The Ediacaran emergence of bilaterians: Congruence between the genetic and the geological fossil records. *Philosophical Transactions of the Royal Society of London B* 363: 1435–1443.

Prinz J (Chapter 17 in this volume). Attention, working memory, and animal consciousness.

Shevlin H (forthcoming). Understanding suffering: A sensory-motivational account of unpleasant experience.

Sneddon L, Elwood RW, Adamo SA, and Leach MC (2014). Defining and assessing animal pain. *Animal Behaviour* 97: 201–212.

Tononi G, and Koch C (2015). Consciousness: Here, there and everywhere? *Philosophical Transactions of the Royal Society of London B* 370: 20140167. http://dx.doi.org/10.1098/rstb.2014.0167

Trestman M (2013). The Cambrian explosion and the origins of embodied cognition. *Biological Theory* 8: 80–92.

PART IV

Mindreading

21

ANIMAL MINDREADING

The problem and how it can be solved

Robert Lurz

Introduction

For many species of animal, the ability to predict the behavior of others is vital to their well-being and reproductive success.[1] In the field of animal social cognition, there are two generally recognized types of strategies that animals are understood to use to make such predictions. *Behavior-reading* is one type of strategy. This strategy involves predicting the behavior of others on the basis of observable cues that are perceived, believed, or otherwise represented to obtain *without interpreting those cues as signs of underlying mental states* (Lurz 2009, 2011; Povinelli and Vonk 2003). The observable cues can include bodily appearances (e.g., threatening posture), behaviors (e.g., reaching toward a particular object or place), and environmental relations (e.g., looking in the direction of a particular object or place); and the predictive process itself can be the result of individual learning or innate mechanisms. The other behavior-predicting strategy is *mindreading* (aka theory of mind). This strategy involves *inferring others' mental states*, such as sensory experiences, desires, and beliefs, from represented observable cues, and using this information about others' mental states to predict their behavior (Premack and Woodruff 1978). Here, too, the inferential and predictive processes involved may be the result of individual learning or innate mechanisms.[2]

Although mindreading and behavior-reading are different predictive strategies, they are not mutually exclusive. Humans are capable of both (Apperly and Butterfill 2009; Doherty 2011), and some animals are capable of behavior-reading (Lurz, Kanet and Krachun 2014). But are any animals capable of mindreading? And if some are, what sort of empirical tests would validly demonstrate this? This last question, in particular, has been a central question in animal social cognition research for over four decades. During that time, researchers have tested a range of animals on a number of different types of mindreading tests. Although the tests have varied along a number of dimensions (e.g., the apparatuses used or whether the tests involved a cooperative or competitive task), they all followed a *standard methodology*.

On the standard methodology, an animal A_1 is given an experimental and a control test.[3] In the experimental test, A_1 is presented with an observable cue C that is a sign that another animal A_2 is in some type of mental state M. For example, A_1 might observe that A_2 is looking at a piece of food on the ground, which is a sign that A_2 sees the food.[4] In the experimental test, there is also an expected behavior B of A_2 that is contingent upon A_2 being in the mental state

M. The expected behavior, for example, might be that A_2 will go for the food, since A_2 sees it. The control test is just like the experimental test except that the observable cue C is absent, as well as A_2's mental state M and expected behavior B. For example, in the control test, A_1 might observe that a piece of food on the ground is not in A_2's line of gaze (since it is hidden behind an opaque barrier), indicating that A_2 cannot see the food and, as a result, will not go for it. On the standard methodology, if A_1 successfully predicts that A_2 will do B in the experimental test but not in the control test, and there is no evidence that A_1 has learned to make such a prediction during the course of testing (e.g., by being rewarded for making such predictions), then A_1 is taken to pass the mindreading test.

On some tests that employ the standard methodology, animals have failed (e.g., Call and Tomasello 1999; Povinelli and Eddy 1996), while on others they have passed (e.g., Hare, Call, Agnetta, and Tomasello 2000; Hare, Call, and Tomasello 2001). Does the fact that some animals have passed such tests provide sufficient grounds to believe that they are capable of mindreading? The answer, of course, depends upon the validity of the tests. If the tests are such that they could just as plausibly be passed by animals using a behavior-reading strategy, then they are not valid and passing them should not be taken as sufficient grounds for believing that the animal in question is capable of mindreading.

The logical problem

A handful of researchers (Heyes 1998; Perner 2008; Povinelli and Vonk 2003; Lurz 2009; Lurz and Krachun 2011) have argued that tests that employ the standard methodology are invalid. The reasons for this are that (a) the observable cues used in these tests are confounded with the mental states being investigated, and that (b) the design of the tests leaves open the reasonable possibility that the animals know in advance of the experimental test that these cues correlate with the type of behavior they are asked to predict. To illustrate, consider the example of the standard methodology above. In that example, A_2's line of gaze to the food (observable cue) is confounded with A_2's seeing the food (mental state). Furthermore, if A_1 is like most social animals that compete for food, it is quite possible that A_1 knows (either from past experience or innately) in advance of the experimental test that A_2 (or animals like A_2) typically go for food in their line of gaze. As a result of the confound and reasonable possibility mentioned, we cannot say whether A_1's successful prediction of A_2's behavior in the experimental test is due to A_1 understanding that A_2 sees the food (mindreading) or to A_1 understanding that A_2 (or animals like A_2) typically go for food in their line of gaze (behavior-reading). This problem of experimentally ruling out such plausible behavior-reading explanations is what Povinelli and Vonk (2003) call the *logical problem* (aka Povinelli's problem). Povinelli and Vonk, along with other researchers (Heyes 1998; Lurz 2009; Lurz and Krachun 2011), argue that empirically answering the question of whether animals mindread requires solving the logical problem, and that solving the logical problem requires designing tests that use a methodology that is fundamentally different from the standard methodology. It is important to note that the logical problem is presented as an instance of the rather common methodological problem in science of confounding variables; it is not presented as the insoluble problem of designing an experiment that can rule out every conceivable behavior-reading hypothesis (see Halina, Chapter 22 in this volume).[5] Many fields of empirical research face similar problems of confounding variables, and there are different strategies that researchers employ to control for confounding variables. One such strategy is designing alternative test procedures in which the confounding variables are dissociated. This is the strategy that Povinelli, Vonk, and others recommend using to solve the logical problem.

In very general terms, it is perhaps not too difficult to see what this alternative test procedure might be. It would involve testing an animal A_1 to see if the animal would predict that another animal A_2 will perform some type of behavior B when a novel observable cue C is represented as obtaining, where the following conditions are satisfied:

(i) *Prior knowledge condition*: On the assumption that A_1 is capable of mindreading and possesses the mental state concept M, it is plausible to suppose that prior to the experimental test, A_1 knows that A_2 (or animals like A_2) tend to perform B-type behaviors when they are in an M-type mental state.

(ii) *Learning condition*: Prior to the experimental test, A_1 is allowed to learn that the novel observable cue C is a sign for a type of mental state M.[6]

(iii) *Novel cue condition*: Prior to the experimental test, A_1 has no independent reason[7] to expect that A_2 (or animals like A_2) will do B when the observable cue C is represented as obtaining. That is to say, the observable cue C is such that there is no plausible reason to think that A_1 has experienced A_2 (or animals like A_2) prior to the experimental test doing B when C was represented as obtaining, or that A_1 is hardwired to instinctively expect animals like A_2 to do B when C is represented as obtaining.

(iv) *No confounding cue condition*: There is no observable cue C′ that obtains (or that might be represented as obtaining) in the experimental test but not in the control test such that it is plausible to suppose that A_1 has a reason, prior to the experimental test, to expect that A_2 (or animals like A_2) will do B when C′ is represented as obtaining.

If the *no confounding cue condition* is satisfied, then A_1 will not be capable of using a behavior-reading strategy to successfully predict that A_2 will do B in the experimental test. However, if the *novel cue, learning,* and *prior knowledge conditions* are satisfied, A_1 could use a mindreading strategy to predict that A_2 will do B. With A_1's prior knowledge that A_2 (or others like A_2) tend to perform B-type behaviors when in an M-type mental state, and with A_1's newly acquired knowledge that the novel observable cue C is a sign for the mental state M, A_1 could infer that A_2 is in the mental state M when C is represented as obtaining and is likely to perform a B-type behavior in the experimental test. Thus, with a test where these four conditions are satisfied, and where A_1 succeeds in predicting that A_2 will do B in the experimental test as a result of representing that observable cue C obtains, we can be confident that A_1 is making this prediction using a mindreading strategy and not a behavior-reading one. Such a test, then, would be a valid mindreading test and would solve the logical problem. But what sort of test would this actually be?

How not to solve the logical problem

A number of researchers have argued that an *experience-projection test with transparent and opaque barriers* would satisfy the four conditions above and solve the logical problem (Bugnyar, Reber, Buckner 2016; Heyes 1998; Karg, Schmelz, Call and Tomasello 2015; Povinelli and Vonk 2003). So far, just three such tests have been conducted – two with chimpanzees (Karg et al. 2015; Vonk and Povinelli 2011) and one with ravens (Bugnyar et al. 2016). The test with ravens is the most recent, and because of its rather elegant design and clear argumentation by the researchers, it provides an excellent illustration of the methodology of the experience-projection test and the reasons some researchers believe that such a test solves the logical problem.

In their study, Bugnyar and colleagues allowed a group of ravens ($N = 10$) to cache food under three different test conditions. In the *window-open test*, a (focal) raven was given food to hide in a caching room while another raven (competitor) watched from an adjacent room through an open window. After the focal raven hid its food, the competitor was let into the caching room and allowed to search for the hidden food in the presence of the focal raven. The window-open test was used as a baseline in which the focal ravens' caching strategies would be compared to those used in the experimental and control tests (described below). If the ravens' caching strategies in the window-open (baseline) test were found to be significantly similar to those used in the experimental test and significantly different from those used in the control test, the ravens would be taken to pass the mindreading test.

The *window-closed test* (control test) was just like the window-open test except that the window between the rooms was covered by an opaque panel which prevented the competitor from seeing the caching room. Results from the two tests showed that the focal ravens were significantly more likely to hide their food quicker and to return to cache sites less often in the window-open test than in the window-closed test. Such caching strategies, the researchers point out, make ecological sense, since food that is cached quickly and cache sites that are not returned to while competitors are watching are less likely to be noticed by competitors and, therefore, less likely to be pilfered later.

On the assumption that ravens are capable of mindreading and possess the mental state concept *see*, it is plausible to suppose, as the researchers do, that the focal ravens employ different cache strategies in these two tests because they understand that the competitor can *see* them caching in the window-open condition but not in the window-closed condition, and they know from prior experience that caches that are *seen* by competitors are less likely to be pilfered if the caching is done quickly and the cache site is not returned to while competitors are watching. And so it would appear that at this point, we can say that Bugnyar and colleagues' study satisfies the *prior knowledge condition*.

After completing the window-open and window-closed tests, the focal ravens were given a *familiarization trial*. In the trial, the ravens were moved into the competitor's room while the competitor was absent and allowed to look through a peephole cut into the panel that covered the window separating the competitor's room and the caching room. While the raven peered through the peephole, an experimenter hid a piece of food in the caching room, after which the raven was allowed back into the caching room to find the hidden food. The objective of the trial was to introduce the focal ravens to a novel observable cue – the peephole – that, on the assumption that the ravens are capable of mindreading and possess the mental state concept *see*, they would reasonably interpret as a sign for *seeing* the caching room after their experience of looking through the peephole and seeing the caching room. And so it would appear that Bugnyar and colleagues' study satisfies the *learning condition*, too.

Once the ravens passed the familiarization trial, they were given the *peephole test* (experimental test). In the test, the panel with the peephole covered the window separating the two rooms, and a focal raven was given food to hide in the caching room while the researchers played pre-recorded sounds of a familiar competitor raven through a loudspeaker in the competitor's room. After the focal raven hid its food, the researcher stopped playing the recording and allowed the actual competitor raven, from whom the sounds were recorded, to enter the caching room and search for hidden food in the presence of the focal raven.

According to the researchers, the peephole in the experimental test is a novel observable cue, since the ravens "lack a specific associative history of caching in the presence of peepholes" (Bugnyar et al. 2016: 4). That is, the focal ravens have had no experience, prior to the peephole test, with competitor ravens pilfering food from caches that were made behind opaque barriers with peepholes, and thus it is unlikely that the ravens could have any knowledge prior to the experimental test about how competitors would behave toward caches made behind an opaque barrier with a peephole.[8] Thus, according to the researchers, the peephole test satisfies the *novel cue condition*.

The researchers also claim that there is no confounding cue in the peephole test, since there is "no actual competitor whose gaze could be read" (Bugnyar et al. 2016: 3). Without an actual competitor raven present in the peephole test, the researchers maintain, there is no confounding observable cue, such as the line of gaze of the competitor raven, that the focal ravens could plausibly be taken to represent and use to predict pilfering behavior by the competitor similar to that observed in the window-open test. And so, according to the researchers, the *no confounding cue condition* is also satisfied.

On the assumption that the researchers' arguments above are sound, it would appear that their experience-projection test satisfies the four conditions of a valid mindreading test and, therefore, solves the logical problem. Since the peephole test supposedly satisfies the *no confounding cue condition*, it is unlikely that the focal ravens, were they behavior-readers, would be able to predict similar kinds of behavior from the (real/imagined) competitor in both the peephole and open-window tests, since there is (apparently) no common observable cue in these two test conditions that the focal ravens could represent and use to predict similar kinds of behavior from the competitor. But this is not unlikely if the ravens are mindreaders and possess the mental state concept *see*. For in both tests, the ravens could infer that the (real/imagined) competitor can *see* the caching room – an inference which, in the peephole test, could be based on the knowledge learned in the familiarization trial that peepholes afford *seeing* the caching room and which, in the window-open test, could be based on prior knowledge that competitors that have a line of gaze to the caching room can *see* the caching room. The ravens could then apply their prior knowledge that caches that are *seen* by competitors are less likely to be pilfered if the caching is done quickly and the cache site is not revisited to undertake similar caching strategies in both the window-open and peephole tests, which is precisely what the ravens did. In both the window-open and peephole tests, the average duration to caching a piece of food and the average number of returns to cache sites were nearly the same and significantly lower than in the window-closed test. From these results, the researchers concluded that

> ravens treat the [peephole] test condition like the [window-open] test condition, indicating that they can generalize from their own experience using the peephole as a pilferer [in the familiarization trial] and predict that audible [imagined] competitor could potentially see their caches.
>
> (Bugnyar et al. 2016: 3, emphasis added)[9]

A number of researchers have argued that the visual experience-projection test with transparent and opaque barriers does not solve the logical problem precisely because it fails to satisfy the no confounding cue condition (Andrews 2005; Hurley and Nudds 2006; Lurz 2009, 2011; Perner 2012). I am afraid that Bugnyar and colleagues' study is no different on this score from earlier visual experience-projection tests using transparent and opaque barriers. Contrary to what the researchers claim, the fact that there is no actual competitor in the peephole test does not mean that there is no confounding observable cue, such as line of gaze, that the ravens could reasonably be taken to represent and use to predict similar behavior from the (real/imagined) competitor in both the peephole and window-open tests. Although there was no actual competitor in the peephole test, the focal ravens were made to think that there was and, therefore, they might well have thought that this (imagined) competitor could potentially have a line of gaze to the caching room through the peephole. If asked why the focal ravens might think this, the answer is that the ravens could have learned in the familiarization trial that peering through the peephole affords a line of gaze to the caching room and use this knowledge to infer that the (imagined) competitor could potentially have a line of gaze to the caching room if it peered through the peephole.[10] This explanation incidentally is analogous to, and thus no less plausible than, the one that Bugnyar and colleagues give to the similar question: why might the focal ravens think that the (imagined) competitor could potentially *see* the caching room, given that there was no actual competitor for the ravens to observe? The researchers' answer is that the focal ravens, from their experience with peering through the peephole, learn that the peephole affords *seeing* the caching room and use this knowledge to infer that the (imagined) competitor could potentially *see* the caching room if it peered through the peephole.

Therefore, it appears that the focal ravens could have just as easily passed Bugnyar and colleagues' test if they had used a behavior-reading strategy. Due to their past experience with caching food in competitive contexts, it is plausible that the focal ravens had knowledge prior to the peephole test that caches that competitor ravens have a line of gaze to are less likely to be pilfered if the caching is done quickly and the cache site is not returned to; and they could use this prior knowledge, together with the knowledge they learned in the familiarization trial, that the peephole affords a line of gaze to the caching room, to predict the same kind of behavior from the (imagined/real) competitor in the peephole and window-open tests.

How to solve the logical problem

Designing a mindreading test for animals in which all of the four conditions above are satisfied is difficult but not impossible (see Lurz 2009, 2011; Lurz and Krachun 2011). Although I do not believe that Bugnyar and colleagues' study solves the logical problem, I do believe that a modified version of it can. What is needed is an experimental test in which the competitor can *see* but does *not* have a line of gaze to the caching room. One way to achieve this is through the use of mirrors, since mirrors allow one to see things, such as one's face or the room behind one's head, that one does not or cannot have a line of gaze to.[11]

Let us imagine, then, that the ravens are given the following three tests. The *window-open test* (baseline) is just like the one given to the ravens in Bugnyar and colleagues' study in which the competitor can easily peer through the window and into the caching room while the focal raven hides its food. The *window-up test* (control), however, involves placing the window high up on the wall separating the competitor's room and the caching room so that the competitor cannot peer through the window and into the caching room. In both tests, the focal raven is given food to hide in the caching room while a competitor is in the adjacent room, after which the competitor is released into the caching room to find the hidden food in the presence of the focal raven.

After taking these two tests, the ravens would be given a *mirror familiarization trial*. In this trial, the focal ravens are transferred to the competitor's room while the competitor is absent. In the room, the window is high up on the wall, preventing the focal ravens from peering through the window and into the caching room. However, a mirror is placed high up on the wall opposite to the window and angled downward, allowing the focal ravens to see the caching room when they look at the mirror.[12]

After the mirror familiarization trial, the ravens are given the *mirror test* (experimental test). In this test, the focal ravens are given food to hide in the caching room while the window is high up on the wall and the competitor is in the adjacent room. In addition, the mirror is placed in the competitor's room, as it was in the familiarization trial. The placement of the mirror performs two functions. It allows the competitor to see the caching room by looking at the mirror, and it allows the focal raven in the caching room to see the mirror through the open window. Since the window is placed high up on the wall, just like in the window-up test, the focal ravens can see that the competitor is prevented from having a line of gaze to the caching room. Furthermore, during the mirror familiarization trial, the focal ravens were given no reason to think that looking at the mirror affords a line of gaze to the caching room. When the ravens looked at the mirror, it was the mirror, not the caching room, to which they had a line of gaze. What the mirror allowed the focal raven to do was to *see* the caching room, not to have a line of gaze to the caching room. Thus, unlike Bugnyar and colleagues' peephole test, it is *not* plausible to suppose that the focal ravens in the mirror test might think that the competitor in the adjacent room could potentially have a line of gaze to the caching room. On the reasonable assumption that line of gaze is the only confounding cue that the focal ravens might plausibly be understood to represent and use to predict the same kind of behavior from the competitor in the window-open and mirror tests, it would appear that the mirror test satisfies the *no confounding cue condition*.

Without a confounding observable cue for the focal ravens to represent in the mirror test, they cannot employ a behavior-reading strategy to predict the same kind of behavior from the competitor in the window-open and mirror tests. But the ravens could make such a prediction if they are capable of mindreading and possessed the mental state concept *see*. For in both tests, the ravens could infer that the competitor in the adjacent room can *see* the caching room – an inference which, in the mirror test, could be based on the knowledge learned in the mirror familiarization trial that looking at the mirror affords *seeing* the caching room and which, in the window-open test, could be based on prior knowledge that competitors that have a line of gaze to the caching room can *see* the caching room. The ravens could then apply their prior knowledge, that caches that are *seen* by competitors are less likely to be pilfered if the caching is done quickly and the cache site is not revisited, to undertake similar caching strategies in both the window-open and mirror tests.

Thus, there are ways of designing a valid mindreading test for animals – the logical problem has a solution. Yet these types of tests have not been used to assess animals' mindreading capacities, and therefore we do not know whether animals are capable of mindreading. Until such tests are used and animals pass them, we should remain agnostic – though, optimistic – about the possibility of animal mindreading (Lurz, Kanet and Krachun 2014).

Notes

1 Throughout, 'animal' is used to stand for nonhuman animals.

2 Vincent and Gallagher (Chapter 26 of this volume) put forward a third type of strategy, the *interaction theory*, which holds that chimpanzees predict the behavior of others by directly perceiving their mental states. Interaction theory and mindreading agree that chimpanzees represent the mental state of others; they disagree over whether such representations take the form of perception or inferred belief. In this essay, I follow tradition and present the 'logical problem' as existing between behavior-reading and mindreading accounts of animal social behavior. The problem could just as well be presented as existing between behavior-reading and the interaction accounts (Cf. Gallagher and Povinelli 2012).

3 Typically, groups of animals are tested. However, for easy of explaining the standard methodology, I use an individual animal.

4 'Line of gaze to' and 'looking at' are used throughout as synonyms for the observable spatial relation that holds between a subject's eyes and non-occluded objects in front of the subject's eyes. It is important to note that line of gaze/looking at is *not* seeing. Seeing is a state of awareness and, thus, a mental state; line of gaze/looking at is a spatial relation, not a mental state. Although line of gaze/looking at is not seeing, it is an important observable cue used to infer what someone is seeing.

5 After all, most possible behavior-reading hypotheses are not even antecedently plausible and, thus, do not need to be ruled out by a test procedure.

6 It is important to note that A_1 does not learn that C is a sign for M by learning that C is correlated with a type of behavior B that A_1 knows to be caused by M. Rather, A_1 must learn that C is a sign for M by learning, via introspection, that C correlates with A_1's own mental state M.

7 That is, A$_1$ has no reason other than what A$_1$ can infer from what it has learned in the learning condition about the relation between C and M, and what it supposedly knows from the prior knowledge condition about the relation between M and behavior B in others.

8 It is also unlikely that the ravens might instinctively know how competitors would behave in such a condition, given the novelty of the peephole situation.

9 In contrast to this mindreading proposal, Bugnyar and colleagues at one point argue for the more "ecumenical proposal" that the focal ravens attribute an "intervening variable" to the competitor (Cf. Whiten 1996). On this proposal, the focal ravens are hypothesized to expect similar types of behavior from competitors in the window-open and peephole tests because they attribute a common intervening variable that they understand to cause such behaviors in "perceptually dissimilar situations" (p. 4). The researchers argue that since the window-open and peephole tests are perceptually dissimilar, the intervening variable proposal offers a better account of the focal ravens' behavior than any behavior-reading proposal. The researchers are mistaken, however, that the window-open and peephole tests are perceptually dissimilar, or so I argue. If my argument is correct, their study not only fails to provide convincing evidence that ravens are mindreaders rather than behavior-readers, but also that ravens are attributors of intervening variables rather than behavior-readers.

10 Previous studies have shown that ravens are capable of representing others' line of gaze (Bugnyar, Stöwe and Heinrich 2004; Schloegel, Kotrschal and Bugnyar 2007). It is quite plausible, therefore, that the focal ravens possess the concept *line-of-gaze* and use it to represent this spatial relation holding between their own eyes and the caching room when they peer through the peephole.

11 Recall that line of gaze is the observable spatial relation that one bears to non-occluded objects in front of one's eyes. Hence, by looking into a mirror, one does not have a line of gaze to one's face or the room behind one's head, since these non-occluded objects are not in front of one's eyes.

12 Ravens are corvids and some corvids (e.g., magpies and crows) have been shown to understand the reflective properties of mirrors (Medina, Taylor, Hunt and Gray 2011; Prior, Schwarz and Güntürkün 2008). It is plausible, then, that the ravens, upon looking at the mirror, take themselves to be seeing the real caching room behind them and not some virtual caching room behind the mirror.

Further reading

K. Andrews, *Do Apes Read Minds?* (Cambridge, MA: MIT Press, 2012) is an excellent book on the question of whether animals have a theory of mind and the different uses of theory of mind in humans and animals. T. Suddendorf, *The Gap: The Science of What Separates Us From Other Animals* (New York: Basic Books, 2013) is an equally excellent book on theory of mind in animals as well as related questions of self-recognition and mental time travel in animals.

References

Andrews, K. (2005) "Chimpanzee Theory of Mind: Looking in All the Wrong Places?" *Mind & Language* 20: 521–536.

Apperly, I., and Butterfill, S. (2009) "Do Humans Have Two Systems to Track Beliefs and Belief-Like States?" *Psychological Review* 4: 953–970.

Bugnyar, T., Reber, S., and Buckner, C. (2016) "Ravens Attribute Visual Access to Unseen Competitors." *Nature Communications* 7: 10506. doi:10.1038/ncomms10506.

Bugnyar, T., Stöwe M., and Heinrich, B. (2004) "Ravens, *Corvus corax*, Follow Gaze Direction of Humans Around Obstacles." *Proceedings of the Royal Society B* 271: 1331–1336.

Call, J., and Tomasello, M. (1999) "A Nonverbal False Belief Task: The Performance of Children and Great Apes." *Child Development* 70: 381–395.

Doherty, M. (2011) "A Two-System Theory of Social Cognition." In J. Roessler, H. Lerman and N. Eilan (eds.), *Perception, Causation, and Objectivity*. Oxford: Oxford University Press.

Gallagher, S., and Povinelli, D. (2012) "Enactive and Behavioral Abstraction Accounts of Social Understanding in Chimpanzees, Infants, and Adults." *Review of Philosophy and Psychology* 3: 145–169.

Hare, B., Call, J., Agnetta, B., and Tomasello, M. (2000) "Chimpanzees Know What Conspecifics Do and Do Not See." *Animal Behavior* 59: 771–785.

Hare, B., Call, J., and Tomasello, M. (2001) "Do Chimpanzees Know What Conspecifics Know?" *Animal Behavior* 61: 139–151.

Heyes, C. (1998) "Theory of Mind in Nonhuman Primates." *Behavioral and Brain Sciences* 21: 101–148.

Hurley, S., and Nudds, M. (2006) *Rational Animals?* Oxford: Oxford University Press.

Karg, K., Schmelz, M., Call, J., and Tomasello, M. (2015) "The Goggles Experiment: Can Chimpanzees Use Self-Experience to Infer What a Competitor Can See?" *Animal Behavior* 105: 211–221.

Lurz, R. (2009) "If Chimpanzees Are Mindreaders, Could Behavioral Science Tell? Toward a Solution to the Logical Problem." *Philosophical Psychology* 22: 305–328.

Lurz, R. (2011) *Mindreading Animals: The Debate Over What Animals Know About Other Minds.* Cambridge, MA: MIT Press.

Lurz, R., Kanet, S., and Krachun, C. (2014) "Animal Mindreading: A Defense of Optimistic Agnosticism." *Mind & Language* 29: 428–454.

Lurz, R., and Krachun, C. (2011) "How Could We Know Whether Nonhuman Primates Understand Others' Internal Goals and Intentions? Solving Povinelli's Problem." *Review of Philosophy and Psychology* 2: 449–481.

Medina, F., Taylor, A., Hunt, G., and Gray, R. (2011) "New Caledonian Crows' Responses to Mirrors." *Animal Behaviour* 82: 981–993. doi:10.1016/j.anbehav.2011.07.033.

Perner, J. (2008) "Who Took the Cog Out of Cognitive Science? Mentalism in an Era of Anti-Cognitivism." In P. A. Frensch and R. Schwarzer (eds.), *International Congress of Psychology: 2008 Proceedings.* Hove: Psychology Press.

Perner, J. (2012) "Mini-Meta: In Search of Minimal Criteria for Metacognition." In M. Beran, J. Brandl, J. Perner and J. Proust (eds.), *The Foundations of Metacognition.* Oxford: Oxford University Press.

Povinelli, D., and Eddy, T. (1996) "What Young Chimpanzees Know About Seeing." *Monographs of the Society for Research in Child Development* 61: 1–152.

Povinelli, D., and Vonk, J. (2003) "Chimpanzee Minds: Suspiciously Human?" *Trends in Cognitive Sciences* 7: 157–160.

Premack, D., and Woodruff, G. (1978) "Does the Chimpanzee Have a Theory of Mind?" *Behavioral and Brain Sciences* 1: 515–526.

Prior, H., Schwarz, A., and Güntürkün, O. (2008) "Mirror-Induced Behavior in the Magpie (*Pica pica*): Evidence of Self-Recognition." *PLoS Biology* 6: e202. doi:10.1371/journal. pbio.0060202.

Schloegl, C., Kotrschal, K., and Bugnyar, T. (2007) "Gaze Following in Common Ravens (*Corvus corax*): Ontogeny and Habituation." *Animal Cognition* 74: 769–778.

Vonk, J., and Povinelli, D. (2011) "Social and Physical Reasoning in Human-Reared Chimpanzees: Preliminary Studies." In J. Roessler, H. Lerman and N. Eilan (eds.), *Perception, Causation, and Objectivity.* Oxford: Oxford University Press.

Whiten, A. (1996) "When Does Smart Behavior-Reading Become Mind-Reading?" In P. Carruthers and P. Smith (eds.), *Theories of Theories of Mind.* Cambridge: Cambridge University Press.

22

WHAT APES KNOW ABOUT SEEING

Marta Halina

Introduction

Humans are able to infer what objects another agent can or cannot see, given that other agent's point of view. Psychologists refer to this as level 1 visual perspective taking (Flavell 1974). Visual perspective taking is generally characterized as a form of mindreading because it requires that an individual reason about the perceptual states of other agents. Mindreading, in turn, is thought to underlie many other important cognitive abilities, such as empathy, self-awareness, and even phenomenal consciousness (Baron-Cohen 1997; Carruthers 2009; Apperly 2011). Given this, there has been much interest in the question of whether our nearest primate relatives, such as chimpanzees (*Pan troglodytes*), have visual perspective taking abilities. Over the last decade, comparative psychologists have conducted many experiments with the aim of determining this. The results of these experiments have been mainly positive, leading some researchers to conclude that chimpanzees are capable of this form of mindreading (see Call and Tomasello 2008 for a review).

This essay examines what constitutes evidence for level 1 visual perspective taking (hereafter, VPT1) in nonhuman primates. Specifically, it evaluates the view that the dominant research paradigm used to test for this ability in apes is flawed (Povinelli and Vonk 2004; Penn et al. 2008; Penn and Povinelli 2007; Penn 2011; Lurz 2009, 2011; Lurz and Krachun 2011; see also Whiten 2013). There are various strands to this view; however, one of the central claims is that the current research program fails to provide evidence for VPT1 because there is an alternative behavior-reading explanation for the positive results of the experiments conducted thus far. This point is coupled with the further claim that there is an alternative research paradigm (namely, experience projection tasks) that succeeds in eliminating these behavior-reading alternatives, and it is not until subjects pass tests in this new paradigm that we have evidence for VPT1 in nonhuman animals.

If the critics are correct, then contrary to the current consensus in comparative psychology, we lack compelling evidence that chimpanzees have visual perspective taking abilities. However, in this chapter, I argue that the critics' position is misguided. First, the new paradigm advanced by the critics does not succeed in eliminating behavior-reading explanations – that is, behavior reading can still account for the positive results of these experiments. Second, our inability to eliminate behavior-reading explanations is unsurprising, given their nature: they are a version of what Carl Hempel identified as the "theoretician's dilemma." This dilemma states that when a theory positing unobservable entities allows one to establish an observable regularity in the world, then these unobservable posits are no longer necessary because one can always redescribe that regularity in terms of observable entities alone. Applied to mindreading research, the claim is that we can reinterpret any mindreading ability in terms of an agent's ability to recognize and act on observable regularities. Given this, the critics' position is best understood as a general skeptical problem, rather than an empirical or methodological problem that psychologists must solve before concluding that nonhuman animals are capable of visual perspective taking (see Halina 2015).

Level 1 visual perspective experiments and the behavior-reading alternative

The main experimental strategy used to investigate whether chimpanzees are capable of VPT1 is to present a subject (A) with a social situation that involves interacting with another agent (B). Researchers then vary some property so as to affect what B can see. This may be a property of B (open versus closed eyelids or head turned toward versus away from some object), or a property of the environment (a transparent versus opaque barrier or a well-lit versus dark room). The question is whether A will recognize these changes and respond in the manner of someone who takes into account the perceptual states of others. For example, will A prefer to use begging gestures toward a recipient who can see those gestures and prefer to steal food from a competitor who cannot see that food? If chimpanzees consistently behave in a wide variety of circumstances in the manner of individuals capable of VPT1, then comparative psychologists take this as evidence that they, in fact, have this ability.[1] And indeed, this is what the experimental results suggest (see, for example, Hare et al. 2000; Tomasello et al. 2003; Kaminski et al. 2004; Liebal et al. 2004; Melis et al. 2006; Tomasello and Call 2006; Bräuer et al. 2007; Tempelmann et al. 2011).

Critics of the above approach argue that the results obtained from such experiments are confounded by learned or evolved behavioral rules. The reason for this is that the observable properties that psychologists vary across experimental conditions are all properties that normally covary with an agent's ability to see or not see objects. Thus, one should expect these observable properties to covary with seeing and not-seeing behaviors in a chimpanzee's natural environment. For example, the property of there being no opaque barrier between an agent's eyes and an object should regularly co-occur with that agent exhibiting behaviors consistent with seeing that object (such as approaching that object if it is desirable food, retreating from that object if it is a harmful predator, etc.); while the property of there being an opaque barrier between an agent's eyes and an object should regularly covary with that agent exhibiting behaviors consistent with not seeing that object (such as not approaching it even if it is desirable food, not retreating from it even if it is a harmful predator, etc.). Given these co-occurrences, chimpanzees might have learned or evolved behavioral rules that link these observable properties with seeing and not-seeing behaviors. Although the regular co-occurrence of a particular observable property and a suite of behaviors may be caused by an underlying mental state, an individual adapted to this observable regularity need not reason about these mental states in order to successfully predict behavior.

According to the critics, an experiment cannot provide evidence for mindreading unless it excludes the possibility that subjects are solving the experimental task using complementary behavior reading, where complementary behavior reading (CBR) operates on precisely those observable regularities caused by an underlying mental state (Lurz 2011). The advocates of this position (whom I will refer to as CBR theorists) do not take their argument as rendering mindreading empirically intractable, however. Their point is rather that comparative psychologists are using the wrong experimental approach for testing for VPT1 in nonhuman animals. It is not until the appropriate experiments are conducted – those capable of eliminating behavior-reading alternatives – that psychologists can claim that they have evidence for or against mindreading in nonhuman animals. The CBR theorists go on to maintain that the appropriate experiments to conduct are "experience projection tasks."

In the following section, I present two versions of the experience-projection task that CBR theorists cite as the most promising way forward for visual perspective taking research. I then argue that both versions of this task fail to eliminate alternative behavior-reading explanations. Thus, they fail to satisfy the criteria imposed by their designers.

Experience-projection experiments

The general idea behind an experience-projection experiment is that a subject is given the opportunity to learn that some situation S_1 reliably leads her to experience the psychological P_1, while some other situation S_2 reliably leads her to experience the psychological state P_2. Once the subject learns to associate S_1 with P_1 and S_2 with P_2 in herself, the researcher then tests if the subject will reason that S_1 leads to P_1 and S_2 to P_2 in other agents. For CBR theorists, an experience-projection experiment seems like a promising way to prevent subjects from relying on complementary behavior reading because experimenters can make S_1 and S_2 differ in some arbitrary way – that is, in a way that does not normally vary with the psychological states P_1 and P_2. Given this, subjects purportedly have no reason to infer that S_1 will lead to P_1-like behaviors in another agent, unless they reason that S_1 will lead to P_1 in that agent.

Cecilia Heyes (1998) proposed one of the first experience-projection experiments, which has been cited as an exemplar of the CBR experimental approach (see Povinelli and Vonk 2004; Penn and Povinelli 2007). In Heyes's experiment, an ape subject is given the opportunity to interact with two pairs of goggles. The goggles are designed so that their external features are identical except that one pair has red trim and the other pair has blue trim. However, when the subject puts on these goggles, she discovers another important difference between them: she can see through the lenses of the blue-trimmed goggles, but not through the lenses of the red-trimmed goggles. By familiarizing herself with these goggles, the subject is expected to learn to associate the observable state of wearing blue-trimmed goggles with the psychological state of being able to see and the observable state of wearing red-trimmed goggles with the psychological state of not being able to see. Once the subject learns these properties, the question is, will she expect agents wearing the blue-trimmed goggles to behave as if they can see, and agents wearing the red-trimmed goggles to behave as if they cannot see? If so, CBR theorists hold, the subject must be capable of attributing perceptual states to others because there is no other reason to expect seeing and not-seeing behaviors from agents wearing blue-trimmed and red-trimmed goggles. The only way to come to this conclusion is by analogically inferring that when other agents wear these goggles, they are having the same perceptual experiences that I have when I wear them.

As commentators on this experiment have pointed out, however, the above is not the only means of inferring that agents wearing the blue and red goggles will behave in ways consistent with seeing and not-seeing, respectively. For example, Andrews (2005) points out that subjects might experience themselves behaving like seeing agents while wearing the blue-trimmed goggles (walking around, manipulating objects, etc.) and experience themselves behaving like not-seeing agents while wearing the red-trimmed goggles (colliding with objects and agents, failing to perform familiar tasks, etc.). From these behavioral experiences, a subject might reason analogically that other agents will behave as I do when wearing these blue- and red-trimmed goggles. To make this inference, the subject need not attribute to agents the psychological states of seeing and not seeing. Lurz (2011) also points out that even if subjects were not to attempt to move around or do anything while wearing the goggles, they could still recognize that wearing the red-trimmed goggles is like having an opaque barrier in front of one's eyes, while wearing the blue-trimmed goggles is like not having an opaque barrier in front of one's eyes. Given that the property of having an opaque barrier in front of one's eyes normally covaries with an inability to see, and the property of not having an opaque barrier in front of one's eyes normally covaries with an ability to see, subjects could rely on the learned or innate behavioral rule: expect agents with an opaque barrier in front of their eyes to exhibit X behaviors (behaviors normally exhibited by not-seeing agents in this context) and expect agents with no opaque barrier in front of their eyes to exhibit Y behaviors (behaviors normally exhibited by seeing agents in this context). The original experience-projection task proposed by Heyes, then, can be solved using complementary behavior reading alone and thus does not constitute a test for visual perspective taking in nonhuman animals according to the criteria advanced by the critics.

Lurz (2011; Chapter 21 in this volume) maintains that all experiments aimed at testing a nonhuman animal's ability to attribute perceptions of reality fail to reject the behavior-reading hypothesis. The reason for this is that normal visual experiences of real objects involve having a direct line of gaze to those objects, and normal visual experiences of not being able to see real objects involve not having a direct line of gaze to those objects (where a direct line of gaze to an object X is a spatial relationship between one's eyes and X, such that one can draw an imaginary line from one to the other). Thus, the attribution of visual experiences of reality will always be confounded with the observable property of having or lacking a direct line of gaze (Lurz 2011: 82–83). Given this, Lurz argues that our best bet for empirically identifying whether apes can attribute visual perceptions to others is to determine whether they can attribute non-veridical perceptual experiences to others.

To this end, Lurz designs a set of experiments aimed at testing whether a subject can attribute to others the perception that an object appears to be one way, when the subject knows that it is in reality another way. The particular example that I will focus on here is an experiment that relies on size-distorting lenses; however, the analysis of this experiment extends to the others in this paradigm. In Lurz's size-distorting-lens experiment, a subordinate subject competes over food with a dominant conspecific in a room that contains strategically placed transparent barriers – some of which have size-distorting properties. Before the test begins, a subject is familiarized with the fact that the dominant competitor will take the larger of two rewards (let us say bananas) when given the opportunity. The subject is also familiarized with the effects that three types of transparent barriers have on objects that are located behind them. A blue-trimmed magnifying barrier makes objects appear larger, a red-trimmed minimizing barrier makes objects appear smaller, and a black-trimmed barrier has no distorting effect on the appearance of objects.[2]

After this pretraining phase, the subject and competitor are placed in separate rooms on opposite sides of an adjoining competition room (Figure 22.1). In the middle of the competition room are two barriers, each with one banana behind it. The bananas are located on the subject's side of the room, so that when the subject and competitor enter the room, the subject has visual access to both bananas, while the competitor is only able to view the bananas through the barriers. Imagine, as depicted in Figure 22.1, that the subject and competitor are competing over two same-sized bananas, one of which is located behind a blue-trimmed magnifying barrier and the other of which is located behind a red-trimmed minimizing barrier. When the subject and competitor enter the room, which banana will the subject expect the competitor to retrieve?

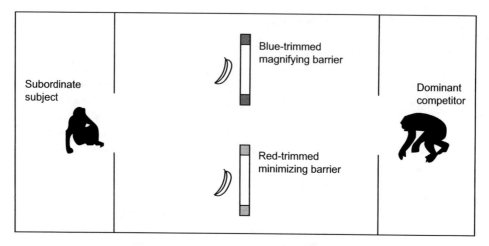

Figure 22.1 An experience-projection experiment that uses distorting transparent barriers. The subject anticipates which banana the competitor will attempt to retrieve.

According to Lurz, a subject that reasons about both observable properties and mental states will expect that the competitor will retrieve the banana behind the blue-trimmed magnifying barrier. Such a subject knows that both of the bananas are equal in size, but also knows that the banana behind the blue-trimmed magnifying barrier appears larger than the banana behind the red-trimmed minimizing barrier from the competitor's point of view. The subject can see that the competitor must view the bananas through the barriers and knows that the competitor has no experience with the distorting effects of these barriers.[3] Given this, the subject will predict that the competitor will retrieve the banana that appears to be the largest to him, which is the one behind the blue-trimmed barrier.

What will a subject that reasons only in terms of observable properties predict that the competitor will do in this situation? According to Lurz, there are two possibilities, neither of which is the same as the prediction made by a mindreading subject. The first possibility is that the subject views the competitor as having a direct line of gaze to both bananas. Under this scenario, the subject has learned that when it comes to the blue- and red-trimmed barriers, the reality of the situation is what lies behind the barriers, and the reality is that two same-sized bananas lie behind these barriers. Thus, the subject will predict that the competitor will choose randomly between the two bananas because that is how agents generally behave when having a direct line of gaze to two identical food items. The second possibility is that the subject has learned that when objects are placed behind the blue- and red-trimmed barriers, images appear on the surfaces of these barriers. The reality of the situation for the subject in this case is that there are two same-sized bananas behind the blue- and red-trimmed barriers, but the competitor cannot establish a direct line of gaze to these bananas because the images on the barriers block the competitor's line of gaze to them. Given this, the subject will expect the competitor to retrieve neither banana – at least not until the competitor has the opportunity to walk around one of the barriers and establish a direct line of gaze to one of them.

If Lurz's analysis is correct, then it is empirically possible to reject the hypothesis that apes reason on the basis of complementary behavior reading alone.[4] From this, CBR theorists can argue that until apes pass such a test, one cannot conclude that they attribute mental states to others. They can also argue that if apes fail this task, then that is all the more reason to doubt the positive results obtained by comparative psychologists thus far. As with the original experience-projection experiment, however, it is possible to pass this task on the basis of behavior reading alone, as I will now argue.

When chimpanzees first encounter size-distorting lenses, they are fooled by the effects of these lenses and treat the distorting glass as non-distorting transparent glass (Krachun et al. 2009). Thus, when encountering the red- and blue-trimmed barriers for the first time, we should expect subjects to interact with them as if they were normal transparent barriers. Such subjects could be said to be acting on the behavioral affordances that such normal transparent barriers have. For example, they would recognize that the way to retrieve **A** (the apparent object as seen through the barrier or the image of the object as it is projected onto the barrier) in such a situation is to walk around the barrier towards **R** (the object behind the barrier) (see Figure 22.2).

This is how agents typically respond to transparent barriers. They do not treat them as opaque barriers (ignoring the objects behind them) nor as the absence of a barrier (trying to walk through them). Later, after becoming familiar with the effects of the blue- and red-trimmed barriers, subjects will revise their understanding of the situation. Specifically, in order for the experiment to succeed, subjects must learn during the pretraining phase that there is a regular, predictable relationship between **R** and **A**.[5] In this case, because the blue-trimmed barrier magnifies objects and the red-trimmed barrier minimizes objects, subjects must learn that **A** on the blue-trimmed-barrier will always be a larger version of **R** behind it and that **A** on the red-trimmed-barrier will always be a smaller version of **R** behind it.

Although subjects are expected to learn during the pretraining phase the properties of the blue- and red-trimmed barriers, there is nothing preventing them from recalling that when they first encountered these barriers, they responded to them (or would have responded to them) as if they were normal transparent barriers. With this recollection in mind, subjects could reason that any agent encountering these barriers for the first time is likely to respond to them as if they were normal transparent barriers. This is all that is needed in order to predict that a competitor will attempt to retrieve the banana behind the blue-trimmed barrier on the basis of behavior reading alone. Such a subject might reason that the competitor has a direct line of gaze to the apparent banana (**A**) and hold that for every action the competitor is likely to perform on **A**, he will perform this action on **R** because this is how agents typically behave around transparent barriers. In other words, the competitor will treat this as a normal transparent barrier and thus behave like agents typically behave around transparent barriers, with the added caveat that the relationship between **A** and **R** for this particular barrier is a function other than **A** equals **R**.

The above technique can be applied to all of the new experience-projection tasks proposed by Lurz.[6] This is because any subject with the observable information necessary for mindreading

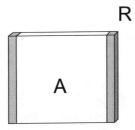

Figure 22.2   A transparent size-distorting barrier, where **R** is the object behind the barrier and **A** is the apparent object as seen through the barrier or the image of the object as it is projected onto the barrier.

will also have the information necessary for behaving like a mindreader using behavioral reading. Specifically, if you give a subject the chance to experience that a situation has the effect of making **R** (some real object) appear as **A** (the illusory state), and also give the subject a chance to learn that **R** is not really **A**, then that subject will have also learned that when they were new to the situation, they treated (or would have treated, if given the opportunity) **R** as if it were **A**. Such a subject would then have the information needed to predict that other naïve agents (agents new to the situation) will respond to **R** as if it were **A**. This does not mean that the subject understands that the other agent perceives **R** (the observable state) *as* **A** (a mental state). Rather, the subject could simply reason that the agent will behave as naïve agents generally behave in this situation (as an agent responding to **A**).

The mindreader's dilemma

The new experience-projection tasks do not succeed in eliminating behavior-reading hypotheses as possible explanations for the positive results of visual perspective taking experiments. What are the consequences of this on the investigation of what apes know about seeing? Elsewhere I have argued that it is impossible to eliminate all behavior-reading alternative explanations of mindreading experiments (Halina 2015). The reason for this is similar to Carl Hempel's well-known "theoretician's dilemma." Hempel (1958) noted that if a theory positing unobservable entities is successful at capturing some observable regularity in the world, then the unobservable posits in that theory are no longer necessary, because the theory can be redescribed in terms of observable entities alone. This leads to a dilemma because either a theory positing unobservable entities fails to capture an observable regularity, in which case it is simply an unsuccessful theory, or it is successful at capturing such a regularity, in which case it is unnecessary because it can be cast in terms of observable entities alone. Similarly, we have a mindreader's dilemma: if the attribution of mental states allows an agent to capture some observable regularity in the world (between colored barriers and the behavior of a competitor, for example), then that attribution is unnecessary because the agent could be relying on some innate or learned rule that captures this observable regularity directly instead.

Does the mindreader's dilemma render the question of what apes know about seeing empirically intractable? I do not think it does. Rather, it tells us that eliminating all possible complementary behavior-reading explanations is an impossible task and thus cannot serve as the standard for evidential success in mindreading research. Instead, we should rely on other standards, such as controlling for those variables that we know might serve as confounds in our experiments (see Heyes 2015 for a move in this direction). Comparative psychologists, however, already adhere to this evidential standard. Pointing out empirically plausible confounds is a constructive way to move the field of animal mindreading research forward; arguing that we have no evidence for animal mindreading until we exclude all possible complementary behavior-reading hypotheses is not. Given the positive results of the experiments conducted thus far (including a recent goggles test, see Karg et al. 2015), I suggest that the evidence currently favors the hypothesis that nonhuman apes know a lot about seeing.

Notes

1   See Halina (2015) for an account of the logic behind this experimental approach in terms of Mill's methods.
2   When a subject is familiarized with these barriers, controls are put into place so that he does not learn that objects behind the blue-trimmed magnifying barrier are more likely to be approached or retrieved than objects behind the red-trimmed minimizing barrier. Also, the objects that the subject will be

competing for during the experiment (in this case, bananas) are not used during the pretraining phase, so that the subject has no experience of preferring bananas located behind one type of barrier over another.

3   It is not clear from Lurz's description of the experiment how a subject is to know that the competitor is naïve to the distorting effects of the barriers. It seems possible that a subject would infer from the fact that she has had experience with these barriers that a competitor might have experience with them too. Let us assume that there is a way to control for this and that the subject knows that the competitor is ignorant of the effects that the blue- and red-trimmed barriers have on the objects behind them (because, for example, the subject has never observed the competitor interacting with these barriers).

4   This is under the assumption that a failure to pass this task is best attributed to a failure of mindreading as opposed to a failure in one of the inferential steps not involving mindreading (such as that noted in note 3).

5   Recall that in the testing phase of this experiment, subjects have visual access only to **R**, not **A**. Thus, they must infer **A** on the basis of **R** and the color of the barrier. If they could not do this, they would not know what **A** is and would be unable to make any predictions about the competitor's response to **A**.

6   See Halina (2013) for a more detailed presentation of this argument and Buckner (2013) for a similar analysis with respect to Lurz's "transparent colored barrier" variation of this experiment (Lurz 2011: 96–101).

References

Andrews, K. (2005) "Chimpanzee Theory of Mind: Looking in All the Wrong Places?" *Mind & Language*, 20(5), 521–536.

Apperly, I. (2011) *Mindreaders: The Cognitive Basis of "Theory of Mind"*, New York: Psychology Press.

Baron-Cohen, S. (1997) *Mindblindness: An Essay on Autism and Theory of Mind*, Cambridge, MA: MIT Press.

Bräuer, J., Call, J., and Tomasello, M. (2007) "Chimpanzees Really Know What Others Can See in a Competitive Situation," *Animal Cognition*, 10, 439–448.

Buckner, C. (2013) "The Semantic Problem(s) With Research on Animal Mind-Reading," *Mind & Language*, 29, 566–589.

Call, J., and Tomasello, M. (2008) "Does the Chimpanzee Have a Theory of Mind? 30 Years Later," *Trends in Cognitive Sciences*, 12(5), 187–192.

Carruthers, P. (2009) "How We Know Our Own Minds: The Relationship Between Mindreading and Metacognition," *Behavioral and Brain Sciences*, 32, 121–138.

Flavell, J. (1974) "The Development of Inferences About Others," in T. Mischel (ed.) *Understanding Other Persons*, Oxford: Blackwell.

Halina, M. (2013) "The Role of Visual Perspective Taking in Great Ape Social Cognition: A Philosophical and Empirical Analysis," *University of California, San Diego, Dissertation*.

Halina, M. (2015) "There Is No Special Problem of Mindreading in Nonhuman Animals," *Philosophy of Science*, 82, 473–490.

Hare, B., Call, J., Agnetta, B., and Tomasello, M. (2000) "Chimpanzees Know What Conspecifics Do and Do Not See," *Animal Behaviour*, 59, 771–785.

Hempel, C. G. (1958) "The Theoretician's Dilemma: A Study in The Logic of Theory Construction," *Minnesota Studies in the Philosophy of Science*, 2, 173–226.

Heyes, C. M. (1998) "Theory of Mind in Nonhuman Primates," *Behavioral and Brain Sciences*, 21, 101–148.

Heyes, C. M. (2015) "Animal Mindreading: What's the Problem?" *Psychonomic Bulletin and Review*, 22(2), 313–327.

Kaminski, J., Call, J., and Tomasello, M. (2004) "Body Orientation and Face Orientation: Two Factors Controlling Apes' Begging Behavior From Humans," *Animal Cognition*, 7, 216–223.

Karg, K., Schmelz, M., Call, J., and Tomasello, M. (2015) "The Goggles Experiment: Can Chimpanzees Use Self-Experience to Infer What a Competitor Can See?" *Animal Behaviour*, 105, 211–221.

Krachun, C., Call, J., and Tomasello, M. (2009) "Can Chimpanzees (*Pan troglodytes*) Discriminate Appearances From Reality?" *Cognition*, 112, 435–450.

Liebal, K., Pika, S., Call, J., and Tomasello, M. (2004) "To Move or Not to Move: How Apes Adjust to the Attentional State of Others," *Interaction Studies*, 5(2), 199–219.

Lurz, R. W. (2009) "If Chimpanzees Are Mindreaders, Could Behavioral Science Tell? Toward a Solution to the Logical Problem," *Philosophical Psychology*, 22(3), 305–328.

Lurz, R. W. (2011) *Mindreading Animals: The Debate Over What Animals Know About Other Minds.* Cambridge, MA: MIT Press.

Lurz, R. W., and Krachun, C. (2011) "How Could We Know Whether Nonhuman Primates Understand Others' Internal Goals and Intentions? Solving Povinelli's Problem," *Review of Philosophy and Psychology*, 2(3), 449–481.

Melis, A. P., Call, J., and Tomasello, M. (2006) "Chimpanzees (*Pan troglodytes*) Conceal Visual and Auditory Information From Others," *Journal of Comparative Psychology*, 120(2), 154–162.

Penn, D. C. (2011) "How Folk Psychology Ruined Comparative Psychology and What Scrub Jays Can Do About It," in R. Menzel and J. Fischer (eds.) *Animal Thinking: Contemporary Issues in Comparative Cognition*, Cambridge, MA: MIT Press.

Penn, D. C., Holyoak, K. J., and Povinelli, D. J. (2008) "Darwin's Mistake: Explaining the Discontinuity Between Human and Nonhuman Minds," *Behavioral and Brain Sciences*, 31(2), 109–178.

Penn, D. C., and Povinelli, D. J. (2007) "On the Lack of Evidence That Chimpanzees Possess Anything Remotely Resembling a 'Theory of Mind,'" *Philosophical Transactions of the Royal Society B*, 362, 731–744.

Povinelli, D. J., and Vonk, J. (2004) "We Don't Need a Microscope to Explore the Chimpanzee's Mind," *Mind & Language*, 19(1), 1–28.

Tempelmann, S., Kaminski, J., and Liebal, K. (2011) "Focus on the Essential: All Great Apes Know When Others Are Being Attentive," *Animal Cognition*, 14(3), 433–439.

Tomasello, M., and Call, J. (2006) "Do Chimpanzees Know What Others See – Or Only What They Are Looking At?" in S. Hurley and M. Nudds (eds.) *Rational Animals?* New York: Oxford University Press.

Tomasello, M., Call, J., and Hare, B. (2003) "Chimpanzees Understand Psychological State – The Question Is Which Ones and to What Extent," *TRENDS in Cognitive Sciences*, 7(4), 153–156.

Whiten, A. (2013) "Humans Are Not Alone in Computing How Others See the World," *Animal Behaviour*, 86, 213–221.

23

USING CAUSAL MODELS TO THINK ABOUT MINDREADING

Hayley Clatterbuck

Introduction

A plausible account of mindreading ought to provide satisfying answers to the following two sets of questions. First, what is the function of mindreading? What advantages does it confer, and why might it have evolved? Second, how could we tell whether a subject is mindreading? These two questions are closely related, for to answer either one, we must give an account of which behaviors we should expect from a mindreader that we would not expect from a subject that does not reason about the mental states of others. In addition, to answer either requires an investigation of alternative cognitive processes that a subject may be utilizing. Finally, both questions require us to say what mindreading *is* so that we investigate what it does and where it can be found.

In this chapter, I will examine an influential account of mindreading, most prominently forwarded by Andrew Whiten (1994, 1996, 2013), according to which mental state attributions serve as *intervening variables*, intermediary causal links between a subject's beliefs about various observable cues, including others' present behavior, and her subsequent predictions about how others will behave. Importantly, these variables can unify perceptually disparate cue-behavior links, yielding more flexible predictions in a variety of contexts. Thus, a mindreader's social inferences in different contexts may be represented by a single, unified causal model containing an intervening mental-state variable. In contrast, it is claimed, a subject that reasons about contingencies among observables alone is best represented by distinct causal models for each predictive context.[1]

On this account, we can conceive of empirical investigations of mindreading as attempts to determine which causal model most accurately represents a subject; e.g. is it one that contains an intervening mental state variable or one that does not? To answer such questions, we can turn to the field of causal modeling, an increasingly dominant approach among statisticians, epistemologists, computer scientists, and psychologists. Causal modeling provides tools for inferring causal structure from observable correlations, including tools for revealing the presence and content of intervening variables. It can also shed light on which models are particularly apt for playing various epistemic roles. Thus, the intervening variable approach seems to suggest promising empirical avenues for testing mindreading in children and nonhuman animals.

In this chapter, I will first provide a brief description of the intervening variable approach and some straightforward applications of the causal modeling framework that it suggests. Then

I will examine several significant obstacles for using causal models to think about mindreading; these raise questions about whether we can appropriately represent mindreading via causal models and, if so, how we could know which causal model best represents some actual subject's cognitive process.

The intervening variable approach

Any attempt to answer questions about the function of mindreading and how to test for it runs into an immediate problem. Suppose we have a subject A who makes the prediction that B will perform some behavior P in the presence of observable cues O. For example, suppose that chimpanzee A observes that dominant chimpanzee B is oriented toward a piece of food (O), predicts that B will punish A if A goes for the food (P), and as a result, A refrains from taking it.

The mindreading hypothesis (MRH) states that A made this behavioral choice by attributing some mental state, M, to B; for example, A believed that B could *see* the food and that if B could see the food, B would punish A for taking it. The natural alternative is the behavior-reading hypothesis (BRH), according to which A predicted the behavior of another on the basis of O alone; for example, A believed that B was oriented toward the food and that if B is oriented toward the food, he will punish him for taking it (Lurz 2009).[2]

Because the mental states of others are not directly observable, any act of mindreading would require A to first attend to various observable cues in order to infer the likely mental state of B[3]; in our example, A must know that the dominant is oriented toward the food and that this means that he can see it. How, then, could we know that our subject A made his prediction about B's likely behavior on the basis of both O and M (as the MRH would have it) or O alone (as the BRH would have it)? Further, given that A was necessarily behavior-reading on either hypothesis, when "would it become valid to say that a non-verbal creature was reading behavior in a way which made it of real interest to say they were mind-reading?" (Whiten 1996, 279).[4]

This so-called "logical problem" has been used to cast doubt on experiments that have purported to demonstrate mindreading in nonhuman animals and has received considerable attention in the psychological and philosophical literatures (the problem is most forcefully presented by Povinelli and Vonk 2004, and Penn and Povinelli 2007; for a sampling of critical discussions, see Lurz 2009, Andrews 2005, Halina 2015, Clatterbuck 2016, and Chapters 21 and 22 in this volume by Lurz and Halina, respectively). Povinelli and Vonk (2004) describe the logical problem as follows:

> The general difficulty is that the design of these tests necessarily presupposes that the subjects notice, attend to, and/or represent, precisely those observable aspects of the other agent that are being experimentally manipulated. Once this is properly understood, however, it must be conceded that the subject's predictions about the other agent's future behavior could be made either on the basis of a single step from knowledge about the contingent relationships between the relevant invariant features of the agent and the agent's subsequent behavior, or on the basis of multiple steps from the invariant features, to the mental state, to the predicted behavior.
>
> (8–9)

We can cast the problem in terms of the causal models that the MRH and BRH generate. An MRH model of A's prediction will posit that some observable state, O, of the environment caused A to have a belief that O obtains. From this belief, A inferred that B was in mental state

M, which in turn caused A to predict that B would perform some behavior P. Finally, this causes some observable response from A (see Figure 23.1).

However, there is also a BRH model of A's behavior, according to which A's belief that O obtains directly caused it to predict that B would P (see Figure 23.2).

In these causal models, the beliefs of the subject are represented as variables that may take alternative states (e.g. A does or does not believe that O obtains), and the arrows between them denote causal relations. We can add a parameter to each arrow denoting the direction and strength of the causal relationship via the conditional probability of the effect given its cause (e.g. Pr[A believes that O | O is present]).

It is possible to assign parameters to the two models in such a way that will guarantee that they are able to fit our data equally well; that is, they can make the same predictions about the probability that A would perform his adaptive response given the observable state of the environment.[5] If this is the case, then observations of A's behaviors will be evidentially neutral between the MRH and BRH. How, then, can we tell which of these models is true of A?[6] Further, if A's belief about O would, by itself, suffice for P, what function does the additional mental state attribution play?

These problems arise when we compare single causal chain MRH and BRH models. However, Whiten's key insight into this problem is that mental state attributions need not merely serve as intermediary links between a single observable cue and single behavioral prediction. Instead, a subject may posit mental states to explain what many different behaviors in different observable circumstances have in common, thereby uniting various known cue-behavior links as instances of a single mental state.

Consider the following example from Whiten (1996) of how we might attribute the mental state of "thirst." A purely behavior-reading subject may represent separate contingencies between various observable cues (e.g. B is fed dry food) and behavioral consequences (e.g. B drinks a large volume of water). A mindreader, on the other hand, may notice a pattern in the data, given that diverse inputs are all leading to the same outputs, and thereby posit thirst as an intervening variable, "the value of which can be affected by any or all of the input variables, and having changed, can itself affect each of the outputs" (Whiten 1996, 284). The behavior-reader and mindreader can be depicted by the causal models shown in Figure 23.3.

If the arrows in each graph have positive parameter values, then according to either, the subject will predict that responses on the right will follow from inputs on the left (and again, given the parameters we assign, they might predict the very same conditional probabilities).

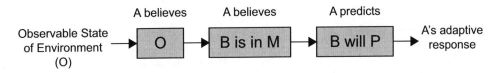

Figure 23.1 An MRH model of A's social inference

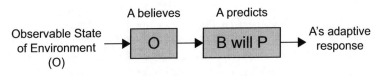

Figure 23.2 A BRH model of A's social inference

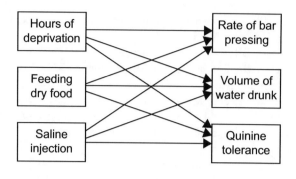

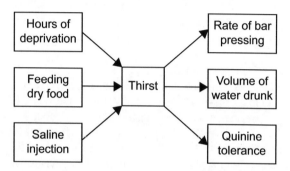

Figure 23.3 Models of thirst behavior without an intervening variable (top) and with an intervening mental state variable (bottom)

Source: Reprinted from Whiten (1996, 286).

What, then, would allow us to distinguish between the two models? And is there any advantage to being as described by one rather than the other?

Intervening variables as simplifying models

Whiten (1996, 2013) identifies two key differences between these two models. The first has to do with the predictions that a mindreader can make in novel observable contexts. A mindreader

> codes another individual as being in a certain state such as 'fearing', 'wanting' or 'knowing' on the basis of a host of alternative indicator variables, and uses that information more efficiently to take actions that are apt for different adaptive outcomes in different circumstances than would be possible if the vast number of alternative pairwise links had to be learned.
>
> (Whiten 2013, 217)

For example, consider a behavior-reader that knows the links between the first two inputs on the left-hand side of the model (hours of deprivation and dry food) and each of the three behavioral consequences on the right-hand side, and observes that a saline injection also leads to a high rate of bar pressing. If these stimuli are treated as distinct from the other two, the subject would still have to learn whether saline injections would also lead to, say, a high volume of water drunk. On the other hand, this observed contingency might suffice for a mindreader to link saline injections to the known "thirst" variable, in turn linking it to the known consequences of thirst without having to observe these contingencies.[7]

In addition to making past observed contingencies relevant to new cases, the introduction of an intervening variable also has a more syntactic effect on a causal model, reducing the number of causal arrows it contains (in Figure 23.3, from nine to six). For every new cue that is added to the behavior-reading model, separate arrows must be created which link it to each output variable. However, an intervening variable serves as an "informational bottleneck" which requires the addition of just one additional arrow.

Whiten argues that mindreading models are thus simpler and "more economical of representational resources" (Whiten 1996, 284). However, if mindreading's function lies in the simplicity of the models it generates, then a seeming paradox arises. The best candidates for mindreading are large-brained primates and corvids, suggesting that the process of positing intervening variables to capture complex patterns requires significant neural and cognitive resources. Further, on Whiten's conception, this process does not obviate the need to recognize a complex system of cue-response links first before the mindreading variable can be introduced. In what sense, then, are mindreading models simpler in a way that yields benefits for its users?

An answer to this question is suggested by Sober's (2009) application of model selection criteria to the case at hand. As noted above, it is possible to assign parameter values to the BRH and MRH models such that they will make similar predictions; that is, they can be made to fit to the data (roughly) equally well. However, introducing an intervening variable reduces the number of causal arrows, and thus adjustable parameters, required by a causal model. Interestingly, this has important epistemic consequences.

One of the central challenges of modeling is to strike the right balance between underfitting (failing to pick up on the "signal") and overfitting one's data (picking up on the "noise"). Models with more parameters typically allow for a closer fit to data but also run the risk of overfitting to noise; hence, it is well known by modelers that simpler models are often more predictively accurate (Bozdogan 1987, Forster and Sober 1994). Model selection criteria are attempts to formally describe this trade-off between fit and complexity (as measured by the number of parameters). Sober employs one such criterion,[8] the Akaike Information Criterion (AIC), which has been proven to provide an unbiased estimate of a model's predictive accuracy.[9] AIC takes into consideration a model's fit to data (Pr[data | L(M)]) and subtracts a penalty for the number of adjustable parameters, k:

AIC score of model M = log [Pr(data | L(M))] − k

Thus, models that fit the data roughly equally well can differ in their AIC scores, with more complex models suffering lower expected predictive accuracy.

The upshot is that while the BRH and MRH models may fit the data equally well, the latter will often contain fewer adjustable parameters as a result of its intervening mental state variable. Therefore, a subject that *uses* such a mental model can be expected to make more accurate predictions.[10] This buttresses Whiten's contention that for a mindreader, "behavioral analysis can become efficient on any one occasion, facilitating fast and sophisticated tactics to be deployed in, for example, what has been described as political maneuvering in chimpanzees" (Whiten 1996, 287). This also demonstrates that even if the only function of mindreading were to systematize already-known observable regularities, it might still contribute significantly to prediction.

However, there are several problems with the suggestion that the distinctive function of postulating intervening mental state variables is in allowing their users to make the same predictions but faster and more accurately. First, this function is difficult to test for; what baseline speed or accuracy should we expect from a behavior-reader, in order that we may compare it to a mindreader? Second, we might wonder whether mindreading would be worth the investment if it did not provide genuinely new kinds of predictive abilities.[11] Lastly, as we will soon see, there are also behavior-reading intervening variables that may serve the same syntactic role of simplifying models.

Distinguishing between models with different causal structures

While model selection considerations shed light on the advantages of using a model containing intervening variables, they don't provide a methodology for testing for them. However, other tools from causal modeling are more promising to this end.

According to the intervening variable approach, the predictions that mindreaders make in various contexts all have a common cause, a variable denoting the presence or absence of a mental state. In contrast, the predictions of behavior-readers across observationally disparate situations are independent of one another. For simplicity, consider the two models of predictions made in observable contexts, O_1 and O_2, where there is a direct causal connection between two variables if and only if there is an arrow linking them shown in Figure 23.4.

For example, O_1 might be a context in which a dominant chimp is oriented toward a piece of food and O_2 might be one in which the dominant is within earshot of a piece of food (where this is an observable property, such as distance) that would be noisy to obtain (as in the experiments of Melis *et al.* 2006). Each of these states is associated with the dominant punishing the subordinate for taking the food (P_1), going for the food himself (P_2), and so on. A mindreading chimp represents both of these situations as one in which the dominant is in some mental state M, such as *perceiving* the subordinate taking the food or *knowing* where the food is. A behavior-reading chimp represents them via distinct learned contingencies.

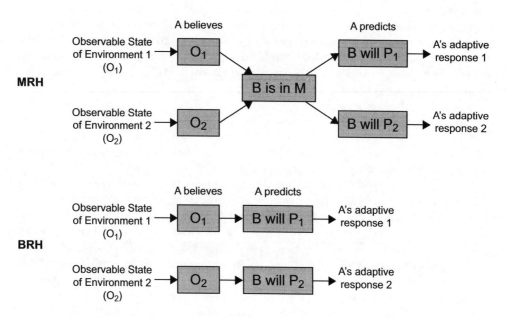

Figure 23.4   MRH and BRH models of predictions made in observationally distinct contexts

Each of these models predicts that A will exhibit adaptive responses in both observable contexts. However, they make different higher-order predictions about the correlations between those behaviors.[12] This follows from the Causal Markov Condition (CMC), a fundamental assumption of most prominent causal-modeling approaches. Informally, it says that once we know the states of a variable's direct causes (its "parents"), then that variable will be independent of all other variables in the graph *except* the variables that it causes (its "descendants"). Slightly less informally, if there is a causal arrow from A to B (and no other arrows into B), then conditional on the state of A, the state of B is independent of all other variables in the graph except for any variable C for which there is a directed causal path from B to C.[13]

Applied to the BRH model in Figure 23.4, the CMC states that once we take into account the observable states of the environment, A's belief that O_1 will be independent of all other variables in the graph except those that it causes; thus, it will be independent of any of its beliefs or behaviors in context 2 (the variables in the bottom row). A behavior-reader's responses in the two situations will be probabilistically independent once we have conditioned on the observable state of the environment. That is, a behavior-reader who performs an adaptive response in context 1 will be no more likely to do so in context 2 (or vice versa).

This is not true of the MRH, however. If we merely condition on the observable states of the environment, we have not yet accounted for a common cause of the adaptive responses in both contexts. Because the belief about B's mental state is a more proximate cause of those behaviors and we expect that the effects of a common cause will be correlated,[14] we should expect that a mindreader's behaviors in the two contexts will be probabilistically dependent, even once we have conditioned on the observable states of the environments.

In theory, then, we can experimentally distinguish between these two models by testing whether a chimp that performs the successful behavior in one experiment is more likely to perform the successful behavior in the other. In our working example, if chimps who successfully avoided the food that the dominant is oriented toward are no more likely to avoid the food that the dominant can hear, then this is good evidence that they were reasoning via separate, behavioral contingencies rather than an intervening mental state attribution.[15]

Let us grant that independence in behaviors across context is evidence against mindreading.[16] Is the converse true? Does a correlation in behaviors indicate that a subject was indeed mindreading? Unfortunately, the inference in this direction is far more fraught and has opened the intervening variable approach to significant objections.

The central predictive difference between the MRH and BRH – the presence or absence of a correlation in behaviors, conditional on observable contexts – depends on the assumption that an intervening mental state attribution variable is the only thing that could impose such a correlation. However, there are other causal connections among mental representations in different contexts that could also lead to correlated behaviors, and unless these are controlled for, the intervening variable approach will have difficulty establishing the presence of mindreading.

The first class of alternative behavior-reading explanations for a correlation in behaviors across observable contexts posits that while there is no intervening variable in use, there may be other causal links between the observable states or the subject's representations of them (see Figure 23.5).

Heyes (2015) suggests two mechanisms through which this could occur. First, if the O_1 stimuli is perceptually similar to that in O_2, stimulus generalization may cause a subject to treat the O_2 context as if it were the O_1 (the second dashed arrow in Figure 23.5). Second, situations in which O_1 is present might typically be ones in which O_2 is also present; for instance, situations in which a dominant is oriented toward food might also be ones in which he is in earshot of food (the first dashed arrow in Figure 23.5). In this case, mediating conditioning can cause

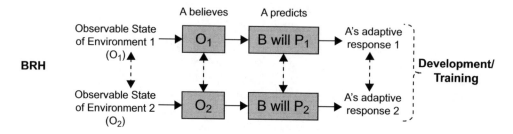

Figure 23.5   BRH model in which the subject's behaviors may be correlated across contexts, despite the absence of an intervening variable. Dashed arrows denote possible causal connections that may impose a correlation.

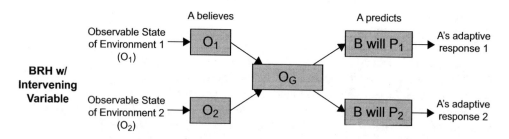

Figure 23.6   A BRH model containing an intervening variable.

the stimuli to "become associated with each other such that presentation of one of these stimuli would activate representations of them both, and thereby allow 'pairwise' learning involving the stimulus that was not physically present" (Heyes 2015, 319).

Still other confounds may be present. There may be correlations between the adaptive responses that are called for in each situation, such that a subject who produces one often produces the other. Lastly, for reasons of development or subjects' prior experience, a subject who possesses the top pairwise link may be more likely to possess the other (for example, perhaps only particularly astute or experienced chimps will pick up on both).

Controlling for these possibilities is indeed a central methodological concern among mind-reading researchers, and we might hope that good experimental design could solve such problems.[17] However, there is another alternative behavior-reading hypothesis that poses a somewhat more vexing challenge (see Figure 23.6).

The problem here is that a behavior-reader may also use an intervening representation that unites both observable contexts. This variable denotes some observable generality (O_G) of which both O_1 and O_2 are instances; this may be some single feature that both share, a common prototype that is used to represent both,[18] or some other perceptually based category that nevertheless seems to fall short of a genuine mental state attribution. For example, in response to experiments that purport to show that chimpanzees know what others *see*, skeptics of the MRH have argued that chimpanzees could solve these tasks by representing various experimental contexts as ones in which the dominant had a "line of sight" to the food, where this is an observable, geometric property of the environment (Lurz 2009; Kaminski et al. 2008).

The logical problem re-emerges, then, at the level of intervening variables. Given that an intervening behavior-reading variable will also impose a correlation in behaviors across contexts, this simple test will not suffice to distinguish between that model and the MRH. Additionally, if such variables are often available as heuristic stands-in for mental state attributions, what is the unique function of "genuine" mindreading?[19]

Conclusion

The methodological problems raised above arose from the fact that we were testing for a merely syntactic property of models (whether effects were correlated). Because MRH and BRH models with intervening variables have the same syntactic properties, this test will not distinguish between them. What is needed, then, is an approach that is sensitive to the semantic differences between mental state attributions, on the one hand, and representations of their perceptual analogs, on the other.

A few avenues for resolving this problem suggest themselves. First, we might insist that there is no real semantic difference between "genuine" mindreading variables and observable-level variables that unite particularly complex and sophisticated webs of observable contexts.[20] Alternatively, we might insist that there is a real difference and test for whether a subject makes novel predictions (that is, beyond the known cue-behavior links to which the intervening variable was introduced) that are instances of a mental regularity but not a corresponding observable-level regularity, or vice versa; however, doing so will involve an in-depth examination of the semantics of mental state attributions (Clatterbuck 2016, Heyes 2015). Likewise, we might abandon the idea that there is some bright line distinguishing mindreading and behavior-reading at any single point in time and instead focus on subjects' learning trajectories over time, evaluating "candidate mental state representations by seeing whether the animal can revise them to be sensitive to new and additional sources of evidence for the target mental state" (Buckner 2014, 580).

We might have hoped that the intervening variable approach could offer a quick fix to some of the empirical and theoretical problems that beset investigations of mindreading: if mindreading models have a different causal structure than behavior-reading models, then simple syntactic tools might easily distinguish between them. However, as the foregoing discussion shows, there are many factors that complicate this picture and demand both careful experimental controls for confounding variables and a renewed focus on the semantic differences between mindreading and other types of social cognition.

Notes

1 This assumption will be called into question in what follows.
2 See Butterfill (Chapter 25 of this volume) for a discussion of how to formulate a "pure" BRH and minimal mindreading alternatives that do not attribute full-fledged representations of mental states.
3 Characterizing this as an inference may be tendentious, but I will continue to do so for ease of exposition. If one likes, they can read "inference" as "The representation of O causes the representation of M" or "The O variable causes the M variable."
4 Here, I will focus more on the epistemological question and less about the semantic question of what counts as mindreading, though of course these are intimately related. For a discussion of a "logical problem" with respect to the latter, see Buckner (2014).
5 One has to make certain assumptions to ensure that the MRH and BRH have equal fit to data (Penn and Povinelli 2007, Sober 2009, Clatterbuck 2015).
6 As presented by Povinelli and Vonk (2004) and Penn and Povinelli (2007), the logical problem has two parts. The first is that for any MRH model like this, there will always be a BRH model that fits the data equally well. The second part states that this BRH model will be more parsimonious, in virtue of its attributing fewer beliefs to A, and therefore ought to be favored on those grounds. I will not address this second claim here. See Fitzpatrick (2009) and Sober (2015) for more general discussions of parsimony in the debate over mindreading.

7 Whether this capacity is restricted to mindreaders will be discussed in the next section.

8 For an overview of various model selection criteria, see Zucchini (2000).

9 "By predictive accuracy of a model M we mean how well on average M will do when it is fitted to old data and the fitted model is then used to predict new" (Sober 2009, 84).

10 Sober (2009) uses model selection considerations to show that *we* can more accurately predict subjects' behaviors via MRH models and that this gives us some reason to believe that those models are true. Clatterbuck (2015) argues that this argument is problematically instrumentalist, and instead, we should use Sober's insight to shed light on the advantage of possessing an MRH model, not merely being described by it.

11 See Andrews (2005, 2012) for a defense of the view that the distinctive function of mindreading is not to predict behavior but rather to explain and/or normatively assess behavior.

12 See Sober (1998) for a comprehensive, and perhaps the first, application of this technique to the mindreading debate, and Sober (2015) for an elaboration of the technique.

13 I am glossing over a great many technical details of the CMC which vary somewhat relative to the formal frameworks in which it is used. See Hausman and Woodward (1999), Spirtes *et al.* (2000), and Pearl (2000). For a helpful introduction, see Hitchcock (2012).

14 This will only be true, in general, if we assume Faithfulness. See Spirtes *et al.* (2000, Ch. 3).

15 In the Melis *et al.* (2006) work that inspired this example, it was shown that chimps more often than not chose to pursue food in ways that their competitor could not see, in one task, and in ways their competitor could not hear, in another. The authors took this to be some evidence that chimps may understand what others perceive, in such a way that is not limited to a particular sensory modality. Notably, the experimenters only tested for whether their chimps, in the aggregate, succeeded above chance levels in each of the two experiments. They did not test for whether individual performances were correlated on the two tasks.

16 A problem here is that a mindreader could use separate mental state attributions in each context, in which case, her subsequent behaviors would still be independent.

17 For a good example, see Taylor *et al.* (2009). For a discussion of how to control for developmental confounds, see Gopnik and Melzoff (1997).

18 For a discussion of how different types of mental categorizations, such as prototypes or examplars, can be represented using directed acyclic graphs, see Danks (2014).

19 For a presentation and critical examination of an argument for why such observable-level variables will always be available, see Clatterbuck (2016).

20 Whiten suggests that one can count as a mentalist if one uses a single variable which represents another as being in a certain state, even if one doesn't have a fully fledged concept of beliefs as being "in the heads" or as being internal causes of their behaviors (1996, 286).

Further reading

For a comprehensive examination of the various roles that parsimony plays in causal inference and its relation to the animal mindreading debate, see E. Sober, *Ockham's Razors* (Cambridge: Cambridge University Press, 2015). D. Danks, *Unifying the Mind: Cognitive Representations as Graphical Models* (Cambridge, MA: MIT Press, 2014) presents a unified framework for thinking about many types of mental representations and activities in terms of causal models, as well as a helpful and accessible introduction to the technical details of various causal modeling frameworks.

References

Andrews, K. (2005). Chimpanzee theory of mind: Looking in all the wrong places? *Mind & Language*, *20*(5), 521–536.

——— (2012). *Do apes read minds? Toward a new folk psychology*. Cambridge, MA: MIT Press.

Bozdogan, H. (1987). Model selection and Akaike's information criterion (AIC): The general theory and its analytical extensions. *Psychometrika*, *52*(3), 345–370.

Buckner, C. (2014). The semantic problem(s) with research on animal mindreading. *Mind & Language*, *29*(5), 566–589.

Clatterbuck, H. (2015). Chimpanzee mindreading and the value of parsimonious mental models. *Mind & Language, 30*(4), 414–436.

———— (2016). The logical problem and the theoretician's dilemma. *Philosophy and Phenomenological Review.* DOI:10.1111/phpr.12331

Danks, D. (2014). *Unifying the mind: Cognitive representations as graphical models.* Cambridge, MA: MIT Press.

Fitzpatrick, S. (2009). The primate mindreading controversy: A case study in simplicity and methodology in animal psychology. In R. Lurz (Ed.), *The Philosophy of Animal Minds* (pp. 258–277). Cambridge: Cambridge University Press.

Forster, M., and Sober, E. (1994). How to tell when simpler, more unified, or less ad hoc theories will provide more accurate predictions. *The British Journal for the Philosophy of Science, 45*(1), 1–35.

Gopnik, A., and Meltzoff, A. (1997). *Words, thoughts, and theories.* Cambridge, MA: MIT Press.

Halina, M. (2015). There is no special problem of mindreading in nonhuman animals. *Philosophy of Science, 82,* 473–490.

Hausman, D., and Woodward, J. (1999). Independence, invariance, and the causal Markov condition. *British Journal for the Philosophy of Science, 50,* 1–63.

Heyes, C. M. (2015). Animal mindreading: What's the problem? *Psychonomic Bulletin and Review, 22*(2), 3113–327.

Heyes, C., and Frith, C. (2014). The cultural evolution of mind readings. *Science, 344*(6190), 1357–1363.

Hitchcock, C. (2012). Probabilistic causation. In Edward N. Zalta (ed.), *The Stanford Encyclopedia of Philosophy* (Winter 2012 Edition), http://plato.stanford.edu/archives/win2012/entries/causation-probabilistic/

Kaminski, J., Call, J., and Tomasello, M. (2008). Chimpanzees know what others know, but not what they believe. *Cognition, 109,* 224–234.

Lurz, R. (2009). If chimpanzees are mindreaders, could behavioral science tell? Toward a solution to the logical problem. *Philosophical Psychology, 22,* 305–328.

Meketa, I. (2014). A critique of the principle of cognitive simplicity in comparative cognition. *Biology & Philosophy, 29*(5), 731–745.

Melis, A. P., Call, J., and Tomasello, M. (2006). Chimpanzees (Pan troglodytes) conceal visual and auditory information from others. *Journal of Comparative Psychology, 120*(2), 154.

Pearl, J. (2000). *Causality: Models, reasoning, and inference.* Cambridge: Cambridge University Press.

Penn, D. C., and Povinelli, D. J. (2007). On the lack of evidence that non-human animals possess anything remotely resembling a 'theory of mind'. *Philosophical Transactions of the Royal Society of London B: Biological Sciences, 362*(1480), 731–744.

Povinelli, D. J., and Vonk, J. (2003). Chimpanzee minds: Suspiciously human? *Trends in Cognitive Sciences, 7*(4), 157–160.

———— (2004). We don't need a microscope to explore the chimpanzee's mind. *Mind & Language, 19*(1), 1–28.

Sober, E. (1998). Black box inference: When should intervening variables be postulated? *The British Journal for the Philosophy of Science, 49*(3), 469–498.

———— (2009). Parsimony and models of animal minds. In R. Lurz (ed.), *The Philosophy of Animal Minds.* New York: Cambridge University Press.

———— (2015). *Ockham's razors.* Cambridge: Cambridge University Press.

Spirtes, P., Glymour, C., and Scheines, R. (2000). *Causation, prediction, and search* (2nd ed.). Cambridge, MA: MIT Press.

Taylor, A. H., Hunt, G. R., Medina, F. S., and Gray, R. D. (2009). Do New Caledonian crows solve physical problems through causal reasoning? *Proceedings of the Royal Society B, 276,* 247–254.

Whiten, A. (1994). Grades of mindreading. In C. Lewis and P. Mitchell (Eds.), *Children's early understanding of mind* (pp. 277–292). Cambridge: Cambridge University Press.

———— (1996). When does smart behavior-reading become mind-reading? In P. Carruthers and P. Smith (Eds.), *Theories of theories of mind* (pp. 277–292). Cambridge: Cambridge University Press.

———— (2013). Humans are not alone in computing how others see the world. *Animal Behaviour, 86*(2), 213–221.

Zucchini, W. (2000). An introduction to model selection. *Journal of Mathematical Psychology, 44,* 41–61.

24

DO CHIMPANZEES REASON ABOUT BELIEF?

Kristin Andrews

Introduction

For almost 40 years, psychologists and philosophers have been devising experiments and testing chimpanzees on the question first asked by Premack and Woodruff in 1978: "Does the chimpanzee have a theory of mind?" With this question, they meant to ask whether chimpanzees do what they assumed we do, namely, attribute beliefs and desires in order to predict behavior. This capacity is known as *mindreading* or *theory of mind*. After 30 years of chimpanzees failing all the tests we put to them, some researchers concluded that chimpanzees probably don't reason about belief (Call and Tomasello 2008).[1] Ten years later, those same researchers were part of a team that reversed course: "our results, in concert with existing data, suggest that apes solved the task by ascribing a false belief to the actor, challenging the view that the ability to attribute reality-incongruent mental states is specific to humans" (Krupenye et al. 2016).[2]

The claim that passing the false belief task is evidence of false belief ascription is one that requires critical scrutiny. For one, there is no consensus on what is involved in ascribing belief, given the lack of agreement regarding the nature of belief. And, given that we don't directly observe anyone ascribing belief, but infer it from behavior, we must consider alternative explanations for the behavior. However, the typical alternative explanations considered are all of the variety that apes are not mentalists. There is good reason to think that apes are mentalists who see other apes and other animals as intentional agents. Nonetheless, they may not be mentalists who ascribe beliefs.

I will argue that before accepting that apes ascribe false beliefs, we need to specify what is involved in ascribing beliefs, and we need to consider other mentalist hypotheses for how apes might pass. This doesn't mean that chimpanzees don't understand false beliefs in much the way we do. It might be instead that we understand false beliefs in much the way chimpanzees do.

Forty years of false belief tests

Premack and Woodruff (1978) asked whether a 14-year-old chimpanzee named Sarah could attribute states of mind to a human actor in order to predict what the actor would do next. They asked Sarah to watch videos of a human trying to achieve a goal, such as warming up a cold room with a heater or opening a door. Sarah was asked to indicate the human's goal by choosing a photograph of the object the human would need to achieve their goal, e.g., a key to open the door. Sarah solved these problems (except for human actors she didn't like; she tended to choose a useless object when her enemy was portrayed in the video). Premack and Woodruff concluded that Sarah understood that the human actor had a certain intention, and that she ascribed intention and knowledge (or desire and belief) to the actor.

Critics were not convinced. Sarah could have solved this task using a simple form of associative reasoning, by associating the match with the heater and the key with the door, without having to think anything about the mental states of the actor. To avoid this simple associative explanation for Sarah's behavior, Daniel Dennett (1978), Jonathan Bennett (1978), and Gilbert Harman (1978) each suggested an alternative experiment based on asking whether chimpanzees can think that others have *false* beliefs. If a person falsely believes that two things go together, then simple association will not allow a subject to predict how the person will act, because the two things *in fact* do not go together. Instead, to predict a falsely believing person's action, a subject would have to consider how the person sees the world. If we accept that belief and desire together cause behavior, and that beliefs and desires are *propositional attitudes* – representational states consisting of an attitude toward a proposition which can be true or false – then to predict someone's false belief behavior, one could attribute the false belief along with a desire to the target. For example, if we can say that Sharine believes that the key will open the door, and that she desires to open the door, we can predict that Sharine will insert the key into the door's lock, even if we know that the key doesn't fit the lock.

This idea led to the moved-object false belief task, which became the standard means for testing belief reasoning in children (Wimmer and Perner 1983). A version goes like this: children watch a puppet show in which Maxi hides a piece of chocolate and then leaves the room. While Maxi is out, his mother finds the chocolate and moves it to another location. Then Maxi comes back to get his chocolate. The story is stopped and children are asked where Maxi will go to look for his chocolate. Children who predict that Maxi will look for the chocolate where he left it pass the test. Children who predict that Maxi will look for the chocolate where it really is fail. Passing the test is interpreted as being able to reason about beliefs.

While human children pass this task between four and five years old (Wellman et al. 2001), and human infants appear to pass a nonverbal version of the task in the first two years of life (e.g. Buttelmann et al. 2015; Onishi and Baillargeon 2005; Southgate et al. 2007), chimpanzees failed many versions of this task given over the years. In one, chimpanzees learned that a communicator could see in which of two boxes a hider placed a food reward, though the chimpanzees could not see for themselves (Call and Tomasello 1999). After the hider placed the food, the communicator marked the box that contained the treat by placing a token on top of the box. Then the chimpanzees had the chance to choose one box and receive the contents. Once chimpanzees were competent at this task, they were given the false belief task. The situation started out the same, but after the hider placed the treat, the communicator left the room; and while she was gone, the hider switched the location of the two boxes, which were identical in appearance. When the communicator returned, she marked the box sitting in the location of the original placement of the treat, which, unbeknownst to her, was empty. Chimpanzees, like four-year-old children, failed this test. Five-year-old children, however, passed. Despite efforts to change the structure of the task by making the chimpanzee compete with a human (Krachun et al. 2009) or with another chimpanzee (Kaminski et al. 2008), and by removing both cooperative and competitive aspects (Krachun et al. 2010), these changes failed to elicit false belief tracking.[3]

What all these attempts had in common was using food to motivate chimpanzees to track false belief behavior. The experimental material that finally motivated chimpanzees to pay attention to false belief had nothing to do with food (Krupenye et al. 2016). The story the

Figure 24.1 False belief 2 condition from Krupeyne et al.'s (2016) experiment 1. The chimpanzee subject watches as the human sees King Kong hide in the right haystack and then goes inside to get the stick, closing the door behind him. While the human isn't watching, King Kong moves from the right haystack to the left, and then leaves the scene. Then the door opens, the human comes out with the stick raised over his head, and the chimpanzee subjects look more at the rightmost haystack, where the human last saw King Kong. These looks are interpreted as a prediction that the human will hit the rightmost haystack, and an attribution of a false belief that King Kong is hiding in the right haystack.

chimpanzees watched involved a human who was attacked by someone in a gorilla suit (King Kong). Chimpanzees first saw King Kong attack the human, and then run into one of two haystacks to hide. The human grabbed a stick and hit the haystack where King Kong was hiding. In the false belief conditions, the human had to leave the scene to get the stick, at which point King Kong changed position and left the scene. When the humans came back, the chimpanzee subjects looked at the haystack in which King Kong hid before the human left, anticipating that the human would beat that haystack with the stick (see Figure 24.1).

One innovation which made this experiment successful was using chimpanzee-relevant materials. Another was the eye-tracking technology and chimpanzee training which permitted careful analysis of where chimpanzees were looking. In addition, this study was modeled on the study widely touted as demonstrating belief reasoning in two-year-old children, including all the controls and the test trial types (Southgate et al. 2007).

The authors think that this study shows that chimpanzees can ascribe false beliefs. This parallels Southgate and colleague's interpretation of the toddler study: "The data presented in this article strongly suggest that 25-month-old infants correctly attribute a false belief to another person and anticipate that person's behavior in accord with this false belief" (Southgate et al. 2007, p. 590).

However, we should only conclude that infants and apes attribute beliefs to others if we first understand what is involved in attributing beliefs, and if attributing beliefs is the best explanation for passing this task.

What is involved in attributing beliefs

To understand belief mindreading, we can start by comparing it with other kinds of mindreading. Over the past 15 years, we've seen a number of studies that appear to demonstrate that chimpanzees mindread perceptions (see Butterfill's Chapter 25, Clatterbuck's Chapter 23, Halina's Chapter 22, and Lurz's Chapter 21 in this volume). Perceptual mindreading, broadly defined, is the capacity to understand what others can and cannot see. Subtypes of perceptual mindreading can also be identified. According to Flavel (1974), level-1 perspective taking consists of knowing that *what* one sees may differ from what others see, whereas level-2 perspective taking consists of knowing that *how* one sees things can differ from how others see things. While children have been tested on both level-1 and level-2 perspective taking, the chimpanzee perceptual mindreading studies have been focused only on level-1 perspective taking.

Level-1 perspective taking differs from both level-2 perspective taking and mindreading belief in that level-1 perspective taking is conceptually light, level-2 perspective taking is a bit heavier, and mindreading belief is heavier yet. To explain, let's compare the three kinds of mindreading:

(A) Mindreading level-1 visual perception: Mindreader believes that subject sees object.
(B) Mindreading level-2 visual perception: Mindreader believes that subject sees object as q.
(C) Mindreading belief: Mindreader believes that subject believes that P.

Now let's consider the cognitive and conceptual requirements for each of these types of mindreading. They all require that the mindreader has beliefs, and that is a point granted by all parties engaged in the debate. For (A), a mindreader only needs the concept of *see*. The object can be understood as "this thing" *de re* and need not be characterized in terms of how it appears to another, *de dicto*. What is it to understand that another can see a thing? That's a good question. Lurz (Chapter 21 in this volume) suggests that seeing is a mental state concept, and it is distinct from what he calls "direct line of gaze" – an observable relational concept between the body of a gazer and an object. While he previously identified the mental state concept of seeing with level-2 perspective taking (Lurz 2011), today he presents seeing as a mental state that can also compatible with level-1 perspective taking. As a *mental* state, at least part of what would be needed to know that another sees something as something else is, plausibly, some understanding of the other as a conscious intentional agent.

Once we get to (B), we see that the mindreader needs the concept *see* along with additional, and contrasting, descriptive concepts. The level-2 perspective taker can know that the eraser looks like a piece of candy to someone else. This adds a greater conceptual competence to the mindreader, and requires the ability to consider the mode of presentation of the object to another person, and to understand that a perspective might not correspond to reality.

In (C), a belief mindreader has an even greater conceptual burden, since one has to have the concept *believe* as well as the ability to correctly attribute propositional attitudes. What is belief? That's a really good question. Belief is typically understood as an attitude toward a truth-evaluable proposition which is mentally represented, though the vehicle of the mental representation is debated (see Bermúdez's Chapter 11, Glock's Chapter 8, and Rescorla's Chapter 3 in this volume). We might represent propositions sententially in a language of thought, as maps, as causal relations, as probabilistic relations, or as some combination of these. Of course, the cognitive load of belief attribution will differ depending on the vehicle of belief in play.

In addition to those who disagree about the vehicle of belief, there are others who do not accept the representational nature of belief. Dispositionalists or instrumentalists such as Braithwaite (1933); Davidson (1984); Dennett (1987, 1991, 2009); Marcus (1990, 1995); Ryle (1949); Schwitzgebel (2001, 2002); and Sellars (1981) all advocate various alternative accounts of belief. (See also Vincent and Gallagher, Chapter 21 in this volume.) So-called radicals in cognitive science deny any role for representation, given their view that explanations in terms of dynamical systems can explain our cognitive capacities (e.g. Barrett 2011; Chemero 2009; Hutto and

Myin 2012). Yet others think that much of what has been called mental representation can be understood in terms of externalized deeds or action (e.g. Rowlands 2006; Thompson 2007; Varela et al. 1991).

Finally, the folk have their own understanding of belief, though English speakers in North America typically use the word "think" rather than "believe" (Buckwalter et al. 2015). In the colloquial understanding, thinking that P can either mean that one represents and stores P as information, or in a thicker sense, it can mean that one might "like it that P is true, emotionally endorse the truth of P, explicitly avow or assent to the truth of P, or actively promote an agenda that makes sense given P" (Buckwalter et al. 2015, p. 2). The thicker sense of "think" is consistent with representational, dispositional, and enactive views of belief.

So, what it means to have a concept of belief is disputed, and different theorists will have different criteria for thinking that one has a belief. Take three quick examples. According to Schwitzgebel's phenomenal–dispositional account of belief:

> To believe that P, on the view I am proposing, is nothing more than to match to an appropriate degree and in appropriate respects the dispositional stereotype for believing that P. What respects and degrees of match are to count as "appropriate" will vary contextually and so must be left to the ascriber's judgment.
>
> (Schwitzgebel 2002, p. 253)

The dispositional stereotype for a belief that P will consist of the cluster of behavioral and phenomenal dispositions we tend to associate with the belief. And the dispositional stereotype for a belief that someone has a belief would likewise consist of the cluster of behavioral and phenomenal dispositions associated with thinking that someone else has the set of behavioral and phenomenal dispositions associated with the attributed belief. So, for example, to believe that a person believes that there is a monster in the rightmost haystack may be associated with the disposition to expect that the person feels more scared approaching the rightmost haystack, runs away from the rightmost haystack, attacks the rightmost haystack, etc., and to be surprised if the person didn't act as expected. The Krupenye et al. study would suggest the chimpanzee has this belief about the human actor's belief, on the phenomenal dispositional account.

On Dennett's (2009) intentional systems theory, beliefs are interpretive gambits that permit us to better understand and predict patterns of behavior. Because believers are rational, they act in predictable ways that are explained in terms of how they should act given the beliefs they should have. This intentional system is holistic, such that the mental concepts of the system are related to one another, and to behavior, providing a coherent explanatory system. As a holistic system, it is important to interpret behaviors from within a larger context, because the interpretation of a single behavior is a function of how it fits into the larger pattern of behavior.

If the intentional system includes the platitude that seeing is believing, then, given the evidence across circumstances that chimpanzees understand seeing, the Krupenye et al. findings would support interpreting all the mindreading studies as evidence of mindreading belief. If it doesn't, then we can interpret the Krupenye et al. findings as evidence that chimpanzees understand seeing, but not belief – because the chimpanzees could have anticipated the human's action, because that's where the human last saw King Kong, and people seek out things where they last saw them. Either way, the Dennettian approach requires us to take into account a large body of behaviors in order to know how best to interpret any one of them, and it would be a mistake to interpret the result of a single study outside of the larger context.

Because an intentional system tracks robust patterns, an interpretation would also have to take into account the chimpanzees' failure to track false belief in previous studies. Whether the pattern is robust enough to warrant the interpretation of belief attribution would be open to debate, and likely would require further evidence. The intentional systems view may be incompatible with Krupenye and colleagues' explanation for why apes failed earlier false belief tests: "Differential performance between tasks may reflect differences in task demands or context, or less flexible abilities in apes compared with humans" (Krupenye et al. 2016, p. 113). If false belief capacities in chimpanzees are much less flexible than those in humans, such that the pattern doesn't hold, then on the intentional systems view we shouldn't call them false belief capacities.

Like Dennett's intentional systems theory, on Davidson's interpretationism a belief is also understood in terms of attributions, but on this account the attributions are essentially tied up to language. We understand other creatures by applying a principle of charity to them, thinking that they are rational and that their utterances are largely true. Furthermore, we understand other creatures by thinking that they understand us in much the same way. Davidson writes,

> My thesis is rather that a creature cannot have a thought unless it has language. In order to be a thinking, rational creature, the creature must be able to express many thoughts, and above all, be able to interpret the speech and thoughts of others.
>
> (1982, p. 100)

Thus, we see that the only empirical data that would be relevant to determining whether a chimpanzee could mindread belief would come from a research program studying linguistic abilities.

And finally, consider one realist account of belief, Fodor's Language of Thought (LOT). On this account, a belief is a representation of sentential content in a language-like vehicle (Fodor 1975; see also Beck Chapter 4 in this volume). On this view, in order to mindread beliefs, one must be able to represent a belief about someone else's belief, which requires having the concept of belief. Like on Davidson's interpretationism, a LOT mindreader needs a significant amount of conceptual resources, including the concept of belief, in addition to linguistic competence (though unlike Davidson, Fodor thinks that having an external language isn't required for thinking in the language of Mentalese). That is, a mindreader would have to represent mental sentences about others' mental sentences, attribute those mental sentences, and understand that the other is thinking the target mental sentence. On this view, passing the false belief task wouldn't automatically provide evidence of belief ascription, if alternative LOT explanations are possible. Insofar as there are alternative mentalist explanations for passing the task, which I argue for in the next section, passing wouldn't entail false belief ascription on the LOT account of belief, either.

The takeaway message is that we can't say that chimpanzees or infants attribute beliefs without specifying the account of belief that we are working with. These and other accounts of belief, rationality, and representation (in this volume, see Beck Chapter 4, Bermúdez Chapter 11, Boyle Chapter 10, Gauker Chapter 2, Proust Chapter 13, and Rescorla Chapter 3) can also provide different criteria and different explanations for what passing the false belief task requires. They differ in how intellectual belief ascription is, yet they all can explain passing the tasks in terms of attributing beliefs.

Let us now look briefly at explanations for passing false belief tasks that do not require belief attribution.

Alternative mentalist explanations for infant and chimpanzee false belief prediction

Is there a way to be a mentalist and predict false belief behavior without being a belief min-dreader? There are three main approaches: a two-systems account, a developing one-system account, and a pluralistic account.

Apperly and Butterfill (2009, 2013) defend a two-system account of mindreading, according to which there is a fast automatic system that permits tracking false beliefs without represent-ing them as such, and a slower conceptual system that takes the familiar form (see Butterfill, Chapter 25 in this volume). Key to the view is how the early-developing system trades in non-psychological proxies for mental states: "*encountering*" and "*registration*" (Apperly and Butterfill 2009, p. 962). The encountering representation tracks perceptions, and so would rule out objects being in a target's field if, for example, they are located behind an opaque barrier relative to the target. *Registering* an object involves encountering it at one location and nowhere else. Together with the capacity for representing goals nonmentalistically, these states allow subjects to track at least some of the mental states of targets without the conceptual apparatus required for rep-resenting belief as such. This theory would explain the ability of the chimpanzee to predict the behavior of the human who attacks King Kong as a case of the human registering King Kong in the rightmost haystack.

Carruthers advocates a developing one-system model such that from infancy, humans already have concepts such as *thinks*, *likes*, and *is aware of*, and they use these concepts in ascribing propo-sitional attitudes to others (Carruthers 2016). This ability matures over time, as humans learn how to apply the concepts more generally by coming to see the kinds of perceptual access that give rise to various propositional thoughts. On this view, we may see the ape ability to pass this false belief task as evidence that apes have these proto-belief concepts without having the con-cept of belief, given that they work well enough to predict false belief behavior. However, unlike the children, apes would be stuck at this intellectual stage of development.

A third alternative, which I advocate, arises from a challenge to the commitment about the function of propositional attitude attributions. On both hypotheses discussed above, adult humans are thought to attribute beliefs and desires to predict behavior. While it may seem intui-tive that we predict behavior by thinking about people's beliefs and desires, that intuition might be a post hoc rationalization of our capacity to easily track behavior. The last few decades of social psychology research has taught us that humans are particularly bad at introspecting the mechanisms we use to act (e.g. Nisbett and Wilson 1977).

I argue for Pluralistic Folk Psychology (PFP), according to which we predict behavior in various ways, including stereotypes; self-reference; primary intersubjectivity; situation; inductive generalizations over past behavior; norms; non-propositional mental states such as moods, emo-tions, and goals; teleology; and trait attribution (Andrews 2012, 2015a). According to Pluralistic Folk Psychology, we build models of individuals and types of individuals that consist of informa-tion such as personality traits, social roles, emotions, histories, goals (and yes, in many humans, beliefs too), and manipulate these models to predict behavior. And, even when we are not attributing beliefs (which is most of the time), we do see others as minded, intentional creatures.

Essential to PFP is the idea that prediction and explanation are not symmetrical; a model can predict without explaining. If this is right, then it is also right that the false belief moved-object task will not paradigmatically elicit reasoning about beliefs. Given that we explain our own behavior in terms of our beliefs when we are looking to justify our actions (Malle et al. 2000), and that justifying anomalous behavior permits the development of cumulative culture,

I argue that the function of belief attribution is to explain – and justify – anomalous behavior (Andrews 2012).

Given this brief description of PFP, we can interpret the chimpanzee false belief tracking behavior in terms of registration as Apperly and Butterfill suggest, without accepting their complete two-systems account of belief. Rather, the encountering and registration relationships can be included as important parts of the folk psychological toolkit. On PFP, evidence of belief attribution would come not from passing some other form of the false belief task. Rather, it would come from observing a range of explanation-seeking behaviors, best interpreted as an attempt to understand why individuals act in the way they do, and accepting others even when they act eccentrically.

Conclusion

Apes and infants are sensitive to others' false beliefs. But we can't yet say *tout court* that they have a concept of belief – because we're not yet in agreement about what counts as understanding belief, and there are alternative explanations for their actions that do not require belief ascription. But does this mean that apes lack our theory of mind?

In a commentary in *Science* on the Krupenye et al. study, Frans de Waal writes:

> Theory of mind is probably part of a much larger picture that includes empathy, social connectedness, and the way bodies relate to other bodies. It is no accident that the tests conducted here focus on the body, i.e., subjects' eyes following the physical movements of actors. As such, the study by Krupenye et al. may help us move away from the prevailing assumption that theory of mind relies on a cognitive simulation of what is going on in the heads of others. Reading others' minds is beyond anybody's capacity. All we can do – and what apes apparently do in similar ways – is read bodies.
>
> (de Waal 2016, p. 40)

Here, de Waal challenges what has for so long been taken for granted – that we humans read minds. While we do interpret people, and offer explanations for people's actions, we shouldn't expect a great deal of accuracy in our explanations of others' actions. Yet, we're really good at coordinating our behavior with others, which means we are good at anticipating what others will do. Predicting behavior, and explaining behavior, are two different practices, and have two different functions; we need to stop seeing them as always caused by the same processes.

Why is it, then, that infants pass the implicit tasks, but not until age four do children pass the explicit verbal tasks? PFP has an answer: the verbal tests raise a puzzle for subjects, and elicit reasoning systems that need not come on line when one is simply anticipating behavior in a real-life situation. The question "Where is Maxi going to look for his chocolate?" raises a challenge for children that they have to figure out. An important difference between the implicit tasks, including the Buttelmann et al. (2009) active helping task, on the one hand, and the Maxi task on the other, is that the first task is about acting, and the second is about engaging in an act of charity to figure out what a reasonable person would do in a situation like that. The explicit tasks are akin to seeking a justification.

To conclude that apes do engage in belief reasoning is premature, but, as well, it would be premature to conclude that they do not. First, we need to get clearer on what we mean by belief attribution. Second, given that it took humans 40 years of looking to find evidence that chimpanzees can track false belief behavior, we should not be too quick to judge inability, especially since we haven't even started looking for evidence that apes explain behavior in terms of discrepant representational states. For all this time, we've been looking for evidence of ape belief reasoning in all the wrong places (Andrews 2005). Maybe now, with the knowledge that apes can make predictions that track someone's false belief, we can begin to examine other belief-relevant behaviors; and then, with a particular theory of belief in hand, we might be able to say whether apes actually have the concept of belief, and whether they use it to explain the strange things their friends and families sometimes do.

Further reading

For some alternative ways of thinking about the function of belief attribution, see Tadeusz Zawidzki's book *Mindshaping* (Cambridge, MA: MIT Press, 2013) and Victoria McGeer's articles, "The regulative dimension of folk psychology" (2007, in D. D. Hutto and M. Ratcliffe (Eds.), *Folk Psychology Re-Assessed* (pp. 137–156), Dordrecht, The Netherlands: Springer) and "Mind-making practices: The social infrastructure of self-knowing agency and responsibility" (2015, *Philosophical Explorations*, *18*(2), 259–281), as well as my book *Do Apes Read Minds?*, which is more about mindreading in the human ape than the nonhuman ones.

Acknowledgments

Thanks to Jacob Beck, Cameron Buckner, Brian Huss, and Brandon Tinklenberg for helpful comments on earlier drafts of this chapter.

Notes

1 At the end of their review of the status of chimpanzee theory of mind research program after 30 years of research, Call and Tomasello wrote, "chimpanzees probably do not understand others in terms of a fully human-like belief – desire psychology in which they appreciate that others have mental representations of the world that drive their actions even when those do not correspond to reality. And so in a more narrow definition of theory of mind as an understanding of false beliefs, the answer to Premack and Woodruff's question might be no, they do not. Why chimpanzees do not seem to understand false beliefs in particular – or if there might be some situations in which they do understand false beliefs – are topics of ongoing research" (Call and Tomasello 2008, p. 191).
2 An important lesson to be taken away from the 40 years of testing chimpanzees on false belief tracking is that we need to be very cautious making claims of inability; not finding evidence of a capacity in an experimental setting can say more about the researchers than the chimpanzees. It took people who understand the chimpanzee's point of view—who think like a chimpanzee—to create materials that would interest a chimpanzee. The development of eye-tracking technology was also crucial.
3 For a detailed description of these studies, see Andrews (2017).

References

Andrews, K. (2005). Chimpanzee theory of mind: Looking in all the wrong places? *Mind and Language, 20*, 521–536.
Andrews, K. (2012). *Do Apes Read Minds? Toward a New Folk Psychology*. Cambridge, MA: MIT Press.
Andrews, K. (2015a). The folk psychological spiral: Explanation, regulation, and language. *The Southern Journal of Philosophy, 53*, 50–67.
Andrews, K. (2015b). Pluralistic folk psychology and varieties of self-knowledge: An exploration. *Philosophical Explorations, 18*(2), 282–296.
Andrews, K. (2017). Chimpanzee mindreading: Don't stop believing. *Philosophy Compass 12*(1), e12394. DOI:10.1111/phc3.12394

Apperly, I. A., and Butterfill, S. A. (2009). Do humans have two systems to track beliefs and belief-like states? *Psychological Review, 116*(4), 953–970.

Apperly, I. A., and Robinson, E. J. (2001). Children's difficulties handling dual identity. *Journal of Experimental Child Psychology, 78*, 374–397.

Apperly, I. A., and Robinson, E. J. (2002). Five-year-olds' handling of reference and description in the domains of language and mental representation. *Journal of Experimental Child Psychology, 83*, 53.

Baillargeon, R., Scott, R. M., and He, Z. (2010). False-belief understanding in infants. *Trends in Cognitive Sciences, 14*(3), 493–501.

Barrett, L. (2011). *Beyond the Brain: How Body and Environment Shape Animal and Human Minds*. Princeton, NJ: Princeton University Press.

Bennett, J. (1978). Commentary on three papers about animal cognition. *The Behavioral and Brain Sciences, 1*, 556–560.

Braithwaite, R. B. (1933). The nature of believing. *Proceedings of the Aristotelian Society, 33*, 129–146.

Buckwalter, W., Rose, D., and Turri, J. (2015). Belief through thick and thin. *Noûs, 49*(4), 748–775.

Buttelmann, D., Carpenter, M., and Tomasello, M. (2009). Eighteen-month-old infants show false belief understanding in an active helping paradigm. *Cognition, 112*(2), 337–342.

Buttelmann, F., Suhrke, J., and Buttelman, D. (2015). What you get is what you believe: Eighteen-month-olds demonstrate belief understanding in an unexpected- identity task. *Journal of Experimental Child Psychology, 131*, 94–103.

Butterfill, S. A., and Apperly, I. A. (2013). How to construct a minimal theory of mind. *Mind & Language, 28*(5), 606–637.

Call, J., and Tomasello, M. (1999). A nonverbal false belief task: The performance of children and great apes. *Child Development, 70*, 381–395.

Call, J., and Tomasello, M. (2008). Does the chimpanzee have a theory of mind? 30 years later. *Trends in Cognitive Sciences, 12*(5), 187–192.

Carruthers, P. (2016). Two systems for mindreading? *Review of Philosophy and Psychology, 7*(1), 141–162.

Chemero, A. (2009). *Radical Embodied Cognitive Science*. Cambridge, MA: MIT Press.

Davidson, D. C. (1975). Thought and talk. In S. Guttenplan (Ed.), *Mind and Language* (pp. 7–24). Oxford: Oxford University Press.

Davidson, D. C. (1982). Rational animals. *Dialectica, 36*, 317–327.

Davidson, D. C. (1984). *Inquiries Into Truth and Interpretation*. Oxford: Oxford University Press.

Dennett, D. C. (1978). Beliefs about beliefs. *Behavioral and Brain Sciences, 4*, 568–570.

Dennett, D. C. (1987). *The Intentional Stance*. Cambridge, MA: MIT Press.

Dennett, D. C. (1991). Real patterns. *Journal of Philosophy, 87*, 27–51.

Dennett, D. C. (2009). *Intentional Systems Theory*. In B. McLaughlin, A. Beckermann, and S. Walter (Eds.), *The Oxford Handbook of Philosophy of Mind*. Oxford: Oxford University Press.

de Waal, F. B. M. (2016). Apes know what others believe. *Science, 354*(6308), 39–40.

Flavell, J. H. (1974). The development of inferences about others. In T. Mischel (Ed.), *Understanding Other Persons* (pp. 66–116). Oxford: Blackwell.

Flavell, J. H. (1977). The development of knowledge about visual perception. *The Nebraska Symposium on Motivation, 25*, 43–76.

Flavell, J. H. (1992). Perspectives on perspective-taking. In H. Beilin and P. B. Pufall (Eds.), *Piaget's Theory: Prospects and Possibilities*. The Jean Piaget symposium series (Vol. 14, pp. 107–139). Hillsdale, NJ: Erlbaum.

Fodor, J. (1975). *The Language of Thought*. New York: Thomas Y. Crowell.

Hare, B., Call, J., Agnetta, B., and Tomasello, M. (2000). Chimpanzees know what conspecifics do and do not see. *Animal Behaviour, 61*, 771–785.

Hare, B., Call, J., and Tomasello, M. (2001). Do chimpanzees know what conspecifics know? *Animal Behaviour, 61*(1), 139–151.

Harman, G. (1978). Studying the chimpanzees' theory of mind. *Behavioral and Brain Sciences, 1*, 576–577.

Hutto, D., and Myin, E. (2012). *Radicalizing Enactivism: Basic Minds Without Content*. Cambridge, MA: MIT Press.

Kaminski, J., Call, J., and Tomasello, M. (2008). Chimpanzees know what others know, but not what they believe. *Cognition, 109*, 224–234.

Krachun, C., Carpenter, C. M., Call, J., and Tomasello, M. (2009). A competitive nonverbal false belief task for children and apes. *Developmental Science, 12*(4), 521–535.

Krachun, C., Carpenter, C. M., Call, J., and Tomasello, M. (2010). A New Change-of-Contents False Belief Test: Children and Chimpanzees Compared. *International Journal of Comparative Psychology, 23*(2), 145–165.

Krupenye, C., Kano, F., Hirata, S., Call, J., and Tomasello, M. (2016). Great apes anticipate that other individuals will act according to false beliefs. *Science, 354*(6308), 110–114.

Leslie, A. M. (2005). Developmental parallels in understanding minds and bodies. *Trends in Cognitive Sciences, 9*(10), 459–462.

Lurz, R. (2011). *Mindreading Animals*. Cambridge, MA: MIT Press.

Malle, B. F. (2004). *How the Mind Explains Behavior: Folk Explanations, Meaning and Social Interaction*. Cambridge, MA: MIT Press.

Malle, B. F., Knobe, J., O'Laughlin, M. J., Pearce, G. E., and Nelson, S. E. (2000). Conceptual structure and social functions of behavior explanations: Beyond person-situation attributions. *Journal of Personality and Social Psychology, 79*, 309–326.

Marcus, R. B. (1990). Some revisionary proposals about belief and believing. *Philosophy and Phenomenological Research, 50*, 133–153.

Marcus, R. B. (1995). The anti-naturalism of some language centered accounts of belief. *Dialectica, 49*(2/4), 113–129.

Nisbett, R. E., and Wilson, T. D. (1977). Telling more than we can know: Verbal reports on mental processes. *Psychological Review, 84*(3), 231.

Onishi, K. H., and Baillargeon, R. (2005). Do 15-month-old infants understand false beliefs? *Science, 308*, 255–258.

Povinelli, D. J., and Vonk, J. (2004). We don't need a microscope to explore the chimpanzee's mind. *Mind and Language, 19*, 1–28.

Premack, D., and Woodruff, G. (1978). Does the chimpanzee have a theory of mind? *Behavioral and Brain Sciences, 1*, 515–526.

Rowlands, M. (2006). *Body Language: Representation in Action*. Cambridge, MA: MIT Press.

Ryle, G. (1949). *The Concept of Mind*. New York: Barnes & Noble.

Schwitzgebel, E. (2001). In-between believing. *The Philosophical Quarterly, 51*, 76–82.

Schwitzgebel, E. (2002). A phenomenal, dispositional account of belief. *Nous, 36*, 249–275.

Scott, R. M., and Baillargeon, R. (2009). Which penguin is this? Attributing false beliefs about object identity at 18 months. *Child Development, 80*(4), 1172–1196.

Sellars, W. (1981). Mental events. *Philosophical Studies, 81*, 325–45; reprinted in ISR: 282–300.

Southgate, V., Senju, A., and Csibra, G. (2007). Action anticipation through attribution of false belief by 2-year-olds. *Psychological Science, 18*, 587–592.

Thompson, E. (2007). *Mind in Life: Biology, Phenomenology, and the Sciences of Mind*. Cambridge, MA: Belknap Press of Harvard University Press.

Varela, F. J., Thompson, E., and Rosch, E. (1991). *The Embodied Mind*. Cambridge, MA: MIT Press.

Wellman, H. M., Cross, D., and Watson, J. (2001). Meta-analysis of theory-of-mind development: The truth about false belief. *Child Development, 72*, 655–684.

Wimmer, H. J., and Perner, J. (1983). Beliefs about beliefs: Representation and constraining function of wrong beliefs in young children's understanding of deception. *Cognition, 13*, 103–128.

25

TRACKING AND REPRESENTING OTHERS' MENTAL STATES

Stephen A. Butterfill

1 Introduction

Few things matter more than the mental states of those nearby. Their ignorance defines limits on cooperation and presents opportunities to exploit in competition. (If she's seen where you stashed those mealworms she'll pilfer them when you're gone, leaving you without breakfast. And you won't get that grape if he hears you sneaking past.) What others feel, see and know can also provide information about events otherwise beyond your ken. It's no surprise, then, that abilities to track others' mental states are widespread. Many animals, including scrub jays (Clayton, Dally and Emery 2007), ravens (Bugnyar, Reber and Buckner 2016), goats (Kaminski, Call and Tomasello 2006), dogs (Kaminski et al. 2009), ring-tailed lemurs (Sandel, MacLean and Hare 2011), monkeys (Hattori, Kuroshima and Fujita 2009) and chimpanzees (Karg et al. 2015), reliably vary their actions in ways that are appropriate given facts about another's mental states. What underpins such abilities to track others' mental states?

There is a quite widely accepted answer. As in humans, so in other animals: abilities to track others' mental states are underpinned by representations of those mental states. Some people seem less confident about lemurs or monkeys than chimpanzees, perhaps in part because these animals' abilities to track others' mental states appear less flexible (e.g. Burkart and Heschl 2007). Others caution that there is currently insufficient evidence to accept that any nonhuman animals ever represent others' mental states (e.g. Whiten 2013). But overall, the view that abilities to track others' mental states are underpinned by representations of those mental states is endorsed by many of those cited above for at least some nonhuman animals.

The simple answer will appear inescapable if we assume that tracking others' mental states must, as a matter of logic, involve representing others' mental states. But this assumption is incorrect. Contrast representing a mental state with tracking one. For you to track someone's mental state (such as a belief that there is food behind that rock) is for there to be a process in you which nonaccidentally depends in some way on whether she has that mental state. Representing mental states is one way, but not the only way, of tracking them. In principle, it is possible to track mental states without representing them. For example, it is possible, within limits, to track what another visually represents by representing her line of sight only. More sophisticated illustrations of how you could, in principle, track mental states without representing them abound (e.g. Buckner 2014, p. 571f). What many experiments actually measure is whether certain subjects can track mental states: the question is whether changes in what another sees, believes or desires are reflected in subjects' choices of route, caching behaviours, or anticipatory looking (say). It is surely possible to infer what is represented by observing what is tracked. But such inferences are never merely logical. To learn what underpins abilities to track others' mental states, we would therefore need to evaluate competing hypotheses. In recognising this, we immediately face two requirements. The first requirement is a theoretically coherent, empirically motivated and readily testable hypothesis on which tracking mental states does not involve representing mental states. This requirement is currently unmet (Halina 2015, p. 486; Heyes 2015, p. 322) and, as the next section argues, surprisingly difficult to meet.

2 Pure behaviour reading: cast the demon out

Pure behaviour reading is the process of tracking others' behaviours, including their future behaviours, independently of any knowledge, or beliefs about, their mental states. Can research on pure behaviour reading supply hypotheses on which tracking mental states does not involve representing mental states?

Contrast two approaches to theorising about behaviour reading. One focusses on the behaviourist counterpart of Laplace's demon. The behaviour-reading demon has unlimited cognitive capacities, perfect knowledge of history and can conceptualise behaviours in any way imaginable. Although blind to mental states, it can predict others' future behaviours at least as well as any mindreader (Andrews 2005, p. 528; Halina 2015, p. 483f). Invoking the behaviour-reading demon makes vivid the point that the existence of abilities to track others' mental states does not logically entail representations of mental states. But the behaviour-reading demon is little use when it comes to generating testable hypotheses. Not even the most exacting rigour requires excluding the possibility that an animal is a behaviour-reading demon before accepting that it can represent mental states.

The other approach to theorising about behaviour reading concerns actual animals rather than imaginary demons. Byrne (2003) studied a particularly sophisticated case of behaviour reading in Rwandan mountain gorillas. The procedure for preparing a nettle to eat while avoiding contact with its stings is shown in Figure 25.1. It involves multiple steps. Some steps may be repeated varying numbers of times, and not all steps occur in every case. The fact that gorillas can learn this and other procedures for acquiring and preparing food by observing others' behaviour suggests that they have sophisticated behaviour-reading abilities (Byrne 2003, p. 513). If we understood these behaviour-reading abilities and their limits, we might be better able to understand their abilities to track mental states too.

We seek an account of pure behaviour reading to generate testable hypotheses about tracking mental states without representing them. This will involve at least three components: segmentation, categorisation and structure extraction.

First, it is necessary to segment continuous streams of bodily movements into units of interest. Humans can readily impose boundaries on continuous sequences of behaviour even as infants (Baldwin and Baird 2001). How could such segmentation be achieved? Commencement and completion of a goal or subgoal typically coincide with dramatic changes in physical features of the movements, such as velocity (Zacks, Tversky and Iyer 2001). Baldwin and Baird express this idea graphically with the notion of a 'ballistic trajectory' which provides an 'envelope' for a unit of action (Baldwin and Baird 2001, p. 174). Research using schematic animations has shown that adults can use a variety of movement features to group behavioural chunks into units (Hard, Tversky and Lang 2006).

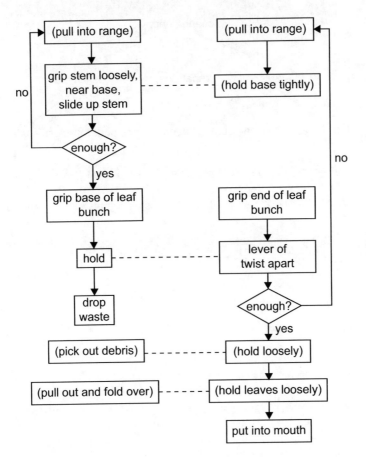

Figure 25.1   Read this! An analysis of the steps performed by the left and right hands in preparing nettles to eat without getting stung.

Source: Byrne (2003), figure 1 (p. 531).

A second component of behaviour reading is categorisation. Adult humans spontaneously label units of behaviour as 'running', 'grasping', or 'searching' (say). This is categorisation: two units which may involve quite different bodily configurations and joint displacements and which may occur in quite different contexts are nevertheless treated as equivalent. How are categories identified in pure behaviour reading? One possibility is that some categorisation processes involve mirroring motor cognition. When a monkey or a human observes another's action, there are often motor representations in her that would normally occur if it were her, the observer, who was performing the action (see Rizzolatti and Sinigaglia 2010 for a review). Further, in preparing, performing and monitoring actions, units of action are represented motorically in ways that abstract from particular patterns of joint displacements and bodily configurations (e.g. Koch et al. 2010). These findings indicate that one process by which units of action are categorised is the process by which, in other contexts, your own actions are prepared.

A third component of behaviour reading is structure extraction. Many actions can be analysed as a structure of goals hierarchically ordered by the means-ends relation (see Figure 25.2 for an illustration). A behaviour reader should be able to extract some or all of this structure. But

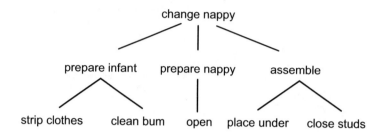

Figure 25.2 A routine action with a complex, hierarchical structure

how? Units of behaviour that are all involved in bringing about a single outcome are more likely to occur in succession than chunks not so related. This suggests that transitional probabilities in the sequence of units could, in principle, be used to identify larger structures of units, much as phonemes can be grouped into words by means of tracking transitional probabilities (Gómez and Gerken 2000). We know that human adults can learn to group small chunks of behaviour into larger word-like units on the basis of statistical features alone (Baldwin et al. 2008). A statistical learning mechanism required for discerning such units is automatic (Fiser and Aslin 2001), domain-general (Kirkham, Slemmer and Johnson 2002) and probably present in human infants (Safran et al. 2007) as well as other species, including songbirds (Abe and Watanabe 2011) and rats (Murphy, Mondragón and Murphy 2008). It is therefore plausible that some animals use statistical learning to extract some of the hierarchical structure of actions.

Our primary concern here with behaviour reading is as a potential basis for abilities to track others' mental states without representing them. But behaviour reading matters in other ways too. In mindreaders, behaviour reading enables mental state ascriptions (Newtson, Engquist and Bois 1977, p. 861; Baldwin et al. 2001, p. 708). Behaviour reading may also matter for efficiently representing events (Kurby and Zacks 2008), identifying the likely effects of actions (Byrne 1999), predicting when an event of interest will occur (Swallow and Zacks 2008, p. 121), and learning through observation how to do things (Byrne 2003). And of course a special case of pure behaviour reading, 'speech perception', underpins communication by language in humans.

What are the limits of pure behaviour reading? It is perhaps reasonable to assume that structure extraction depends on domain-general learning mechanisms. After all, such mechanisms appear sufficient, and there is currently little evidence for domain-specific mechanisms. This assumption allows us to make conjectures about the limits of pure behaviour reading. One limit concerns non-adjacent dependencies. There is a non-adjacent dependency in my behaviour when, for example, my now having a line of sight to an object that is currently unobtainable because of a competitor's presence results in me retrieving the object at some arbitrary later time when the competitor is absent. In this case, my retrieving the object depends on my having had it in my line of sight, but there is an arbitrary interval between these events. The hypothesis is that structures involving non-adjacent dependencies are relatively difficult to learn and identify, and that difficulty increases as the number of non-adjacent dependencies increases.[1] More generally, since birdsongs are discriminable and involve diverse behavioural structures (Berwick et al. 2011), we might take the Birdsong Limit as a rough working hypothesis: structures not found in birdsong cannot be extracted in pure behaviour reading.

Although not designed to test such limits, some existing experimental designs involve features which plausibly exclude explaining subjects' performance in terms of pure behaviour reading only. To illustrate, consider the sequence of events in the 'misinformed' condition of Hare, Call and Tomasello (2001, Experiment 1). A competitor observes food being placed [A], the competitor's access is blocked [B], stuff happens [X^N], food is moved [C], more stuff happens [Y^N], and the competitor's access is restored [D]. Finding evidence that chimpanzees can learn to identify patterns of this form [$ABX^N CY^N D$] and use them to predict the conspecifics' behaviours would represent a major discovery.

While it is probably impossible and certainly unnecessary to exclude the possibility that an animal is a behaviour-reading demon, it turns out to be quite straightforward (in theory, at least) to exclude the possibility that its actual behaviour-reading abilities are what underpin its abilities to track others' mental states. Even in advance of knowing much about the processes and representations involved in pure behaviour reading, the assumption that structure extraction depends on domain-general learning mechanisms makes it unlikely that the relatively sophisticated abilities of corvids and great apes (say) to track others' mental states could be underpinned by pure behaviour reading only.

3 End false belief about false belief

In the absence of an alternative, should we accept, provisionally, that in at least some nonhumans, tracking mental states does, after all, involve representing them? There are at least two obstacles to accepting this.

The first is a false belief about false belief. The false belief task (Wimmer and Perner 1983) is sometimes regarded as an acid test of mental state representations (see Bennett's, Dennett's and Harman's influential responses to Premack and Woodruff 1978). Awkwardly, chimpanzees and other nonhuman animals have so far mostly thwarted efforts to show that they can track others' false beliefs (e.g. Marticorena et al. 2011). False belief tasks continue to yield many important discoveries concerning humans (e.g. Milligan, Astington and Dack 2007; Devine and Hughes 2014). But there are reasons to doubt that the false belief task, despite its enormous value, is an acid test of mindreading. First, it is possible to track others' false beliefs without actually representing them (Butterfill and Apperly 2013). Second, there is evidence that typically developing humans can represent incompatible desires before they can represent false beliefs (Rakoczy, Warneken and Tomasello 2007). Having an ability to track false beliefs is therefore not sufficient for being able to represent beliefs, and probably not necessary for being able to represent mental states. So whether we accept that any nonhumans can represent others' mental states should not hinge on whether they can track false beliefs. As Premack and Woodruff (1978, p. 622) suggest, a false belief task is 'another arrow worth having in one's quiver rather than the assured bullseye that the philosophers suggest it is.'

There is a second, more challenging obstacle to accepting that some nonhumans can represent mental states. After claiming that 'chimpanzees understand . . . intentions . . . perception and knowledge', Call and Tomasello (2008) qualify their claim by adding that 'chimpanzees probably do not understand others in terms of a fully human-like belief-desire psychology' (p. 191). This is true. The emergence in human development of the most sophisticated abilities to represent mental states probably depends on rich social interactions involving conversation about the mental (e.g. Moeller and Schick 2006), on linguistic abilities (Milligan, Astington and Dack 2007), and on capacities to attend to, hold in mind and inhibit things (Devine and Hughes 2014). These are all scarce or absent in chimpanzees and other nonhumans. So it seems unlikely that the ways humans at their most reflective represent mental states will match the ways non-humans represent mental states. Reflecting on how adult humans talk about mental states is no way to understand how others represent them. But then what could enable us to understand how nonhuman animals represent mental states?

The view that tracking mental states involves representing them leaves too many options open, as Call and Tomasello's nuanced discussion shows. It is not a hypothesis that generates readily testable predictions. We need a theoretically coherent, empirically motivated and readily testable hypothesis on which tracking mental states does involve representing mental states (compare Heyes 2015, p. 321). Identifying such a hypothesis is the second requirement we would have to meet in order to evaluate competing hypotheses about what underpins abilities to track others' mental states. And to meet this second requirement, we must first reject a dogma.

4 Reject the dogma of mindreading

Representing physical states, such as the masses or temperatures of things, requires having some model of the physical. Little follows directly from the fact that an individual can represent weight or other physical properties: everything depends on which model of the physical underlies her capacities. And if we ask, 'What model of the physical characterises her thinking?', we find that there are multiple, experimentally distinguishable candidate answers (e.g. Kozhevnikov and Hegarty 2001). Her physical cognition might be characterised by a Newtonian model of the physical, or perhaps on an Aristotelian model. And it might involve one or another measurement scheme. Perhaps, for example, she distinguishes the weights of things relative to her abilities to move them. Or maybe she relies on a system of comparisons. Different models of the physical and different systems of measurement generate different predictions about the limits of her abilities to track physical events.

Likewise for mental properties. The conjecture that someone can represent mental states – that she is a mindreader, or that she has a 'theory of mind' – does not by itself generate readily testable predictions. Everything depends on which model of the mental characterises her mindreading.

In asking which model of the mental – or of the physical – characterises a capacity, we are seeking to understand not how the mental or physical in fact are, but how they appear from the point of view of an individual or system. Specifying a model is a key part of providing what Marr calls a 'computational description' of a system (Marr 1982). The model need not be something used by the system: it is a tool the theorist uses in describing what the system is for and broadly how it works.

When an animal is suspected of mindreading, we must ask, 'How does she model the mental?' But it will make no sense to ask this question as long as we are in the grip of a dogma. The dogma is that all models of the mental comprise a family in which one of the models, the best and most sophisticated model, contains everything contained in any of the models.

This dogma implies that only animals whose capacities approximate those that humans exhibit in talking about mental states can be mindreaders. In rejecting the dogma, we also remove any reason to make this assumption. Different mindreaders may rely on different, incommensurable models of the mental and different schemes for distinguishing mental states. Mindreading in other animals need not be an approximate version of mindreading in adult humans any more than medieval physical thought approximates contemporary physical theories.

To see how strange endorsing the dogma would be, contrast the mental with the physical. The briefest encounter with the history of science reveals that there are several models of physical phenomena like movement, mass and temperature. Some models are more accurate but also relatively costly to apply, while others are easier to apply but less accurate. And there appear to be different kinds of physical cognition which involve different – and incommensurable – models of the physical (e.g. Helmet et al. 2006). It would be astonishing to discover that there is one privileged model such that all physical cognition can be understood by reference to that particular model. The dogma of mindreading tacitly guides discussion only because, by contrast with the rich array of flawed theories of the physical, there is a scarcity of scientific theories of the sort of mental states which animals can track. But this scarcity can be alleviated.

5 Construct models of the mental

What is a model of the mental? On a widely accepted view, mental states involve subjects having attitudes toward contents (see Figure 25.3). Possible attitudes include believing, wanting, intending and knowing. (Not every model of the mental need include these attitudes.) The content is what distinguishes one belief from all others, or one desire from all others. The content is also what determines whether a belief is true or false, and whether a desire is satisfied or unsatisfied.

There are two main tasks in constructing a model of mental states. The first task is to characterise some attitudes. This typically involves specifying their distinctive functional and normative roles by developing a theory of the mental. The second task is to find a scheme for specifying the contents of mental states. This typically involves one or another kind of proposition.

One model of the mental is specified by minimal theory of mind (Butterfill and Apperly 2013, 2016), which repurposes a theory offered by Bennett (1976) in building on insights offered by Gómez (2009) and Whiten (1994), among others. This theory – or, rather, series of nested theories – specifies states with stripped-down functional roles whose contents are distinguished by tuples of objects and properties rather than by propositions. These features ensure that, although minimal theory of mind is capable of underpinning abilities to track mental states, including false beliefs, in a limited but useful range of situations, realising minimal theory of mind need involve little conceptual sophistication or cognitive resources.

The construction of minimal theory of mind enables us to specify some simple models of the mental, and to generate testable hypotheses about how mindreaders model minds. One such hypothesis concerns infant humans. The hypothesis is that a minimal theory of mind describes the model of the mental which underpins mindreading processes in these subjects. A key prediction of this hypothesis has so far mostly been confirmed (see Low et al. 2016). A minimal model

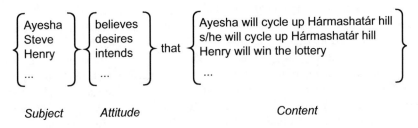

Figure 25.3 Mental states involve subjects having attitudes toward contents

of the mental might capture how minds appear from the point of view of some mindreading processes in some humans.

Consider a related hypothesis about nonhuman animals: abilities to track mental states in some nonhumans are underpinned by capacities to represent mental states which involve a minimal model of the mental. (This hypothesis was suggested by Apperly and Butterfill 2009.) This hypothesis avoids objections arising from views on which nonhumans have representational powers whose emergence in human development involves linguistic abilities and communicative exchanges. It also generates testable predictions about the limits of mindreading in nonhumans, including predictions which distinguish hypotheses about minimal theory of mind from hypotheses about pure behaviour reading. And there is already a hint that one such prediction is correct (see Karg et al. 2016; they don't mention this, but a signature limit of minimal mindreading is inability generally to do level-2 perspective taking).

Constructing models of the mental enables us to identify theoretically coherent, empirically motivated and readily testable hypotheses on which representations of mental states underpin abilities to track them. But of course this is just a first step towards understanding varieties of animal mindreading, one that opens the way for further theorising about the kinds of processes that underpin mindreading.

6 Conclusion

What underpins abilities to track others' mental states? To answer this question, we would need to evaluate at least two competing hypotheses. First, we would need a theoretically coherent, empirically motivated and readily testable hypothesis on which tracking mental states does not involve representing mental states. Although no such hypothesis currently exists (Halina 2015, p. 486; Heyes 2015, p. 322), there is a body of research on behaviour reading from which a theory capable of generating readily testable predictions might be derived (see Section 2). Second, we would need a readily testable hypothesis on which representations of mental states underpin abilities to track them. The construction of minimal theory of mind enables us to generate one such hypothesis (Section 5).

How plausible are these hypotheses? Even in advance of having a theory of behaviour reading, we might assume that extracting structure in behaviour reading depends on domain-general learning mechanisms only. Given this assumption, it seems unlikely that nonhumans' most flexible mental-state tracking abilities are underpinned by behaviour reading only (Section 2). This may motivate the search for alternative theories on which tracking others' mental states does not involve representing them. It may even justify accepting, provisionally at least, that some animals other than humans represent mental states.

To accept this is not yet to have a theory about mindreading capable of generating readily testable predictions, however (Section 3). Understanding abilities to track others' mental states is not simply a matter of categorising them as involving or not involving representations of mental states. Instead, we need to understand how different mindreaders model the mental.

Because different mindreaders may rely on different, incommensurable models of the mental and different schemes for distinguishing mental states, we need to identify models of the mental that we can use to generate readily testable hypotheses about different mindreaders' capacities (Section 4). The construction of minimal theory of mind illustrates how to do this.

The hypothesis that abilities to track mental states in some nonhumans, including great apes and corvids, are underpinned by capacities to represent mental states which involve a minimal model of the mental, has three things going for it. It makes precise what researchers should care about in asserting that animals other than humans can represent others' mental states. It isn't already known to be false, and there is even a hint that its predictions are correct (Section 5). And it has no theoretically coherent, empirically motivated and readily testable competitors – at least not yet. So if a minimal model of the mental doesn't characterise any nonhuman animals' abilities to track other mental states, what does?

Note

1 Compare deVries et al. (2012). Of course, whether non-adjacent dependencies are intrinsically difficult depends on the cognitive architecture (Uddén et al. 2012). There is evidence that monkeys (Ravignani et al. 2013) and chimpanzees (Sonnweber, Ravignani and Fitch 2015) can learn patterns involving one non-adjacent dependency.

References

Abe, Kentaro, and Dai Watanabe. 2011. 'Songbirds possess the spontaneous ability to discriminate syntactic rules'. *Nature Neuroscience* 14 (8): 1067–1074, August. doi:10.1038/nn.2869.

Andrews, Kristin. 2005. 'Chimpanzee theory of mind: Looking in all the wrong places?' *Mind & Language* 20 (5): 521–536, November. doi:10.1111/j.0268–1064.2005.00298.x.

Apperly, Ian A., and Stephen Butterfill. 2009. 'Do humans have two systems to track beliefs and belief-like states?' *Psychological Review* 2009 (116): 4.

Baldwin, Dare, Annika Andersson, Jenny R. Safran, and Meredith Meyer. 2008. 'Segmenting dynamic human action via statistical structure'. *Cognition* 106 (3): 1382–1407.

Baldwin, Dare, and Jodie A. Baird. 2001. 'Discerning intentions in dynamic human action'. *Trends in Cognitive Sciences* 5 (4): 171–178.

Baldwin, Dare, Jodie A. Baird, Megan M. Saylor, and M. Angela Clark. 2001. 'Infants parse dynamic action'. *Child Development* 72 (3): 708–717.

Bennett, Jonathan. 1976. *Linguistic Behaviour.* Cambridge: Cambridge University Press.

Berwick, Robert C., Kazuo Okanoya, Gabriel J. L. Beckers, and Johan J. Bolhuis. 2011. 'Songs to syntax: The linguistics of birdsong'. *Trends in Cognitive Sciences* 15 (3): 113–121, March. doi:10.1016/j. tics.2011.01. 002.

Buckner, Cameron. 2014. 'The semantic problem(s) with research on animal mind-reading'. *Mind & Language* 29 (5): 566–589, November. doi:10.1111/mila.12066.

Bugnyar, Thomas, Stephan A. Reber, and Cameron Buckner. 2016. 'Ravens attribute visual access to unseen competitors'. *Nature Communications* 7: 10506, February. doi:10.1038/ncomms10506.

Burkart, Judith Maria, and Adolf Heschl. 2007. 'Understanding visual access in common marmosets, Callithrix jacchus: Perspective taking or behaviour reading?' *Animal Behaviour* 73 (3): 457–469, March. doi:10.1016/j.anbehav.2006.05.019.

Butterfill, Stephen A., and Ian A. Apperly. 2013. 'How to construct a minimal theory of mind'. *Mind and Language* 28 (5): 606–637.

Butterfill, Stephen A., and Ian A. Apperly. 2016. 'Is goal ascription possible in minimal mindreading?' *Psychological Review* 123 (2): 228–233, March. doi:http://0-dx.doi.org.pugwash.lib.warwick.ac.uk/ 10.1037/ rev0000022.

Byrne, Richard W. 1999. 'Imitation without intentionality. Using string parsing to copy the organization of behaviour'. *Animal Cognition* 2 (2): 63–72.

Byrne, Richard W. 2003. 'Imitation as behaviour parsing'. *Philosophical Transactions: Biological Sciences* 358 (1431): 529–536.

Call, Josep, and Michael Tomasello. 2008. 'Does the chimpanzee have a theory of mind? 30 years later'. *Trends in Cognitive Sciences* 12 (5): 187–192.

Clayton, Nicola S., Joanna M. Dally, and Nathan J. Emery. 2007. 'Social cognition by food-caching corvids: The western scrub-jay as a natural psychologist'. *Philosophical Transactions of the Royal Society B* 362: 507–552.

de Vries, Meinou H., Karl Magnus Petersson, Sebastian Geukes, Pienie Zwitserlood, and Morten H. Christiansen. 2012. 'Processing multiple non-adjacent dependencies: Evidence from sequence learning'.

Philosophical Transactions of the Royal Society B: Biological Sciences 367 (1598): 2065–2076, July. doi:10.1098/rstb.2011.0414.

Devine, Rory T., and Claire Hughes. 2014. 'Relations between false belief understanding and executive function in early childhood: A meta-analysis'. *Child Development* 85 (5): 1777–1794, September. doi:10.1111/cdev. 12237.

Fiser, József, and Richard N. Aslin. 2001. 'Unsupervised statistical learning of higher-order spatial structures from visual scenes'. *Psychological Science* 12 (6): 499–504.

Gómez, Juan Carlos. 2009. 'Embodying meaning: Insights from primates, autism, and Brentano'. *Neural Networks, What It Means to Communicate*, 22 (2): 190–196, March. doi:10.1016/j.neunet.2009.01.010.

Gómez, Rebecca, and LouAnn Gerken. 2000. 'Infant artificial language learning and language acquisition'. *Trends in Cognitive Sciences* 4 (5): 178–186.

Halina, Marta. 2015. 'There is no special problem of mindreading in non- human animals'. *Philosophy of Science* 82 (3): 473–490. doi:10.1086/ 681627.

Hard, Bridgette Martin, Barbara Tversky, and David S. Lang. 2006. 'Making sense of abstract events: Building event schemas'. *Memory & Cognition* 34: 1221–1235.

Hare, Brian, Josep Call, and Michael Tomasello. 2001. 'Do chimpanzees know what conspecifics know?' *Animal Behaviour* 61 (1): 139–151.

Hattori, Yuko, Hika Kuroshima, and Kazuo Fujita. 2009. 'Tufted capuchin monkeys (Cebus apella). *Animal Cognition* 13 (1): 87–92, June. doi:10. 1007/s10071-009-0248-6.

Helme, Anne E., Josep Call, Nicola S. Clayton, and Nathan J. Emery. 2006. 'What do bonobos (Pan paniscus) understand about physical contact?' *Journal of Comparative Psychology* (Washington, DC: 1983) 120 (3): 294–302, August. doi:10.1037/0735-7036.120.3.294.

Heyes, Cecilia. 2015. 'Animal mindreading: What's the problem?' *Psychonomic Bulletin & Review* 22 (2): 313–327, August. doi:10.3758/s13423- 014-0704-4.

Kaminski, Juliane, Juliane Bräuer, Josep Call, and Michael Tomasello. 2009. 'Domestic dogs are sensitive to a human's perspective'. *Behaviour* 146 (7): 979–998. doi:10.1163/156853908X395530.

Kaminski, Juliane, Josep Call, and Michael Tomasello. 2006. 'Goats' behaviour in a competitive food paradigm: Evidence for perspective taking?' *Behaviour* 143: 1341–1356, November. doi:10.1163/156853906778987542.

Karg, Katja, Martin Schmelz, Josep Call, and Michael Tomasello. 2015. 'Chimpanzees strategically manipulate what others can see'. *Animal Cognition* 18 (5): 1069–1076, May. doi:10.1007/s10071–015–0875-z.

Karg, Katja, Martin Schmelz, Josep Call, and Michael Tomasello. 2016. 'Differing views: Can chimpanzees do Level 2 perspective- taking?' *Animal Cognition* 19 (3): 555–564, February. doi:10.1007/ s10071-016-0956-7.

Kirkham, Natasha Z., Jonathan A. Slemmer, and Scott P. Johnson. 2002. 'Visual statistical learning in infancy: Evidence for a domain general learning mechanism'. *Cognition* 83 (2): B35–B42.

Koch, Giacomo, Viviana Versace, Sonia Bonnì, Federica Lupo, Emanuele Lo Gerfo, Massimiliano Oliveri and Carlo Caltagirone. 2010. 'Resonance of cortico – cortical connections of the motor system with the observation of goal directed grasping movements'. *Neuropsychologia* 48 (12): 3513–3520, October. doi:10.1016/j.neuropsychologia.2010.07.037.

Kozhevnikov, Maria, and Mary Hegarty. 2001. 'Impetus beliefs as default heuristics: Dissociation between explicit and implicit knowledge about motion'. *Psychonomic Bulletin & Review* 8 (3): 439–453. doi:10.3758/ BF03196179.

Kurby, Christopher A., and Jefrey M. Zacks. 2008. 'Segmentation in the perception and memory of events'. *Trends in Cognitive Sciences* 12 (2): 72–79.

Low, Jason, Ian A. Apperly, Stephen A. Butterfill, and Hannes Rakoczy. 2016. 'Cognitive architecture of belief reasoning in children and adults: A primer on the two-systems account'. *Child Development Perspectives* n/a–n/a, May. doi:10.1111/cdep.12183.

Marr, David. 1982. *Vision: A Computational Investigation Into the Human Representation and Processing of Visual Information*. San Francisco, CA: W.H. Freeman.

Marticorena, Drew C.W., April M. Ruiz, Cora Mukerji, Anna Goddu, and Laurie R. Santos. 2011. 'Monkeys represent others' knowledge but not their beliefs'. *Developmental Science* 14 (6): 1406–1416, November. doi:10.1111/j.1467–7687.2011.01085.x.

Milligan, Karen, Janet Wilde Astington, and Lisa Ain Dack. 2007. 'Language and theory of mind: Meta-analysis of the relation between language ability and false-belief understanding'. *Child Development* 78 (2): 622–646, March. doi:10.1111/j.1467-8624.2007.01018.x.

Moeller, Mary Pat, and Brenda Schick. 2006. 'Relations between maternal input and theory of mind understanding in deaf children'. *Child Development* 77 (3): 751–766, May. doi:10.1111/j.1467–8624.2006. 00901.x.

Murphy, Robin A., Esther Mondragón, and Victoria A. Murphy. 2008. 'Rule learning by rats'. *Science* 319 (5871): 1849–1851, March. doi:10 .1126/science.1151564.

Newtson, Darren, Gretchen A. Engquist, and Joyce Bois. 1977. 'The objective basis of behavior units'. *Journal of Personality and Social Psychology* 35 (12): 847–862.

Premack, David, and Guy Woodruff. 1978. 'Does the chimpanzee have a theory of mind?' *Behavioral and Brain Sciences* 1 (4): 515–526. doi:10.1017/S0140525X00076512.

Rakoczy, Hannes, Felix Warneken, and Michael Tomasello. 2007. '"This way!", "No! That way!" – 3-year olds know that two people can have mutually incompatible desires'. *Cognitive Development* 22 (1): 47–68. doi:10.1016/j.cogdev.2006.08.002.

Ravignani, Andrea, Ruth-Sophie Sonnweber, Nina Stobbe, and W. Tecumseh Fitch. 2013. 'Action at a distance: Dependency sensitivity in a New World primate'. *Biology Letters* 9 (6): 20130852, December. doi:10.1098/ rsbl.2013.0852.

Rizzolatti, Giacomo, and Corrado Sinigaglia. 2010. 'The functional role of the parieto-frontal mirror circuit: Interpretations and misinterpretations'. *Nature Reviews: Neuroscience* 11 (4): 264–274. doi:10.1038/ nrn2805.

Safran, Jenny R., Seth D. Pollak, Rebecca L. Seibel, and Anna Shkolnik. 2007. 'Dog is a dog is a dog: Infant rule learning is not specific to language'. *Cognition* 105 (3): 669–680, December. doi:10.1016/j.cognition. 2006.11.004.

Sandel, Aaron A., Evan L. MacLean, and Brian Hare. 2011. 'Evidence from four lemur species that ringtailed lemur social cognition converges with that of haplorhine primates'. *Animal Behaviour* 81 (5): 925–931, May. doi:10.1016/j.anbehav.2011.01.020.

Sonnweber, Ruth, Andrea Ravignani, and W. Tecumseh Fitch. 2015. 'Non- adjacent visual dependency learning in chimpanzees'. *Animal Cognition* 18 (3): 733–745, January. doi:10.1007/s10071–015–0840-x.

Swallow, Khena M., and Jefrey M. Zacks. 2008. 'Sequences learned without awareness can orient attention during the perception of human activity'. *Psychonomic Bulletin & Review* 15: 116–122.

Uddén, Julia, Martin Ingvar, Peter Hagoort, and Karl M. Petersson. 2012. 'Implicit acquisition of grammars with crossed and nested non-adjacent dependencies: Investigating the push–down stack model'. *Cognitive Science* 36 (6): 1078–1101, August. doi:10.1111/j.1551–6709.2012. 01235.x.

Whiten, Andrew. 1994. 'Grades of mindreading'. In *Children's Early Understanding of Mind*, edited by Charlie Lewis and Peter Mitchell, 47–70. Hove: Erlbaum.

Whiten, Andrew. 2013. 'Humans are not alone in computing how others see the world'. *Animal Behaviour* 86 (2): 213–221, August. doi:10. 1016 /j.anbehav.2013.04.021.

Wimmer, Heinz, and Josef Perner. 1983. 'Beliefs about beliefs: Representation and constraining function of wrong beliefs in young children's understanding of deception'. *Cognition* 13: 103–128.

Zacks, Jefrey M., Barbara Tversky, and Gowri Iyer. 2001. 'Perceiving, remembering, and communicating structure in events'. *Journal of Experimental Psychology: General* 130 (1): 29–58.

26

FROM FALSE BELIEFS TO TRUE INTERACTIONS

Are chimpanzees socially enactive?[1]

Sarah Vincent and Shaun Gallagher

In their 1978 paper, psychologists David Premack and Guy Woodruff posed the question, "Does the chimpanzee have a theory of mind?" They treated this question as interchangeable with the inquiry, "Does a chimpanzee make inferences about another individual, in any degree or kind?" (526). Here, we offer an alternative way of thinking about this issue, positing that while chimpanzees may not possess a theory of mind in the strict sense (to be explained shortly), we ought to think of them as enactive perceivers of practical and social affordances. As such, we reframe the question: "Are chimpanzees socially enactive?"

In the first section, we briefly review the well-known theory of mind and behavior-reading accounts. We then present a more detailed account of the enactivist approach to social cognition. In the second section, we contrast these three accounts as they apply to a number of empirical studies related to social cognition in chimpanzees (*Pan troglodytes*), defending an enactivist interpretation of the data.

Theory of mind, behavior-reading, and interaction theory

Theory of mind (ToM) approaches have traditionally assumed that we do not have direct access to the minds of others (Sellars 1956; Gallagher 2016).[2] Accordingly, ToM claims that only some form of inference (i.e., either theoretical inference or simulation) makes possible one's understanding (or "mindreading") of the mental states of others.

Behavior-reading (BR) accounts offered the first alternative to ToM views. As accounts of mindreading began to emphasize its predictive purchase (i.e., with respect to behaviors), some argued that we are able to predict the behavior of others on the basis of observations about the relationship between current behavior and the environment in which the behavior occurs – without attributing mental states (Povinelli 2000; Povinelli and Vonk 2004; Penn and Povinelli 2007). According to this camp, what some take to be evidence of ToM is in fact only evidence of associative learning.

The enactivist account of social cognition, sometimes termed 'interaction theory' (IT), is an alternative to both ToM and BR views – an alternative, we argue, that is especially useful for making sense of social cognition among chimpanzees (and perhaps in other species more generally). Drawing on phenomenological resources, especially the work of Merleau-Ponty, IT challenges ToM's assumption that we do not have direct access to other minds, in part by defining minds as embodied and situated. In most of our everyday encounters with others, we do not assume a spectatorial view, observing others from a third-person perspective. Rather, IT claims, mindreading by theoretical inference or simulation is a relatively rare, more specialized approach to gaining understanding of another in peculiar circumstances or when interaction and communicative processes involved in most of our everyday encounters fail. Crucially, rather than merely observing, we tend to *interact* with others in highly contextualized social settings, via communicative acts, or in normatively circumscribed and sometimes prescribed relations, which often support our direct enactive perception of the embodied intentions and emotions of others. Put simply, interaction theorists hold that we understand others primarily through embodied and situated instances of interaction – directly perceiving others as minded beings (Gallagher 2008, 2012). We are not primarily observers but rather participants with respect to social cognition.

IT takes social perception to be enactive (or action-oriented), involving sensory-motor skills rather than the passive reception of sensory inputs (Varela et al. 1991; Hurley 1998; Noë 2004). Generally, we perceive the world as affording action (practical affordances), and we perceive others as affording interaction (social affordances). We also perceive intentions and emotions in others' postures, movements, gestures, facial expressions, gaze direction, vocal intonations, etc. In this regard, IT references embodied cognition research and specific conceptions of intention and emotion.

Importantly, intentions are not hidden mental states. They include bodily or motor intentions (so-called 'M-intentions') reflected in the kinematics of movement and action, as well as present or proximal intentions ('P-intentions' or intentions-in-action) where a prior intention is specified in terms of present context (Pacherie 2006, 2008; Searle 1983). That M- and P-intentions can be perceived in the other's actions is not an *a priori* claim; there is good scientific evidence to support this claim. If I pick up a cup to drink from it, the shape of my grasp is different than if I pick it up to throw it (Jeannerod 1997). The intentional aspects of bodily movements are intrinsic to and reflected in the dynamic kinematics of movement (Ansuini et al. 2006, 2008; Marteniuk et al. 1987; Sartori et al. 2011). As Becchio et al. (2012) have shown experimentally, even in the absence of contextual information, these intentions can be perceptually differentiated as such in bodily movement. Indeed, this is a capacity that develops early in infancy. Seven- to nine-month-old infants can perceive certain ambiguous acts, like offering and withdrawing an object, as reflecting playful intentions, with different goals and outcomes than when the same intentions are interpreted literally (Legerstee 2005; Reddy 2008). P-intentions are closely tied to context, and there is evidence for the perception of P-intentions (as well as emotions) in studies of bodily kinematics and the dynamics of social attention and contextualized interaction in adults (Atkinson et al. 2007; Lindblom 2015).

Emotions, too, involve aspects of embodied mind. Emotions are not just internal experiences; they are complex patterns that include bodily states and expressions. If we think of emotions as "individuated in patterns of characteristic features (Newen et al. 2015: 187) – features that may include bodily expressions, behaviors, action expressions, etc. – then emotion perception can be considered a form of perceptual pattern recognition (Izard 1972; Izard et al. 2000; Newen et al. 2015). We can directly perceive a pattern of expressions and behaviors – and as such, directly perceive a sufficient amount of the pattern that constitutes the emotion. Philosophers like Scheler (1954: 260–261), Wittgenstein (1967: §229; 1980: §170, §570), and Merleau-Ponty (2012) have argued for this view.

The case for enactive cognition in chimpanzees

Which of these approaches to social cognition best fits with our present knowledge regarding nonhuman animals? At the instigation of Dennett (1978), much of the ToM theorizing about social cognition focuses on false-belief tests, regarded as the standard experimental design for assessing ToM in children (Wimmer and Perner 1983; Baron-Cohen et al. 1985; Leslie and Frith 1988; Onishi and Baillargeon 2005; Senju et al. 2011).

Call and Tomasello (1999) presented great apes (including five chimpanzees) with a nonverbal false-belief task. The experiment involved two humans (a hider [*H*] and a communicator [*C*]) and one ape. Two boxes were placed between *H* and the ape, with one containing food. *C* was able to see which box the food was placed in, but the ape was not. The ape saw *C* place food in a box, walk away, and turn her back to *H* and the ape, while *H* switched the location of the food. The switch was made obvious to the ape, but the ape still did not know which box the food was in. When *C* returned, she placed a marker (a previously trained signal to the ape about where the food was located) on the box that originally (but no longer) contained the food. None of the apes succeeded at selecting the correct box containing the food when both boxes were subsequently presented to them, which suggests that they failed to recognize the false belief of *C*. Call and Tomasello concluded that the apes did not have a theory of mind. They were careful to point out, however, that apes nonetheless do have sophisticated cognitive and social abilities and interact with each other in intelligent ways.

As an alternative to a false-belief task, Tomasello et al. (2003), following Hare et al. (2000), utilized food-competition experiments to assess social cognition in chimpanzees. In the original experiment, Hare et al. (2000) positioned a subordinate chimpanzee and a dominant chimpanzee in separate rooms that were linked by a shared space. In the shared space, a food item was placed in view of both chimpanzees, while additional food was placed behind a barrier that prevented the dominant chimpanzee from seeing it. The subordinate chimpanzees approached the latter food, which was not visible to the dominant chimpanzees – even when the subordinates were allowed to enter the mutual space first. Tomasello et al. analyze this behavior as follows: "Chimpanzees actually know something about the content of what others see and, at least in some situations, how this governs their behavior" (155). They then describe chimpanzees as possessing "a social-cognitive schema enabling them to go a bit below the surface and discern something of the intentional structure of behavior and how perception influences it" (156) – but (consistent with the Call and Tomasello 1999 results) not as possessing a full-blown ToM.

Povinelli and Vonk (2004), however, offered an alternative BR account. According to their analysis, chimpanzees may be able to reason only about behaviors (as opposed to construing those behaviors in terms of mental states). With respect to the Hare et al. (2000) experiment, Povinelli and Vonk suggest that a subordinate chimpanzee needs only to have two beliefs: (a) that there is no barrier between the dominant chimpanzee and the first food item, and (b) that the subordinate chimpanzee could be punished for taking that food. Here, in contrast to the ToM-based analysis, there is no need for the subordinate chimpanzee to have a third kind of belief (i.e., concerning the mental states of the dominant chimpanzee). The BR view, according to the researchers, is then a more parsimonious explanation and should be preferred.[3] [For a further discussion of BR and mindreading, see Lurz, Chapter 21 in this volume.]

An enactive analysis of the Hare et al. (2000) experiment would include the idea that chimpanzees are aware of affordances in the situation. The subordinate chimpanzee can see that the dominant chimpanzee can see some things and not others (Povinelli and Eddy 1997). The affordances are not only physical, in terms of whether the chimpanzee is able to reach and grab the food, for example; they are also social. Much of what unfolds in this food-competition experiment has to do with the social roles of the chimpanzees, that influence the subordinate chimpanzees' perception with respect to possibilities for action (e.g., getting one food item as opposed to the other) and for interaction (e.g., avoiding repercussions from a dominant chimpanzee if the mutually visible food is selected). From previous interactions with the dominant chimpanzees and other group mates, the subordinate chimpanzees have become just that: subordinate. A subordinate's perception of the mutually observable food item is already informed by her history of interactions. This is more than associative learning; in order to grasp the meaning of the situation at hand, one has to be able to interact *with* the other and *in* their shared world; one has to be able to perceive affordances defined by social context.

Although IT and BR views may be generally consistent with each other, crucially, the enactivist approach offers a specification about the meaning that is implicit in the action and potential interaction. The meaning isn't deduced from a set of beliefs or rules, as if it were an abstract theoretical or intellectual process of puzzle-solving; and it is not simply the result of an association of a current situation with a past situation. It's a matter of "practical or pragmatic (and specifically social) reason" (Gallagher and Povinelli 2012: 154) – being able to see what is possible in a socially constrained situation. Meaning, in this sense, affords certain implicit consequences that the perceiver is able to anticipate. Call et al. (2004), for example, found that chimpanzees became angry when an experimenter chose not to provide a reward to them – but not when she was unable to provide the reward. This suggests an awareness of what actions were available in their shared social world, and importantly, the responses from the chimpanzees modulated in accordance with changes to those social affordances (i.e., changes to how the chimpanzees could expect to interact with the experimenter). [For a related discussion of perspective-taking in chimpanzees, see Halina, Chapter 22 in this volume.]

A different kind of food-competition experiment offers additional support for the enactivist/IT interpretation. Kaminski et al. (2008) placed three cups between two chimpanzees, one subject and one competitor. The competitor, distracted by the researcher, was able to see the location of only one food item, while the subject was able to see both food items as they were placed into two of the three cups. In cases where the subject selected a cup first, she would pick the cup containing the food that the competitor knew was there – maximizing her potential for food acquisition. The researchers reject the ToM interpretation and conclude that "chimpanzees have a basic goal-perception psychology" (233). That is, chimpanzees can see what another's goal is; they can see what the other sees of the situation (what it affords the other chimpanzee), without necessarily understanding any hidden mental states related to that goal. This is consistent with experimental data regarding chimpanzees tracking the gaze of humans, again suggesting an awareness of what others see, and therefore what their affordances are in the shared environment. In one study, for example, chimpanzees as young as 13 months engaged in gaze-tracking (Okamono et al. 2002); and in other studies, chimpanzees used the information gained by gaze-tracking to find food that was initially not visible to them (Itakura et al. 1999; Bräuer et al. 2005).

There is also evidence of chimpanzees responding differently to the affective states of conspecifics, displayed on the faces of those conspecifics. For example, Kano et al. (2008) found that chimpanzees were more likely to remember the photos of aggressive chimpanzees than of relaxed conspecifics. This is consistent with the enactivist view about direct social perception; the aggressive chimpanzees' faces offer clearer information about social affordances and would therefore be more memorable or salient for the observing chimpanzee. In an actual interaction situation, in contrast to the experimental presentation of photos, this recognition would not be reduced to a pure association, since in such circumstances current affordances (and not just previous social contexts) are what primarily drive the effect.

The failing of false-belief tasks, too, can be explained through the lens of IT. For example, three-year-old children fail elicited false-belief tests (i.e., those in which experimenters ask the child for a judgment about the behavior of someone who is observed), although much younger infants at 13 months pass spontaneous false-belief tests (Onishi and Baillargeon 2005). In the spontaneous tasks, infants observe a toy being moved from a green box to a yellow box, unbeknownst to an agent returning to the room with the false belief that the toy is still in the green box. Experimenters measure violation of expectation in terms of looking times or anticipated looking at targets to show that young infants anticipate that the agent will look in the original green box for the toy. The standard ToM interpretation is that the infant is a passive observer who infers that the agent has a false belief (Baillargeon et al. 2010). The BR interpretation is that the infant has already learned the rule that agents look for things where they last saw them, and they infer that is where the agent will look (Ruffman and Perner 2005; Perner and Ruffman 2005; Povinelli and Vonk 2003). Like the ToM interpretation, BR understands the process as inferential. Indeed, this account still requires inferences on the part of the infant (Heyes 2014).

In contrast to what would be demanded in terms of inferential ability by either ToM or BR interpretations in these cases, the enactivist IT interpretation maintains that since infants have interacted with others throughout their first year of life in very basic, embodied (primary intersubjective) engagements (Trevarthen 1979), their perceptions of others are already shaped in ways that recognize the possibilities afforded to others and to themselves by specific situations. That such possibilities for meaningful interactions with others shape the way that they perceive such situations is made clear in experiments that allow infants to interact with the agents (e.g., by directing the agent to the right box) (Buttelmann et al. 2009; Southgate et al. 2010). These experiments suggest that in their active response to the agent, infants discriminate between situations in which the agent has seen *versus* has not seen the toy being moved.

In an experiment with three-year-olds who typically fail the explicit false-belief test, Rubio-Fernández and Geurts (2013) allow the three-year-olds to interact with the agent, and they show that the more a three-year-old is able to act and interact in the situation, the more likely the child is able to get the right answer. Interaction not only allows the three-year-old to gain the right answer; it also helps to explain why the same three-year-old fails the explicit false-belief test. In the latter test, the child is interacting only with the experimenter, answering her questions, and not with the agent whose behavior he is asked to predict from a third-person perspective. The saliency of the second-person interaction with the experimenter, and the social affordances connected with it, however, bias the child's answer towards what both the experimenter and the child know – the actual location of the toy – which then motivates the wrong answer (Gallagher 2015). As Ciaunica (2014) explains, in evolutionary terms of survival, the immediacy of intersubjective interaction takes priority over any merely observational task. In experiments that rearrange the task to make the interaction with the experimenter support (rather than distract from) the child's ability to track the perspective of the agent (e.g., Rubio-Fernández and Geurts 2013), the three-year-old passes the false-belief test.

If we extrapolate from what seems to be happening in the human child case to what might be the problem in the chimpanzee case, a potential answer emerges as to why chimpanzees struggle with false-belief tasks. In the Call and Tomasello (1999) study, one problem may be that the salience of the communicative interaction between chimpanzee and communicator may bias the chimpanzee into following the lead of the communicator's behavior, even when the communicator has not seen the location change. Another problem may be that the kind of situation confronting the chimpanzee, both in terms of problem-solving and in terms of social (intersubjective) structure is significantly different from primary intersubjective situations in the wild. While human infants have a year of primary intersubjective interactions shaping their perception, it is not clear that primary intersubjectivity is the same for chimpanzees, so the specific situations of false-belief tests may not offer the same affordances (or are not necessarily as meaningful) as for human infants.

We note that most of the chimpanzee experiments that have been completed involve interspecies tasks; we should not be surprised to see different results emerge if, in addition to the food-competition design, more experimental designs emerge that rely on intraspecies interaction. Action and interaction affordances, and therefore possible responses, may be different in interspecies *versus* intraspecies situations. As Byrne and Whiten (1992) noted, following Jolly (1966) and Humphrey (1976), primates in naturalistic settings do not encounter the kinds of technical challenges that many of our existing experimental designs employ; rather, primates tend to respond to social problems (e.g., avoidance of conflict). Especially when we consider the fact that experimental designs take chimpanzees out of the wild and remove them from their pre-existing social groups, we should expect to see our results affected by both the nature of the tasks with which they are presented and their removal from naturalistic settings.

We also note that the importance of the false-belief task is a matter of debate. Some philosophers who study social cognition in nonhuman animals have called for a new experimental paradigm in which implicit, violation-of-expectation tests replace standard, explicit false-belief tests (Andrews 2005; Lurz 2011). We want to go further and suggest that it is not clear that mental state attribution is of central importance for social cognition in either chimpanzees or humans. As Call and Tomasello remark at the end of their study, there is so much more to social cognition than mental state attribution (mindreading). Apes do have sophisticated cognitive and social abilities, some of which they share with humans, and some which may be quite different due to differences in affordances offered by their own natural environments. Call and Tomasello mention conspecific gaze-following, behavioral coordination during hunting, vocal and gestural communication with group mates, social learning, and joint actions in contests for dominance and resources: "These all involve understanding complex social situations and creating sophisticated social strategies for dealing with them" (1999: 394). They all involve sensory-motor capacities and embodied interactions that provide sufficient information relevant to the practical and social situation without the need for mindreading or worrying about false beliefs.

As philosophers, we need to make sense of what is obviously complex social cognition that may not amount to a proper ToM in chimpanzees. IT is able to acknowledge and can begin to make sense of the different, but still rich, meaning-laden social worlds that vary across species, while recognizing that humans alone may be capable of higher-order mindreading (available to us, for example, when direct perception fails).[4]

Notes

1   SG thanks the Humboldt Foundation's Anneliese Maier Research Award for supporting his research on this topic.
2   But see Lavelle 2012 and Carruthers 2015 for the idea that we may have perceptual access to some mental states.
3   This claim has been met with some criticism (Carruthers 2008; Fitzpatrick 2009; Sober 2015).
4   Some clarification may be achieved by considering how IT relates to two other proposals. (1) Povinelli and Giambrone (1999) argue that in the human, an acquired ToM capacity with the possibility of reinterpreting behavior in terms of hidden mental states may come to co-exist with the primary behavioral-reading skills that characterize both chimpanzee and young infant behavior. (2) Likewise, Heyes and Frith (2014) suggest that the kind of explicit mindreading that starts around four years of age in humans, and that goes beyond the abilities of young infants, is a learned cultural skill (much like the skill of reading a text). IT can agree with all of these theorists on this point – that ToM is something learned as the child develops – with two important provisos: that learning this skill is very much informed by the interaction capacities of primary and secondary intersubjectivity found in human infants, and that mindreading does not typically become the default or automatic way that humans understand each other, as Povinelli and Eddy (1997) suggest.

Further reading

L. Barrett's *Beyond the Brain: How Body and Environment Shape Animal and Human Minds* (Princeton, NJ: Princeton University Press, 2011) provides a provocative discussion of the evolution of minds and the relationship of minds to environments. For an interdisciplinary discussion of the importance of understanding the mind as embodied, see F. J. Varela, E. Thompson, and E. Rosch, *The Embodied Mind* (Cambridge, MA: The MIT Press, 1993). For an introduction regarding research on chimpanzee cognition, see E. V. Lonsdorf, S. R. Ross, and T. Matsuzawa, *The Mind of the Chimpanzee: Ecological and Experimental Perspectives* (Chicago: The University of Chicago Press, 2010). For a detailed discussion of the phenomenological tradition that informs IT, see S. Gallagher and D. Zahavi, *The Phenomenological Mind*, 2nd edition (New York: Routledge, 2012).

References

Andrews, K. (2005) "Chimpanzee theory of mind: Looking in the all the wrong places?" *Mind & Language* 20/5, 521–536.

Ansuini, C., L. Giosa, L. Turella, G. M. Altoè, and U. Castiello. (2008) "An object for an action, the same object for other actions: Effects on hand shaping," *Experimental Brain Research* 185, 111–119.

Ansuini, C., M. Santello, S. Massaccesi, and U. Castiello. (2006) "Effects of end-goal on hand shaping," *Journal of Neurophysiology* 95, 2456–2465.

Atkinson, A. P., M. L. Tunstall, and W. H. Dittrich. (2007) "Evidence for distinct contributions of form and motion information to the recognition of emotions from body gestures," *Cognition* 104, 59–72.

Baillargeon, R., R. M. Scott, and Z. He. (2010) "False-belief understanding in infants," *Trends in Cognitive Sciences* 14/3, 110–118.

Baron-Cohen, S., A. M. Leslie, and U. Frith. (1985) "Does the autistic child have a 'theory of mind'?" *Cognition* 21, 37–46.

Becchio, C., V. Manera, L. Sartori, A. Cavallo, and U. Castiello. (2012) "Grasping intentions: From thought experiments to empirical evidence," *Frontiers of Human Neuroscience* 6, art. 117.

Bräuer, J., J. Call, and M. Tomasello. (2005) "All great ape species follow gaze to distant locations and around barriers," *Journal of Comparative Psychology* 119, 145–154.

Buttelmann, D., M. Carpenter, and M. Tomasello. (2009) "Eighteen-month-old infants show false belief understanding in an active helping paradigm," *Cognition* 112, 337–342.

Byrne, R. W., and A. Whiten. (1992) "Cognitive evolution in primates: Evidence from tactical deception," *Man* 27/3, 609–627.

Call, J., B. Hare, M. Carpenter, and M. Tomasello. (2004) "'Unwilling' versus 'unable': Chimpanzees' understanding of human intentional action," *Developmental Science* 7, 488–498.

Call, J., and M. Tomasello. (1999) "A nonverbal false belief task: The performance of children and great apes," *Child Development* 70/2, 381–395.

Carruthers, P. (2008) "Meta-cognition in Animals: A skeptical look," *Mind & Language* 23/1, 58–89.

Carruthers, P. (2015) "Perceiving mental states," *Consciousness and Cognition* 36, 498–507.

Ciaunica, A. (2014) "Under pressure: Processing representational decoupling in false-belief tasks," *Review of Philosophy and Psychology* 5/4, 527–542.

Dennett, D. (1978) "Beliefs about beliefs," *Behavioral and Brain Sciences* 1, 568–570.

Fitzpatrick, S. (2009) "Simplicity and Methodology in Animal Psychology: A Case Study," in R. Lurz (ed.) *The Philosophy of Animal Minds*, Cambridge: Cambridge University Press.

Gallagher, S. (2008) "Inference or interaction: Social cognition without precursors," *Philosophical Explorations* 11/3, 163–174.

Gallagher, S. (2012) "Neurons, Neonates and Narrative: From Empathic Resonance to Empathic Understanding," in A. Foolen, U. M. Lüdtke, T. P. Racine, and J. Zlatev (eds.) *Moving Ourselves, Moving Others, Motion and Emotion in Intersubjectivity, Consciousness and Language*, Philadelphia: John Benjamins Publishing Company, 167–196.

Gallagher, S. (2015) "The Problem with 3-Year-Olds," *Journal of Consciousness Studies* 22/1–2, 160–182.

Gallagher, S. (2016) "The Minds of Others," in D. O. Dahlstrom, A. Elpidorou, and W. Hopp (eds.) *Philosophy of Mind and Phenomenology: Conceptual and Empirical Approaches*, New York: Routledge, 117–138.

Gallagher, S., and D. Povinelli. (2012) "Enactive and behavioral abstraction accounts of social understanding in chimpanzees, infants, and adults," *Review of Philosophy and Psychology* 3, 145–169.

Hare, B., J. Call, B. Agnetta, and M. Tomasello. (2000) "Chimpanzees know what conspecifics do and do not see," *Animal Behaviour* 59, 771–785.

Heyes, C. (2014) "False belief in infancy: A fresh look," *Developmental Science* 17/5, 647–659.

Humphrey, N. (1976) "The Social Function of Intellect," in P. P. G. Bateson and R. A. Hinde (eds.) *Growing Points in Ethology*, Cambridge: Cambridge University Press.

Hurley, S. L. (1998) *Consciousness in Action*, London: Harvard University Press.

Itakura, S., B. Agnetta, B. Hare, and M. Tomasello. (1999) "Chimpanzee use of human and conspecific social cues to locate hidden food," *Developmental Science* 2, 448–456.

Izard, C. E. (1972) *Patterns of emotions: A new analysis of anxiety and depression*, New York: Academic Press.

Izard, C. E., B. P. Ackerman, K. M. Schoff, and S. E. Fine. (2000) "Self-Organization of Discrete Emotions, Emotion Patterns, and Emotion Cognition Relations," in M. D. Lewis and I. Granic (eds.) *Emotion, development, and self-organization*, Cambridge: Cambridge University Press, 15–36.

Jeannerod, M. (1997) *The Cognitive Neuroscience of Action*, Oxford: Blackwell Publishers.

Jolly, A. (1966) "Lemur social behavior and primate intelligence," *Science* 153, 501–506.

Kaminski, J., J. Call, and M. Tomasello. (2008) "Chimpanzees know what others know, but not what they believe," *Cognition* 109, 224–234.

Kano, F., M. Tanaka, and M. Tomonaga. (2008) "Enhanced recognition of emotional stimuli in the chimpanzee (Pan troglodytes)," *Animal Cognition* 11/3, 517–524.

Lavelle, J. S. (2012) "Theory-theory and the direct perception of mental states," *Review of Philosophy and Psychology* 3/2, 213–230.

Legerstee, M. (2005) *Infants' Sense of People: Precursors to a Theory of Mind*, Cambridge: Cambridge University Press.

Leslie, A. M., and U. Frith. (1988) "Autistic children's understanding of seeing, knowing and believing," *British Journal of Developmental Psychology* 6, 315–324.

Lindblom, J. (2015) *Embodied Social Cognition*, Switzerland: Springer International Publishing.

Lurz, R. W. (2011) *Mindreading Animals: The Debate over What Animals Know About Other Minds*, Cambridge, MA: MIT Press.

Marteniuk, R. G., C. L. MacKenzie, M. Jeannerod, S. Athenes, and C. Dugas. (1987) "Constraints on human arm movement trajectories," *Canadian Journal of Psychology* 41/3, 365–378.

Merleau-Ponty, M. (2012) *The Phenomenology of Perception*, London: Routledge.

Newen, A., A. Welpinghus, and G. Juckel. (2015) "Emotion recognition as pattern recognition: The relevance of perception," *Mind and Language* 30/2, 187–208.

Noë, A. (2004) *Action in Perception*, Cambridge, MA: MIT Press.

Okamono, S., M. Tomonaga, K. Ishii, N. Kawai, M. Tanaka, and T. Matsuzawa. (2002) "An infant chimpanzee (Pan troglodytes) follows human gaze," *Animal Cognition* 5/2, 107–114.

Onishi, K. H., and R. Baillargeon. (2005) "Do 15-month-old infants understand false beliefs?" *Science* 308, 255–258.

Pacherie, E. (2006) "Towards a dynamic theory of intentions," in S. Pockett, W. P. Banks, and S. Gallagher (eds.) *Does Consciousness Cause Behavior? An Investigation of the Nature of Volition*, Cambridge, MA: MIT Press, 145–167.

Pacherie, E. (2008) "The phenomenology of action: A conceptual framework," *Cognition* 107, 179–217.

Penn, D. C., and D. J. Povinelli. (2007) "On the lack of evidence that non-human animals possess anything remotely resembling a 'theory of mind'," *Philosophical Transactions of the Royal Society* 362, 731–744.

Perner, J., and T. Ruffman. (2005) "Infants' insight into the mind: How deep?" *Science* 308, 214–216.

Povinelli, D. J. (2000) *Folk Physics for Apes: The Chimpanzee's Theory of How the World Works*, Oxford: Oxford University Press.

Povinelli, D. J., and T. J. Eddy (1997) "Specificity of gaze-following in young chimpanzees," *British Journal of Developmental Psychology* 15, 213–222.

Povinelli, D. J., and S. Giambrone (1999) "Inferring other minds: Failure of the argument by analogy," *Philosophical Topics* 27, 167–201.

Povinelli, D. J., and J. Vonk. (2003) "Chimpanzee minds: Suspiciously human?" *Trends in Cognitive Sciences* 7/4, 157–160.

Povinelli, D. J., and J. Vonk. (2004) "We don't need a microscope to explore the chimpanzee's mind," *Mind & Language* 19, 1–28.

Premack, D., and G. Woodruff. (1978) "Does the chimpanzee have a theory of mind?" *The Behavioral and Brain Sciences* 1, 515–526.

Reddy, V. (2008) *How Infants Know Minds*, Cambridge, MA: Harvard University Press.

Rubio-Fernández, P., and B. Geurts. (2013) "How to pass the false-belief task before your fourth birthday," *Psychological Science* 24/1, 27–33.

Ruffman, T., and J. Perner. (2005) "Do infants really understand false belief? Response to Leslie," *Trends in Cognitive Sciences* 9/10, 462–463.

Sartori, L., E. Straulino, and U. Castiello. (2011) "How objects are grasped: The interplay between affordances and end-goals," *PLoS ONE* 6/9, e25203. http://dx.doi.org/10.1371/journal.pone.0025203.

Scheler, M. (1954) *The Nature of Sympathy*, London: Routledge and Kegan Paul, 1923.

Searle, J. R. (1983) *Intentionality: An Essay in the Philosophy of Mind*, Cambridge: Cambridge University Press.

Sellars, W. (1956) "Empiricism and the philosophy of mind," in H. Feigl and M. Scriven (eds.) *Minnesota Studies in the Philosophy of Science, Volume I: The Foundations of Science and the Concepts of Psychology and Psychoanalysis*, Minneapolis: University of Minnesota Press, 253–329.

Senju, A., V. Southgate, C. Snape, M. Leonard, and G. Csibra. (2011) "Do 18-month-olds really attribute mental states to others? A critical test," *Psychological Science* 22, 878–880.

Sober, E. (2015) *Ockham's Razors: A User's Manual*, Cambridge: Cambridge University Press.

Southgate, V., C. Chevallier, and G. Csibra. (2010) "Seventeen-month-olds appeal to false beliefs to interpret others' referential communication," *Developmental Science* 13/6, 907–912.

Tomasello, M., J. Call, and B. Hare. (2003) "Chimpanzees understand psychological states – the question is which ones and to what extent?" *Trends in Cognitive Science* 7, 153–56.

Trevarthen, C. B. (1979) "Communication and Cooperation in Early Infancy: A Description of Primary Intersubjectivity," in M. Bullowa (ed.) *Before Speech*, Cambridge: Cambridge University Press.

Varela, F., E. Thompson, and E. Rosch. (1991) *The Embodied Mind*, Cambridge, MA: MIT Press.

Wimmer, H., and J. Perner. (1983) "Beliefs about beliefs: Representation and constraining function of wrong beliefs in young children's understanding of deception," *Cognition* 13, 103–128.

Wittgenstein, L. (1967) *Philosophical Investigations*, Oxford: Blackwell.

Wittgenstein, L. (1980) *Remarks on the Philosophy of Psychology*, Chicago: University of Chicago Press.

PART V

Communication

27

PRAGMATIC INTERPRETATION AND SIGNALER-RECEIVER ASYMMETRIES IN ANIMAL COMMUNICATION

Dorit Bar-On and Richard Moore

Gricean communication and the evolution of language

Prominent theorists of language evolution have converged on the idea that pragmatic phenomena are of fundamental importance to the emergence of language (Tomasello 1999, 2008; Sperber and Wilson 2002; Scott-Phillips 2014, 2015). In particular, some of these authors have argued that it is the emergence of capacities for 'Gricean' or 'ostensive-inferential' communication that is the seed of human language. At the heart of these arguments is a conception of human linguistic communication that goes back to Paul Grice (Grice 1957). Grice's central idea was that human communication is made possible by hearers' interpretive comprehension of speakers' communicative intentions. What he called 'speaker meaning' is a matter of a speaker producing an utterance with the intention of (a) producing an effect on the psychological states of some receiver, and with the further intention of (b) producing that effect in part by means of the receiver's recognition of that intention. The speaker (or gesturer) *intentionally* and *overtly* (or '*ostensively*') produces an utterance with the intention of soliciting some response from her interlocutor (typically by aiming to produce some belief in her, or to solicit some action). The hearer infers the speaker's communicative goal through recognizing the speaker's intention to communicate, and infers the content of this intention on the basis of what the speaker said. The speaker's intention is fulfilled just when the receiver recognizes her intention (and when this recognition plays some part in producing the intended effect). Call this the *Classical Gricean* picture of communication.

On the Gricean view, communicative intentions can play a foundational role in understanding the nature of language because they are *independent* of language. Grice took speaker meaning to be conceptually prior to linguistic meaning (Grice 1967[1987]) and envisaged an explanation of the standard meanings of words and sentences in terms of community-wide, conventionalized speaker meanings. This suggests a '*pragmatics-first*' approach to the evolution of language, since it explains the emergence of conventional *semantic* properties of linguistic items (such as words and sentences) from acts of producing utterances with communicative intentions.

The Classical Gricean picture requires more than that sender and receiver possess concepts and draw inferences (conscious or unconscious) that deploy those concepts. It requires that both senders and receivers have a 'Theory of Mind' (hereafter ToM); that is, a capacity to ascribe beliefs and other psychological states to others (see the chapters in Part IV: Mindreading). Insofar as Gricean communication presupposes such social cognition, a Gricean approach to understanding the evolution of language introduces a clear explanatory task: to account for the phylogenetic emergence of these capacities in our hominin ancestors. As Origgi and Sperber put it, it implies that

> language as we know it developed as an adaptation in a species already involved in inferential communication, and therefore already capable of some serious degree of mindreading . . . the existence of mindreading in our ancestors was a precondition for the emergence and evolution of language.
>
> (2000: 20)[1]

This approach is controversial, since explaining the emergence of such social cognition – including a capacity for propositional and even recursive thoughts – *prior* to the emergence of propositional–compositional language would seem no less difficult than explaining the evolution of language itself. Incorporating the Classical Gricean view into an account of language evolution thus means trading the 'language Rubicon' for a 'psychological Rubicon' (see Bar-On 2013, and Chapter 28 in this volume).

Gricean communication and signaler-receiver asymmetries

The Classical Gricean view supposes that Gricean communicators must be capable not only of intentionally producing and responding to signals, but also of acting with and attributing *communicative intentions*. The production of utterances with communicative intentions and their comprehension is cognitively demanding, because according to the Classical Gricean view (Sperber 2000; Scott-Phillips 2014, 2015), they require entertaining fourth-order meta-representations of mental states – something that has yet to be identified even in ten-year-old children (Liddle and Nettle 2006; see also 2016c). Despite this evidence, researchers have often taken it for granted that the abilities required for Gricean communication are present in young children but not in nonhuman animals (e.g., Sperber 2000; Tomasello 2008; Corballis 2011; Scott-Phillips 2014, 2015). Even assuming that nonhuman animals have *first-order* thoughts (i.e. thoughts about the world, including others' behavior), can attribute simple mental states to others (including intentions, if not beliefs; Call and Tomasello 2008), and possess concepts with which they can draw inferences (consciously or unconsciously), Tomasello, Scott-Phillips and others doubt that they have higher-order thoughts about others' mental states. Consequently, Tomasello, Call, and Hare conclude that "in contrast to human children, chimpanzees may not understand . . . such things as . . . communicative intentions" (Tomasello et al. 2003: 156).

Even apart from animals' comparative lack of ToM capacities, there seems to be a difficulty in regarding animal vocalizations, specifically, as a source of insight into human communication. It has long been assumed that primate vocalizations, especially, are involuntary emotional responses to salient stimuli (e.g., Tomasello 2008). If this assumption is correct, then primate calls are not a species of intentional behavior. For this reason, many researchers (most recently Wheeler and Fischer 2012) have argued that we should focus on the *comprehension* and not the *production* of primate calls to tell us what we want to know about language evolution.[2]

Some of those who adopt the Gricean approach to language evolution have argued that the receiver's side of the sender-receiver relationship raises no problems peculiar to human communication, since nonhuman receivers can make context-sensitive inferences about the significance of (even unintentionally produced) con- and extra-specific signals. This, it is claimed, reveals a fundamental *asymmetry* between animal senders and receivers. According to Fitch (2010), the real explanatory challenge for language evolution research is to explain the emergence of *senders* who act with Gricean communicative intentions. The problem of the receivers' contribution was solved long ago; so we can assume that, at least on the receivers' side, the psychological Rubicon had already been crossed (though one may wonder how).[3]

Findings from primate vocal communication appear to support the signaler-receiver asymmetry claim. Wheeler and Fischer (2012) review evidence suggesting that nonhuman primates lack the voluntary control over their vocalisations that humans have. In their words,

> the same neurobiological circuits that are responsible for innate vocalizations, including laughter and reactions to pain in humans, exist in both nonhuman primate and human nonverbal vocal production systems; the more derived parts responsible and necessary for voluntary control of vocalizations seem to be limited to humans, or at least have not been identified in other primates.
>
> (2012: 197)

Thus, as Seyfarth and Cheney observe, when primates learn about the world from hearing another's screams, they "acquire information from signalers who do not, in the human sense, intend to provide it" (2003: 168).

Unlike (at least some) human utterances, calls produced by primates also appear not to be produced with sophisticated other-directed goals in mind. For example, Seyfarth and Cheney have shown that vervet monkeys produce calls that dramatically affect the *behavior* of their audience, but without seeming to take into account the psychological states of their audience (Seyfarth and Cheney 2003). In producing, e.g. 'contact barks', baboon callers also seem to show little awareness of their listeners' states (of mind or otherwise) (Cheney et al. 1996). Thus, on the part of signalers, there seem to be only affective *reactions* to a perceived situation, albeit ones that may exhibit sensitivity to the presence of a suitable audience.[4]

Whereas animal vocal production therefore appears unsophisticated, animal receivers show an impressive capacity for making contextual inferences to extract information from others' signals. Thus, Seyfarth cites experiments (Bergman et al. 2003) that show that baboon listeners who witness a sequence such as 'A threat-grunts to B and B screams' must be attributing to A a disposition to act toward B in a very specific way. Seyfarth thinks this supports the view that, *as listeners*, "baboons (and probably many other animals) deduce information about events and scenes in the world from the vocalizations that other animals make" even in the absence of intentional production (personal communication). Tomasello, too, finds a "stark contrast" between the "flexible comprehension" exhibited by call receivers and the inflexibility exhibited by call producers (2008: 16f.), and he cites as the reason for the lack of flexibility the fact that nonhuman vocalizations "are mostly very tightly tied to emotions" (2008: 17). So there seems to be an asymmetry between inflexible signalers and sophisticated receivers in at least some animal vocal communication systems.

With this asymmetry in mind, Wheeler and Fischer conclude that "any continuities or parallels that exist between the communication systems of humans and our extant primate relatives reside not in the ability of signal producers to transmit symbolically encoded information, but in the flexible, learned responses of receivers" (2012: 199). Accordingly, they recommend that "a more productive framework" for primate communication research should be "pragmatics, the field of linguistics that examine the role of context in shaping the meaning of linguistic utterances" (2012: 203).

Combining the asymmetry claim with a Gricean conception of the task for a theory of the evolution of language, Fitch draws the following conclusion:

> [A]nimal communication, before language, largely involved signalers who generate signals either automatically (e.g. innate calls) or selfishly ("manipulations"), and thus obeyed no Gricean maxims. *Listeners, on the other hand, have been processing these signals inferentially, fulfilling their half of the Gricean equation, for the entire history of communication systems.* . . . The component of this Gricean model that demands special evolutionary explanation is . . . the speaker's contribution to this cooperative endeavor. *'Going Gricean,' then, required a fundamental change in the rules of animal communication on the part of signalers*, and this step is a logical necessity before language could get off the ground.
>
> (2010: 135, emphases added; see also §4.11)

This shifts the target of language evolution research. Followers of Grice take the primary task of language evolution research to be to provide an account of the social and ecological selection pressures that led to the emergence of subjects' capacities to *both* act with *and* understand communicative intentions (Sperber and Wilson 1995; Origgi and Sperber 2000; Tomasello 2008; Scott-Phillips 2014). On their view, animal communication systems differ from human languages precisely in being fully captured by the (non-Gricean) 'code model', on which *neither* animal signalers nor animal receivers exhibit Gricean mindreading capacities. Thus, they would have to deny that there is a signaler-receiver asymmetry that is relevant to the emergence of Gricean communication. By contrast, Fitch claims that animal receivers have long been 'fulfilling their half of the Gricean equation' (quoted above). If Fitch's view is right, then our nonhuman ancestors already had the cognitive abilities needed for *Gricean* interpretation, so that all that would require explanation is the phylogenetic emergence of *speakers* who were motivated to produce utterances with Gricean intentions. (See also Hurford 2007: 332 and *passim*.)

So, despite agreement about the need for a pragmatics-first approach to language evolution, there are now two different agendas on the table. On the first, an account of language evolution must explain the phylogenic emergence of subjects who can act with and attribute communicative intentions. On the second, language evolution research need explain only the emergence of *speakers* who can put already-existing cognitive capacities to use in the *production* of communicative acts.

The apparent disagreement stems, at least in part, from the presence of two different conceptions of pragmatics. The signaler-receiver asymmetry described above is relevant to the explanation of the evolution of language on one but not the other. If theorists of language evolution are to embrace a pragmatics-first approach, then they must be clear on this distinction before they can settle on the right agenda for a theory of language evolution.

Signaler-receiver asymmetries and pragmatics

On the approach advocated by Tomasello, Scott-Phillips, Sperber and Wilson, and others, it is not enough that animal receivers extract rich information from signals. What needs to be established is that, when interpreting signals, receivers make inferences *about signalers' communicative intentions*. But from the fact that receivers extract rich information from the signals they receive (*even if* they do so inferentially), it does not follow that their doing so depends on their employment of (even a rudimentary) ToM. Many creatures extract rich information about their physical environment without attributing mental states to anyone.

The ability to make context-sensitive inferences about the significance of calls is one that Grice himself would contrast with the ability to understand communicative intentions. His notion of speaker meaning is introduced in contrast with what he labeled *natural meaning*. The latter is the sort of significance we assign to various natural signs, as when we say, e.g., "Those dark clouds mean rain". In contrast to utterances that possess speaker (or 'nonnatural') meaning, natural signs possess natural meaning independently of anyone's intending to communicate any-thing by them. An astute observer can learn to recognize natural meaning by learning the causal correlations between the sign and what it signifies. Thus, the hearer of an animal call can learn that it correlates with the presence of some specific danger, whether or not it was produced intentionally, and thereby derive the call's natural meaning without attributing communicative intentions.

Returning to Fitch's formulation of the speaker-hearer asymmetry, if animal signals are issued unintentionally, then it would seem odd to credit receivers with a *Gricean* interpretation of them. For this would suggest that hearers regularly attribute communicative intentions where none exist. If animal *signalers* do not 'fulfill *their* half of the Gricean equation', then at best we could credit animal receivers with regularly – but *falsely* – *attributing* communicative intentions. If signal-ers never act with Gricean intentions, such attributions would at best be idle. Moreover, on the face of it, 'receivers' and 'signalers' designate different *roles*, not distinct subcategories of creatures with different psychological profiles. The receiver of an alarm call on one occasion is a producer on another. So whatever psychological capacities animals are thought to possess as receivers, they are unlikely to disappear when the same animals become signalers. Either *both* signalers and receivers should be credited with a capacity for ostensive-inferential communication, or *neither*.

Perhaps when Fitch claims that animal receivers 'fulfill their half of the Gricean equation', he has in mind something cognitively less demanding than the ability to attribute communicative intentions. Perhaps his idea is simply that animal receivers are astute interpreters of the *natural* significance of *unintentionally produced* signals. He does write that there is "strong evidence that sophisticated inference is common among primates" (2010: 189). However, while Fitch argues that monkeys, prairie dogs, suricates, ground squirrels, many birds, and even chickens all pro-duce calls that are "inferentially interpreted" by receivers despite the absence of any "intentional encoding" (2010: 191), this would not support the conclusion that these species are Gricean interpreters.

But if animal receivers are not *Gricean* interpreters, then Fitch's 'pragmatics-first' approach is different from the one advocated by Origgi and Sperber, Tomasello, and others. The form of the pragmatics-first approach that focuses primarily on contextual inference would then be only indirectly relevant to their theories of language evolution. Moreover, once it's acknowledged that animal receivers neither act with *nor* attribute communicative intentions, then whatever asymmetry there is between vocal signalers and receivers, it is not relevant to a Gricean under-standing of what is required to explain the emergence of language.

Signaler-receiver asymmetry and pragmatic interpretation: diagnosis

There are at least two different sorts of cognitive prerequisites for genuinely Gricean com-munication. First, there are *rational mindreading* (that is, ToM) capacities: the capacity to issue utterances with other-directed informative-communicative intentions, and the capacity for attributing them to others. In addition, at least on the hearer's side, *inferential* capacities are also needed to figure out the *specific content* of the message the speaker is trying to convey. When drawing a sharp distinction between animal and human communication, and when speculating on the Rubicon that must have been crossed to explain the advent of language, post-Gricean thinkers focus on the first set of (mindreading) capacities. By contrast, Fitch, Hurford, Wheeler and Fischer, and others (including Scarantino and Clay 2015), who are looking to find evidence for precursors of language in the behaviors of existing animals, focus on the second set of (inferential) capacities. Assuming 'inference' is understood in a suitably relaxed fashion, it is uncontroversial that inferential capacities exist in the animal kingdom. However, this observation does little to support the conclusion that animal receivers are *Gricean* interpreters. But then the puzzle for language evolution is as much to explain the emergence of Gricean interpreters as it is to explain how signalers have become Gricean producers.

If this diagnosis is correct, it reveals that, when Fitch talks about animal receivers as engaging in pragmatic interpretation and 'fulfilling their half of the Gricean equation', he must have in mind something much weaker than is required by the Classical Gricean view. For contextual interpretation need not presuppose the attribution of communicative intentions, and so it is not part of any Gricean equation.

Fitch's Gricean reading of the asymmetries likely turns on a conflation of two different sorts of pragmatic phenomena, which have been described independently by Carnap (1942) and Grice (1957). Carnap introduced the term 'pragmatics' to cover the study of those aspects of meaning that are dependent on contextual (or 'situational') factors. On this reading, pragmatic phenomena include the various ways in which the same sentence (type) might be interpreted differently in different contexts. (So, for example, "It's raining" might be used to convey a different proposition on different occasions.) Pragmatics in the Carnapian sense can also cover the ways in which an animal alarm call (understood as a type) might have different significance in different circumstances. Consider, for example, the finding by Palombit et al. (1997) that male baboons are more likely to respond to calls produced by females with whom they have mated than other females – particularly where those females have dependent offspring and are in the presence of a potentially infanticidal male. Wheeler and Fischer's treatment of such differential responses as pragmatic phenomena is in keeping with the Carnapian notion.

Although Grice's work on pragmatics encompassed the ways in which the interpretation of words and sentences can vary with their use (and thus context), he was primarily interested in a deeper phenomenon than the context-sensitivity of interpretation – namely the dependence of linguistic meaning on a special kind of (communicative, audience-directed) intentions. He offered an analysis designed to capture the structure of those intentions, which must be understood by hearers if they are to comprehend the speaker's intended meaning. In addition to an analysis of the nature of speaker meaning, Grice (1975) introduced a set of heuristics – 'Conversational Maxims' – to which hearers can appeal in trying to make sense of speakers' communicative intentions (referred to by Fitch 2010: 135, quoted above).

On the Gricean view, to engage in pragmatic interpretation just is to attribute communicative intentions. Therefore, on the Carnapian *but not* the Gricean version of pragmatics, there can be phenomena of pragmatic interpretation even in the absence of intentional communication. To recap:

> Carnapian pragmatics is the study of the variation (and derivation) of the significance of sentence (or signal) types with the context of production.
>
> Gricean pragmatics is the study of the production of utterances with communicative intentions and their mindreading interpretation by interlocutors.

These different notions of pragmatics have made their way into the literature on animal communication without being properly distinguished. Moreover, they yield different accounts of what is involved in a pragmatics-first approach to language evolution. If we treat Fitch, Wheeler and Fischer, and Cheney and Seyfarth as making claims about Carnapian pragmatic phenomena, then it is clear that what they have in mind is not the attribution of communicative intentions, but simply hearers' ability to make discriminations about the significance of various bits of environmental information – including information derived from unintentionally produced alarm calls. This is not the sense of pragmatics to which Tomasello and others are appealing when giving an account of the Gricean foundations of language evolution.

Conflating these two different senses of pragmatics threatens to be pernicious. For example, when observing that primate receivers of calls can derive different messages from the same calls in different situations – and thus engage in *Carnaptian* interpretation – one can mistakenly conclude that understanding such interpretation can help account for the phylogenetic emergence of abilities needed for Gricean communication. While there may be some overlap in the abilities deployed in Carnapian contextual interpretation and Gricean mindreading interpretation, the former are not sufficient for the latter. Since Gricean but not Carnapian interpretation requires possession of sophisticated ToM, there could be (and likely are) creatures capable of Carnapian contextual interpretation alone.

At times, the slide between the two senses of 'pragmatics' is made explicitly. For example, Scott-Phillips (2014, 2015) argues that there is a fundamental, qualitative difference between animal communication, which can be fully understood on the 'code model', and human communication, which is essentially 'ostensive-inferential' (Scott-Phillips 2014, 2015). On the neo-Gricean view that he defends, it is the absence of the ability for ostensive-inferential communication that explains why non-human great apes did not develop language. Pragmatic phenomena on *this* approach are understood in the Gricean way. Yet, Scott-Phillips reverts to the Carnapian conception when defining pragmatics as "the branch of linguistics that studies meaning and language use in context" (2015: glossary; see also Scott-Phillips 2010). His use of the term 'pragmatics' is thus not univocal.[5] The same equivocation seems to be present in work by Fitch (2010), Hurford (2007), and sometimes even Tomasello (2008: 14–15).

Concluding remarks

There *are* interesting asymmetries between signalers and receivers in animal communication – including these described by Fischer and Wheeler (2012) and others. Even within Gricean dyads, there are marked differences in 'cognitive load' between speakers and hearers (Moore 2013). For example, Gricean communication requires that hearers infer speakers' communicative goals – but not that the speakers infer their own goals. However, this suggests that Gricean communication is cognitively more demanding on *hearers*, reversing the asymmetry claims considered earlier.

Our goal here has not been to argue against the assumptions that motivated the original asymmetry claims. For example, the possibility that some primate calls are not produced voluntarily is at least partly independent of questions about the phylogenetic emergence of Gricean communication. Some empirical evidence suggests that great apes' call production may involve more voluntary control than has been assumed (Slocombe and Zuberbühler, 2007; Slocombe et al. 2010; Crockford et al. 2012). However, while voluntary control over production is necessary for acting with Gricean intentions, it is not sufficient. So this empirical evidence does not show that these calls are produced with Gricean intentions.

We hope to have shown that the pragmatic asymmetries highlighted by Fitch (2010) and Wheeler and Fischer (2012) are, at least on Gricean approaches, only indirectly relevant to the study of language evolution. Failure to recognize this is likely to undermine our interpretation of comparative data, since an equivocal use of the label 'pragmatics' risks masking deep differences between the two conceptions of the task of language evolution research. For example, on the Carnapian conception of pragmatics, existing forms of animal communication may seem to be more continuous with language than on the traditional Gricean conception. That is why Tomasello, Scott-Phillips, and others have argued that animal communication does *not* illuminate the origins of language, and that language evolution required the emergence in phylogeny of a completely new form of communication that presupposed the capacity to act with and understand communicative intentions.

Our view is that language evolution research would now be best served by asking what could constitute genuine precursors to Gricean communication, and by looking for evidence of such precursors in animal communication. One way to pursue this line of research (favored by Bar-On 2013, and Chapter 28 in this volume) would be to consider what forms of language (or proto-language) might have emerged in phylogeny via the operation of *non*-Gricean mechanisms, and prior to the emergence of a capacity to produce and comprehend utterances with communicative intentions. Recognizing forms of animal communication, like *expressive communication*, that resemble Gricean communication in certain (but not all) respects; and identifying non-Gricean mechanisms (such as ontogenetic ritualization, voluntary control, and imitation), may then provide valuable insights into the emergence of human communication in phylogeny.

An alternative approach (Moore 2016a, 2016b, 2016c) argues that classical interpretations overstate the socio-cognitive abilities that Gricean communication requires, and that once we reconsider the demands of Gricean communication, it is appropriate to conclude that great apes are *already* Gricean communicators. On this approach, other instances of Gricean communicators in the animal kingdom may not be rare – rendering the study of animal communication directly relevant to understanding the evolution of language after all.

These different approaches to studying precursors or early forms of Gricean communication may well be complementary rather than incompatible. Indeed, there may be several different paths to progress in language evolution research. All approaches could benefit from a more fine-grained characterization of the various asymmetries that exist in animal communication systems, as well as from a more nuanced account of what is entailed by a pragmatics-first approach to language evolution.[6]

Notes

1 Additionally, Tomasello (2008) argues that Gricean communication is a cooperative, reciprocal endeavor, and that consequently it could emerge only "within the context of collaborative activities" (2008: 7). Moore (2016a) argues against this claim.

2 Other authors (most notably Tomasello – e.g., 2008) take evidence of the lack of intentional vocal production in great apes to be a reason for looking to their gestural communication to find precursors of language, since great apes' gestures are uncontroversially under voluntary control. Proponents of the assymetry view typically work in the field of primate vocal communication.

3 See Bar-On (Chapter 28 in this volume) for relevant discussion.

4 Some recent evidence undermines aspects of this asymmetry claim. For example, see Crockford et al. (2012) for evidence that chimpanzee vocalizations are both produced voluntarily and sensitive to the others' knowledge states.

5 In a short paper written after the completion of this chapter, Scott-Phillips (2017) introduces a distinction between 'weak' and 'strong' pragmatics that roughly corresponds to the one we draw above between Carnapian and Gricean pragmatics.

6 Parts of this chapter derive from a talk presented by Bar-On in Leipzig and Edinburgh in the summer of 2012. Final versions of the material were presented at the Humboldt-Universität zu Berlin and at the Rethinking Animal Minds And Meanings workshop at the Wissenschaftskolleg zu Berlin in the spring of 2016. We thank the audiences for helpful discussions.

Further reading

Cheney and Seyfarth's (2008) *Baboon Metaphysics: The Evolution of a Social Mind* and Tomasello's (2008) *Origins of Human Communication* are classic books on primate cognition and communication. Tomasello's book, especially, develops an important account of language evolution; as does Fitch's *The Evolution of Language* (2010). For the authors' views on the role of communicative intentions in language evolution, see Bar-On (2013, Chapter 28 in this volume) and Moore (2016, Forthcoming b).

References

Bar-On, D. (1995) "Reconstructing 'meaning': Grice and the naturalization of semantics," *Pacific Philosophical Quarterly* **76**: 83–116.

———— (2013) "Origins of meaning: Must we 'go Gricean'?" *Mind & Language* 28(3): 342–375.

———— (2018) Gricean intentions, expressive communication, and origins of meaning. In Kristin Andrews and Jacob Beck (eds.) *Routledge Companion to the Philosophy of Animal Minds*. London and New York: Routledge.

Bergman, T., Beehner, J., Cheney, D., and Seyfarth, R. (2003) "Hierarchical classification by rank and kinship in baboons," *Science* 302: 1234–1236.

Call, J., and Tomasello, M. (2008) "Does the chimpanzee have a theory of mind? 30 years later," *Trends in Cognitive Sciences* 12/5: 187–192.

Carnap, R. (1942) *Introduction to Semantics*, Cambridge, MA: Harvard University Press.

Cheney, D., and Seyfarth, R. (2008) *Baboon Metaphysics: The Evolution of a Social Mind*, Chicago: Chicago University Press.

Cheney, D., Seyfarth, R., and Palombit, R. (1996) "The function and mechanisms underlying baboon contact barks," *Animal Behaviour* 52: 507–518.

Corballis, M. (2011) *The Recursive Mind: The Origins of Human Language, Thought, and Civilization*, Princeton, NJ: Princeton University Press.

Crockford, C., Wittig, R. M., Mundry, R., and Zuberbühler, K. (2012) "Wild chimpanzees inform ignorant group members of danger," *Current Biology* 22(2): 142–146.

Fitch, T. (2010) *The Evolution of Language*, Cambridge: Cambridge University Press.

Grice, P. (1957) "Meaning," in P. Grice (1989) *Studies in the Way of Words*. London: Harvard University Press.

———— (1967/1987) "Utterer's meaning and speaker's intentions," in P. Grice (1989) *Studies in the Way of Words*. London: Harvard University Press.

———— (1975) "Logic and conversation," in P. Grice (1989) *Studies in the Way of Words*. London: Harvard University Press.

Hurford, J. (2007) *The Origins of Meaning: Language in the Light of Evolution*, Oxford: Oxford University Press.

Liddle, B., and Nettle, D. (2006) "Higher-order theory of mind and social competence in school-age children," *Journal of Cultural and Evolutionary Psychology* 4(3–4): 231–244.

Moore, R. (2013) "Evidence and interpretation in great ape gestural communication," *Humana.Mente* 24(1): 27–51.

———— (2016a) "Meaning and ostension in great ape gestural communication," *Animal Cognition* 19(1): 223–231.

———— (2016b) "Gricean communication, joint action, and the evolution of cooperation," *Topoi*, 1–13. doi: 10.1007/s11245-016-9372-5.

———— (2016c) "Gricean communication and cognitive development," *Philosophical Quarterly*, doi: 10.1093/pq/pqw049.

Origgi, G., and Sperber, D. (2000) "Evolution, communication, and the proper function of language," in P. Carruthers and A. Chamberlain (eds.) *Evolution and the Human Mind: Modularity, Language, and Meta-Cognition*. Cambridge: Cambridge University Press, pp. 140–169.

Palombit, R., Seyfarth, R., and Cheney, D. (1997). "The adaptive value of 'friendships' to female baboons: Experimental and observational evidence," *Animal Behaviour* 54: 599–614.

Scarantino, A., and Clay, Z. (2015) "Contextually variable signals can be functionally referential," *Animal Behaviour 100*: e1–e8.

Scott-Phillips, T. (2010) "Animal communication: Insights from linguistic pragmatics," *Animal Behaviour* 79(1): e1–e4.

——— (2014) *Speaking Our Minds*, London: Palgrave Macmillan.

——— (2015) "Nonhuman primate communication, pragmatics, and the origins of language," *Current Anthropology* 56(1): 56–80.

——— (2017) "Pragmatics and the aims of language evolution," *Psychonomic Bulletin and Review* 24(1): 186–189.

Seyfarth, R., and Cheney, D. (2003) "Signalers and receivers in animal communication," *Annual Review of Psychology* 54: 145–173.

Slocombe, K., Kaller, T., Turman, L., Townsend, S., Papworth, S., and Zuberbuehler, K. (2010) "Production of food-associated calls in wild male chimpanzees is dependent on the composition of the audience," *Behavioral Ecology and Sociobiology* 64(12): 1959–1966.

Slocombe, K., and Zuberbühler, K. (2007) "Chimpanzees modify recruitment screams as a function of audience composition," *Proceedings of the National Academy of Sciences of the United States of America* 104: 17228–17233.

Sperber, D. (2000) "Metarepresentations in an evolutionary perspective," in Sperber (ed.) *Metarepresentations: A Multidisciplinary Perspective*. Oxford: Oxford University Press.

Sperber, D., and Wilson, D. (1986/1995) *Relevance: Communication and Cognition*, 2nd edition, Oxford: Basil Blackwell.

Sperber, D., and Wilson, D. (2002) "Pragmatics, modularity, and mind-reading," *Mind and Language* 17(1–2): 3–23.

Tomasello, M. (1999) *The Cultural Origins of Human Cognition*, Cambridge, MA: Harvard University Press.

Tomasello, M. (2008) *Origins of Human Communication*, Cambridge, MA: MIT Press.

Tomasello, M., Call, J., and Hare, B. (2003) "Chimpanzees understand psychological states–the question is which ones and to what extent," *Trends in Cognitive Science* 7(4): 153–156.

Wheeler, B., and Fischer, J. (2012) "Functionally referential signals: A promising paradigm whose time has passed," *Current Anthropology* 21: 195–205.

28

COMMUNICATIVE INTENTIONS, EXPRESSIVE COMMUNICATION, AND ORIGINS OF MEANING

Dorit Bar-On

Even a cursory look at the literature on animal communication reveals that, on a dominant view, the theoretical task of explaining the evolution of linguistic meaning is to be understood in (at least roughly) Gricean terms. After raising some difficulties for the Gricean approach to the emergence of meaning, I will motivate an alternative conception of the explanatory task, which focuses on the potential of non-Gricean, *expressive communication* for illuminating the origins of meaning. This conception not only seems ethologically plausible and philosophically cogent, but it also renders the puzzle of language evolution more tractable by treating meaningfulness as a multifaceted phenomenon with potentially divergent evolutionary roots.

The Gricean approach to origins of meaning[1]

To make progress in addressing the puzzle concerning the origins of linguistic meaning, one needs to have a relatively clear sense of the *target* phenomenon – that is, of meaningfulness as it is found in human language. But there is little agreement on what should be taken as the hallmark(s) of linguistic meaningfulness. The following is a (partial) list of different features that have been emphasized as essential to meaning by different theorists: *arbitrariness* or *conventionality*, *stimulus-independence*, *discrete & symbolic* character, *referential displacement* or *intentionality*, *learnability*, *flexibility* and *voluntary control* of use, *communicative intentions* and use of *Theory of Mind*, *cooperative motivation*, possibility of *prevarication*. Some of the features on the list pertain to *acts* of signaling or communicating (e.g. voluntary control, communicative intentions), others pertain to the *products* of such acts, or *vehicles* of communication (e.g. symbolic or arbitrary character, referential displacement). And it is not clear how the various features (or even subsets of them) hang together. Specifically, what does the symbolic or arbitrary character of language have to do with whether or not it's produced with communicative intentions? And what does having displaced reference have to do with learnability or with prevarication? (Indeed, at times it seems that behind the emphases on different features lie rather divergent perspectives on language – viz., thinking of language as a relatively fixed *system* of encoded rules for generating sound-meaning mappings vs. thinking of language in terms of the rational-reflective-cooperative capacities that are manifested in its *use*.)

The heterogeneity of the highlighted features suggests that meaningfulness itself may be a multifaceted phenomenon, with different aspects possibly having different precursors and distributed across various regions of evolutionary space, so to speak. Yet a long tradition with deep philosophical roots invites us to focus on a specific subset of features – those that locate the roots of meaningful language in *individual rational insight or creative invention*. Along these lines, when Darwin turned to discuss the evolution of language, he suggested that what it would take to effect a transition from the purely expressive vocalizations of musical protolanguage to meaningful speech sounds is for "some *unusually wise* ape-like animal" to "have *thought of imitating* the growl of a beast of prey, *so as to indicate to his fellow monkeys* the nature of the expected danger" (1871: 57, emphases added).

In philosophy of language, this theme – of tying the emergence of linguistic intentionality (in Brentano's sense) to *individual intentions to communicate* – is associated with Paul Grice (1957, 1968, 1989). In the language evolution literature, Grice's "communication–intention" perspective has been sharply contrasted with the so-called "code model" of communication.[2] As followers of Grice see it, there are at least two (related) features that distinguish human language from paradigmatic codes.

(i)   Human communicators can have elaborate understanding of each other *without* a fixed code, and their communicative interactions have a distinctive, *overt* (or 'ostensive') character.

Suppose that, during a performance, my friend catches my eye and scrunches her face in an exaggerated manner, holding her nose. Presumably, she *means that* she hates the performance. And I would normally come to understand that by *recognizing* that she is *intentionally* – but also *openly* and *without deceit* – letting me know how she feels.[3] On the Gricean view, this kind of *overtness* – whereby speaker and hearer have mutual awareness of the speaker's intentions, is the hallmark of successful linguistic exchanges.

(ii)   For human communicators, even when a code-like conventional system is in place (i.e., a learned language like English), coded meanings are just the beginning of meaningful linguistic communication.

Suppose you hear someone saying "It was too slow." You understand the individual words, and their mode of composition, but you understand very little of what the speaker meant. Successful linguistic communication requires – and speakers essentially rely on – *contextual inference*. On the Gricean view, "humans do not just associate a linguistic meaning [with] the sound of a sentence; they also use information on the speech situation, the interlocutors, their past interactions, the background knowledge they share, and so on"; the meanings encoded in utterances at most provide meaningful "fragments . . . without a definite import" (Sperber and Origgi 2010: 124).

So, on the Classical Gricean picture of communication, paradigmatic cases of human communication are built on *overt communicative intentions*, on the part of speakers, and their *reflective contextual interpretation*, on the part of hearers. What Grice called "speaker meaning" is a matter of a speaker producing an utterance (acoustic, written, gestural, or otherwise) with the intentions of

(a)   producing an effect on the psychological states of some receiver, and, further,
(b)   producing the effect in (a) in part *by means of* the receiver's recognition of that intention.

The relevant communicative intentions can (though they do not *have* to) rely on non-arbitrary "natural meaning," or on iconic relations. Gricean speaker meaning is also independent of convention, of compositional structure, and of learnability (or "cultural transmission"). Indeed, on the Gricean view, linguistic *conventions* are to be analyzed as resulting through processes of "ossifying" individual speaker meanings.

The Classical Gricean picture implies that communicators can possess a capacity to form and attribute intentions concerning beliefs, intentions, and other psychological states of creatures other than themselves – a so-called "Theory of Mind" – *before* they have language. However, there is little evidence that even our closest primate relatives are capable of sophisticated awareness of (and concern with) others' states of mind of the sort required for Gricean communication.[4] (And there are several arguments in the philosophical literature to the effect that, even if first-order intentional states do not require language, *Gricean* mindreading – *which is both recursive and propositional* – does.[5]) But the more evidence we have that nonlinguistic animals (as well as prelinguistic children) lack the full battery of cognitive states required by the Classical Gricean theory, the less plausible this Gricean evolutionary trajectory

Complex communicative intentions → Speaker meaning → Conventional language

would seem to be. The Gricean trajectory would require our nonhuman ancestors to have crossed a *psychological* Rubicon before they could venture crossing the language Rubicon. This is because they would have had to acquire a psychological capacity for sophisticated "mindreading," which was not remotely possessed by their nonhuman predecessors, before they could be in a position to engage in Gricean communication (i.e. to issue and interpret utterances with speaker meaning). Yet, from an evolutionary perspective, explaining the presence of a capacity for full-dress Gricean propositional thoughts in some extinct languageless species seems no less problematic than explaining the emergence of language itself.[6] (And this should motivate us to explore alternative trajectories.)

But perhaps the explanatory task facing theories of language evolution can be reconceived. Rather than focusing on the question of what might have motivated our ancestors to become deliberate, reflective Gricean communicators, perhaps we should be looking for ways that *non-Gricean* communication might have gradually evolved so as to take on linguistic character. In the next section, I want to propose that we can be helped in this task by attending to a specific type of non-Gricean communication that we share with many diverse species of nonhuman animals (and not just other great apes): expressive communication.

Expressive communication and origins of meaning[7]

In a survey of a half-century of ethological research, Peter Marler (2004) examines a wide and impressive range of avian calls, including predator alarm calls, calls for courtship, aggression, announcement and exchange of food, distress, group proximity maintenance, even rain anticipation. Marler suggests that a bird's alarm call can – and often does – fulfill its communicative role by showing the bird's fear *at the same time as* it reveals the fear's intentional content (2004: 176). Similarly, Snowdon has recently argued that chickens' "food calls can both be referential and communicate an affective state, perhaps of social invitation" (2008: 75).

On Marler's and Snowdon's way of understanding them, birds' alarm calls, though *unlearned*, still prefigure certain semantic and pragmatic aspects of linguistic communication. An alarm call is directed at a predator of a particular type, in virtue of expressing a relatively complex (albeit not compositionally structured) psychological state. The call shows – and its designated audience can recognize – a more or less intense agitation *at*, or fear *of*, a predator of a certain broad type. Coupled with a head tilt or directed gaze, the call can point to a specific predator of the relevant type.

Understood as affective displays, alarm calls belong in a broad class of expressive behaviors – in our own species and others – including growls; hisses and lip-smacks; facial expressions such as those associated with anger, fear, pain, etc.; and bodily demeanor, posture, and various gestures. A threatening growl is not simply a natural sign of its producer's fierceness (an *index*, in the sense of Maynard Smith and Harper 2003); and it not only represents its producer as possessing a certain resource, but also reveals his readiness to defend it if challenged. A vervet monkey's alarm call not only indicates the presence of an aerial predator, but also reveals the caller's fear or agitation, and thereby moves others to take a specific action to avoid the danger. Even one dog's cowering demeanor upon encountering another will display to a suitably endowed recipient the dog's fear (kind of state), *how* afraid they are (quality/degree of state), *of* whom they are afraid (the state's intentional object), and how they are disposed to act (slink away or hide behind its owner's leg). (Similar remarks apply to dogs' play bows.) Expressive communication, in general, is in a sense Janus-faced. It points inward, to the psychological state it expresses, at the same time as it points outward, toward the object or event at which the state is directed, as well as toward ensuing behaviors.[8]

"Expressive signals" (as we may call them) differ from mere natural signs, symptoms, and other reliable indicators in terms of their psychological, semantic, and pragmatic profile. The functionally *referential* character of alarm calls has been widely discussed.[9] But some alarm-call systems exhibit a predicative dimension, for the acoustic intensity of an alarm call is closely associated with the perceived level of predator danger. For example, suricates are said to have acoustically different alarm calls in response to different predator types, "but their call structure also varies depending on the level of urgency. (Low urgency calls tend to be harmonic across all predator types, while high urgency calls are noisier)" (Manser 2001: 2315). And prairie dogs, who have distinct calls for dogs, coyotes, hawks, and humans, have been reported to have acoustically distinct calls for humans with different color shirts (Slobodchikoff et al. 2009).[10] In this way, alarm calls may be *functionally predicative* in addition to being functionally referential. Thus, despite not being issued with communicative intentions (we may assume), and despite lacking compositional semantic structure, alarm (and other) calls appear to share an interesting meaning-relevant property with propositional linguistic utterances: they can be systematically differentially keyed to different features of the environment in a way that bears directly on their communicative function and significance.

Inasmuch as expressive signals are *directed at* objects and features of an animal's environment *as apprehended* (or "psychologically filtered") by the animal, they contrast with automatic physiological reactions, or hormonally dictated changes, and may be said to exhibit a measure of *intentionality* (in Brentano's sense). Moreover, experimental evidence suggests that, even if alarm and other calls are not *intentionally produced* (let alone produced in order to affect the audience's psychological states), their production can be brought under control in many mammals and all primates tested so far, as well as in many birds (a point to which I will later return).[11] And, as suggested earlier, even functionally referential signals can reveal producers' complex states of mind to suitably attuned receivers. (Note that to say that a state is complex is *not* to say that it has recombinable *parts* or components that correspond to the dimensions or aspects of psychological complexity. Instead, it should be understood as a *non-propositional, yet still world-directed* affective and action-guiding state. Likewise, a behavioral signal that expresses a complex affective state may also lack composite structure.[12]

On the view I advocate, expressive communication is a form of *social, intersubjective, world-directed*, and *open* communicative behavior that is (not intentionally but) biologically designed to enable expressers to *show* their *intentional states of mind* to suitably endowed observers, so as to move them *to act* in certain ways (toward the expresser or the object of her expressed state), in part by foretelling the expresser's *impending behavior*.[13] On this view, natural design takes the place of individual audience-directed communicative intentions and reflective inferential interpretations in securing the communicative significance, effectiveness, and openness of expressive communication. The communicative work of expressive communication is done through the spontaneous production of signals that are *designed* to *manifest* or reveal (rather than conceal; hence "open") complex states of mind of producers, and to *elicit appropriate, active responses* on the part of receivers. The producers themselves do not *intend* to show their states of mind, nor do they rely on their audience's *figuring out* their intentions. The receivers, in turn, do no reflectively interpret the expressive behavior, but are rather in a position to recognize immediately and non-inferentially the states expressed – their presence, intentional object, degree, behavioral profile, etc. – as well as being moved to act in appropriate ways, perhaps via contagion, or "resonance," or empathy and similar mechanisms.

While animal signaling is ubiquitous, not all animals that signal engage in expressive communication. The above characterization seems to go beyond the characterization of signals proposed by Evolutionary Game Theory, by taking into account the *psychological*, and *open-social* underpinnings of specifically *expressive* signals. According to the Expressive Communication (EC) approach, the displays (vocal, facial, gestural, postural, etc.) that comprise the repertoires of creatures capable of expressive communication are designed *openly* to convey information about the environment (as seen through the eyes of a minded producer), to foretell the producer's behavior, and to move the like-minded or relevantly affected audience to appropriate action by, specifically, commanding attention to the expressive performances themselves. This world-directed, intersubjective, and open character of expressive signals gives them a kind of *social natural meaning*. But the social meaningfulness and overtness of expressive signals is not earned through the labor of individual insight or invention. For, in general, animal expressers do not *intentionally express* their states of mind *in order to communicate messages*, and their observers do not make *rational inferences* about the intentions behind the expressive behavior. So *neither* half of the expressive communicative equation is Gricean. Given its non-Gricean character, expressive communication clearly places much weaker demands on the cognitive capacities of both producers and consumers than does full-blown Gricean communication.

Now the expressive character of alarm calls is often seized upon as a way of illustrating the great distance between animal communicative behaviors and language.[14] Tomasello, for example, sees a "sharp contrast" between what he calls "communicative displays" (among which he includes alarm calls), on the one hand, and "communicative signals that are chosen and produced by individual organisms flexibly and strategically for particular social goals, adjusted in various ways for particular circumstances" (2008: 14), on the other hand. He takes it that "the *starting point* for communication from a *psychological point of view*" must lie with signals that are "*intentional* in the sense that the individual controls their use flexibly toward the goal of influencing others" (2008: 14, emphases added). It's only when producers begin to attempt to "influence the behavior or psychological states of recipients intentionally" that we "have the starting point for communication from a psychological point of view" (2008: 14).[15]

On the non-Gricean EC approach advocated here, however, expressive behavior, and the kind of communication it affords, form a theoretically significant category of behavior that lies somewhere between the two endpoints Tomasello describes – i.e., *merely reflexive-reactive* affective displays and *fully reflective-creative* intentional utterances. (And there may, of course, be additional significant "joint'" in between.) To begin with, in agreement with the recommended "psychological point of view," EC's starting point is behavior that shows and affects the *psychological states* of producers and receivers, respectively. Moreover, EC draws on current research showing that animals belonging to a wide variety of species can bring their expressive behaviors (including alarm, food, aggression, courtship, and other calls) under voluntary control – showing a capacity for suppressing, modulating, and even intentionally producing the behavior for instrumental purposes.[16] This suggests that, although expressive behavior is not, in general, a form of *intentionally communicative behavior*, it is wrong to assimilate it to the model of purely reflexive, innately fixed reaction patterns or behavioral routines. It is important to distinguish in this connection between expressive *acts* (or *performances*) and the expressive *vehicles* used. In the case of alarm calls, for instance, what is innately fixed and not learned is the call *repertoire*, which constitutes the set of *expressive vehicles* at the disposal of an animal of a given species.[17] It is far less clear that individual expressive *acts* (or performances) of producing the calls are innately determined in all cases.

In general, expressive signals such as grooming grunts, food-begging gestures, nursing pokes, and ground-slaps, and various other "intention movements" and "attention getters,"[18] form *unlearned, shared repertoires of expressive vehicles*. As a matter of fact, diachronically speaking, the relatively stable (often innate) character of expressive vehicles contributes to their potential as *bearers of specific informative significance* – they constitute natural analogues of shared (albeit rudimentary) vocabularies. Such repertoires have at least one advantage over intentionally produced gestures that are very context-specific. As noted by Cartmill and Maestripieri (2012), the latter are *too* flexible, and require recipients to figure out what the gesturer is trying to achieve. Insofar as context-specific gestures have no fixed association with a gesturer's ends, and thus no stable meaning, their efficacy as communicative signals is reduced.

So far, I've argued that despite the fact that the production of expressive signals is innocent of Gricean intentions, expressive communication foreshadows linguistic communication in virtue of (at least) the following characteristics:

(i) Expressive signals carry complex *social meaning*, despite lacking compositional structure, in virtue of showing signalers' world-directed states of mind (*both* affective *and* cognitive) and their impending behavior to relevant others, as well as moving them to act appropriately.

(ii) Expressive signals inherit their complexity from the complexity of the psychological states they express; they are designed to show the intentional objects of these states, as well as their type and degree, and to elicit appropriate responses. Expressive signals are thus "psychologically involved"; despite not being intentionally designed to affect the audience's states of mind, they reflect and affect producers' and recipients' current psychological states.

(iii) Being naturally, rather than intentionally, designed to suit the social-biological purposes of co-habiting *groups* of animals, expressive signals – as *vehicles* – enjoy stable significance and specific function that prefigure the semantic-pragmatic stability of linguistic signs. In a sense, they embody *shared natural conventions* (see later).

(iv) Expressive *performances* – unlike mere "informative displays" – can be brought under considerable voluntary control. Unlike the signal repertoires they utilize, the performances are not entirely fixed, and they form intricate patterns of active intersubjective engagements.

Recognizing these features of the production, uptake, and vehicles involved in expressive communication should have consequences for our understanding of the question of the origins of meaning with which we began. When projecting back, we ought to keep in mind that our nonhuman predecessors, being social, minded, and expressive creatures, would have *already* been proficient – though non-Gricean – communicators, with a natural tendency openly to share information about their current states of mind and impending behavior, as well as about their environment, to suitably responsive others.[19] As producers, they would have already had fixed signal repertoires, readily recognizable by their audience, with which to *show* others how things are with them *and* how things are in the world (as well as moving them to respond in specific ways).

If this is right, then the alleged *Gricean* evolutionary puzzle – to do with the fact that "giving information away would seem prima facie to be against the individual interests of the information-giver" (Hurford 2007: 331) – was in a sense already solved with the emergence of expressive communication. This should relieve language evolution theorists of the need to offer specifically evolutionary explanations for why our immediate predecessors should have become motivated to share information with each other about various matters. It would free them to focus on what is perhaps a more tractable (even if still immensely difficult) problem. This is the problem of identifying additional non-Gricean capacities that we have in common with nonhuman animals that – in concert with the capacity to use unlearned but shared expressive communicative vehicles – could have conspired to put our ancestors on their way to the kind of flexible, intentional use of symbolic vehicles characteristic of meaningful speech. Below, I very briefly highlight several such capacities, as these have featured in recent suggestive studies of animal communication.

From expressive communication to meaningful speech?

In a recent paper, Pika and Bugnayer (2011) report Australian ravens' "object-oriented behaviours" of showing and offering non-food items of interest "to already attending recipients of the opposite sex". The relevant behaviors are said to be "always directed to a recipient," to be "mechanically ineffective," and to "receive a voluntary response," as well as show "goal-directedness and sensitivity to the attentional state of recipients." The authors characterize these as "triadic referential signals," which (they claim) show similarity to declarative pointing and showing behavior in human children. (They cite the fact that ravens, like humans, rely heavily on cooperation between pair-partners as providing reason to look beyond our "closest phylogenetic relatives," since "examples of convergent evolution in distant-related species" can "provide crucial clues to the types of problems that particular morphological or behavioural mechanisms were 'designed' to solve.")

It does not seem quite right to speak of the ravens' showing and offering behaviors as either triadic or referential. At any rate, it is clear that they are not referential in the same sense in which alarm calls are said to be (functionally) referential. The ravens' behaviors are *object-oriented* and *object-involving*, but they are not "object specifying"; the ravens show and offer objects, but their behaviors are not semantically *about* those objects. By contrast, an eagle alarm call can function like a holophrastic label – it has the communicative function of alerting relevant receivers to the presence of eagles, or some threat-from-above. It also seems that the ravens' showing and offering is not *declarative* in the sense in which babies' pointing to salient attractions is said to be, inasmuch as the ravens' behavior involves (literally) *bringing* an object to another's attention, as opposed to *drawing* the other's attention to a (third) object. But even if the behaviors are not referential, triadic, and declarative, they manifest object-involvement, an interesting type of audience-sensitivity (gauging of the other's attention), flexibility, and non-imperatival use – and, importantly, on the part of a *producer*.

Pika et al. (2005), Leavens et al. (2005), and Cartmill and Byrne (2007) have demonstrated strategic use of communicative signals by both chimps and orangutans. For instance, when partially successful in getting what they want, orangutans repeatedly used gestures that were attempted previously. When unsuccessful, they avoided failed signals and attempted more novel gestures, trying each only once or twice. In a review of these experiments, Cartmill and Maestripieri (2012) point out that the orangutans had to keep in memory gestures and actions previously attempted so they could redeploy behaviors that had achieved partial success in obtaining the desired food and avoid them when they had failed. They take the study to show that apes have a greater sensitivity to recipients' responses and to the efficacy of their own communicative actions than had been previously thought. Interestingly, Cartmill and Byrne (2007) emphasize the importance of what they call "conventional gestures" – by which they mean species-wide, unlearned, and arbitrary gestures, which contrast with the imitative gestures used in pantomime. They claim that these might be better candidates than iconic gestures as elements of an early "protolanguage," as they place weaker cognitive demands on producers (and presumably on their receivers, too). And they suggest that we should seek insights into the origins of "intentional meaning" in the "grey area" between hardwired reactive behaviors and highly context-specific communicative signals (such as pointing).

A nice illustration of the grey area, as well as of a remarkably fine-tuned audience sensitivity, comes from a recent report by Crockford et al. (2012). They describe recent experiments with wild Ugandan chimpanzees who emit snake calls highly selectively, depending on whether or not the call receivers have themselves seen the snake, whether they have been within earshot of a snake call, how far away they are relative to the caller, and how affiliated they are with the caller. It may be debatable whether the callers "assess the state of knowledge" of the receivers (as the authors claim). But it seems undeniable that the callers are attuned to, monitor, and recall, specifically, other subjects' attention to – and impending behavior toward – a salient ("third") object of potential interest or significance to both producer and receiver, as witnessed by the intricate pattern of their call production. And the call receivers are moved to take specific actions to avoid the threat of which the call informs them, skirting the path to avoid the location of the threat (which is invisible to them).

The wild chimps' case illustrates how, beginning with an unlearned, but shared and stable, naturally meaningful repertoire of *vocal* signals, a producer who is endowed with instrumental or practical understanding,[20] and who has voluntary control over the production of the signals, as well as enhanced intersubjective sensitivity, might be able to bootstrap themselves to using "mechanically ineffective" signals as tools (or means) for accomplishing other-directed ends, exploiting their natural meaning, rather than having creatively to *endow* an otherwise meaningless, novel sound or gesture with a Gricean speaker meaning.

In recent years, several researchers have suggested that the capacity for *imitative vocal learning* (which humans share with birds, and some cetaceans, but *not* with non-human primates) may shed light on the evolution of linguistic communication. This idea is illustrated by one of the more successful instances of training members of a nonprimate species – grey parrots – "to use the elements of English speech to communicate referentially with humans" (Pepperberg 2007: 359). Capitalizing on these birds' keen interest in various items in the lab, Alex (and later Griffin) were taught (among other things) to say "paper," "cork," "corn" – and later "want paper/cork/corn" – to request the relevant items and label them correctly, as well as the template "wanna x/y/z" (e.g. "wanna go back/eat") to make various action requests. The parrot's productions of English word sounds were not instances of rote, purposeless mimicry; they were goal-directed, novel, and referential. So they appear to meet standard current definitions of *imitation*.[21]

Of special interest in the present context are similarities between parrot-human interactions and some familiar paradigms of children's word acquisition. Specifically, consider a familiar acquisition paradigm: the child produces nonlinguistic voluntary expressive behavior and the adult offers a label for the intentional object or other aspects of the child's performance. So, for example, as we witness prelinguistic children's expressive behaviors, we sometimes say things like: "You're tired, aren't you?", "You want *Teddy*, don't you?" "You're so *scared* of this dog," and so on. What the linguistic adult does in such cases is effect a transition to incipient linguistic behavior by passing onto the child a new *expressive vehicle* for articulating aspects of the psychological state that are shown through the behavior – the state's character, degree, intentional object, and other features. (This paradigm of "transmission of expressive vehicles," I submit, underwrites some of the language-learning protocols of not only parrots, but also apes and dolphins, and the acquisition by animals of human gestures such as pointing.) It's at least in part because Alex was able to *show* his trainers his affective *and* cognitive states – *what* was holding his attention, *where* his focus was, what he was curious about, wanted or needed, whether he was bored, excited, tired, agitated, alarmed, and so on – that the trainers were able to offer him appropriate labels that he could then (thanks to his ability for vocal imitation) appropriate and use in effective communication that deployed speech sounds.[22]

The expressive paradigm of avian learning of labels is suggestive of one possible non-Gricean trajectory. What we'd be looking for is an analogue in phylogeny of the sort of human-to-animal expressive-vehicle-transmission just described. In abstract terms, what we need is something like the following evolutionary progression: at an initial stage, we have a creature producing an expressive, unlearned, functionally referential vocalization; and we have a recipient whose attention is drawn to the referential target of the vocalization. At the next stage, we have the recipient spontaneously imitating the vocalization in resonance with the intentional psychological state expressed by the producer. The recipient has become a (voluntary) producer.

In creatures capable of vocal control and vocal imitation, what begins life as an expressive signal could gradually become detached from producers' states of mind, while retaining its social meaning and communicative function. What imitation and control enable is the *appropriation* of signals and their use as "mechanically ineffective" communicative means. Voluntary control allows the intentional use of an already naturally meaningful expressive signal as a tool for accomplishing a social goal (as in the wild chimps' case). Imitation can yield a use of a label to articulate in a distinct form what is only inarticulately shown through expressive behavior (as in Alex's case.) With the right selection pressures, vocal patterns that are voluntarily producible and reproducible could be detached from their tight connection to expressed psychological states, and used instrumentally to draw attention to objects or other aspects of a shared surrounding. Further detachment from the presence of the normal environmental triggers of the vocalizations could lead to their gaining currency as standard *stand-ins* for the different intentional objects of the states characteristically expressed when producing them. And they can propagate throughout a social group as standard ways of communicating *about* those objects, even in their absence. For example, one can sensibly imagine along these lines that what begins its life as a food call, signaling a producer's excitement upon seeing food (and moving others to come get it), could become detached from producers' excitement and attached to their intentional target, so that a voluntary production of the call could take on the force of a *request* for food that isn't there. Alarm calls for different sources of threat could similarly be attached to alarmed states' triggers (e.g., leopards vs. eagles) and used even when the trigger isn't there so as to obtain the desired result of others' scattering. As the calls begin to be used more the way Alex used labels, they can form, in effect, a rudimentary vocabulary whose elements resemble symbolic one-word sentences with relatively specific content – a so-called "Protolanguage." (The same may apply to gestures.) Thus, even without the wisdom of Darwin's "ape-like creature," who *intends* to use a vocalization "as a sign or symbol for" the relevant source of danger, the ability to use, control, and imitate the production of expressive vehicles could be exploited in overt communicative interactions that exhibit early trappings of intentional use of meaningful, and even conventional, communication.

Limitations of space prevent a fuller survey of cases. Such a survey, I believe, would support the following additional claims:

(v) Even when using innately fixed repertoires, nonhuman animals exhibit various sorts of flexibility (e.g., audience-effects and context-sensitivity) in *acts* of expressive communication. The *production* of expressive signals (even unlearned ones) can be not only suppressed and modulated, but can even be intentional.

(vi) Among apes, gestural communication, specifically, exhibits individual and group variability, and can be modified via learning and intersubjective interactions.[23]

(vii) Expressive communication is at times triadic, relying on shared attention mechanisms that allow signalers and receivers to attend together to objects or events of mutual concern.

(viii) Through learning to use already meaningful signals as *mechanically ineffective* tools for achieving goals, a measure of symbolic arbitrariness is achieved (through the exploitation of social natural meaning, rather than through convention).[24]

★★★

There are important meaning-relevant differences – psychological, semantic, and pragmatic – between nonhuman animal communication (expressive communication included), on the one hand, and human linguistic communication, on the other. And it is not unreasonable to suggest that, to move beyond mere informative signaling, our ancestors would have had to engage in some form of intentional communication. However, I have tried to make plausible the idea that, *at its inception*, intentional communication need not require the communicator to *intend to communicate some message to her audience* – at least not if by that we mean that she has to have a conception of what her audience thinks, or wants, or intends, etc. *and* intentionally to design her communicative behavior so as to accomplish a desired goal. Expressive behaviors, which (on the account I have sketched) are *naturally designed* for the purpose of intersubjective communication, may be sufficient to put communicators on the right path – the behavioral repertoire itself need not be invented or learned. For once communicators gain voluntary control over the production of expressive signals that are already in their unlearned repertoire – and once, moreover, they are capable of acquiring signals from others through imitation and other kinds of transmission – new forms of communication become possible. Once appropriated, and caught up in intentional actions, expressive signals can propagate and stabilize, and come to have a semantic-pragmatic life of their own.[25]

Notes

1 For fuller discussion, see Bar-On (2013a).
2 See Bar-On and Moore, Chapter 27 in this volume.
3 The example is due to Bennett (1976: 13).
4 For a useful early discussion of the question whether nonhuman animals might meet less demanding, 'sub-Gricean' conditions on meaning, see Bennett (1976). And see Bar-On and Moore (Chapter 27 in this volume) for additional discussion and references.
5 See, e.g. Bermúdez (2003) and Carruthers (2008).
6 Of course, several philosophers have seen a *conceptual* difficulty here (known as the "circularity objection" to Grice's analysis of meaning), which has prompted a search for accounts of meaning that bypass altogether the appeal to Gricean intentions (see, e.g. Millikan 1984). For relevant discussion, see Blackburn (1984: Ch. 3) and Bar-On (1995) and (2013a).
7 This section relies on ideas developed in Bar-On and Green 2010, Bar-On and Priselac (2011), and Bar-On (2013a, b). See also Green (Chapter 29 in this volume) and Stegmann (Chapter 30 in this volume) for related discussions.
8 See Tormey (1971).
9 See Marler et al. (1992), Macedonia and Evans (1993), and Zuberbühler (2000)
10 See also Cheney and Seyfarth (2007: 221).
11 On the voluntary control of animal vocalizations, see Fitch 2010: 4.9.3.
12 For further discussion, see Bar-On and Priselac (2011) and Bar-On (2013a). And see Gomez (2009) for a related suggestion.
13 See references in previous note, as well as Bar-On (2013b).
14 See, e.g. Fitch (2010: 4.9).

15 It is for this reason that Tomasello maintains that nonhuman primates' gestures are "the best place to look for the evolutionary roots" of human communication (Fitch 2010: 4.9).

16 See, e.g. Zuberbühler (2000), Seyfarth and Cheney (2010), Fitch (2010), Hurford (2007), Snowdon (2008), and Fitch and Hauser (2002).

17 See Bar-On (2015).

18 For a partial catalogue of primate expressive behaviors, see Tomasello (2008: Ch. 2).

19 To reiterate, expressive communication only occurs among creatures who engage in overt acts of showing their *states of mind* to suitable others through behavioral performances. Expressive signals, on my view, have meaning that is different from what Green (Chapter 29 in this volume) refers to as the "organic meaning" possessed by biological signals that do not rely on such showing.

20 Of the sort that appears manifested in chimps' and corvids' tool use.

21 See Fitch (2010: 162).

22 Which is not to say that he was using English *words*, or fully engaging in linguistic communication. (See Pepperberg 1999.)

23 This contrasts with the signaling behaviors of bees and other eusocial insects, and may support the common-sense intuition that the latter belong in a different biological category, despite their impressive complexity. (Further vindication of this intuition, however, would require an investigation into the natural design of bee dances and the mental life of arthropods more generally.)

24 Relevant here is what Tomasello (2008: 5.3.1) describes as "drift to the arbitrary."

25 Thanks to several audiences attending presentations of earlier versions of this chapter between the summers of 2012 and 2015 (at the Max Planck Institute for Evolutionary Anthropology, Leipzig, Psychology Colloquium, St. Andrews University, Smith College, Cognitive Science Colloquium, SUNY Buffalo, the Center for the Study of Mind in Nature, University of Oslo, and the Wissenschaftskolleg zu Berlin). Special thanks to Carol Voeller for discussions and comments on earlier drafts.

Acknowledgments

Work on this chapter was completed while a fellow at the Wissenschaftskolleg zu Berlin from 2015–2016.

References

Bar-On, D. (1995) "Reconstructing 'meaning': Grice and the naturalization of semantics," *Pacific Philosophical Quarterly* 76: 83–116.

——— (2013a) "Origins of meaning: Must we 'go Gricean'?" *Mind and Language* 28(3): 342–375.

——— (2013b) "Expressive Communication and Continuity Skepticism," *Journal of Philosophy* 110(6): 293–330.

——— (2015) "Expression: Acts, Products, and Meaning," in S. Gross et al. (eds.) *Meaning Without Representation: Essays on Truth, Expression, Normativity, and Naturalism*, Oxford: Oxford University Press.

Bar-On, D., and Green, M. (2010) "Lionspeak: Communication, expression, and meaning," in J. R. O'Shea and E. Rubenstein (eds.) *Self, Language, and World: Problems From Kant, Sellars, and Rosenberg*, Atascadero, CA: Ridgeway Publishing Co., pp. 89–106.

Bar-On, D., and Priselac, M. (2011) "Triangulation and the beasts," in C. Amoretti and G. Preyer (eds.) *Triangulation: From an Epistemological Point of View*, Heusenstamm: Ontos Verlag, pp. 121–152.

Bennett, J. (1976) *Linguistic Behaviour*, Cambridge: Cambridge University Press.

Bermúdez, J. (2003) *Thinking Without Words*, Oxford: Oxford University Press.

Blackburn, S. (1984) *Spreading the Word*, Oxford: Oxford University Press.

Carruthers, P. (2008) "Metacognition in animals: A skeptical look," *Mind and Language* 23: 58–89.

Cartmill, E. A., and Byrne, R. W. (2007) "Orangutans modify their gestural signaling according to their audience's comprehension," *Current Biology* 17: 1345–1348.

Cartmill, E. A., and Maestripieri, D. (2012) "Socio-cognitive specializations in nonhuman primates: Evidence from gestural communication," in J. Vonk and T. K. Shackelford (eds.) *The Oxford Handbook of Comparative Evolutionary Psychology*, Oxford: Oxford University Press, pp. 166–193.

Cheney, D., and Seyfarth, R. M. (2007) *Baboon Metaphysics*, Chicago: University of Chicago Press.

Crockford, C., Wittig, R. M., Mundry, R., and Zuberbüler, K. (2012) "Wild chimpanzees inform ignorant group members of danger," *Current Biology* 22(2): 142–146.

Darwin, C. (1871) *The Descent of Man, and Selection in Relation to Sex*, London: John Murray.

Fitch, W. T. (2010) *The Evolution of Language*, Cambridge: Cambridge University Press.

Fitch, W. T., and Hauser, M. D. (2002) "Unpacking 'honesty': Vertebrate vocal production and the evolution of acoustic signals," in A. M. Simmons, R. R. Fay, and A. N. Popper (eds.) *Acoustic Communication*, New York: Springer, pp. 65–137.

Gomez, J. (2009) "Embodying meaning: Insights from primates, autism, and Brentano," *Neural Networks* 22: 190–196.

Grice, P. (1957) "Meaning," *The Philosophical Review* 66: 377–388.

——— (1968) "Utterer's meaning, sentence-meaning, and word-meaning," *Foundations of Language* 4: 225–242.

——— (1989) *Studies in the Way of Words*, Cambridge, MA: Harvard University Press.

Hurford, J. (2007) *The Origins of Meaning: Language in the Light of Evolution*, Oxford: Oxford University Press.

Leavens, D., Hopkins, W., and Bard, K. (2005) "Understanding the point of chimpanzee pointing: Epigenesis and ecological validity," *Current Directions in Psychological Science* 14: 185–189.

Macedonia, J. M., and Evans, C. S. (1993) "Variation among mammalian alarm call systems and the problem of meaning in animal signals," *Ethology* 93: 177–197.

Manser, M. B. (2001) "The acoustic structure of suricates' alarm calls varies with predator type and the level of response urgency," *Proceedings of the Royal Society B: Biological Sciences* 268(1483): 2315–2324.

Marler, P. (2004) "Bird calls: A cornucopia for communication," in P. Marler and H. Slabbegoorn (eds.) *Nature's Music: The Science of Birdsong*, New York: Elsevier, pp. 132–177.

Marler, P., Evans, C. S., and Hauser, M. D. (1992) "Animal signals: Reference, motivation or both?" in H. Papousek, U. Jürgens, and M. Papousek (eds.) *Nonverbal Vocal Communication: Comparative and Developmental Approaches*, Cambridge: Cambridge University Press, pp. 66–86.

Maynard Smith, J., and Harper, D. (2003) *Animal Signals*, Oxford: Oxford University Press.

Millikan, R. (1984) *Language, Thought, and Other Biological Categories*, Cambridge, MA: Bradford Books/ MIT Press.

Pepperberg, I. M. (1999) *The Alex Studies: Cognitive and Communicative Abilities of Grey Parrots*. Cambridge, MA: Harvard University Press.

——— (2007) "Emergence of linguistic communication: Studies on Grey parrots," in C. Lyon, C. L. Nehaniv, and A. Cangelosi (eds.) *Emergence of Communication and Language*. London: Springer, pp. 355–386.

Pika, S. and Bugnyar, T., (2011) "The Use of Referential Gestures in Ravens (Corvus corax) in the Wild", *Nature Communications* 2: 1–5.

Pika, S., Liebal, K., Call, J., and Tomasello, M. (2005) "The gestural communication of apes," *Gesture* 5(1/2): 41–56.

Seyfarth, R. M., and Cheney, D. (2010) "Production, usage, and comprehension," *Brain & Language* 115: 92–100.

Slobodchikoff, C. N., Paseka, A., and Verdolin, J. L. (2009) "Prairie dog alarm calls encode labels about predator colors," *Animal Cognition* 12(3): 435–439.

Snowdon, C. T. (2008) "Contextually flexible communication in nonhuman primates," in D. K. Oller and U. Griebel (eds.) *Evolution of Communicative Flexibility: Complexity, Creativity, and Adaptability in Human and Animal Communication*. Cambridge, MA: MIT Press, pp. 71–92.

Sperber, D., and Origgi, G. (2010) "A pragmatic perspective on the evolution of language," in R. K. Larson, V. Déprez, and H. Yamakido (eds.) *The Evolution of Human Language: Biolinguistic Perspectives*, Cambridge: Cambridge University Press, pp. 124–132.

Tomasello, M. (2008) *Origins of Human Communication*, Cambridge, MA: Bradford Books/MIT Press.

Tormey, A. (1971) *The Concept of Expression*, Princeton, NJ: Princeton University Press.

Zuberbühler, K. (2000) "Referential labeling in wild diana monkeys," *Animal Behavior* 59: 917–927.

29

HOW MUCH MENTALITY IS NEEDED FOR MEANING?

Mitchell S. Green

Intention-Based Semantics

Some entities and processes exhibit meaning of a sort that is germane to communication. These include words and phrases, as well as gestures, facial expressions, and perhaps also manifestations of biological traits such as bioluminescence, scent-marking, alarm calls, and stridulation. Theoretical questions about these communicative forms of meaning fall into two broad types: (1) In virtue of what do words (phrases, etc.) have meaning? and (2) How shall we best characterize such meaning as words (phrases, etc.) have? One may remain neutral on the type-1 question while focusing on the second, in the course of which debates about the adequacy of truth conditions, possible worlds, sense and reference, context-change potential, and the like, come to the fore. Or one may keep type-2 questions in the background and consider whether words (phrases, etc.) have their meaning given by iconicity (*sensu* Plato's characterization of Socrates' attempt to develop Cratylus's idea in the dialogue of that name), or conventions, or minds, or some combination of these three.

Our focus in what follows will be on type-1 questions, and in particular on whether words, phrases, or any other entities can possess semantic, or at least communicative significance, only as a result of the action of minds. According to a longstanding tradition, a necessary condition of such entities as these having meaning is their being acted upon in a certain way by minded creatures. Locke popularized this view, which was reinvigorated in the last century by Grice and those who followed him into what came to be known as Intention-Based Semantics (IBS).[1] On the IBS strategy, we imagine two agents A and B who share no common language, when A attempts to convey a message to B (that there is quicksand down that path, say). A does something, perhaps gesturing, or miming the process of being sucked under by quicksand, with the intention of getting B to think there is quicksand down that path, and further intending that B come to believe this at least in part as a result of his recognition of A's intention that he so believe. Suppose that B does cotton on and later uses a similar strategy to warn a third traveler of quicksand. Repeated interactions along these lines could result in the particular gesture-mime combination having a conventional significance among travelers in this region. Similar processes might result in other gestures, vocalizations, facial expressions, and the like acquiring distinct conventional significance among these agents ("water nearby"; "where is food"; "let me hold the baby"; etc.).

One virtue of this story is that it resolves a qualm about answers to type-1 questions that appeal to convention. The qualm is that such answers appear circular: how can words be imbued with meaning without the conveners already possessing a conventional medium of communication? The proponent of IBS may reply that the above quicksand story presupposes no conventions. Instead, it presupposes that agents A, B, and others behave intentionally, ascribe intentions to others and to themselves, can discern similarities between behaviors and worldly states of affairs, can remember what they learn, and can behave with a modicum of rationality. On a view of convention as a behavioral regularity with a degree of arbitrariness as well as normative force (which may only flow from practical rationality), one can envision the emergence of meaning conventions from conditions not themselves conventional. Flush with success, the proponent of IBS might also urge that insofar as stridulation and bioluminescence are communicative, they are in a way so radically different from what we find in human communication that they merit a wholly distinct treatment.

Natural and speaker meaning

In referring above to forms of meaning germane to communication, I suggested that other forms of meaning are not so germane, thereby invoking a distinction that has, for the last half-century, been an established part of the philosophical landscape. This is Grice's (1957) separation of 'natural' from 'non-natural' meaning, although the latter term has since been supplanted by the phrase 'speaker meaning.' According to this distinction, we invoke the concept of natural meaning when we say such things as "Those spots mean measles," whereas we invoke the concept of speaker meaning in such utterances as "That traffic cop's gesture means that the road is closed." Grice elucidates each of these concepts by suggesting that for the first kind of case, five conditions hold, while for the second kind of case, none of those five conditions holds. The conditions are as follows:

1   One cannot consistently say, "Those spots mean measles, but he hasn't got measles." That is, 'mean' in its "natural" usage is factive.
2   One cannot argue from "Those spots mean measles" to any conclusion about what is or was meant by those spots.
3   One cannot argue from "Those spots mean measles" to any conclusion about what anyone meant by those spots.
4   One cannot restate the above example in terms that involve direct discourse. That is, one cannot rephrase "Those spots mean measles" by saying "Those spots meant 'measles'" or "Those spots meant 'He has measles.'"
5   One can restate "Those spots mean measles" as "The fact that he has spots means that he has measles."

Grice makes clear that he expects these five conditions most likely stand or fall together (1957, p. 215), and to my knowledge did not entertain the question whether some but not all of them can be satisfied. Further, Grice analyzes the concept of speaker meaning as follows: *agent A speaker means that P* just in case A performs an action with the intention of producing a psychological effect on another agent B, while further intending that this effect be produced at least in part as a result of B's recognition of A's intention. This is known as a reflexive communicative intention. While the reflexive dimension of Grice's definition has been challenged,[2] it is widely agreed that at least overt intentions are characteristic of communication in our own species. Together with Grice's assumption that conditions 1–5 above stand or fall together, this dominant framework affords little room for making sense of more primitive forms of meaning that we might discover among nonhuman animals, or for that matter within our own species.

To give some reason why such a primitive kind of meaning deserves notice, consider a case that a biologist would treat as exemplifying it. Amazonian tree frogs typically bear pigments enabling them to camouflage in the jungle flora in which they reside. This is one strategy, known as crypsis, for deterring predation. Other species of tree frog in that region pursue a distinct strategy of bearing coloration that makes them easy to spot. Such salient anurans are also typically highly poisonous (Maan and Cummings 2012). Biologists will describe such frogs' bright coloration as a *warning signal*, placing it in the broader category of aposematism (Poulton 1880). In so doing, these scientists do not impute intentions to frogs, to say nothing of communicative intentions, and they do not suggest that they or the species of which they are members perform speech acts in the sense of that term used in contemporary philosophy of language. But neither are these biologists speaking metaphorically. Instead, they are making use of the notion of a signal, which for now we may gloss as a feature of an organism that conveys information, and that also was designed (if only by virtue of a process of natural selection) to convey that information to an appropriate audience.[3] Further, in the particular case of the brightly colored tree frog, the suggestion is that this creature's possession of bright coloration is a signal *that it is noxious*. So, too, it is natural to say of such a case that the tree frog's bright coloration *means* that it is noxious. But what kind of meaning is this?

To answer this question, it helps to observe that it is possible to signal deceptively. A population of warningly colored, toxic tree frogs could, after all, find within its midst a mutation that is warningly colored but not toxic. Such a frog is not intending to deceive, but will gain an advantage over its peers by deterring predators without paying the cost of harboring toxic chemicals. Of such a brightly colored, nontoxic tree frog, we might say that although its bright coloration means that it is noxious, in fact it is not.

Consider, then, how deceptive aposematism plays out with Grice's five conditions:

1F One *can* consistently say, "That red patch means he is poisonous, but he isn't poisonous." That is, 'mean' in its organic usage is not factive.

2F One *can* argue from "That red patch means he is poisonous" to a conclusion about what is or was meant by that red patch.

3F One cannot argue from "That red patch means he is poisonous" to any conclusion about what anyone meant by that red patch.

4F One cannot restate the above example in terms that involve direct discourse. That is, one cannot rephrase "That red patch means he is poisonous" by saying, "That red patch means 'poisonous,'" or "That patch means, 'I am poisonous.'"

5F One *cannot* restate "That red patch means he is poisonous" as "The fact that he has a red patch means he is poisonous."

I have italicized the conditions that flip when we go from spots meaning measles to the poisonous tree frog: 1, 2, and 5. If this is correct, then Grice was mistaken to suppose that conditions 1–5 stand or fall together. It follows as well that the extensions picked out by Grice's original sets of conditions (1–5, and the denial of each of 1–5) are classes that are not jointly exhaustive. That is, there are cases of meaning that are neither natural- nor speaker-meaning.[4] Might this open up an avenue to an Intention-Free Semantics?

Limitations of Intention-Based Semantics

Notwithstanding its attractions, IBS faces two challenges which we may term *the problem of analytical priority*, and *the problem of cognitive load*. According to the former, IBS problematically takes intentions to be more explanatorily basic than is word meaning. For instance, some have claimed that we have no idea how to ascribe the complex intentions that are needed in Grice's analysis to creatures that cannot be presumed already to possess a language (Davidson 1974). Avramides (1989) offers an alternative account on which IBS provides a non-reductive analysis of semantic concepts. However, if we were previously puzzled about how communicative forms of meaning can come into being, it is not clear how such an analysis will assuage that puzzlement.[5]

According to the problem of cognitive load, IBS places unduly high cognitive demands on speakers whom we would, intuitively, think capable of meaning things (Glüer and Pagin 2003; Breheny 2006). Such speakers include young children as well as those who, regardless of their age, have a compromised theory of mind. In either case, it is not plausible that the speaker would have the cognitive sophistication to intend to bring about an effect in an audience's cognitive state by means of that audience's recognition of their intention.[6]

Issues of cognitive load also have implications for our understanding of language evolution. A theorist aspiring to naturalize meaning, while also aiming to be at least consistent with the empirical facts of language evolution, may well also wish to see how meaning could emerge along a plausible evolutionary path. Yet in spite of the excitement associated with the recent comparative cognition research (well represented in this volume), little persuasive evidence exists to support the attribution to nonhuman animals of the kinds of complex intentions that speaker meaning requires. Thus, while a majority of scientists and philosophers are by now comfortable ascribing cognitive states to nonhuman animals, few are prepared to ascribe to nonhuman animals the sorts of reflexive communicative intentions required for speaker meaning. Nor do we possess credible evidence of such cognitive sophistication in extinct ancestors of modern humans. As a result, if anything like meaning emerges among nonhuman animals, it will be a challenge to explain how it does so with the tools of IBS.

Biological signaling

Explanatory priority and cognitive load are not immediately fatal to IBS; perhaps no better account is to be found of the ontogeny and phylogeny of semantic phenomena than is offered by this program. Before accepting that conclusion, however, we do well to follow the scent that has just emerged. Although every physical object is a source of information, for the great majority of such objects, we do not gain an explanatory advantage by noting their information-bearing properties. Earth's tides are influenced by the moon's gravitational pull, but it would generally be explanatorily idle to add – what is also true – that these tides carry information about the moon's proximity. If a creature relies on moonlight for navigation, however, accounting for its behavior may well rely on noting that high tide is informationally significant for it. More generally, many organisms are able to exploit the information-conveying powers of their surroundings to aid their survival. A mosquito uses the presence of a higher-than-typical level of carbon dioxide in the air to find a meal, typically in the blood of a mammal (Gillies 1980). The concentration of carbon dioxide in the air is thus a cue for the mosquito, though it may not be for other animals. More officially, we may say *C is a cue for organism O* just in case O is competent to use C for the acquisition of information for its benefit. That the presence of a higher-than-typical level of carbon dioxide in the air is a cue for organism O does not imply that anything (either natural selection or a sentient creature's intention) designed carbon dioxide to play that role. Cues can even be produced by things that are neither artifacts nor animate. So, too, an organism's use of a cue does not imply that it understands or in some other way produces a mental representation of any piece of information. Competence may but need not be underwritten by mental representation.

An organism's use of a cue is not yet communication. I am not communicating with the mosquito when it enjoys a meal at my vascular expense; nor is it communicating with me. Nevertheless, cues can be precursors to communication. For a related notion, consider that instead of gathering information from other objects for its own purposes, a creature could manipulate that information to exploit others. Crypsis is a case in point, in which a creature uses camouflage in order to avoid predation or to make potential prey more vulnerable to its attack (Ruxton et al. 2004). Crypsis can also aid sexual selection. Two males might be vocalizing in competition for a female, but one of them might also produce a vocalization designed to mask the effect of the other's mating call (Legendre et al. 2012). Following standard usage in the biological literature, we may call *coercion* any trait or behavior in which an organism manipulates information to gain an advantage in its interaction with others.

When an organism uses a cue, it has an evolved response to the transmission of information; but the entity transmitting that information does not do so as a result of an evolved response. By contrast, in coercion an organism uses a trait that is evolved to manipulate information for its benefit. So in cues we have receivers of information making adaptive use of it; and in coercion we have potential senders of information manipulating it for their own ends. If we now combine these two concepts in such a way that both the sender and receiver of information make adaptive use of information, we approach communication. One process by which this occurs is ritualization.

In a study of domestic dogs, Quaranta et al. (2007) observed that due to hemispheric specialization for different affective responses, together with contralateral muscular control, a dog whose right hemisphere is stimulated will tail-wag in a way skewed to the left; a left-hemisphere stimulation will cause the wagging to skew right. A subsequent (Siniscalchi et al. 2013) study showed that conspecifics are responsive to this asymmetry – showing increased cardiac activity and higher scores of anxious behavior when observing left- rather than right-biased tail wagging. The observing dogs thus appear to use this asymmetrical wagging as a cue to the wagging dog's affective state. We might also imagine a process aided by artificial selection resulting in the wagging dog's skewing its wag more dramatically, thereby making its affective state easier for conspecifics to detect. Such a development would likely increase the chances of appropriate encounters and decrease the likelihood of unwarranted conflicts. We would here have a case of the sender (wagging dog) gaining an advantage from manipulating information, and a receiver (viewing dog) gaining an advantage from the information's being manipulated. In so doing, the wagging would have been ritualized to become a signal. A single dog would, of course, be both sender and receiver, but would only signal to itself in exceptional cases.

Signalers and receivers need not be of the same species, and may be single- or multi-celled organisms. Likewise, nothing in the definition of signaling rules out plants or living things in other kingdoms as potential signalers or receivers. So long as the notions of information, transmission, and adaptation apply to a pair of entities, they are capable of participating in a signaling transaction. Such a transaction does not, however, require intentions to communicate, to say nothing of reflexive communicative intentions. Signals constitute what I will term *organic meaning*, which overlaps with natural meaning[7] while including speaker meaning as a special case. A Venn diagram illustrates the relations among these notions (Figure 29.1).

May we say anything non-metaphorical about what signals organically mean? Our first observation should be that in a given case, there may be considerable indeterminacy as to the

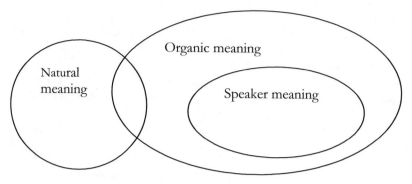

Figure 29.1   Relations among natural, organic, and speaker meaning

Species	Behavior or trait	Putative organic meaning	Audience
Ethiopian wolves (*Canis simensis*)	Scent marking	"Our territory"; also signifies pack composition[9]	Conspecifics of rival packs
Poison tree frogs (*Dendrobates pumilio*)	Bright coloration	"I'm toxic"[10]	Avian predators
Millipedes (genus *Mytoxia*)	Bioluminescence	"I'm toxic"[11]	Mammalian predators
Bottlenose dolphins (*Tursiops truncatus*)	Signature whistles	"NN is here", where 'NN' functions like a proper name[12]	Other pod members
Black–capped chickadees (*Poecile atricapilla*)	"Seet" alarm call	"Moving raptor nearby"[13]	Other flock members
Black–capped chickadees (*Poecile atricapilla*)	"Chick-a-dee" call and variants	Signifies degree of danger of stationary raptor	Other flock members
Doestic chickens (*Gallus gallus domesticus*)	"Scream" or "whistle" calls	"aerial predator"; "terrestrial predator"; "food"[14]	Other flock members
Vervet monkey (*Chlorocebus pygerythrus*)	"Chuttr"; "chirp"; "rraup"	"snake"; "leopard"; "eagle"[15]	Other troop members

Figure 29.2   Signals used by certain nonhuman animals and their putative organic meaning

exact characterization of what is meant. For instance, a signal might be interpreted in terms of the grammatical category of a Noun Phrase (NP), as expressing a property, or on the other hand, it might be construed in propositional terms. For now, however, we can acknowledge that each of these approaches may be adequate to the empirical facts without there being a further fact of the matter making one of these uniquely correct. That attitude need not differentiate animal from human communication, since we find no shortage of indeterminacy among our own kind.[8]

Second, what, if anything, a trait or behavior organically means will only be established after painstaking empirical investigation. A tiny sample from a vast array of results is shown in Figure 29.2.

Some of these (organically) meaningful signals may be produced without presupposing any mentality on the part of their producer: tree frog coloration and millipede bioluminescence are cases in point. Others, however, require that the signaler can differentially sense aspects of its environment and translate the result of what it senses into an appropriate signal. Chickadees and Ethiopian wolves evidently need to do this. None of these cases, however, presupposes that the signaler intends to transmit information when it signals.[16]

Organic meaning and semanticity

We have thus far developed a notion of meaning that is compatible with but does not require mentality, to say nothing of communicative intentions. To this it might be replied that although the point is all well and good, organic meaning is a far cry from the sort of meaning that we observe in our own species. For in our own species, meaningful units are compositional (and thus productive), they are produced intentionally, and they exhibit displacement[17] – not to mention our capacity to use meaningful units for implicature, metaphor, litotes, and synechdoche.

Our species may be uniquely capable of carrying out all of these feats. However, we need to distinguish three questions:

1   Is it possible to explain all of human communication without appeal to the cognitive apparatus underwriting speaker meaning?
2   Is it possible to account for a communicative form of meaning without appeal to the cognitive apparatus underwriting speaker meaning?
3   Can we explain the institution of semantic facts without appeal to the cognitive apparatus underwriting speaker meaning?

I suspect that the answer to the first question is no, and have argued that the answer to the second is yes. I'll end with some reasons to answer the third question in the affirmative.

Attributions of semanticity only begin to have use in application to organically meaningful units that are separable from the organism producing them. It is otiose to ascribe semantic value to a frog's bright coloration or a millipede's bioluminescence; instead, it is enough to describe these traits as bearers of organic meaning. While it is less than clear how we might rigorously characterize the relevant notion of separability, reasonable candidates for bearers of semanticity are the products of vocalizations among nonhuman primates. These will be our focus in what follows. Darwin (1872) had originally suggested that animal vocalizations are readouts of internal states of arousal, and thus do not refer to external objects or otherwise bear semantic properties. However, this conclusion only follows if such internal states are not themselves world-directed. A readout of an internal state of perception, awareness, or attention, for instance, may well inherit that state's world-directedness. Yet much literature on the topic of nonhuman animal communication stops short of ascribing semantic properties to such readouts because of their apparent differences from such phenomena in our species. For instance, alarm calling and like signaling are not normally under the voluntary control of the animals producing the calls,[18] whereas humans can typically choose whether to refer to an object verbally, in some other way, or not at all. Another reason is that humans often use language with reflexive communicative intentions, or at least intentions to produce cognitive effects in others. For instance, Cheney & Seyfarth write:

> The calls given by monkeys in social interactions . . . appear to serve many of the same purposes as human speech, in the sense that they act to mediate social interactions, to

appease, and to reconcile. Other calls function to inform individuals about the caller's location and to maintain group contact and cohesion. . . . Despite these functional similarities, however, the mental mechanisms underlying non-human primate vocalizations appear to be fundamentally different from the mechanisms underlying adult human speech. When calling one another, monkeys seem to lack one of the essential requirements of human speech: the ability to take into account their audience's mental states.

(Cheney and Seyfarth 1996, p. 72)[19]

Much literature in the ethology of communication adopts a similar attitude, as reflected in the widespread use of the term *functionally referential* to describe alarm calls.[20] On this usage, terms that are functionally referential behave as if they are referring terms, even if not produced by creatures intending to refer to an object or intending to draw another organism's attention to that object. These latter conditions, it would seem, are characteristic of human uses of referring terms, whereas intentions to refer or to direct another's attention to an object are difficult to establish among nonhuman animals, and of course *post hoc* verbal interrogations are not an option outside our own species. (An analogous case of scientific timorousness can be imagined for the concept of functional predication.)

Calling certain organically meaningful traits and behaviors functionally referential or predicative may just reflect laudable theoretical parsimony. However, use of this label is often accompanied by a denial that such traits or behaviors are "true" words or otherwise bear genuine semantic properties. This denial would be justified if the above features characterizing human use of words *distinctively* also characterized their use *essentially*. However, that an entity or a class of entities exhibit a property distinctively, does not imply that they do so essentially. (I uniquely occupy this particular spatiotemporal location, but I could easily move without ceasing to be the same individual.) More broadly, many features of language use are not found in other species, either extant or, so far as the fossil record suggests, extinct. The capacity for irony is one. But few would argue that the capacity for irony is essential to a community's having a language. Likewise, when we refer with a meaningful expression, we typically do so with specific intentions. It does not follow that in the absence of such intentions, the most that a creature can do is "functionally refer."

Think, then, of a noun as an artifact used for referring to an object, and a predicate as an artifact for ascribing a property to an object. No doubt, a vocal pattern or other repeatable will only come to take on such a role in a community of agents who use such parts of speech with sufficient regularity and success. Accordingly, imagine a future race of creatures – call them New World Vervets (NWVs) – descended from actual vervets (*Cercopithecus aethiops*), who can describe their environment with some precision, both referring and predicating in response to a variety of situations, and by virtue of these acts elicit appropriate responses from their conspecifics. In addition to four noun-like terms for different kinds of predator a (raptor), b (leopard), c (snake), and d (raptor[21]), they also possess four predicate-like terms for characterizing them: F (large), G (small), H (near), and K (far). Concatenations of such expressions will produce sixteen possible Vervish expressions exhibiting truth conditions such as the following:

'Fa' is true iff there is a large raptor;
'Kc' is true iff there is a distant snake;
'Gb' is true iff there is a small leopard; and so on.

Natural selection may have endowed these creatures with the capacity to respond to environmental situations with phrases of Vervish, but not in a way under their voluntary control. Yet when such calls are produced, other members of the group respond appropriately. For instance, in response to a 'Kc' call, the NWVs scan the landscape but do no more; however, in response to a call of 'Hc', NWVs rush to the ground to surround the nearest snake and mob it, attacking it with stones and sticks.

We may also note that the morphology of Vervish expressions is not uniquely determined by the situation to which they respond: other acoustic patterns could have borne the semantic properties we've ascribed above. Accordingly, such calls satisfy one condition for conventionality, namely arbitrariness. We have stipulated that their use satisfies another condition, namely regularity. Finally, their use is norm-governed in the following sense: an adaptive response to a predator threat is to alarm-call with the appropriate terminology. This is adaptive because it increases the troop's chances of emerging from an encounter with that predator without losing members. Together, these conditions (arbitrariness, regularity, and normativity) are enough to show that Vervish is conventional.

Vervish lacks connectives and devices of embedding, and as a result has only a finite number of strings. It is tempting to suggest that it is essential to a system of communication's being a language that it contains an infinite set of well-formed expressions. If so, the conclusion would need to be supported by some other reason than that human communication is uniquely productive. Productivity is surely important to human communication. But even that does not imply that it is essential to it. (Recall that irony is important to human communication.) Yet we've no need to show that Vervish is a language in anything like the sense that Croatian or Inupiatun are. Our task has only been to argue that Vervish exhibits semanticity. For if it does, we may conclude that Intention-Free Semantics is a viable avenue for exploring type-1 questions about meaning.[22]

Notes

1 See Bennett 1976; Schiffer 1972, 1982; and Loar 1981. See Borg 2006 for an overview.
2 Vlach 1981 provides an overview of many of the most important such challenges. See also Neale 1992.
3 This definition is inspired by Maynard Smith and Harper 2004, but differs from them in making explicit use of the notion of information. Also, here and below I use the notion of design with no imputation that evolutionary explanations are teleological. Instead, features of organisms have consequences for their behavior, and thus survival, and thus for their chances of passing on their genes. In this sense, bird feathers are designed *inter alia* for thermoregulation.
4 Reboul 2007 also argues that the natural/non-natural distinction is not exhaustive, and proposes intentional (but not reflexively intentional) behaviors as a source of a third type of meaning. The gist of our discussion so far is that natural selection can stand in for intentions to produce a third type of (communicatively significant) meaning.
5 See Bar-On and Green 2010, and Bar-On 2013, for fuller discussion.
6 Horisk and Cocroft 2013 address this issue in greater detail.
7 Organic and natural meaning overlap in that there are cases of signaling that also naturally mean what they signal. These are *indices*, and help organisms establish their signals' reliability. See Green 2009 for fuller discussion.
8 Green 1999 offers a fuller discussion of varieties of indeterminacy in meaning and attitude ascription. Millikan 1996 argues that many animal signals should be seen as having both directive and assertoric force. The indeterminacy claim mooted here does not imply this view, but suggests instead that there may be no fact of the matter whether such signals have one of these forces rather than the other.
9 Silliero-Zubiri and Macdonald 1998.
10 Mann and Cummings 2012.
11 Marek et al. 2011.

12 Sayigh et al. 2007.
13 Templeton et al. 2008.
14 Evans and Evans 2007.
15 Price et al. 2015.
16 Space limitations preclude a discussion of the conditions under which signals are *stable*, in the sense of being resistant to exploitation by deceptive signalers. See Maynard Smith and Harper 2004 for a canonical treatment, and Green 2009 for an application of some of the themes at issue to the phenomenon of expressive behavior.
17 Readers of Jackendoff 1999, p. 273, will suspect that what we are here calling semanticity emerges prior to what he construes as the first step in the evolution of language, namely "the use of symbols in a non-situation-specific fashion." (Other authors call this 'displacement'.) If this suspicion is correct, it may call for an elaboration of Jackendoff's hierarchy. Alternatively, we might question the clarity of the notion of displacement. How much "distance" is required to satisfy this condition? Also, assuming that what matters in the notion is epistemic rather than spatio-temporal displacement, observe that many creatures signal information about their genetically determined fitness level – which level is not open to sensory inspection to predators or potential mates. Such signals are in one respect far removed from what they are signals of.
18 Price et al. 2015 argue for this claim. Great ape gestural communication appears to be an exception; see Cartmill and Byrne 2010.
19 Earlier in this same article, these authors cite Grice's distinction between natural and non-natural meaning as a basis for concluding that "truly linguistic communication does not occur unless both signaler and recipient take into account each other's state of mind" (Cheney and Seyfarth 1996, p. 62).
20 Macedonia and Evans (1993) appear to have introduced this term.
21 Like their Old World ancestors, the NWVs appear to have a pair of synonyms in their lexicon.
22 Invoking, as a next step, a notion of *expression* of a psychological state, may provide further explanatory reach without positing communicative intentions. (Expressive behavior is designed, but not necessarily intended, to manifest psychological states.) See Green 2007, Bar-On and Green 2010, and Bar-On 2013.

References

Avramides, A. (1989) *Meaning in Mind: An Examination of a Gricean Account of Language* (Cambridge, MA: MIT).

Bar-On, D. (2013) 'Origins of meaning: Must we 'go Gricean'?' *Mind and Language* **28**: 342–75.

———, and Green, M. (2010) 'Lionspeak: Expression, meaning, and communication,' in E. Rubenstein (ed.) *Self, Language and World* (Atascadero, CA: Ridgeview): 89–106.

Bennett, J. (1976) *Linguistic Behaviour* (Cambridge: Cambridge University Press).

Borg, E. (2006) 'Intention-based semantics,' in Lepore and Smith (eds.) *The Oxford Handbook of the Philosophy of Language* (Oxford: Oxford University Press): 250–66.

Breheny, R. (2006) 'Communication and folk psychology,' *Mind and Language* **21**: 74–107.

Cartmill, E., and Byrne, R. (2010) 'Semantics of primate gestures: Intentional meaning of orangutan gestures,' *Animal Cognition* **13**: 793–804.

Cheney, D., and Seyfarth, R. (1996) 'Function and intention in the calls of non-human primates,' *Proceedings of the British Academy* **88**: 59–76.

Darwin, C. (1872) *The Expression of Emotions in Man and Animals* (London: Harper Collins).

Davidson, D. (1974) 'Belief and the basis of meaning,' repr. in his *Inquiries Into Truth and Interpretation*, 2nd ed. (Oxford: Oxford University Press, 2001): 141–54.

Evans, C., and Evans, L. (2007) 'Representational signaling in birds,' *Biology Letters* **3**: 8–11.

Gillies, M. (1980) 'The role of carbon dioxide in host finding by mosquitoes (*Diptera: Culicudae*): A review,' *Bulletin of Entomological Research* **70**: 525–32.

Glüer, K., and Pagin, P. (2003) 'Meaning theory and autistic speakers,' *Mind and Language* **18**: 23–51.

Green, M. (2009) 'Speech acts, the Handicap Principle and the expression of psychological states,' *Mind & Language* **24**: 139–63.

——— (2007) *Self-Expression* (Oxford: Clarendon Press).

——— (1999) 'Attitude ascription's affinity to measurement,' *International Journal of Philosophical Studies* **7**: 323–48.

Grice, H. P. (1957) 'Meaning' repr. in Grice (1989): 213–23.

——— (1989) *Studies in the Way of Words* (Harvard).

Horisk, C., and Cocroft, R. (2013) 'Animal signals: Always influence, sometimes information,' in U. Stegman (ed.) *Animal Communication Theory: Information and Influence* (Cambridge: Cambridge University Press): 259–78.

Jackendoff, R. (1987) *Consciousness and the Computational Mind* (Cambridge: MIT Press).

Jackendoff, R. (1999) 'Possible stages in the evolution of the language capacity,' *Trends in Cognitive Science* **3**: 272–9.

Legendre, F., Marting, P., and Cocroft, R. (2012) 'Competitive masking of vibrational signals during mate searching in a treehopper,' *Animal Behaviour* **83**: 361–8.

Loar, B. (1981) *Mind and Meaning* (Cambridge: Cambridge University Press).

Macedonia, J. M., and Evans, C. (1993) 'Variation among mammalian alarm call systems and the problem of meaning in animal signals,' *Ethology* **93**: 177–197.

Mann, M., and Cummings, M. (2012) 'Poison frog colors are honest signals of toxicity, particularly for bird predators,' *American Naturalist* **179**: E1–E14.

Marek, P., Papaj, D., Yeager, J., Molina, S., and W. Moore (2011) 'Bioluminescent aposematism in millipedes,' *Current Biology* **21**: R680–R681.

Maynard Smith, J., and Harper, W. (2004) *Animal Signals* (Oxford: Oxford University Press).

Millikan, R. (1996) 'Pushmi-pullyu representations,' in J. Tomberlin (ed.) *Philosophical Perspectives* IX (Atascadero CA: Ridgeview Publishing): 185–200.

Neale, S. (1992) 'Paul Grice and the philosophy of language,' *Linguistics and Philosophy* **15**: 509–559.

Poulton, E. (1880) *The Colours of Animals* (New York: Appleton & Company).

Price, T., Wadewitz, P., Cheney, D., Seyfarth, R., Hammerschnidt, K., and Fischer, J. (2015) 'Vervets revisited: A quantitative analysis of alarm call structure and context specificity,' *Scientific Reports* **5**: 1–11.

Quaranta, A., Siniscalchi, M., and Vallortigara, G. (2007) 'Asymmetric tail-wagging responses by dogs to different emotive stimuli,' *Current Biology* **17**: R199–R201.

Reboul, A. (2007) "Does the Gricean distinction between natural and non-natural meaning exhaustively account for all instances of communication?" *Pragmatics & Cognition* **15**: 253–76.

Ruxton, G., Sherratt, T., and Speed, M. (2004) *Avoiding Attack: The Evolutionary Ecology of Crypsis, Warning Signals, and Mimicry* (Oxford: Oxford University Press).

Sayigh, L., Esch, C., Wells, R., and Janik, V. (2007) 'Facts about signature whistles of bottlenose dolphins *Tursiops truncatus*,' *Animal Behaviour* **74**: 1631–42.

Schiffer, S. (1982) 'Intention-based semantics,' *Notre Dame Journal of Formal Logic* **23**: 119–56.

——— (1972) *Meaning* (Oxford: Oxford University Press).

Silliero-Zubiri, C., and Macdonald, D. (1998) 'Scent-marking and territorial behaviour of Ethiopian wolves *Canis simensis*,' *Journal of Zoology London* **245**: 351–61.

Siniscalchi, M., Lusito, R., Vallortigara, G., and Quantara, A. (2013) 'Seeing left- or right-asymmetric tail wagging produces different emotional responses in dogs,' *Current Biology* **23**: 2279–82.

Templeton, J., Greene, E., and Davis, K. (2008) 'Allometry of alarm calls: Black-capped chickadees encode information about predator size,' *Science* **308**: 1934–7.

Vlach, F. (1981) 'Speaker's meaning,' *Linguistics and Philosophy* **4**: 359–91.

30

THE CONTENT OF ANIMAL SIGNALS

Ulrich Stegmann

Animal signals are usually defined as structures or behaviors that evolved in order to carry information about the sender or the environment. They are believed to represent or indicate things; they have some kind of "content". The nature of that content or information is not well understood, however. Most researchers of animal communication gravitate towards quantitative information concepts when pressed, but some regard information as awkward baggage that had better be jettisoned. In philosophy, animal signals have mostly figured as a foil for discussing human language or as occasional examples in naturalistic accounts of information and representation. They became the subject of focused inquiries over the last decade or so.

This chapter surveys current views about the content of animal signals. The views are drawn from both the ethological and the philosophical literature. Some of them have not been explicitly articulated before, especially the views in animal behavior studies. For simplicity, I formulate the views in terms of necessary and sufficient conditions and presuppose that certain behaviors mean/indicate something or other. This allows focusing on what makes a signal mean/indicate one thing *rather* than another (i.e. the conditions for content determination).

From human communication to animal signals

Human linguistic communication is usually understood in broadly Gricean terms. On this view, linguistic communication involves not only sentences and their meanings, but also complex mental states, especially intentions to communicate and the ability to attribute mental states to others. In addition, linguistic communication tends to serve as a general paradigm for communication and therefore often informs views on animals. Accordingly, genuine communication in animals is sometimes taken to require communicative intentions and mental state attributions; for otherwise, signals seem little more than automatic manifestations of affective states (Dennett 1983). But Gricean communication demands cognitive sophistication. Some philosophers therefore distinguish between a strong and a weak kind of communication. The strong kind is Gricean communication and the weak kind is information transfer. Animal communication is then regarded as an instance of the latter, in which certain behaviors and structures merely have the biological function to convey information (e.g. Bennett 1976; Green 2007).

The distinction between Gricean communication and information transfer is useful. But it should not be confused with the claim that human and animal communication diverge neatly.

First, even if communicative intentions are unnecessary, animal receivers may need mental representations in order to decode signal content (Tetzlaff and Rey 2009) or motivate action (Rescorla 2013). Second, the general absence in animals of mental abilities required for Gricean communication is contested. Gestural communication in many nonhuman primates, for instance, is under the sender's volitional control (Pika et al. 2007) and conveys a range of meanings (Hobaiter and Byrne 2014). Evidence for control over auditory signal production is at least mixed (e.g. Fedurek and Slocombe 2011; Schel et al. 2013). A complex picture emerges with respect to mental state attributions (e.g. Fedurek and Slocombe 2011; Andrews 2012; Keefner 2016).

Irrespective of these complications, the "signaling model" (Green 2007) chimes with the dominant view in animal behavior studies. On this view, animals communicate by conveying information from senders to receivers, with signals as the physical vehicles by which information is conveyed, and receivers acting on the basis of the information received (e.g. Bradbury and Vehrencamp 2011). The waggle dance of honeybees, for example, does not simply elicit receiver responses. Instead, the dance is believed to convey specific information about the location of a resource to recruits, which then depart in that direction *because* they have been so informed. The informational view of animal communication is entrenched in contemporary animal behavior studies: signals are routinely defined in terms of information (e.g. Otte 1974), several classifications of signals are based on their purported information content,[1] and the evolutionary origin and maintenance of signaling systems is taken to hinge on signals conveying (true) information.[2]

Yet, what is information supposed to be in this context? Some researchers are explicit in asserting that a signal carries information in the sense that it is *about something* or *has content*, and must therefore be distinguished from information in the quantitative sense (e.g. Halliday 1983). But such characterizations are too vague and abstract for some critics of the information view (e.g. Rendall et al. 2009). Moreover, there exists no general and uncontroversial notion of content or information that one could simply apply to animal signals. The informational edifice therefore rests on poorly understood foundations.

Signal content in the ethological literature

In the ethological literature, the term "information" is often used interchangeably with what receivers come to know, infer, or predict when perceiving a signal (e.g. Seyfarth et al. 2010). And acquiring knowledge from signals is often described as reducing a receiver's uncertainty (Wiley 1983; Seyfarth and Cheney 2003; Bergstrom and Rosvall 2011; Wheeler et al. 2011). These practices suggest a first family of views about the content (X) of animal signals (S):

[1] S's content is X iff R infers/predicts/comes to know/becomes more confident that X, given S

Consider a female firefly (R) perceiving a male's light pulse (S). According to [1], the information carried by S depends on what the female infers from it. Plausibly she infers from S that there is a male conspecific willing to mate. The phrase following the *that*-clause therefore describes the content of S. Encouragingly, this is just the kind of content that ethologists have actually attributed to male light pulses: "Here I am in time and space, a sexually mature male of species X that is ready to mate" (Lloyd 1966, p. 69).

However, [1] appeals to several distinct processes. Becoming more confident about X, for instance, does not imply knowing that X is true. Also, inferring and predicting is sometimes taken to include automatic responses based on reflexive associations and evolved dispositions (e.g. Krebs and Dawkins 1984). So, [1] is much too vague to specify the content of animal signals.

And simply settling on one of the processes will not do. A principled argument is required as to why one of the processes, rather than some other, qualifies as determining signal content.

There is evidence that some signals elicit mental representations in receivers. Rather than triggering a reflexive response, these so-called "representational" (Evans and Evans 2007) or "conceptual" signals (Zuberbühler et al. 1999) are assumed to have their effects on receivers via internal representations. Some authors go a step further and distinguish informational from non-informational interactions along these lines. Accordingly, a structure or behavior carries information *only* if it elicits a thought or mental image in the receiver, not if it triggers a reflexive response. The content of signals then tends to be identified with the content of the internal representation (Maynard Smith and Harper 2003; Seyfarth and Cheney 2003). Interestingly, the critics of the informational view have also sought to distinguish between informational and non-informational interactions, and they come to broadly similar conclusions: interactions are informational if the receiver response relies on cortical as opposed to non-cortical processing (Rendall et al. 2009), or on cognitive as opposed to non-cognitive processing (Owings and Morton 1998). In short, at least some of the proponents and opponents of the information view agree to the extent that information is exchanged only if the receiver processes what it perceives by means of a higher-order mechanism. This suggests another group of views about content:

[2] S's content is X iff S elicits in R a cognitive or cortical representation of X/thought of X/ mental image of X

Again, [2] offers several distinct higher-order mechanisms (e.g. cognitive processing does not imply mental imagery), and it is unclear which of these might determine signal content. Furthermore, organisms relying on lower-order mechanisms will not qualify as exchanging information. And this implication does not sit well with the usual understanding of communication in animal behavior studies.

Faced with these challenges, it may be tempting to seek refuge in quantitative frameworks. Two quantities, entropy and mutual information, have become particularly influential in ethology (e.g. Halliday 1983; Seyfarth et al. 2010; Wheeler et al. 2011). Shannon entropy is a measure of the number of different states, and their probabilities, that a system can assume. Systems with many, equally possible states (e.g. the six sides of fair dice) are associated with a higher degree of uncertainty about the system's current state than systems with few possible states, especially if one is very likely (e.g. bank vaults being locked/unlocked). Mutual information captures the statistical association between two such systems. In the 1950s and 1960s, several studies estimated the mutual information between signals and receiver responses (see Halliday 1983). However, since signals are not normally taken to be about their effects on receivers, this measure ("transmitted information", Wiley 1983) cannot capture a signal's information content. Closer to the target is the mutual information between signals and the states they are about ("broadcast information", Wiley 1983). Hence the following idea:

[3] S's content is X iff S has non-zero mutual information with X

However, Shannon's quantities are not equivalent to (or a measure of) information in the colloquial sense of content, a point acknowledged by several early ethologists. One reason is that the quantities average across all the states a system can have, whereas content in the colloquial sense is not an average (Dretske 1981). Another reason is that S's reducing R's uncertainty about X is a three-term relation (involving S, R, and X), whereas mutual information is only a two-term relation between S and X.

Nowadays the preferred quantitative framework in animal behavior studies is statistical decision theory (SDT) (Bradbury and Vehrencamp 2011). Its basic idea is that animals can use current perceptions to update their prior knowledge about events. Background knowledge stems from earlier experiences and/or evolutionary history. SDT employs Bayes' theorem to derive posterior probabilities. The difference between posterior and prior probabilities is understood as measuring the animal's uncertainty reduction about the state whose probability is being updated. The idea might be captured as follows:

[4] *S*'s content is *X* iff *S* updates *R*'s expectation about *X*

Bayesian probabilities are traditionally understood as degrees of belief. This raises the question of the nature of beliefs in, say, invertebrates and organisms lacking nervous systems. Perhaps to avoid these issues, SDT remains explicitly neutral about the mechanisms of updating (e.g. Bradbury and Vehrencamp 2011). But this strategy raises another problem. If SDT is simply employed as a predictive tool, then it justifies construing *S* merely *as if* having content.[3]

Signal content as natural information

Philosophers tend to regard the content of animal signals as an instance of either natural or semantic information.[4] These two types of information are distinguished with respect to whether or not they allow for having false contents. Falsity requires that something can carry the information that *p* despite it's being the case that not-*p*. For instance, the belief that it is Friday carries the information that *it is Friday*, which may or may not be true (semantic information). Tree rings, by contrast, are standard examples of natural information. Six tree rings indicate that the tree is six years old, because the tree would normally not have six rings unless it actually was six years old.

Just as tree rings are reliably caused by an annual period of slow growth, animal signals are often produced reliably in response to certain events or objects, e.g. predators. And so, just as tree rings indicate age, animal signals indicate various events or objects. This core idea has been developed in different ways. Some authors rely on strong versions of natural information, according to which one state indicates another only if the first could not obtain without the second; a signal thus guarantees that the indicated state obtains (Dretske 1981; Adams and Beighley 2013). But most commentators believe that such strict relations rarely obtain. Another group of theories therefore allow that a state can carry information about another even if the first can obtain without the second (Millikan 2004; Shea 2007; Skyrms 2010). A well-articulated theory of this sort is defended by Scarantino (2015).

A centerpiece of Scarantino's theory of natural information is that one state carries information about another when the first makes the second more likely (or less likely):

> Incremental Natural Information (INI): r's being G carries incremental natural information about s's being F, relative to background data d, if and only if p(s is F | r is G & d) ≠ p(s is F | d)
>
> (Scarantino 2015, p. 423)

The key idea can be put as follows. Entity *s* has a certain prior probability of being *F* given some background data. Then *r* is observed to be *G*. This fact may or may not make a difference as to whether *s* is *F*. If it does make a difference to the probability of *s*'s being *F* (by making it more likely, or less likely, that *s* is *F*), then *r*'s being *G* carries information about *s*'s being *F*. Notice that the information content of r's being G is not (only) that s is F. This is because the occurrence of a state of affairs usually affects the probabilities of many states rather than just one. Scarantino's formal definition of information content is too complex to reproduce here; suffice it to say that it includes three features: the identity of the states whose probabilities are changed, the amount of change, and their probabilities after the change. Scarantino holds that animal signals carry information in this sense. For instance, for vervet monkeys, there is always a certain background probability that an eagle approaches. But hearing an eagle-alarm call makes that event much more likely. Eagle alarm-calls therefore carry incremental information about the presence of eagles. Hence:

[5] S's content is X iff S changes the probability of X

Animal signals *do* change the probabilities of other states. However, I am not convinced that this is the kind of information which scientists actually attribute to signals and which figures in their explanations and predictions (Stegmann 2015). First, INI-contents are much broader than the contents attributed by ethologists. For instance, the content ethologists attribute to the eagle-alarm calls of vervet monkeys is that an eagle is approaching. But their INI-content includes an array of additional states, e.g. the eagle having been detected, the eagle's foraging success being reduced, the caller interrupting foraging, the receiver taking evasive action, and so on.

Second, signals carry weak natural information if they are sometimes produced in the absence of the states whose probabilities they change. But are signal *tokens* produced in the absence of the correlated state informative? If yes, then they would appear to carry the information that p despite not-p and, hence, false information. This would contradict the widely held view that natural information cannot be false (e.g. Dretske 1981; Millikan 2004; Adams and Beighley 2013). One might claim, instead, that the information is not actually p alone, but rather a disjunction of all states causing or correlating with the signal, i.e. $<p$ or q or ... $>$. This disjunctive content is true even if, in a particular instance, p does not obtain (Adams and Beighley 2013). This move, however, spells trouble for signals whose contents are taken to be specific (see above). A third option is to deny that such tokens carry any natural information (Millikan 2004). But in that case, carrying information cannot merely be a matter of being an instance of a probabilistically related type, contradicting the very notion of weak natural information (Stegmann 2015). Furthermore, this option is at odds with the ethological practice of classifying such signals as indicating falsely or "dishonestly" (e.g. Maynard Smith and Harper 2003).

Let us step back from these objections and take a broader look. It has been argued that there exists a group of signals that do more than simply carry natural information. So-called "expressive behaviors" (Bar-On and Green 2010) are designed to "express" or "show" an animal's affective states. Affective states are directed towards events or objects, which are their non-propositional intentional objects (e.g. excitement *about* food). Expressive behaviors are said to carry natural information about the things that reliably cause them. But they are also "precursor[s] of linguistic behavior" (Bar-On and Green 2010, p. 104), both because they express states with intentional objects and because they are designed to elicit appropriate receiver responses. One might therefore construe expressive behaviors as having a kind of content:

[6] S's content is X if S is designed to express X, where X = $<$affective state directed at non-propositional intentional object$>$

On this reading, the content of an (expressive) signal is a certain mental state and its intentional object. In a similar vein, Proust (2016) suggests that mental states called "affordance-sensings" mediate the exchange of animal signals. Affordances are, roughly, the behavioral opportunities that a situation allows or requires. Signals convey affordances; they do not refer to states in the world.

It may be objected that even signals expressing affective states can carry propositional content. Arguably, one must distinguish between (1) signal production, which is the expression of an affective state; and (2) the product (signal) itself, which could have propositional content. McAninsh et al. (2009) make this point and argue that at least some animal signals are of this kind. This brings us to theories according to which the content of animal signals is an instance of semantic information or, equivalently, representational content.

Signal content as semantic information

Dretske (1988) proposed a general theory of representational content, according to which a state represents another just in case it has the function to carry natural information about the other. Hence:

[7] *S*'s content is *X* iff *S* has the biological function to carry natural information about *X*

The appeal to function avoids the ubiquity worry raised against probabilistic accounts. But other challenges emerge. One is that many signals do not guarantee that the represented state obtains or even make it likely. Furthermore, some signals evolved in order to "deceive" receivers, i.e. to represent falsehoods, and [7] cannot account for their content. Predatory fireflies, for instance, mimic the light pulses sent by females of other species and consequently lure males of those species to their deaths. For the predators' signals to falsely represent the presence of females, they would need to have evolved in order to indicate the presence of females. But they systematically fail to achieve that function. So probably their function is to mislead males. But then they do not represent females.

While Dretske's (1988) account ties content exclusively to the signal producer, Millikan's account (2004) includes the receiver. Signal-*producing* mechanisms (in the sender) evolved in order to issue signals in response to certain conditions, so that variations in the signals' physical features map to variations in the conditions. The time and location of a beaver's tail splash, for example, correspond to present danger, just as the specific features of a bee's waggle dance correspond to a certain location relative to the hive. Signal-*consuming* mechanisms (in the receiver) evolved to respond with behaviors that benefit both sender and receiver, such as taking cover or flying to the signaled location. Another important component of Millikan's theory are "normal conditions". This is a technical term for the states of affairs that obtain when mechanisms achieve their functions in the way that explains the mechanisms' evolution, rather than by accidental means. For instance, the normal condition of the consuming mechanism of beaver tail-splashes is the presence of danger, because this co-occurrence obtains when the mechanism achieves its function in the way that explains its evolution. Recall that this co-occurrence is also the function of the tail-splash producing mechanisms. So, the normal condition of a consuming mechanism is that the producing mechanism achieves its function, and vice versa; signal-producing and -consuming devices must "cooperate" in this manner. With these elements in place, Millikan identifies representational content as the state of affairs to which the signal evolved to correspond and whose co-occurrence with the signal is the normal condition of the consuming device. The following is meant to capture Millikan's proposal:

[8] *S*'s content is *X* iff (1) *X* is the state to which *S* evolved to correspond and (2) *S*'s co-occurrence with *X* is the normal condition of the consuming mechanism

Millikan's theory reconstructs the specificity of many signals. For instance, in the case of the light pulses of male fireflies, X is the presence of a male firefly ready to mate. [8] also accounts for the possibility that signals can be true or false; they are true when the producing mechanism achieves its function and false when it does not. Hence, some authors are sympathetic to this account (Allen and Saidel 1998; Godfrey-Smith 2013; Artiga 2014).

Deceptive signals remain problematic, however. The producing mechanism of the predatory firefly achieves its function when it produces a mimicking signal in the presence of itself, the predator. But the co-occurrence of female-type light pulses with a predator is not the normal condition of the males' consuming mechanism; it is not the kind of circumstance under which males' responses resulted in matings. The predators' light pulses therefore do not belong to a cooperative system, and hence lack representational content (Stegmann 2009). However, Artiga (2014) maintains that the light pulses can be individuated so that they do belong to a cooperative system. Another move is to accept the argument's conclusion but maintain that it is unproblematic: essentially, males just mistake content-free mimics for meaningful models (Adams and Beighley 2013; Artiga 2014).

I prefer to abandon Millikan's cooperation requirement and simply let receivers determine signal content (Stegmann 2009, 2013). Here is my proposal:

[9] S's content is X iff (1) S elicits a response B in a receiver and (2) the receiver acquired its B-disposition due to past S-tokens that co-occurred with Xs

S is a token structure or behavior; B is a response, behavioral or other; and receivers acquire their responses through learning and/or evolution. Consider firefly signals. A female-type light pulse (S) prompts a male to approach (B), and the male acquired this disposition due to an evolutionary process in which past light pulses of this kind co-occurred with conspecific females (X). The content of the light pulse is therefore the presence of a conspecific female. Crucially, the light pulse has this content independently of whether it was produced by a conspecific female or by a predator. This is because the content is determined only by a historical fact about the receiver. It is worth noting that the co-occurrence of S and X can be a correlation, as in this example, or a one-off coincidence, as in one-trial learning.

One implication of [9] is that signals have specific contents only in virtue of, and relative to, certain receivers. This implication explains why the same signal can mean different things to different receivers (Smith 1977; Stegmann 2009) and renders [9] applicable to *cues*, as well. Furthermore, content attributions become testable. To claim that "this female-type light pulse *signals* the presence of a female" is equivalent to claiming that "the presence of a female is the *acquisition condition* of the receiver's response". Whether or not the latter claim is true can be tested. Finally, [9] renders content attributions explanatory. For example, the presence of females (the acquisition condition/content) explains why male fireflies tend to approach female-type light pulses.

Despite these attractions, [9] faces challenges, like the demarcation of acquisition conditions and complications due to stimulus categorizations by receivers. It is also vulnerable to some of the objections raised against Millikan's theory. Among the latter are the counterintuitive consequences when signals are not triggered by S, but rather by a state Y that shares a common cause with S (Godfrey-Smith 2013), or the view that representational content achieves no explanatory gain over and above correlations (as Rescorla 2013 has argued with respect to bees). Nevertheless, I believe that [9] is a promising basis for developing a theory of signal content.[5]

Notes

1 For instance, the classification based on whether the information is about the sender or a third party (e.g. Halliday 1983; Krebs and Dawkins 1984), or the classification distinguishing between "indices", "icons", and "symbols" (Maynard Smith and Harper 2003).
2 If signals carried (mostly) false information, then responding to them would not be an evolutionarily stable strategy for receivers (Maynard Smith and Harper 2003).
3 Kristin Andrews (pers. comm.) notes that one might understand probabilities in terms of "degrees of cognitive representations" while remaining neutral about whether those cognitive representations are beliefs.
4 The distinction originated with Grice's distinction between "natural" and "non-natural" meaning.
5 For valuable comments, I thank Kristin Andrews and the audience of the 30th Bar Hillel International Workshop on *Information and its Role in Science*.

Further reading

An illuminating, early philosophical treatment of animal communication is J. Bennett, *Linguistic Behaviour* (Cambridge: Cambridge University Press, 1976), §62. According to R. G. Millikan, *The Varieties of Meaning* (Cambridge, MA: MIT Press, 2004), animal signals have representational content. For A. Scarantino, "Information as a Probabilistic Difference Maker," *Australasian Journal of Philosophy* 93 (2015): 419–43, they carry natural information. J. Bradbury and S. Vehrencamp, *Principles of Animal Communication* (Sunderland, MA: Sinauer, 2011) is the principal textbook in the information tradition. Contributors from different fields discuss informational and non-informational accounts in U. Stegmann (ed.), *Animal Communication Theory: Information and Influence* (Cambridge: Cambridge University Press, 2013).

References

Adams, F., and Beighley, S. (2013) "Information, meaning, and animal communication," in U. Stegmann (ed.), *Animal Communication Theory: Information and Influence*, Cambridge: Cambridge University Press.

Allen, C., and Saidel, E. (1998) "The evolution of reference," in D. Cummins and C. Allen (eds.), *The Evolution of Mind*, New York: Oxford University Press, pp. 183–203.

Andrews, K. (2012) *Do Apes Read Minds?* Cambridge, MA: MIT Press.

Artiga, M. (2014) "Signaling without cooperation," *Biology and Philosophy* 29: 357–78.

Bar-On, D., and Green, M. (2010) "Lionspeak: Communication, expression and meaning," in J. O'Shea and E. Rubenstein (eds.), *Self, Language, and World: Problems From Kant, Sellars, and Rosenberg: In Memory of Jay F. Rosenberg*, Atascadero, CA: Ridgeview Publishing Co.

Bennett, J. (1976) *Linguistic Behaviour*, Cambridge: Cambridge University Press.

Bergstrom, C. T., and Rosvall, M. (2011) "The transmission sense of information," *Biology and Philosophy* 26: 159–76.

Bradbury, J. W., and Vehrencamp, S. L. (2011) *Principles of Animal Communication*, Sunderland, MA: Sinauer Associates.

Dennett, D. C. (1983) "Intentional systems in cognitive ethology: The 'Panglossian Paradigm' defended," *The Behavioral and Brain Sciences* 6: 343–90.

Dretske, F. (1981) *Knowledge and the Flow of Information*, Cambridge, MA: MIT Press.

Dretske, F. (1988) *Explaining Behavior: Reasons in a World of Causes*, Cambridge, MA: MIT Press.

Evans, C. S., and Evans, L. (2007) "Representational signalling in birds," *Biology Letters* 3: 8–11.

Fedurek, P., and Slocombe, K. E. (2011) "Primate vocal communication: A useful tool for understanding human speech and language evolution?" *Human Biology* 82: 153–73.

Godfrey-Smith, P. (2013) "Signals, icons, and beliefs," in J. Kingsbury, D. Ryder and K. Williford (eds.), *Millikan and Her Critics*, Chichester: Wiley-Blackwell, pp. 41–58.

Green, M. (2007) *Self-expression*, Oxford: Oxford University Press.

Halliday, T. (1983) "Information and communication," in T. Halliday and P. J. B. Slater (eds.), *Animal Behaviour, Vol. 2: Communication*, Oxford: Blackwell Scientific, pp. 43–81.

Hobaiter, C., and Byrne, R. W. (2014) "The meanings of chimpanzee gestures," *Current Biology* 24: 1596–600.

Keefner, A. (2016) "Corvids infer the mental states of conspecifics," *Biology & Philosophy* 31: 267–81.

Krebs, J. R., and Dawkins, R. (1984) "Animal signals: Mind-reading and manipulation," in J. R. Krebs and N. B. Davies (eds.), *Behavioural Ecology: An Evolutionary Approach*, Oxford: Blackwell, pp. 380–402.

Lloyd, J. E. (1966) "Studies on the flash communication system in Photinus fireflies," *Miscellaneous Publications, Museum of Zoology, University of Michigan* 130: 1–95.

McAninsh, A., Goodrich, G., and Allen, C. (2009) "Animal communication and neo-expressivism," in R. W. Lurz (ed.), *Philosophy of Animal Minds: New Essays on Animal Thought and Conciousness*, Cambridge: Cambridge University Press, pp. 128–44.

Maynard Smith, J., and Harper, D. (2003) *Animal Signals*, Oxford: Oxford University Press.

Millikan, R. G. (2004) *The Varieties of Meaning*, Cambridge, MA: MIT Press.

Otte, D. (1974) "Effects and functions in the evolution of signaling systems," *Annual Review of Ecology and Systematics* 5: 385–417.

Owings, D. H., and Morton, E. S. (1998) *Animal Vocal Communication: A New Approach*, Cambridge: Cambridge University Press.

Pika, S., Liebal, K., Call, J., and Tomasello, M. (2007) "The gestural communication of apes," in K. Liebal, C. Müller and S. Pika (eds.), *Gestural Communication in Nonhuman and Human Primates*, Amsterdam: John Benjamins, pp. 37–51.

Proust, J. (2016) "The evolution of communication and metacommunication in primates," *Mind and Language* 31: 177–203.

Rendall, D., Owren, M. J., and Ryan, M. J. (2009) "What do animal signals mean?" *Animal Behaviour* 78: 233–40.

Rescorla, M. (2013) "Millikan on honeybee navigation and communication," in J. Kingsbury, D. Ryder and K. Williford (eds.), *Millikan and Her Critics*, Chichester: Wiley-Blackwell, pp. 87–102.

Scarantino, A. (2015) "Information as a probabilistic difference maker," *Australasian Journal of Philosophy* 93: 419–43.

Schel, A. M., Townsend, S. W., Machanda, Z., Zuberbühler, K., and Slocombe, K. E. (2013) "Chimpanzee alarm call production meets key criteria for intentionality," *PLoS ONE* 8: e76674.

Seyfarth, R. M., and Cheney, D. L. (2003) "Signalers and receivers in animal communication," *Annual Review of Psychology* 54: 145–73.

Seyfarth, R. M., Cheney, D. L., Bergman, T., Fischer, J., Zuberbühler, K., and Hammerschmidt, K. (2010) "The central importance of information in studies of animal communication," *Animal Behaviour* 80: 3–8.

Shea, N. (2007) "Consumers need information: Supplementing teleosemantics with an input condition," *Philosophy and Phenomenological Research* 75: 404–35.

Skyrms, B. (2010) *Signals: Evolution, Learning, and Information*, Oxford: Oxford University Press.

Smith, W. J. (1977) *The Behaviour of Communication. An Ethological Approach*, Cambridge, MA: Harvard University Press.

Stegmann, U. E. (2009) "A consumer-based teleosemantics for animal signals," *Philosophy of Science* 76: 864–75.

Stegmann, U. E. (2013) "A primer on information and influence in animal communication," in U. E. Stegmann (ed.), *Animal Communication Theory: Information and Influence*, Cambridge: Cambridge University Press, pp. 1–39.

Stegmann, U. E. (2015) "Prospects for probabilistic theories of natural information," *Erkenntnis* 80: 869–93.

Tetzlaff, M., and Rey, G. (2009) "Systematicity and intentional realism in honeybee navigation," in R. W. Lurz (ed.), *The Philosophy of Animal Minds*, Cambridge: Cambridge University Press, pp. 72–88.

Wheeler, B. C., Searcy, W. A., Christiansen, M. H., Corballis, M. C., Fischer, J., Grüter, C., Margoliash, D., Owren, M. J., Price, T., Seyfarth, R., and Wild, M. (2011) "Communication," in R. Menzel and J. Fischer (eds.), *Animal Thinking: Contemporary Issues in Comparative Cognition*, Cambridge, MA: MIT Press, pp. 187–205.

Wiley, R. H. (1983) "The evolution of communication: Information and manipulation," in T. R. Halliday and P. J. B. Slater (eds.), *Animal Behaviour, Vol. 2: Communication*, Oxford: Blackwell, pp. 156–89.

Zuberbühler, K., Cheney, D. L., and Seyfarth, R. M. (1999) "Conceptual semantics in a nonhuman primate," *Journal of Comparative Psychology* 113: 33–42.

31

INTENTIONALITY AND FLEXIBILITY IN ANIMAL COMMUNICATION

Christine Sievers, Markus Wild, and Thibaud Gruber[1]

The question of whether nonhuman animals participate in intentional communication has become central in the comparative research on animal communication. Current research has focused on the signaler displaying intentional behavior (Townsend et al. 2016) mostly by applying the features of the concept of *intentional signals* (Call and Tomasello 2007; Liebal et al. 2014). Here, we will show that current empirical evidence may pick out a signaler's informative and communicative intention, and a recipient's ability to understand "the meaning of the signal" linked to the signaler's intentions, only if researchers adopt a Neo-Gricean definition of intentional communication that views communication as fundamentally inferential. However, adopting such an approach happens mainly for reasons of methodological access to intentional communication in animals and does not exclude calling out to non-inferential accounts of communication, such as the one developed by Millikan (2005).

Furthermore, we will stress that the commonly proposed behavioral criteria for intentional communication focus on the signaler's behavior and therefore determine the presence of *intentional behavior* by the signaler. However, any criteria for intentional communication should also take into account the recipient's response, which must also display instances of intentional behavior. There are two reasons for doing so. First, the recipient's response is a constitutive part of communicative interaction, sign use, and the very nature of a sign (Millikan 2005). This holds for both animal and human communication and for both signals and linguistic utterances. We call this reason the *constitutive reason*. Second, not integrating the recipient's responses nor attempting to link those to the signaler's communicative behavior makes it difficult to evaluate whether recipients merely display instances of decision-making (Wheeler and Fischer 2012), independently of the signaler's potential goal and intentional behavior and the signal's meaning, rather than truly engage in intentional communication. To exclude these cases, we need a framework that allows determining whether signalers and recipients attend to each other's behavior and interact in a flexible, voluntary manner, as evidenced in humans. We call this reason the *methodological reason*.

We will explore both reasons in more details in Section 2. However, before we do so, we recall the main lines of the Gricean account of human communication made prominent in animal communication research by Dennett's (1983) influential paper. We will analyze its shortcomings and lay out Millikan's non-Gricean account of intentional communication in Section 2 to justify implementing an analysis of the recipient's behavior in animal communication interactions in Sections 3 and 4. We illustrate this analysis with a few examples from the animal communication literature.

1 Empirical research on intentional communication in nonhuman primates: the Gricean approach and its limitations for animal communication

Whether nonhuman primates communicate intentionally, that is, whether they rely on intentions, such as goals and beliefs about goals and knowledge states of the recipient, when they produce signals (Tomasello 2008; Liebal et al. 2014; Townsend et al. 2016), has attracted much attention recently in the comparative research on animal communication. This is in part due to the parallels that can be made with human communication (Grice 1957; Sperber and Wilson 1995).

Currently, this question is empirically mostly addressed by identifying so-called *intentional signals*. This term denotes signals intentionally (i.e. goal-directed) produced as opposed to cases where the signaler may not have voluntary control over signal production (e.g. when triggered by its emotional state). While authors have stressed different aspects of potentially intentional signals (Call and Tomasello 2007; Liebal et al. 2004; Leavens et al. 2005), they converge on two central criteria, the context and the timing of the signal behavior.

First, for a signal to be produced intentionally, the signaler must produce the signal for an audience, that is in a *social context*. Empirically, this implies that the signaler displays audience-directed behavior, such as checking the attentional state of the recipient, and audience-specific signals, such as producing the signal to allies but not foes.

Second, the signaler must display response-waiting after signal production, i.e. it must monitor the intended recipient's behavior. This is because signalers are interested in whether their goal has been fulfilled or not. If not, the signaler is expected to display signs of persistence and/or elaboration (Tomasello 2008; Leavens et al. 2010; Cartmill and Byrne 2007; Russon and Andrews 2010; Genty et al. 2014).

In theoretical works on intentional communication, Grice (1957) described what it takes for a situation of triangular communication (i.e. communicating something to someone via a signal, Hurford 2007) to be successful such that signalers successfully deliver the message they intended to deliver, and recipients understand that message. The signaler has to display two intentions involved in signal production (see Moore 2016b):

(i) S utters x intending A to produce a particular response r.

and

(ii) S utters x intending A to recognize that S intends (i).

The first intention is often labeled the *informative intention*: the signaler intends to inform the audience about something. To do so, they produce signal x because it serves the purpose of conveying the information via its meaning. The audience's response here can be communicative or not. The first two features of intentional signals relied upon by comparative research very well pick out such a potential informative intention via the proposed empirical criteria: the signal is used socially, and response waiting is displayed.

The second intention of importance is often labeled the *communicative intention* of the signaler. This communicative intention makes it *overt* to the audience that the produced meaningful signal is important enough to extract because it was intentionally provided by the signaler; this is often referred to as *ostensive* or *overtly intentional* communication (Sperber and Wilson 1995; Scott-Phillips 2015a).

These two features of intentional communication are both about the signaler, but this is not sufficient for labeling a communicative situation an instance of intentional communication. Both signalers and recipients have to participate flexibly and voluntarily in a communicative situation, in order to make the communication successful (Brinck 2001; Carston 2002). Therefore, the recipients must also be able to display particular features. The so-called *Receiver's Capacity* (Scott-Phillips and Kirby 2013: 428) seems especially important:

(iii) the recipient's capacity to infer from evidence presented to her in (i) and (ii) S's intended meaning by uttering x.

It can be isolated empirically by focusing on the recipient's responses and evaluating how they are potentially based on inferences drawn by the recipient from the context and from the signaler's behavior. During human communication, this can be exemplified by the direction in which the signaler gazes (Senju and Csibra 2008; Csibra 2010).

A final but more neglected aspect of intentional communication stressed by Grice (1975) is that communication can be viewed as a cooperative act. Thus, communication can only be successful if all participants *attend to each other* (Brinck 2001) to get the intended message transmitted correctly. Therefore, we need an additional feature to represent Gricean communication such as:

(iv) signaler and recipient flexibly and voluntarily interact with each other.

If signaler and recipient interact flexibly with each other, they will evaluate the communicative behavior of the other and determine how to respond to it to successfully attain their goals and/or communicate their intentions. On a behavioral level, this might cause a turn-taking between participants (Sacks et al. 1974; Levinson 1983; Kimbrough Oller 2000; Wilson and Wilson 2005). The flexible interaction should always be primarily caused by the signal's meaning. Furthermore, this flexible interaction might require being aware of the voluntariness of the behavior of the other as opposed to a signaler just accidently producing a signal (Grice 1982).

As Dennett (1983) pointed out, an individual displaying such an informative and communicative intention must be capable of having mental states, i.e. thoughts about external, non-mental entities in the world, and to metarepresent. Such intentionality comes in reflexive levels. In theory, endless levels of intentionality can be displayed, although they are limited by individuals' cognitive abilities.

In the situation of two signalers' intentions involved in intentional communication, an individual must be capable of displaying second-order intentionality to display informative intentions, that is, the signaler *wants* the audience to *know* about something when producing the signal. Therefore, to ascribe a Gricean informative intention to an individual, the latter must be able to process mental states of the second order. In the original Gricean proposal, where S wants A to know that S has an informative intention (that is, S wants to make the informative intention overt), fourth-order intentionality may even be necessary: the signaler *wants* the audience to *know* that the signaler *wants* the audience to *know* about something by producing the signal.

Such requirement may exclude any nonhuman animal from potentially displaying intentional communication, as it is unclear to what extent other animals, including nonhuman primates, can really take into account each other's mental states (Call and Tomasello 2007). While studies tackling this question bring promising answers (Hare et al. 2000; Crockford et al. 2012; Schel et al. 2013, Liebal et al. 2004), we believe that two additional points must be noted to avoid dismissing *a priori* the idea of nonhuman animals communicating intentionally because of the complex mental processing required to fulfill the Gricean proposal:

(1) The Gricean requirements are requirements for an ideal case of human meaningful and rational communication, but this does not imply that intentional communication in all cases requires such demanding capabilities. They have long been questioned and revised in the philosophy of language and cognitive sciences (Millikan 1984; Moore 2016b; Townsend et al. 2016). In everyday communication, signalers often only want the audience to do something (e.g. to close the window). These utterances are not about the signaler's intention to influence the knowledge state of the recipient, but very simply about the signaler's intention to influence the recipient's behavior, to the point that they only require display of first-order intentionality ('I want you to close the window').

(2) Evidence for a communicative intention might be found in conspecific–directed behavior as simple as gazing: in combination with producing a meaningful signal, it might constitute enough clues to display a communicative intention (Gomez 1994). However, using gaze as an indicator for communicative intentions is debated (Scott-Phillips 2015b and Moore 2016a).

Ultimately, in nonhuman primates, instead of an informative intention, an *imperative* (making someone do something) intention and a communicative intention of second-order intentionality (such as 'S wants the audience to recognize the signal as an expression of a communicative act') is sufficient to ascribe to a signaler the two required intentions for intentional communication.

The proposal laid out here for dealing with the requirements of intentional communication on the signaler's side is summing up a potential re-evaluation of the Gricean framework, and should therefore be labeled a Neo-Gricean approach. This approach emphasizes that proponents of an ostensive-inferential account of intentional communication, such as Grice himself (1957) or Scott-Phillips (2015b), have set the bar too high for cognitive requirements. Ultimately, if one seeks to apply the framework to animal communication, it is wiser not to start with the original Gricean proposal, but rather with a revised Neo-Gricean approach (e.g. Gomez 1994, Moore 2016b).

2 A non-Gricean approach to communication

There are other options apart from a Gricean-inspired approach: Ruth Millikan (1984, 2005, forthcoming), for instance, proposes a perception-based account on communication. Laying out Millikan's account in more detail here will enable us to elaborate on what we previously high-lighted as the constitutive and the methodological reason with respect to identifying intentional communication in nonhuman animals. Millikan rejects Grice's claim that in order to understand what a signaler means, we need to grasp its intended effect. She presents an alternative proposal based on the assumption that the meaning of linguistic signs is determined by their proliferation history, that is, their history of selection and reproduction in a certain domain. To track down the domain of a sign, communicators display perceptual processes rather than inferential ones. Since the meaning of a sign is determined by its proliferation history, and since the domain of a sign can be tracked by perceptual means alone, recognizing the signaler's intentions is not required for understanding what is meant by an utterance. The signaler's inner mental life is not relevant to a receiver who is primarily interested in obtaining information about the world.

According to Millikan, linguistic forms (such as words, syntactic forms, or tonal inflections) are handed down from one person to another because these forms *function* to coordinate receivers' and signalers' behavior. Millikan defines the term *function* here as the kind of effect achieved by the cooperative use of a linguistic form. If the effect is desirable and solves coordination problems, the linguistic form keeps itself in circulation. Millikan calls this kind of function the 'stabilizing function' (Millikan 1984, 2005), which is about equivalent to the semantic meaning of a linguistic form. Linguistic forms with stabilizing functions thus become conventions, and conventions correspond to reproducing lineages of cooperatively used forms. For example, the German word 'Esel' (donkey) has been successfully used often enough to refer in human interactions to one particular species of animal and keeps itself in circulation for this very reason. By becoming a convention, the word 'Esel' serves the function of referring to donkeys whether a signaler intends to do so or not. Unlike animal species, linguistic lineages also frequently acquire new functions without changing their physical forms. Thus, the word 'Esel' might also be used to refer to a stubborn and stupid person. This just creates a new lineage or branch with a stabilizing function. Such novel uses of conventional linguistic forms can be introduced by the signaler's intentions. If the hearer understands the novel use by inferring the signaler's intention, the novel use will then serve as a new coordinating function, either temporarily or permanently. The novel use may also be copied by other signalers, and may in time be directly understood by hearers without the need to unpack the signaler's' intention.

For our purposes, two aspects of Millikan's view on language used in communication are of special importance. First, the recipient does not need to infer any signalers' intentions to understand conventional linguistic forms. The reason for this stems from the fact that the function of linguistic forms is not to point to the signaler's mind but to point to the world (except for words that have the purpose of referring to the signaler's mind, of course). For example, the function of the word 'Esel' is to refer to an animal and not to the signaler's thoughts about this animal. As Millikan puts it, the hearer directly perceives the donkey through the use of the word 'Esel'. If the word is used correctly (i.e. in accordance with its stabilizing function), it carries natural information about donkeys just as donkey shapes, donkey calls, donkey smells, or donkey faces carry natural information about donkeys. By processing this natural information by the various sense modalities, we perceive the object at the source of the natural information in question. In this sense, we perceive objects directly through language (Millikan forthcoming).

Millikan thus departs from Grice's key insight that stimuli that are non-naturally meaningful point to the very intentions that triggered their production in the first place, since she thinks that non-natural (semantic) meaning is on a continuum with natural (informational) meaning. This account is especially compelling for the case of language learning in children, since children are able to learn, use, and understand linguistic forms before they are capable of getting signalers' intentions, and before developing full-fledged mindreading abilities. In Millikan's view, signalers' intentions are not of primary interest for the hearer, and hearers understand utterances non-inferentially by using signals with conventional stabilizing functions.

It is only in problematic cases (such as incorrect, unexpected or novel use of words) that inferences to the signalers' intentions play an important part in successful linguistic communication. In contexts of adult human communication, we always already presuppose that signalers intend to communicate something. In the case of primate communication, however, the more fundamental question arises whether we are dealing with intentional communication or not. Since problematic cases in human communication ask for inferential work on the recipient's side, and since such problematic cases are cases that pose epistemological challenges (e.g. 'What the heck is the signaler talking about?'), we submit that in the case of primate communication, it is necessary to take the recipient's inference to signalers' intentions as a *methodological guide* to answer the question of whether we are confronted with a case of intentional communication or not. This is what we label the methodological reason for adopting an inferential stance of communication.

Another major part of Millikan's cooperative perception-based model of linguistic communication is that the recipient is a constitutive element of a communicative event. We previously outlined this as the *constitutive reason* for taking recipients' behavior into account. In effect, all linguistic forms proliferate and acquire stabilizing functions by being used cooperatively by the signaler and the hearer. Cooperation is successful if the use of a linguistic form is followed by a certain reaction. For instance, when hearing the typical tonal inflection that is associated with a question, the expected reaction is to give an answer. Similarly, when a signaler uses the word 'Esel', the expected reaction of the hearer is to perceive a donkey or to think of a donkey (but not to represent a donkey in the signaler's mind). The reaction of the hearer is therefore part of the linguistic form, because the linguistic form would not have acquired its coordinating function between hearers and signalers if the hearers had not reacted in a certain way often enough for the form to keep itself in circulation. A linguistic convention thus consists in a pattern that includes contributions by both the signaler and the hearer; in fact, the hearer's contribution is as much a part of the convention as the signaler's is (Millikan 2005).

3 The importance of a voluntary, flexible interaction between signaler and recipient

The insight gained from Millikan leads us to investigate animal communication not by considering Gricean communicative intentions, but instead by considering feature (iv) of intentional communication, namely the flexible interaction between the participants of the communicative situation. Such an approach allows us to determine differences and similarities *in degree* between humans and nonhuman primates, relying on behavioral variables such as flexibility – caused by attending to each other – during communication. It also allows us to exclude cases in which the recipient may respond to a signal without knowing what it means, perceiving it as correlating with a certain event and therefore responding in a certain way whenever the signal occurs.

Flexible interaction means that intentional signal production should cause intentional behavior on the recipient's side, and in some cases it means that recipients themselves produce intentional signals as a response to the signal produced by the signaler. Flexible reactions based on the signaler's intentional behavior by the recipient may only be possible if the recipient is somehow aware that this signaler's behavior was intentional, i.e. not accidental. This does not imply that the recipient must display extended metarepresentational abilities: within a Neo-Gricean approach, these potentially complex requirements of flexible interactions can be explained as laid out in Section 1. Such requirements therefore do not assume higher-order intentionality to be fundamental for intentional communication. What the recipient must display is a perceptual awareness of the fact that it is *the signaler* that causes their own (i.e. the signaler's) behavior; additionally, it may also display awareness about the signaler having goals, a capacity within the range of the mental abilities of great apes.

One issue with such a flexible interaction-based method is that identifying the recipient's potentially intentional follow-up behavior caused by the signaler's communicative behavior is difficult. This is because behavior actively displayed by the recipient and caused by the signaler's communicative behavior is difficult to distinguish from behavior involuntarily displayed or not linked to the signaler's communicative behavior (Hobaiter and Byrne 2014; Liebal et al. 2014). Cartmill and Byrne (2007) offer a possible paradigm where orangutans were offered desirable and undesirable food, and displayed response flexibility to the experimenter's behavior to recover their preferred food by either employing elaboration or persistence of signal use, depending on the situation. Thus, the signaler evaluated their level of success regarding the goal they intended to achieve by producing the signal, and modified their communicative behavior flexibly, depending on the recipient's reactions. In communicative situations, the same flexible behavior would have to be displayed by the recipients, i.e. they evaluate the meaning of the signal produced by the signaler and their own motivation to do as signaled. Furthermore, in cases of diverging motivations between signalers and recipients, they should also evaluate their success of communicating their own intention, which implies some reflexive thinking present in signalers and recipients.

4 Criteria for a flexible interaction between signaler and recipient

In this last section, we will run through a few variables that indicate this flexible interaction. Starting on the signaler's side, the variables are (a) behavioral sequences depending on the recipient's behavior, (b) persistence and/or elaboration behavior, and (c) stopping of signaling:

(a) We expect a behavioral sequence involved in signal production, which, though not random, should not be fixed but tied to situation-specific changes and signal's meaning. In contrast, situation-independent fixed behavior does exclude a flexible interaction. Such a sequence may include audience checking, change of body orientation, or gazing towards specific objects or directions (e.g. Gruber and Zuberbühler 2013, Schel et al. 2013). All these variables combined with signal production hint to the signaler trying to make its communicative goal salient to the recipient.

(b) If the communication attempt fails to succeed, the signaler must display signs of persistence or elaboration (Russon and Andrews 2010): if a signal functioning as a sign of persistence is displayed and the recipient still does not react as intended, the signaler may switch to a different signal or behavior (Cartmill and Byrne 2007). Elaboration and persistence behavior may be accompanied by waiting behavior.

(c) In cases where recipients already recognized the signal and this recognition is salient to the signaler, either via the intended recipient's response or via the recipient's attentional state, the signaler is expected to stop signal production (e.g. Crockford et al. 2012), because they succeeded in attaining their goal (Townsend et al. 2016).

Switching to the recipient's side, the variables are: (d) signal production depending on the environmental circumstances, (e) a behavioral pattern dependent on the signaler's behavior, and (f) production of additional behavior to display diverging motivations:

(d) If the recipient perceives the signal and it is not salient to the signaler that the signal was understood (e.g. due to environmental circumstances), the recipient may intend to make salient to the signaler that this in fact is the case by, for example, producing the same call the signaler produced as a response (e.g. Wich and de Vries 2006).

(e) Furthermore, the recipient may also display a behavioral sequence, potentially reflecting that of the signaler and answering to it (e.g. body orientation towards the signaler, gaze following, stopping of previous action). As such, it needs to be assessed whether the recipient's behavioral sequence (respectively, a given behavior) is influenced by the signaler's behavioral sequence (see King and Shanker 2003).

(f) The recipient may also clearly display evidence of diverging motivations, for instance, by turning their body away from the signaler, or resuming the previous action they were engaged in before the interaction. They might produce vocal or gestural signals if the signaler does not cease signaling.

For both communicative situations where signaler and recipient have compatible motivations, but especially where their motivations diverge, a simple turn-taking pattern should be observed. Turn-taking here refers to turn-taking of communicative and non-communicative behavior, leading signalers to reach their goals and recipients to understand the signaler's message as well as successfully displaying their own intentions. The closest to a systematic approach to investigate such flexible turn-taking in nonhuman primate communication is perhaps found in the approaches by Hobaiter and Byrne (2014) and Rossano (2013). Hobaiter and Byrne (2014) applied a behavioral criterion they labeled ASO ("apparently satisfactory outcome") to identify the meaning of gestures by looking at recipients' reactions and signalers' response behavior. Rossano applied conversation analysis to travel initiations in mother-infant dyads in bonobos. Conversation analysis examines how partner-directed behavior leads to mutual understanding (Rossano 2013: 165). Key to mutual understanding is the sequential order of behaviors directed to an individual by taking turns with that individual (see Sacks 1992; Schegloff 2007). Rossano's approach shows how important it is to look at communication multimodally to find flexible interaction.

The focus on flexible interaction is not only important for primates, but for all animal species. Pika and Bugnyar (2011) found evidence for deictic showing and offering gestures in corvids. They also recorded follow-up behavior of signaler and recipient. As a response, the majority of recipients oriented themselves towards the signaler and the object, approached the signaler, and engaged in affiliate interactions with them. Future research, applying either a conversation analysis or ASO approach, could investigate whether such an interpretation is warranted and whether corvids indeed interact flexibly with each other to communicate each other's goals.

5 Conclusion: flexibility in intentional communication

Despite some skepticism towards a re-evaluation of the Gricean framework in the form of downgrading the involved reflexive level of intentionality, our review has shown that nonhuman primates, especially great apes, appear to display intentional behavior when applying a Neo-Gricean approach for informative and communicative intentions. However, we do not think that the recipient's ability to read the signaler's mind or engage in inference about the signaler's intentions is constitutive for intentional communication. Instead, there are two other reasons why the recipient's expected reaction to the signal is important for intentional communication. First, there is a *constitutive reason* for taking into account the recipient's uptake in intentional communication, as illustrated by Millikan's account of communication. Second, we think that the ability of the recipient to infer the signaler's intention from external cues is a useful methodological guide to an answer to our question. This is the *methodological reason* for taking into account the recipient's inferential capacities in intentional communicative interaction.

On an empirical note, the question whether nonhuman animals interact flexibly enough to claim that they participate in intentional communication requires further systematic research. In this respect, we believe the focus should be put on identifying communicative situations where both sides interact flexibly with each other: signaling should cause flexible responses depending on the recipient's motivations, and flexible responses should cause further responses if motivations of signaler and recipient diverge. Currently, the kind of evidence we are looking at still appears scarce in non-primate research, but evidence is building up in the primate literature. A possible reason for the scarcity in non-primate animals may be that they do not interact that flexibly with each other. In this respect, a focus on flexibility may open a new avenue of research to investigate the possible uniqueness of primate communication, or question it.

Note

1 The order of the authors reflects their decreasing contribution to the chapter.

Further reading

Millikan's (2005) *Language: a biological model* provides an overview of her work on communication and language. Liebal et al.'s (2014) *Primate communication: A multimodal approach* sums up empirical research on potentially intentional communication in nonhuman primates, emphasizing the importance of multimodality. For the authors' views on identifying intentional communication in nonhuman animals, see Townsend et al. (2016) and Sievers and Gruber (2016).

References

Brinck, I. (2001) "Attention and the evolution of intentional communication," *Pragmatics & Cognition* 9: 259–277.

Call, J., and Tomasello, M. editors (2007) *The gestural communication of apes and monkeys*, New York: Lawrence Erlbaum.

Carston, R. (2002) *Thoughts and utterances: The pragmatics of explicit communication*, Oxford: Blackwell.

Cartmill, E. A., and Byrne, R. W. (2007) "Orangutans modify their gestural signalling according to their audience's comprehension," *Current Biology* 17: 1345–1348.

Crockford, C., Wittig, R. M., Mundry, R., and Zuberbühler, K. (2012) "Wild chimpanzees inform ignorant group members of danger," *Current Biology* 22: 142–146.

Csibra, G. (2010) "Recognizing communicative intentions in infancy," *Mind and Language* 25: 141–168.

Dennett, D. (1983) "Intentional systems in cognitive ethology: The "panglossian paradigm" defended," *Behavioral and Brain Sciences* 6: 343–355.

Genty, E., Clay, Z., Hobaiter, C., and Zuberbühler, K. (2014) "Multi-modal use of a socially directed call in bonobos," *PLoS ONE* 9: 1–12.

Gómez, J. C. (1994) "Mutual awareness in primate communication: A Gricean approach," In: S. T. Parker, R. M. Mitchell, and M. L. Boccia (eds.) *Self-awareness in animals and humans: developmental perspectives*, Cambridge: Cambridge University Press, 61–80.

Grice, P. (1957) "Meaning," *Philosophical Review* 66: 377–388.

——— (1975) "Logic and conversation," In: P. Cole and J. Morgan (eds.) *Syntax and semantics. 3: Speech acts*, New York: Academic Press, 41–58.

——— (1982) "Meaning revisited," In: N. V. Smith (ed.) *Mutual knowledge*, New York: Academic Press, 223–243.

Gruber, T., and Zuberbühler, K. (2013) "Vocal recruitment for joint travel in wild chimpanzees," *PLoS ONE* 8: 1–9.

Hare, B., Call, J., Agnetta, B., and Tomasello, M. (2000) "Chimpanzees know what conspecifics do and do not see," *Animal Behaviour* 59: 771–785.

Hobaiter, C., and Byrne, R. W. (2014) "The meanings of chimpanzee gestures," *Current Biology* 24: 1596–1600.

Hurford, J. R. (2007) *The origins of meaning*, Oxford: Oxford University Press.

Kimbrough Oller, D. (2000) *The emergence of the speech capacity*, New York: Lawrence Erlbaum.

King, B., and Shanker, S. (2003) "How can we know the dancer from the dance? The dynamic nature of African great ape social communication," *Anthropological Theory* 3: 5–26.

Leavens, D. A., Russell, J. L., and Hopkins, W. D. (2005) "Intentionality as measured in the persistence and elaboration of communication by chimpanzees (Pan troglodytes)," *Child Development* 76: 291–306.

———— (2010) "Multimodal communication by captive chimpanzees (*Pan troglodytes*)," *Animal Cognition* 13: 33–40.

Levinson, S. C. (1983) *Pragmatics*, New York: Cambridge University Press.

Liebal, K., Call, J., and Tomasello, M. (2004) "Use of gesture sequences in chimpanzees," *American Journal of Primatology* 64: 377–396.

Liebal, K., Waller, B. M., Burrows, A. M., and Slocombe, K. (2014) *Primate communication: A multimodal approach*, Cambridge: Cambridge University Press.

Millikan, R. (1984) *Language, thought, and other biological categories*, Cambridge, MA: MIT Press.

———— (2005) *Language: A biological model*, Oxford: Oxford University Press.

———— (forthcoming) *Beyond concepts. Unicepts, language and natural information*, Oxford: Oxford University Press.

Moore, R. (2016a) "Meaning and ostension in great ape gestural communication," *Animal Cognition* 19: 223–231.

———— (2016b) "Gricean communication and cognitive development," *Philosophical Quarterly*. Version of record online: 2 August 2016. doi: 10.1093/pq/pqw049.

Pika, S., and Bugnyar, T. (2011) "The use of referential gestures in ravens (Corvus corax) in the wild," *Nature Communications* 2: 560.

Rossano, F. (2013) "Sequence organization and timing of bonobo mother-infant interactions," *Interaction Studies* 14: 160–189.

Russon, A., and Andrews, K. (2010) "Orangutan pantomime: Elaborating the message," *Biology Letters* 7: 627–630.

Sacks, H. (1992) "Adjacency pairs: Scope of operation," In: G. Jefferson (ed.) *Lectures on conversation: Volume II*, Oxford: Blackwell, 521–532.

Sacks, H., Schegloff, E. A., and Jefferson, G. (1974) "A simplest systematics for the organization of turn-taking for conversation," *Language* 50: 696–735.

Schegloff, E. A. (2007) *Sequence organization in interaction: A primer in conversation analysis*, Cambridge: Cambridge University Press.

Schel, A. M., Townsend, S. W., Machanda, Z., Zuberbühler, K., and Slocombe, K. E. (2013) "Chimpanzee alarm call production meets key criteria for intentionality," *PLoSONE* 8: 1–11.

Scott-Phillips, T. (2015a) "Nonhuman primate communication, pragmatics and the origins of language," *Current Anthropology* 56: 56–80.

———— (2015b) "Meaning in animal and human communication," *Animal Cognition* 18: 801–805.

Scott-Phillips, T., and Kirby (2013) "Information, influence and inference in language evolution," In: U. Stegmann (ed.) *Animal communication theory*, Cambridge: Cambridge University Press, 421–442.

Senju, A., and Csibra, G. (2008) "Gaze following in human infants depends on communicative signals," *Current Biology* 18: 668–671.

Sievers, C., and Gruber, T. (2016) "Reference in human and non-human primate communication: What does it take to refer," *Animal Cognition* 19: 759–768.

Sperber, D., and Wilson, D. (1995) *Relevance: Communication and Cognition*, second edition, Malden, MA: Blackwell.

Tomasello, M. (2008) *Origins of human communication*, Cambridge, MA: MIT Press.

Townsend, S. W., Koski, S., Byrne, R., Slocombe, K., Bickel, B., Braga Goncalves, I., Boeckle, M., Burkart, J., Flower, T., Gaunet, F., Glock, H., Gruber, T., Jansen, D., Liebal, K., Linke, A., Miklosi, A., Moore, R., van Schaik, C., Stoll, S., Vail, A., Waller, B., Wild, M., Zuberbühler, K., and Manser, M. (2016) "Exorcising Grice's ghost: An empirical approach to studying intentional communication in animals," *Biological Reviews*. Version of record online: 2 August 2016. doi:10.1111/brv.12289. [Epub ahead of print]

Wheeler, B. C., and Fischer, J. (2012) "Functionally referential signals: A promising paradigm whose time has passed," *Evolutionary Anthropology* 21: 195–205.

Wich, S. A., and de Vries, H. (2006) "Male monkeys remember which group members have given alarm calls," *Proceedings of the Royal Society Series B* 273: 735–740.

Wilson, M., and T. P. Wilson (2005) "An oscillator model of the timing of turn-taking," *Psychonomic Bulletin and Review* 12: 957–968.

PART VI

Social cognition and culture

32

WHAT IS ANIMAL CULTURE?

Grant Ramsey

Culture from humans to nonhuman animals

Culture in humans connotes tradition, norms, ritual, technology, and social learning, but also cultural events like operas or gallery openings. Culture is in part about what we do, but also sometimes about what we ought to do. Human culture is inextricably intertwined with language, and much of what we learn and transmit to others comes through written or spoken language. Given the complexities of human culture, it might seem that we are the only species that exhibits culture.

How, then, are we to make sense of culture in animals?[1] The study of animal culture is a booming research area. Culture is said to occur in a wide range of vertebrates, from our close kin, chimpanzees (Whiten et al. 1999) and orangutans (van Schaik et al. 2003), to more distant relatives like rats (Galef and Aleen 1995) and whales (Whitehead and Rendell 2015). Could these studies be misleading in that they are not actually studying culture but simply misapplying the term 'culture'? Or is what is labeled culture in animals at the core of human culture, so that although human culture is more elaborate than animal culture, it is different in degree, not kind? While it is certainly easy to intentionally define culture in a way that makes it unique to humans, because of the growing field of animal culture, it would be most useful to attempt to offer a definition of culture that makes sense of how it is used by psychologists, biologists, anthropologists, and others who use the term culture in studies of animal behavior. The challenge is to produce a concept that is broad enough to be able to apply across humans and animals, but not be so anemic that it cannot do justice to human culture. Because of this, I will here construct a definition of animal culture and draw out some of its implications. Let's begin by considering what ingredients should go into such a definition.

Ingredients for a definition of culture

Anthropology has a long tradition of proposing definitions of culture. Kroeber and Kluckhohn (1952) tallied 164 definitions, and many more have been added in the subsequent half century. Some of the definitions of culture focus on cultural products, like Tyler's (1871) understanding of culture as a "complex whole which includes knowledge, belief, art, law, morals, custom, and any other capabilities and habits acquired by man as a member of society" (1). Others focus on social learning or heredity: "*culture* means the social heredity of mankind" (Linton 1936: 78). Still others define culture not in terms of outcomes, but instead in terms of the information that governs behavior and helps create cultural products:

> culture is best seen not as complexes of concrete behavior patterns – customs, usages, traditions, habit clusters – as has, by and large, been the case up to now, but a set of control mechanisms – plans, recipes, rules, instructions (what computer engineers call "programs") – for the governing of behavior.
>
> (Geertz 1973: 44)

Given this diversity of definitions, should we sift through them and try to determine which one is correct? I am inclined not to attempt to pick out the correct one(s), casting others aside. Instead, most of the definitions get at important features of culture. Culture is a form of social heredity, it is something that governs behavior, and it is something that forms the basis of traditions and artifacts. The challenge is not to find the right (or best) definition from those available, but to pick out the essential ingredients of culture and then figure out how to put them together to produce a synthetic definition of culture. Kroeber and Kluckhohn attempted to do just that when they proposed that culture

> consists of patterns, explicit and implicit, of and for behavior acquired and transmitted by symbols, constituting the distinctive achievement of human groups, including their embodiments in artifacts; the essential core of culture consists of traditional (i.e., historically derived and selected) ideas and especially their attached values; culture systems may, on the one hand, be considered as products of action, on the other hand, as conditioning elements of further action.
>
> (1952: 357)

Their definition has the merit of trying to put together important ingredients, but it is of little help for animal culture since it defines culture in terms of humans. And while human culture is clearly highly symbolic and value-laden, these features do not seem to be necessary conditions of culture. For producing the ingredients for a synthetic definition of animal culture, let's consider how animal culture is often understood.

In animal behavior studies, culture often has a negative, operational definition: if there is a behavioral difference across populations that is not explainable in terms of environmental or genetic differences, then it can be attributed to culture. But culture is sometimes given explicit positive definitions as well, for example, "a cultural behaviour is one that is transmitted repeatedly through social or observational learning to become a population-level characteristic" (Whiten et al. 1999: 682). Note that this is not so much a definition of culture, but instead a characterization of a prototypical result of culture. As such, it features characteristics that are commonly associated with culture, like being population-wide, but not necessarily ones we should use as a base for a definition of culture. Similarly, although many genes are homogeneous across populations, it would be misleading to define what genes are in terms of population-level phenotypic characteristics.

Defining culture in terms of outcomes like traditions or group typicality is widespread in the animal culture literature. For example, Allen et al. (2013: 485) define culture in terms of "shared behavior propagated by social learning," and Laland and Janik (2006: 524) understand "culture (or tradition) as all group-typical behaviour patterns, shared by members of animal communities, that are to some degree reliant on socially learned and transmitted information." To understand the various components of the way animal culture is commonly defined in the literature, let's unpack Laland and Janik's definition.

Laland and Janik's definition utilizes three main ingredients. One is an *outcome*, a "group-typical behaviour pattern." Not all behavioral group typicality is cultural, of course, but as they have defined culture, group typicality is a necessary but not sufficient condition for culture. The second ingredient is a *mechanism*; the behaviors are in part due to the mechanism of social learning. The third ingredient is the thing passed on, the *content*, which they describe as "transmitted information." It is rather cumbersome to define culture in terms of outcome, mechanism, and content. Is this complexity necessary, or can we perhaps jettison some of the ingredients? As mentioned above, group typicality is not a desired criterion for culture since it eliminates any cultural variants that are not group-typical, and there is nothing necessary about culture that makes it have to be typical of – or common in – the group. It might, then, be tempting to eliminate this criterion and have culture be defined not in terms of particular kinds of outcomes, but instead in terms of mechanism and content only. Thus, one might think that culture should be defined simply as socially transmitted information.

But to expunge group typicality would be to miss the point that it is inserted into the definition to solve a problem. The problem is that not all information that organisms transmit from one another constitutes culture. Some is mere ephemeral communication – it has an effect on the recipient, but not a lasting one or not one capable of supporting traditions. An alarm call may allow a macaw to learn of an approaching eagle from a conspecific, but what is socially learned by the macaw about the eagle's proximity is not something that forms the basis of a tradition. Similarly, one howling wolf might set the pack howling, but this is not the kind of behavior that is considered cultural. There thus must be a restriction in place, but one that does not require group typicality. I will turn to the question of a replacement restriction in the following section, but let's first consider the other two components, mechanism and content.

Social learning is a component of Laland and Janik's definition and is a common feature of culture definitions. Unfortunately, there are some difficulties with the social learning criterion. As Sterelny (2009) argues, "it is far from clear that there is a distinctive and identifiable form of learning, social learning, that contrasts with (say) individual trial-and-error learning in response to ecological circumstances" (295). And while social learning may be important for culture, it does not suffice for culture. McGrew (2009), for example, holds that

> if culture equals social learning, then many creatures, e.g., octopus, guppy, and lizard, must be granted cultural status. If culture is more than social learning, then we must look elsewhere for essential criteria. On these grounds, it seems sensible to consider social learning as necessary but not sufficient for culture.
>
> (50)

McGrew is certainly correct that social learning is not sufficient for culture. And social learning – or something like it – is necessary. The reason that social learning is a ubiquitous ingredient in definitions of culture is that cultural traditions are sustained by the information that is passed on from one individual to another through behavioral performances. Thus, we need not worry about what, precisely, counts as social learning, and we can sidestep the issues raised by Sterelny. We can do so by simply recognizing that for information to be cultural, it must be transmitted from one individual to another via a behavioral channel.

The final ingredient is the content, what Laland and Janik label *information*. I agree with them that defining culture in terms of information is a good strategy. But one should be cautious. The term 'information' is used in a variety of ways – leaving it unspecified can lead to vacuity, while giving a detailed specification can lead to problems (Lewens 2014). But for the purpose of animal culture, what we want from a concept of information is the reduction of uncertainty. By this I don't mean the *feeling* of uncertainty and its associated anxiety. Instead, if there are multiple ways for, say, a rat to extract seeds from pinecones, and that through the behavioral transfer of information, the number of ways that the rat might use is reduced (down to one, perhaps), then the uncertainty concerning seed extraction has been reduced. Similarly, in a shell game, you gain information about the hidden item by lifting one of the shells to the extent that the uncertainty in the item's whereabouts is reduced by seeing what is under a particular shell. This notion of information is what Dretske (1983) used and developed, and is related to the mathematical accounts of information arising from Shannon and Weaver (Shannon 1948; Shannon and Weaver 1949).

What animal culture is

Let's take stock of the ingredients. Laland and Janik are right that outcome, mechanism, and content are all important ingredients in a concept of animal culture, but there were difficulties with their specific interpretation of these. Let's begin with the last and work backward. Information, suitably defined, seems to be an important part of a definition of culture. In fact, I would go further to argue that culture *is* information – it is a particular kind of information. The other two ingredients are not a part of what culture is, but instead are what help to delimit the kind of information that is culture. The second ingredient, mechanism, is an important way of delimiting this information, though since we are considering the flow of information, the term 'channel' may be more apt. Culture, then, is information transmitted from individual to individual (or between groups of individuals since there may be some forms of cultural information that no individual possesses, but is possessed and transmitted by a group) along a particular kind of channel. The channel that the information must pass through is behavior – it must be transmitted by behavior and not, say, by genes. Thus, taking into account the last two ingredients, we can produce a preliminary, incomplete definition of culture as information transmitted between individuals or groups, where this information flows through the behavior.

From the above example of wolf howl contagion or the startling precipitated by an alarm call, it is clear that not all information that is passed through behavior between individuals or groups is culture. Instead, the outcome the information has is important for whether it is truly culture. In particular, the information must help to bring about the reproduction of the behavior that serves as a channel for the information, and it must have a lasting effect on the behavior of the recipient(s). This idea of culture causing, passing through, and reproducing behavior is not too far from what Kroeber and Kluckhohn were getting at when they held that "culture systems may, on the one hand, be considered as products of action, on the other hand, as conditioning elements of further action" (1952: 357). We can now, following Ramsey (2013), put together the three ingredients into one definition: *Culture is information transmitted between individuals or groups, where this information flows through and brings about the reproduction of, and a lasting change in, the behavioral trait.*

This definition has each of the three ingredients that are common in definitions of culture. But the definition offered here avoids the requirement that culture bring about behavioral homogeneity, and instead of using the somewhat vague and controversial concept of social learning, it simply specifies the channel through which the information must flow in order for it to count as culture. The definition also does not predetermine which taxa exhibit culture. If guppies, lizards, or octopuses transfer information amongst themselves in such a way that it flows through and brings about the reproduction of, and a lasting change in, a behavioral trait, then it is a cultural species. The question of whether or not this concept of culture applies to such taxa has an answer based on empirical evidence, not stipulation.

Culture, environment, and epigenetics

Cultural transmission, as defined here, is certainly distinct from genetic transmission, and cultural explanations of behavioral differences are distinct from and complementary to genetic explanations of difference. Environment, however, is not so easily or cleanly distinguished from culture. The reason is that there can be cultural artifacts, and these artifacts can help furnish the environment. This implies that environment, genes, and culture do not represent three mutually exclusive sources of behavioral differences. Instead, environment is divided into cultural environment and acultural environment.

How, then, can part of the environment such as an artifact be cultural, given the definition of culture provided above? The answer is that while culture necessarily flows through behavior, it can flow through other material things as well. A spear point is a result of behavior, but it can also serve as a channel for cultural information. One can learn some of how to build spear points through the examination of points fashioned by others. Thus, some of the uncertainty in how to build a particular kind of point is reduced through the inspection of such points. Objects become channels for information when they help recapitulate in others the behavior that shaped them. Similarly, animal trails can be cultural artifacts – they decrease the uncertainty of their conspecific's walking behavior, and by walking on them they help to induce like behavior in others. The fact that environment and culture overlap does not mean that it is wrong to operationalize the detection of culture by eliminating environmental and genetic differences. Instead, what one needs to exclude in such assessments are features of the environment fashioned by individuals via cultural behavior. But in studies of culture in animals, this is typically done. For example, if orangutans on one side of a river eat a fruit that a group on the other side does not, what one looks for is whether the fruit is growing on both sides in a similar density and in areas that are similarly accessible.

Where things become more difficult is when there is a significant degree of niche construction (Odling-Smee et al. 2003). Niche construction occurs when organisms modify their environment in a way that can have ecological and evolutionary effects. Beavers building dams is a classic example – the result of their construction creates ponds, and swimming in the ponds they have constructed modifies their selection pressures. But such behavior is not cultural just because it involves niche construction. While there can be cultural niche construction, much niche construction occurs in the absence of culture. The litmus test for whether a part of the environment is cultural is whether its form and/or function is in part the result of a behavior, and whether its having this form and/or function leads others to reproduce in the environment a similar form or function.

Just as culture, as defined above, can flow *outside* of our bodies, it can also flow *inside* and can even affect how genes are transcribed. Being licked by one's mother affects a rat pup's epigenetics (Weaver et al. 2004). Rats that are licked as pups are therefore differently constituted and may therefore behave differently. If being licked as a female pup makes the rat tend to lick her own pups once she matures and eventually has offspring, then this licking behavior is cultural behavior. The licking behavior is traditional and could be disrupted by an intervention in which mother rats were prevented from licking their pups. Thus, even though the licking behavior is in part mediated by epigenetics, it is cultural nevertheless.

Culture and epigenetics are sometimes viewed as alternative ways to explain patterns of behavior. For example, Jablonka and Lamb (2005) distinguish epigenetic and behavioral inheritance mechanisms and place culture within behavioral inheritance only. But under the framework provided here, culture can flow through an epigenetic channel. It therefore follows that culture and epigenetics – like culture and the environment – overlap and are not alternative, mutually exclusive ways of explaining behavioral patterns.

In a similar way, passing on dietary preferences in utero or through milk can count as culture (Galef and Sherry 1973). If the feeding behavior of the mother is reproduced in the young – that is, the dietary uncertainty of the offspring is reduced by the maternal diet – then cultural information flows through the mother's behavior, into her gut, and via biochemical channels to her offspring. Such pathways, like cultural niche construction, can be long and tortuous but, according to the framework provided here, count as culture.

Criteria for recognizing culture in animals

Given the definition of culture offered here, it is natural to ask what observable criteria can serve as evidence of culture. In answering this question, let's consider an influential way of testing for culture, that of McGrew (1992), to see how it compares to this definition. Instead of simply defining what culture is, McGrew offers a set of operational criteria that one can use to determine whether culture is present. He offers eight criteria, which he takes to be individually necessary and jointly sufficient for a species to be cultural: innovation, dissemination, standardization, durability, diffusion, tradition, non-subsistence, and naturalness. Let's consider each in turn.

Innovation is described by McGrew as a "new pattern is invented or modified" (1992, p. 77). There is a growing literature on animal innovation (Reader and Laland 2003), and there is debate concerning how, precisely, we should understand the concept. It is clear that innovation can occur in the absence of culture and if, as McGrew argues, innovation is a necessary condition, then culture cannot exist without innovation. Using the framework provided by Ramsey et al. (2007), while innovation may be the prime source of behavioral novelty, it may not be necessary for such novelty. Instead, mistakes can lead to behavioral novelty, or novel behaviors can be induced by the environment, and this novelty can be transmitted as a cultural tradition. Thus, it is wrong to define culture in terms of innovation, but it may not be wrong to use innovation as an indicator of culture, since there is a good chance that they are empirically highly correlated.

Dissemination is described as "pattern acquired by another from innovator" (1992: 77). Because, as I just argued, there is no definitional link between innovation and culture, I think it is wrong to define dissemination in terms of innovation. That said, because the flow of information in culture transmission is a form of dissemination, I agree with McGrew that dissemination – defined differently – is a necessary condition.

Standardization is described as "form of pattern is consistent and stylized" (1992: 77). To the degree that cultural information is conveyed from one individual to another, behavioral standardization will ensue. Thus, standardized behavior patterns will be a part of any cultural system. That said, consistent behavior patterns may be present with or without culture. Thus, such patterns by themselves bear scant evidence for culture.

Durability is described as "pattern performed outwith presence of demonstrator" (1992: 77). Durability here plays a similar role as that played by the "lasting change" in the behavioral trait, as described above. If the information has a lasting change on behavior, then it will be durable, and it will be performed in the absence of the demonstrator.

Diffusion is described as "pattern spreads from one group to another" (1992: 77). While cultural species will often exhibit diffusion, I do not agree that one should take it to be a necessary condition for culture. There could be species that exist in isolated groups, and that if a foreign individual is accepted into the group, it is required to adopt the cultural norms of the group. In such a species, culture and cultural evolution are possible in the absence of intergroup diffusion. That said, diffusion of behavior is an indication of culture and should thus be understood not as a criterion for culture, but instead as evidence of culture.

Tradition is described as "patterns persist from innovator's generation to next one" (1992: 77). Like diffusion, tradition is a natural consequence of culture: culture spreads from individual to individual, and it is highly probable that many cultural variants will have models from an older generation. That said, is tradition in this transgenerational sense necessary for culture? The framework introduced above implies that culture can (and should) be defined independently of tradition in this sense. Some cultural variants could sweep through a generation, causing lasting changes in their behavior, but die out within that generation. In humans, we would not deny a particular fashion trend to be cultural just because nobody under thirty would be caught dead dawning it. Similarly, one could imagine species whose culture is always confined within a generation. Such a species may be improbable, but is not impossible. Thus, tradition – as defined by McGrew – is an indicator of culture (since culture is almost always associated with traditions), not a necessary condition.

Non-subsistence is described as "pattern transcends subsistence" (1992: 77). This is a condition McGrew added so that culture is present in realms outside of subsistence. For chimpanzees, he offers an example of males from one cultural community tearing up leaves during courtship. Like many of the criteria offered by McGrew, I take this one to be empirically correlated with culture, but not a necessary condition for culture. A species could have all of its cultural variants be related to subsistence.

Naturalness is described as "pattern shown in absence of direct human influence" (1992: 77). The definition of culture offered above requires that the cultural information must flow through the behavior in bringing about culture in others. Thus, if humans change the environment of an animal, thereby changing its behavior, we should not regard this as culture. Although this is true, if a nonhuman animal learns a behavior from a human, but this animal goes on to serve as a model for conspecifics, the 'artificial' behavior could become a cultural norm for the species.

In sum, the criteria offered by McGrew are, for the most part, *indicators* of culture as defined above. His intent was to offer empirically observable, measurable criteria and, as such, his list does a good job pointing to criteria that indicate culture. But these criteria, however, should not be understood as constituting a *definition* of culture. If we ask *what is animal culture?*, then the definition offered in the "What animal culture is" section is a good answer. But if we ask *what are reliable signs of culture?*, then the criteria discussed in this section are a good answer.

Conclusions

The framework provided here accords well with standard practice in the science of animal culture. The common method of discovering behaviors that differ across ecologically similar geographic areas will pick out many cultural variants, though it will leave some undetected. Even if all human groups begin playing the banjo, banjo playing should still count as a cultural behavior. Similarly, it is possible for animal species to have cultural universals. Searching for behavioral differences not linked to environmental or genetic differences should thus be a starting point, not a decisive test. Instead, using the definition of culture elaborated above, we should ask whether the behavioral pattern is maintained by information transmitted via performances of the behavior in others.

The benefit of using the concept of culture here is that it will help us to be clear about what animal culture is and what it takes for a species to be cultural. And it allows us to keep clear about the difference between culture itself and the operational criteria one should use to search for and quantify culture. As we have seen, the criteria offered by McGrew are, for the most part, reliable indicators of culture. In refining these criteria and developing new ones, one can use the definition offered here, asking the question of what observations can reliably indicate culture in this sense.

The conception of culture articulated here is inclusive – any species that uses information in the way described exhibits cultural behaviors. Despite this openness, the conception nevertheless does justice to much of what counts as culture in humans. Patterns of human behavior – languages, techniques, rituals, etc. – are maintained by culture. Some normative aspects of culture, or features linked to class (high vs. low culture), are not a part of culture as conceived here. But this is a strength, not a weakness, since it allows animals to be cultural in the purely informational sense, but also allows culture to be elaborated, supplemented, and transformed into the richly symbolic, normative world of humans.

Acknowledgments

Thank you to Hugh Desmond and Agustin Fuentes for taking the time to carefully read and comment on an earlier draft of this chapter. This chapter was completed while I was on a National Endowment for the Humanities (NEH)-supported fellowship at the National Humanities Center (NHC). I thank the NEH and NHC for their support. Any views, findings, conclusions, or recommendations expressed in this article do not necessarily reflect those of the National Endowment for the Humanities.

Note

1   Nonhuman animals, that is – I will, for simplicity, use 'animals' to denote nonhuman animals.

Further reading

K. N. Laland and B. G. Galef, *The question of animal culture* (Cambridge, MA: Harvard University Press, 2009) offers an excellent collection of articles on culture in animals. G. Ramsey, "Culture in humans and other animals" *Biology & Philosophy* 28 (2013): 457–479 provides a more expansive discussion of animal culture than that found here. K. Laland and V. M. Janik, "The animal cultures debate" *Trends in Ecology & Evolution* 21 (2006): 542–547 offers an overview of recent debates about animal culture and suggests about how to weigh evidence about animal culture. E. Jablonka and M. J. Lamb, *Evolution in four dimensions, revised edition: Genetic, epigenetic, behavioral, and symbolic variation in the history of life* (Cambridge, MA: MIT Press, 2014) centers on human evolution, but proposes a general framework for understanding inheritance systems, including that of culture. Much work on cultural evolution, such as T. Lewens, *Cultural evolution: Conceptual challenges* (Oxford: Oxford University Press, 2015); A. Mesoudi, *Cultural evolution: How Darwinian theory can explain human culture and synthesize the social sciences* (Chicago: University of Chicago Press, 2011); and P. J. Richerson and R. Boyd, *Not by genes alone* (Chicago: University of Chicago Press, 2004) is about human evolution, but these are also insightful for understanding culture in animals.

References

Allen, J., Weinrich, M., Hoppitt, W., and Rendell, L. (2013) "Network-based diffusion analysis reveals cultural transmission of lobtail feeding in humpback whales." *Science, 340*(6131): 485–488.

Dretske, F. (1983) *Knowledge and the flow of information*, Cambridge, MA: MIT Press.

Galef, B. G., and Aleen, C. (1995) "A new model system for studying behavioural traditions in animals." *Animal Behaviour, 50*(3): 705–717.

Galef, B. G., and Sherry, D. F. (1973) "Mother's milk: A medium for transmission of cues reflecting the flavor of mother's diet," *Journal of Comparative and Physiological Psychology*, *83*: 374–378.

Geertz, C. (1973) *The interpretation of cultures*, New York: Basic Books.

Jablonka, E., and Lamb, M. (2005) *Evolution in four dimensions – genetic, epigenetic, behavioral, and symbolic variation in the history of life*, Cambridge, MA: MIT Press.

Kroeber, A. L., and Kluckhohn, C. (1952) *Culture: A critical review of concepts and definitions*, Cambridge: The Museum.

Laland, K. N., and Janik, V. M. (2006) "The animal cultures debate," *Trends in Ecology & Evolution*, *21*(10): 542–547.

Lewens, T. (2014). "Cultural information: Don't ask, don't tell," in Galavotti, M. C., Dieks, D., Gonzalez, W. J., Hartmann, S., Uebel, Th., and Weber, M. (Eds.) *New directions in the philosophy of science* (pp. 369–382), Cham, Heidelberg, New York, Dordrecht, London: Springer International Publishing.

Linton, R. (1936) *The study of man*, New York: Appelton-Century Crofts.

McGrew, W.C. (1992) *Chimpanzee material culture: implications for human evolution*, Cambridge: Cambridge University Press.

McGrew, W. C. (2009) "Ten dispatches from the chimpanzee culture wars, plus postscript (revisiting the battlefronts)," in Laland, K. N., and Galef, B. G. (eds.) *The question of animal culture* (pp. 41–69), Cambridge, MA: Harvard University Press.

Odling-Smee, F. J., Laland, K. N., and Feldman, M. W. (2003) *Niche construction: The neglected process in evolution*. Princeton, NJ: Princeton University Press.

Ramsey, G. (2013) "Culture in humans and other animals," *Biology & Philosophy*, *28*(3): 457–479.

Ramsey, G., Bastian, M. L., and van Schaik, C. (2007) "Animal innovation defined and operationalized," *Behavioral and Brain Sciences*, *30*: 393–437.

Reader, S. M., and Laland, K. N., eds. (2003). *Animal innovation*, Oxford University Press.

Shannon, C. E. (1948) "A mathematical theory of communication," *Bell System Technical Journal*, *27*: 379–423.

Shannon, C. E., and Weaver, W. (1949) *The mathematical theory of communication*, Urbana, IL: University of Illinois Press.

Sterelny, K. (2009) "Peacekeeping in the culture wars," in Laland, K. N., and Galef, B. G. (eds.) *The question of animal culture* (pp. 288–304). Cambridge, MA: Harvard University Press.

Tyler, E. B. (1871) *Primitive culture*, New York: Brentano's.

van Schaik, C. P., Ancrenaz, M., Borgen, G., Galdikas, B., Knott, C. D., Singleton, I., Suzuki, A., Utami, S. S., and Merrill, M. Y. (2003) "Orangutan cultures and the evolution of material culture," *Science*, *299*: 102–105.

Weaver, I. C. G., Cervoni, N., Champagne, F. A., D'Alessio, A. C., Sharma, S., Seckl, J. R., Dymov, S., Szyf, M., and Meaney, M. J. (2004) "Epigenetic programming by maternal behavior," *Nature Neuroscience*, 7: 847–854.

Whitehead, H., and Rendell, L. (2015) *The cultural lives of whales and dolphins*, Chicago: University of Chicago Press.

Whiten, A., Goodall, J., McGrew, W. C., Nishida, T., Reynolds, V., Sugiyama Y., Tutin, C. E. G., Wrangham, R. W., and Boesch, C. (1999) "Cultures in chimpanzees," *Nature*, *399*: 682–685.

33

VARIETIES OF CULTURE

Grant Goodrich

Introduction

The past several decades have seen increased interest in animal culture. Much of the debate has focused on whether any animals have culture, and on how human culture might differ from the culture of animals. Framing the debate in these ways has led to a consideration of culture being a uniquely human phenomenon (Galef 1992), as a single kind of phenomenon that is shared across several (perhaps very many) species (Laland and Hoppitt 2003; Ramsey 2013), or as existing in many species but coming in a unique form in humans (Tomasello 2016). While I think that many species have culture, and that humans may have unique adaptations for cultural learning, the way that most researchers talk about culture is problematic. Most researchers speak of culture as being a single kind of thing that animals either have or don't have, or if both animals and humans have it, what the humans have is its own single kind of thing, "human culture". The problem is, I shall argue, that culture comes in a variety of kinds, and that a single species, including humans, may have multiple kinds of culture.

When I say that most researchers treat culture as a single kind, I mean that (1) they treat it as arising from a single kind of psychological process or mechanism, or (2) that even if it is supported by multiple psychological processes, those different processes and mechanisms all produce the same kind of thing. The problem with (1) is that it risks ignoring certain processes that produce culture, while favoring others. This could lead to researchers ignoring instances of culture in certain species, or it may lead researchers to over-intellectualize culture. The latter problem could lead to researchers ignoring examples of human culture that we might share with many species, and instead leads them to focus on examples of human culture that rely on very complex psychological processes, and to search for those same processes in other animals. The underlying assumption is that all examples of culture in humans arise from complex psychological processes. But this assumption is problematic as it keeps us from understanding the nature of culture in our own species as well as in others. The problem with (2) is that researchers may overlook important differences between instances of culture, both when studying it in a single species and when comparing the cultures of different species. For example, if the spread of tool use in a chimpanzee community is cultural and relies on complex forms of cognition, and the same community also has other cultural traditions that rely on less sophisticated psychological processes, lumping both instances together as simply "culture" risks missing important differences between the two cases.

In this chapter, I argue that current research shows that culture comes in at least two differ-ent kinds: associative and cognitive; that these kinds are present in very many species of animals; and that the same species may have both kinds of culture. While most of the paradigmatic cases of human culture are cognitive in nature, it is possible that humans also have "lower" forms of culture that are often ignored by researchers. A consequence of all of this is that the way we tend to speak about culture is too simplistic. If we are going to compare cultures in different species, we will first need to determine the kinds of culture each species possesses.

What is culture?

I will adopt Ramsey's definition of culture: "culture is information transmitted between indi-viduals or groups, where this information flows through and brings about the reproduction of, and a lasting change in, the behavioral trait" (Ramsey 2013, 2017). This definition of culture has advantages over the most common alternatives which stress culture as tradition produced by some kind of social learning (see, e.g., Galef 1992; Whiten and van Schaik 2007). It is also broad enough to allow that animals have culture and that culture could be supported by a variety of different psychological processes and mechanisms.

The view that culture is a tradition stems from the methods researchers typically employ when studying culture in animals. Researchers often begin by looking for evidence of differ-ent behavioral traditions in different populations of the same species of animal. For example, researchers studying culture in chimpanzees may be interested in how geographically distinct populations construct different tools. A difficulty with this approach to studying culture is that such traditions may arise because of differing ecological constraints or from the genetic makeup of the communities. Accordingly, researchers must rule out the possibilities that the tradition is not cultural. They often do this by restricting "culture" to those traditions that arise from social learning (see, e.g., Whiten and van Schaik 2007).

By requiring that behavioral traditions are the products of social learning, we avoid the problems of the ecological and genetic causes. However, what counts as social learning is con-troversial. Stimulus enhancement occurs when a demonstrator exposes an observer to a single stimulus, and, as a result, the observer's behavior changes with regard to that stimulus. Stimulus enhancement can facilitate the production of widespread behaviors. For example, adult graylag geese will bite at the stems of butterbur plants. Nearby goslings observe this behavior and, as a result, are attracted to the butterbur plant and begin to explore it. The result is that the goslings learn a new feeding technique which becomes widespread in the flock (Fritz et al. 2000). While many researchers hold that such relatively simple forms of learning are examples of social learn-ing (e.g., Heyes 2012), other researchers restrict social learning, or at least the social learning that can produce culture, to those relatively complex forms of learning like imitation, which involve complex cognition (e.g., Galef 1992). If we accept the more conservative definitions of social learning, we risk excluding examples of culture, such as the feeding behaviors of graylag geese, which are acquired by different means.

What is shared across a culture is information. However, "information" is itself a vague term. Genetic information is shared across a species, but sharing genetic information is not the same as sharing cultural information. Ramsey explicitly restricts cultural information to information that "flows through" behavior, and his notion of information is explicitly Drestkean. Dretske employs a teleofunctional account of information where certain states have the function of providing information about some object, event, or relation (Dretske 1980, 1993). Speedom-eters, when properly set up, provide us with information about speed because they have the function of telling us how fast we are going. Similarly, on this view, organs and behaviors that have a natural function from evolution will also carry information. Most importantly, for present purposes, learning produces functional states that carry information. When an organism learns to avoid a predator, it acquires a psychological state that carries information about that predator. Culture arises when such learning "flows through" the behavior of another individual or group and produces a "lasting change in the behavioral trait" (Ramsey 2013, 2017).

Ramsey's definition focuses on what is shared by members of the same culture while also dissolving debates about what should count as social learning. However, given the diversity of mechanisms and psychological processes underlying culture, we might suppose that some instances of culture will be considerably different from other instances. For example, culture that arises from relatively basic forms of social learning might be constrained in ways that other instances of culture are not. In this way, we can treat Ramsey's definition as a general notion under which we can carve out more fine-grained kinds of culture.

Carving up culture: association and cognition

It is common in comparative psychology to distinguish between cognition and association. This distinction has recently come under a considerable amount of scrutiny (see, e.g., Penn and Povinelli 2007; Buckner 2013, 2017). For present purposes, it will not be necessary that certain behaviors be explained wholly by cognition or by association, but only that there are some behaviors that are best explained primarily by associative processes and mechanisms, and other behaviors that are best explained by accounts that are primarily cognitive.

Associationists tend to favor explanations of behavior that rely on contingency learning that is based on stimulus-bound associative mechanisms (Penn and Povinelli 2007). Consider stimulus generalization. Animals may learn to respond to a stimulus in a particular way. When presented with new, perceptually similar stimuli, the animal automatically transfers their learned response to these novel stimuli. In other words, the animal has learned to generalize from one stimulus to all perceptually similar stimuli.

Stimulus generalization is clearly stimulus bound: the animal must detect perceptual similarity in order to respond to a novel stimulus in the same way they responded to past stimuli. Furthermore, it is associative – the organism detects the similar perceptual features of the stimulus and associates these with past rewards or punishments.

Cognitive explanations usually appeal to mental representations, or to complex learning processes that rely on structured information processing. Researchers appeal to cognitive explanations of behaviors when they think that the behavior in question is too complex to be explained by associative learning. For example, Weir and Kacelnik found that their New Caledonian crow, Betty, could develop novel methods to construct hook tools from novel materials (Weir and Kacelnik 2006). Since the materials in question were perceptually different from materials that Betty had previously used, it would seem that Betty's behavior was not stimulus bound. Furthermore, since Betty was developing novel methods for making hook tools, she was able to respond flexibly to the novel materials.

Associative cultures

Dretske's notion of informational systems is silent about whether the system is a product of evolution (e.g., instincts), design (e.g., thermometers), association, or cognition. Ramsey (2013) clearly rules out genetic information from being cultural, and is open to associative learning as giving rise to culture, but he does not distinguish different kinds of culture. However, if we accept a Dretskean approach to information, and we accept that there is a difference between paradigmatic cognitive and associative systems, then we have grounds for distinguishing between cognitive and associative kinds of culture.

Social learning occurs when one learns through others rather than through direct experience (Gariépy et al. 2014). This can occur in many ways ranging from simple stimulus enhancement, e.g., the goslings' learning to eat butterbur (mentioned above), to the explicit pedagogy that humans often use when teaching each other how to make or use something new (Csibra and Gergely 2011). In this section, I will consider social learning that relies on associative processes. Then I will consider why this kind of culture should be treated differently than other kinds.

Battesti et al. (2012) trained female fruit flies to lay their eggs on one of two possible egg-laying locations by lacing one of them with quinine, which fruit flies find aversive. Later the experimenters removed the quinine but found that these females would continue to prefer the same location, even though both sites lacked quinine. Next, they used these conditioned female fruit flies as "demonstrators" for naïve female fruit flies. The naïve fruit flies copied the preferences of the demonstrators. It would seem that the demonstrators' preference for certain sites "enhanced" those sites, which led to the formation of a preference in the naïve fruit flies.

Battesti et al.'s experiment clearly shows that fruit flies are capable of socially transmitting information, via stimulus enhancement, about preferred nest sites. While it is unlikely that the observed social behavior of fruit flies would be stable in the wild, Battesti et al. demonstrated that it is possible to produce an environment that could facilitate the development and persistence of culture in fruit flies. In other words, in the right environment, animals capable of only associative social learning could possess culture.

Some might object that the account above is highly artificial and that animals that rely primarily on associative learning would not produce cultural traditions in their natural environments. While it is true that the case of the fruit fly culture is highly artificial, there is nothing in principle that should prevent organisms whose learning is only associative from possessing culture.

For a more ecologically valid example, consider French grunts (a species of fish). French grunts learn where to rest in coral reefs by observing others. This learning is presumably facilitated by local and stimulus enhancement. The result of this learning is that certain populations prefer certain resting grounds, and this preference is intergenerational (Brown and Laland 2003). Another species of fish, the blue-headed wrasse, learns where to mate from group members and prefers such mating sites for generations (Bshary et al. 2001). In both cases, we have evidence of information being transferred behaviorally where this transfer produces a lasting change in the behavioral trait – French grunts and blue-headed wrasse have culture.

Cognitive culture

Learned associations do not explain all learned behaviors. Some animals produce flexible behaviors that require complex cognition. For example, some animals are able to form and retrieve mental representations or concepts that they use in higher cognitive capacities, such as categorization and inference. Of course, having higher cognitive capacities is not sufficient for having culture. Many complex cognitive capacities serve only individual goals. Nor is having complex cognition and culture sufficient for having cognitive culture; animals with complex cognition may only have associative cultures.

Like associative cultures, cognitive cultures may be formed in a variety of ways. Some animals may transmit culture via imitation; some may share cultural concepts that cause the members of a community to categorize and interact with their surroundings in similar ways. I will consider only one case of cognitive cultures in animals: cultural concepts in chimpanzees. I will begin by first describing cultural concepts in humans, which I take to be uncontroversially cognitive in nature. Then I will draw on studies of wild chimpanzee communities and argue that their behavior is best explained by positing that the chimpanzees have cultural concepts.

Though psychological and philosophical accounts of concepts sometimes diverge, I will adopt an explicitly psychological notion of concepts: concepts are bodies of knowledge stored in long-term memory that underlie our cognitive capacities (Machery 2009). On this view, concepts come in a variety of formats, e.g., prototypes, exemplars, theories, and ideals. The concepts that an organism has enable it to categorize objects and relations, and to make inferences about them.

Individuals may conceptualize the same objects in different ways. This will depend on how they interact and think about the object in question. If one grows up in North America, the kinds of birds that one is likely to see regularly will be different than the kinds of birds that a person living in Central America might experience. Accordingly, we might expect that what individuals from Central America consider to be a typical bird will differ from the birds North Americans consider typical. In this type of case, the populations' having different concepts is explained by ecological factors and perhaps cultural influences.

But not all differences in concepts can be explained by appeals to ecological differences. Consider the case of expert fishermen in Wisconsin. Expert fishermen from the Menominee tribe in Wisconsin categorize fish according to their ecological relations. This differs from the way that expert European-American fishermen living in the same regions categorize fish. For them, what matters are taxonomic and morphological similarities (Medin et al. 2006). The fishermen are using the same waters and are experiencing the same species of fish. However, the different cultures place different values on fish, which results in different ways of interacting with the various fish species. Accordingly, members of the different communities form different cultural concepts – concepts that are widely shared across a community and whose content depends partly on cultural influences (Ross and Tidwell 2010).

Most psychological studies of animal concepts only consider whether animals have concepts and, if so, what conceptual abilities go along with them. For example, some researchers consider whether animals form concepts of objects in their environment (Tanaka 2006) or whether animals form abstract concepts, such as same/different concepts (Wright and Katz 2006). Other studies investigate what animals can do with their concepts, e.g., whether animals can engage in various forms of inference (for a review of the conceptual abilities of animals, see Zentall et al. 2008). Few studies consider the concepts of wild animals, and fewer are interested in whether the concepts that animals have are cultural. Perhaps the studies most suggestive of cultural concepts in animals are from Gruber and his colleagues (Gruber et al. 2009; Gruber et al. 2011; Gruber et al. 2012), so let us turn to examine that research in some detail.

In the Budongo forest, there is a community of chimpanzees known as Sonso chimpanzees. The Sonso community is notable because, unlike many chimpanzee communities, the Sonso chimps do not use tools to procure food. The sole exception is the leaf "sponges", which all wild chimpanzees use. About 180 km away, a different community, the Kanyawara chimpanzees, regularly uses sticks to procure food. Gruber and his colleagues sought to determine if the Sonso chimps would use sticks as tools given the opportunity to do so, and whether the Kanyawara would similarly use sticks given the same task.

Gruber and his colleagues devised a honey retrieval task in which chimpanzees could procure honey from a hole in a log that was lying horizontally on the ground. In the first condition, it was possible for the chimpanzees to retrieve the honey using only their hands; in a second condition, the only way the chimpanzees could retrieve the honey was by using a stick. In the first condition, 2 out of 13 Sonso chimps used leaf sponges to acquire the honey; the rest used their hands. Four Sonso chimps also used leaf "sponges" in the second condition, but only one of them successfully retrieved the honey. Kanyawara chimps tended to use sticks in both conditions:

6 out of 10 in the first condition and 11 out of 12 in the second. Gruber et al. concluded that the differences in the chimps' behavior were due to their cultural knowledge (Gruber et al. 2009).

In a follow-up experiment (Gruber et al. 2011), the second condition was repeated, but this time the condition was modified: a stick with leaves removed from half of it was placed near the hole. The Sonso chimps ignored the stick. Some of the Kanyawara chimps used the stick, while others used sticks from the surrounding environment. In a second condition, with Sonso chimps only, a branch with leaves stripped from half of it was inserted into the hole with honey. Some of the Sonso chimps removed the branch and used the leaves from it to make a sponge; others just removed the branch and tried to obtain honey using their fingers, and others removed the branch and attempted to retrieve the honey using leaf sponges. Some of the chimps smelled the honey on the stick after removing it; four of them consumed the honey on the stick, but none of them tried to use it to procure more honey.

Do the Kanyawara chimpanzees have concepts of their "stick tools"? Experimental studies show that chimpanzees regularly form categories of common objects (including plants) in their surroundings. What's more, these categories are not best explained by stimulus generalization. Tanaka (2006) found that chimpanzees easily spontaneously categorize flowers, weeds, and trees from their surroundings, and that these categories include items that are perceptually dissimilar, e.g., dandelions and camellias.

Besides forming categories of perceptually dissimilar items, chimpanzees are also able to categorize objects based on thematic relations and functions, though it is difficult for them to do so (Tanaka 2006; Hopper et al. 2015). However, Hopper et al. (2015) found that chimpanzees who observe conspecifics using an object will readily learn the functional properties of that object. In their study, Hopper et al. provided chimpanzees with a polycarbonate rod. The rod can be utilized to retrieve a reward via a "poke" technique or a "lift" technique. The "poke" technique can be learned individually, but the chimpanzees in Hopper et al.'s study had not previously employed the lift technique. Accordingly, Hopper et al. set up their apparatus so that the only way for a chimpanzee to retrieve a reward was by utilizing the "lift" technique. Hopper et al. found that none of their chimpanzees were able to learn a "lift" technique through individual learning. However, 15 out of 18 chimpanzees quickly learned the technique after witnessing a human model or a conspecific successfully use the technique. This suggests that chimpanzees are not particularly good at seeing the functional properties of an object unless they have seen a demonstrator exploiting those properties. It is therefore not surprising that the Sonso chimpanzees do not see that a stick could be used as a tool. We might also expect that if they did see a conspecific using a stick as a tool, the behavior would spread across the community.

Given the conceptual abilities of chimpanzees, it is likely that both the Sonso chimps and Kanyawara chimps have some kind of concept of sticks. However, the Kanyawara's concept includes knowledge about the functional properties of sticks that make them useful as tools. Given the fact that chimpanzees do not readily learn the functional properties of an object without first witnessing a conspecific using the object, it is unlikely that they would form such concepts individually. Thus, their concept is cultural in the sense that some of the content of the concept exists because of cultural transmission, and this information is common to most Kanyawara community members' "stick" concept. The Sonso chimpanzees, in contrast, seem to lack a cultural concept of stick as tool, though it is possible that they have some more basic (and non-cultural) concept "stick".

Conclusion

So far we have seen how culture can arise from both association and cognition. Both kinds of culture are significant. Having a culture affects how individuals interact with their environment and with each other. However, just as cognition gives rise to more flexible behaviors, cognitive cultures also give rise to more flexible cultural behavior. Having cultural knowledge of the functional properties of sticks enables Kanyawara chimpanzees to use sticks in a variety of feeding situations and not just the ones with which they are familiar. French grunts have a cultural preference for certain resting sites, but because they (presumably) lack a concept that contains knowledge about what makes a good resting site, they are only able to respond to the presence of a preferred site (which may not be the best option for nesting).

The distinction is not just important for understanding the differences between kinds of cultures, it is also important for how we conceptualize and discuss culture in general. Much of the interest in animal culture has been on the very question of whether animals have it. One problem with asking the question this way is that researchers have been searching for a single thing "culture" that might be common to both animals and humans. I suspect that part of the reason some researchers recoil at the idea of fish and insects having culture is because they believe that the minds of humans and the minds of fish and insects are too different to share anything as rich as culture. Once we distinguish between associative and cognitive cultures, we see that the claim that certain species have culture is not always the same as claiming that those species have the same kind of thing that humans have. This will depend on what kind(s) of culture we think the species in question has.

Distinguishing between associative and cognitive culture also opens up new avenues of research. We typically assume that human culture is cognitive in nature, but it is possible, perhaps likely, that some culture in humans is associative. For example, Behrens and his colleagues have found that the learning of social value in humans is at least some times associative (Behrens et al. 2008). If this learning of social value leads to culture, then we would have good reason for thinking that human culture is sometimes associative.

Distinguishing between kinds of cultures will obviously influence debates about whether human culture and animal culture are homologous or merely analogous (Tomasello 2016). The answer may turn out to be affirmative on both counts. It may turn out that some associative culture in humans (if there is any) is homologous to associative cultures in other taxa; it may also turn out that some cognitive culture in humans is homologous to cognitive cultures in other animals; and it may also turn out that there are some instances of culture in humans that are genuinely unique in that they rely on processes that only exist in humans. If the latter is the case, then there may be examples of culture in animals that are merely analogous to certain examples of culture in humans.

Once we recognize that culture comes in a variety of kinds, we can begin to see the various ways in which cultures can arise, recognize that variety in our own species and others, and better appreciate the continuities and discontinuities that exist between different species.

Further reading

N. Emery, N. Clayton, and C. Frith's (eds.) *Social Intelligence: From Brain to Culture* (Oxford: Oxford University Press, 2007) contains many excellent papers on social cognition and culture in animals. For more on how human social cognition and culture may be different, see M. Tomasello's *A Natural History of Human Thinking* (Cambridge, MA: Harvard University Press, 2014).

References

Battesti, M., Moreno, C., Joly, D., and Mery, F. (2012). "Spread of Social Information and Dynamics of Social Transmission within *Drosophila* Groups". *Current Biology* 22: 309–313.

Behrens, T. E. J., Hunt, L. T., Woolrich, M. W., and Rushworth, M. F. S. (2008). "Associative learning of social value". *Nature* 456: 245–249.

Brown, C., and Laland, K. N. (2003). "Social learning in fishes: a review". *Fish and Fisheries* 4: 280–288.

Bshary, R., Wickler, W., and Fricke, H. (2001). "Fish cognition: A primate's eye view". *Animal Cognition* 5: 1–13.

Buckner, C. (2013). "A property cluster theory of cognition". *Philosophical Psychology* 28: 307–336.

———— (2017). "Understanding Associative and Cognitive Explanations in Comparative Psychology". In: Andrews, K., and Beck, J. (eds.) *Routledge Handbook of Philosophy of Animal Minds*. New York: Routledge.

Csibra, G., and Gergely, G. (2011). "Natural pedagogy as evolutionary adaptation". *Philosophical Transactions of the Royal Society of London B: Biological Sciences* 366: 1149–1157.

Dretske, F. (1980). "The intentionality of cognitive states". *Midwest Studies in Philosophy* 5: 281–294.

————. (1993). "The nature of thought". *Philosophical Studies: An International Journal for Philosophy in the Analytic Tradition* 70: 185–189.

Fritz, J., Bisenberger, A., and Kotrschal, K. (2000). "Stimulus enhancement in greylag geese: Socially mediated learning of an operant task". *Animal Behaviour* 59: 1119–1125.

Galef, B. G. (1992). "The question of animal culture". *Human Nature* 3: 157–178.

Gariépy, J.-F., Watson, K. K., Du, E., Xie, D. L., Erb, J., Amasino, D., and Platt, M. L. (2014). "Social learning in humans and other animals". *Frontiers in Neuroscience* 8: 1–13.

Gruber, T., Muller, M. N., Reynolds, V., Wrangham, R., and Zuberbühler, K. (2011). "Community-specific evaluation of tool affordances in wild chimpanzees". *Scientific Reports* 1: 128. DOI: 10.1038/srep00128.

Gruber, T., Muller, M. N., Strimling, P., Wrangham, R., and Zuberbühler, K. (2009). "Wild chimpanzees rely on cultural knowledge to solve an experimental honey acquisition task". *Current Biology* 19: 1806–1810.

Gruber, T., Singleton, I., and van Schaik, C. P. (2012). "Sumatran orangutans differ in their cultural knowledge but not in their cognitive abilities". *Current Biology* 22: 2231–2235.

Heyes, C. (2012). "What's social about social learning?". *Journal of Comparative Psychology* 126: 193–202.

Hopper, L. M., Lambeth, S. P., Schapiro, S. J., and Whiten, A. (2015). "The importance of witnessed agency in chimpanzee social learning of tool use". *Behavioural Processes* 112: 120–129.

Laland, K. N., and Hoppitt, W. (2003). "Do animals have culture?". *Evolutionary Anthropology: Issues, News, and Reviews* 12: 150–159.

Machery, E. (2009). *Doing Without Concepts*. New York: Oxford University Press.

Medin, D. L., Ross, N. O., Atran, S., Cox, D., Coley, J., Proffitt, J. B., and Blok, S. (2006). "Folkbiology of freshwater fish". *Cognition* 99: 237–273.

Penn, D. C., and Povinelli, D. J. (2007). "Causal cognition in human and nonhuman animals: A comparative, critical review". *Annual Review of Psychology* 58: 97–118.

Ramsey, G. (2013). "Culture in humans and other animals". *Biology & Philosophy* 28: 457–479.

———— (2017). "What is animal culture". In: Andrews, K., and Beck, J. (eds.) *Routledge Handbook of Philosophy of Animal Minds*. New York: Routledge.

Ross, N., and Tidwell, M. (2010). "Concepts and culture". In: Mareschal, D., Quinn, P. C., and Lea, S. E. G. (eds), *The Making of Human Concepts*. New York: Oxford University Press, pp. 133–148.

Tanaka, M. (2006). "Spontaneous categorization of natural objects in chimpanzees". In: Matsuzawa, T., Tomonaga, M., and Tanaka, M. (eds), *Cognitive Development in Chimpanzees*. Tokyo: Springer.

Tomasello, M. (2016). "The ontogeny of cultural learning". *Current Opinion in Psychology* 8: 1–4.

Weir, A. A., and Kacelnik, A. (2006). "A New Caledonian crow (*Corvus moneduloides*) creatively re-designs tools by bending or unbending aluminum strips". *Animal Cognition* 9: 317–334.

Whiten, A., and van Schaik, C. P. (2007). "The evolution of animal 'cultures' and social intelligence". *Philosophical Transactions of the Royal Society of London B: Biological Sciences* 362: 603–620.

Wright, A. A., and Katz, J. S. (2006). "Mechanisms of *same/different* concept learning in primates and avians". *Behavioral Processes* 72: 234–254.

Zentall, T. R., Wasserman, E. A., Lazareva, O. F., and Thompson, R. K. R. (2008). "Concept learning in animals". *Comparative Cognition and Behavior Reviews* 3: 13–45.

34

ANIMAL TRADITIONS

What they are, and why they matter

Rachael L. Brown

Introduction: what are animal traditions?

In the early 1920s, blue tits across Britain were observed stealing milk from the bottles on people's doorsteps by prizing up, or pecking open, their foil tops (Fisher and Hinde 1949). While this behavior alone is interesting enough, its spread through blue tit populations is striking, because birds all over the country adopted the behavior so rapidly that only some form of social transmission could explain it. Indeed, subsequent research into blue tit milk–bottle–opening has shown that the transmission of the trait between individual birds, along with its maintenance in populations over multiple generations, was[1] dependent on a form of social learning – specifically, local enhancement (Sherry and Galef 1990; Sherry and Galef 1984).[2]

Local enhancement is a widespread and relatively "simple"[3] form of social learning. It "occurs when, after or during a demonstrator's presence, or interaction with objects at a particular location, an observer is more likely to visit or interact with objects at that location" (Hoppitt and Laland 2013: 64; Thorpe 1963). In mediating the transmission of learned traits between individuals, it can allow behavioral innovations to spread through animal populations. To illustrate, in the case of blue tit milk–bottle–opening, it is thought that an individual bird (or, more likely, birds (Lefebvre 1995)) hit upon the initial milk–bottle–opening innovation via a combination of luck and asocial learning (such as trial-and-error learning).[4] Following the initial innovation, naïve individuals were then drawn to the milk bottles by local enhancement (i.e. they were more likely to interact with milk bottle tops, having seen the successful demonstrators do so). The naïve birds then, through their own trial and error, learned to open the milk bottles themselves. Given that there are very few possible successful milk–bottle–opening techniques, the same techniques then proliferated through the population. In this way, the milk–bottle–opening trait became widespread and persisted until milk bottle delivery was phased out some years later. Importantly, although asocial learning plays a significant role here, the persistence of the milk–bottle–opening behavior over multiple generations is heavily reliant on social learning (Sherry and Galef 1990; Sherry and Galef 1984).[5]

Blue tits are not the only nonhuman species able to transmit behavior over multiple generations through "simple" forms of social learning such as local enhancement. Stimulus enhancement, observational conditioning, response facilitation, social enhancement, observational R–S learning, emulation, opportunity providing, and inadvertent coaching[6] have also been shown to

362

mediate the transmission and maintenance of various traits in many animals not usually considered particularly cognitively complex, including other species of birds (Krebs and Kroodsma 1980), fish (Brown and Laland 2003; Laland et al. 2003), and rodents (Eisner and Terkel 1991). Importantly, what these cases – which I will broadly call "animal traditions"[7] – demonstrate is that social transmission is not restricted to so-called "smart" animals such as chimpanzees and cetaceans. Indeed, recent laboratory work eliciting the social transmission of a learned skill over multiple generations in bumblebees (Alem et al. 2016) suggests that the basic cognitive ingredients for animal traditions are relatively unsophisticated, and exist far outside those lineages in which we would typically imagine them to reside.

The significance of such (nonhuman) animal traditions is debated (Laland and Galef 2009; Avital and Jablonka 2000; Fragaszy and Perry 2003). Historically, however, those interested in animal cognition, and behavioral and cognitive evolution, in animals (comparative psychologists, behavioral ecologists, ethologists, and animal behaviorists), have tended to overlook them. While there is, of course, much discussion in the literature on social learning and its role in the individual life histories of animals, the type of transgenerational transmission which characterizes animal traditions is often assumed to be of little explanatory importance outside of the primate lineage. In this short chapter, I consider why this has been the norm, and offer some reasons for why animal traditions are far from unimportant in understanding both the evolution of cognition and its proximate mechanisms. To begin with, we shall look at two key claims which motivate the historical view. The first relates to how well simple forms of social learning transfer behaviors between individuals.

Can "simple" mechanisms of social learning facilitate the transmission of traits over multiple generations?

The "simple" mechanisms of social learning underwriting most animal traditions are widely viewed to be incapable of accurately transmitting traits across multiple generations (Laland and Janik 2006; Laland and Galef 2009; Avital and Jablonka 2000; Laland and Hoppitt 2003). We can illustrate this with the blue tit case. Local enhancement does not facilitate the transfer of a *particular* milk-bottle-opening behavior between individuals; rather, it *increases the likelihood* of naïve birds hitting upon the milk-bottle-opening behavior via their own asocial learning. While in this circumstance there are very few ways to open a milk bottle, so we see the spread of a relatively homogenous behavior throughout the population,[8] it is easy to imagine cases where this would not be so. For example, imagine if, rather than requiring an imprecise peck on the lid of the bottles, opening the milk bottles involved a precise or unobvious sequence of behaviors. In such a circumstance, we could reasonably predict that mere local enhancement would be insufficient for milk-bottle-opening to persist in a population. In effect, the animals in question would be in a game of telephone, in which the information required to open the milk bottles is eroded from the population with each imperfect transfer. Not only would it appear impossible for any complex behavioral innovations that arise in such populations to persist via social learning alone, but also unlikely that complex behavioral traits could evolve through any cumulative evolutionary process (such as natural selection) in which social learning acted as a route of multigenerational inheritance.

Expanding a little on this point, the evolution of complex adaptations via natural selection usually involves the gradual accumulation of small fitness-enhancing innovations over multiple generations. It is only via such gradual change that a process like genetic mutation, which is blind to adaptive benefit, is likely to generate complex adaptations. This is because large, undirected changes to the phenotype of an organism (through, say, the duplication or translocation of a large swathe of DNA) are more likely to reduce, rather than increase, the adaptive fit of that organism with their environment. Griffiths and Sterelny (1999) illustrate this nicely with the analogy of trying to crack a combination lock. For a combination lock with six wheels numbered 0–9, for example, there are 151,200 different possible combinations of the wheels if each number can only be used once, and a million different possible combinations if each number can be used more than once. If a safecracker were to attempt to open the lock by getting every number in the combination correct in one go, they would far more likely than not take a very, very long time to succeed. Imagine, however, that there is a "click" when each wheel of the lock is turned into the right position. By carefully turning the first wheel and waiting for the click, and then the second, and so on, the safecracker could quite quickly and easily determine the correct combination to open the lock, and surely in far less time than if they went with the aforementioned wholesale approach. As Griffiths and Sterelny (1999) note, natural selection works something like a safe cracker listening for clicks. Just as there are many more incorrect than correct states of the wheels of a combination lock, there are many more ways for organisms to be maladapted to their environments, and only a few ways to be adapted. By retaining small adaptive innovations (like the safe cracker retaining "one wheel right") and building upon them, however, populations under natural selection gradually build up the required innovations for complex adaptations to evolve. In effect, natural selection solves the problems in the environment through a process of trial and error coupled with the ability to retain small beneficial adaptations, just like the safecracker turning each wheel in turn, listening for clicks.

Although the various mechanisms of asocial learning seen in the animal world are not completely blind to adaptive benefit in the way that genetic mutation is, the most common form of asocial learning – trial-and-error learning – is not "insightful". Animals learning via trial-and-error are not solving the problems they face "in their heads" and then executing the most adaptive behavior the first time. Rather, they are innovating in a relatively random manner and repeating those behaviors which produce a reward. In a manner akin to that described for mutation and selection above, this means that asocial learning is unlikely to facilitate the development of complex behaviors in organisms through anything but an incremental process. Although large adaptive behavioral innovations are, in principle, possible via trial and error, as with genetic mutations, there are many more ways in which an organism can be behaviorally maladapted than adapted to their environment. Small variations on what is currently working are more likely to be, if not adaptive, neutral with respect to survival and reproduction, than large innovations.

Returning again to the hypothetical "complex" milk-bottle-opening technique case again, it is now clear why fidelity of transfer is important. Recall, here we are concerned with a non-obvious and complex behavioral trait. For such a trait to arise and persist, it seems correct to assume that the small innovations in the milk-bottle-opening technique that individuals hit upon via their own *asocial* learning must be propagated and maintained in the population via an accurate mechanism of transmission between individuals (i.e. an accurate social-learning mechanism). If innovations are not able to be transferred between individuals in the population with sufficient fidelity for them to be gradually and cumulatively built upon over time, however, adaptive complexity would be highly improbable.

If this pessimistic, traditional picture of the limited power of simple forms of social learning is correct, any behaviors, skills, or information that is transmitted trans-generationally via "simple" social-learning mechanisms are best understood as temporary effects of the environment. On such a view, any adaptive benefit that such traditional resources confer on organisms is easily accounted for by reference to the fitness of the genes producing the cognitive capacities that explain them given a particular environmental context. In short, although socially learned behaviors, skills, and information can no doubt be fitness enhancing, when we think about how that fitness benefit is transmitted between generations, it is the genetic inheritance of the social-learning capacity that should be invoked rather than the inheritance via social learning of the particular behavior, skill, or bit of information.

An example of this disinterest in animal traditions on the grounds that they lack any long-term evolutionary significance can be seen in the discussion of putative cases of animal culture. As outlined by Ramsey and Goodrich (Chapters 32 and 33, respectively, in this volume), many of those interested in cultural evolution, cultural inheritance, and the cognitive underpinnings of culture have eschewed animal traditions as being different in kind to "true" culture (i.e. the type of complex customs, tools, and structures seen in human societies). Culture, it is claimed, is complex and cumulative, relying heavily on the presence of cognitively demanding forms of social learning, such as explicit teaching and copying. Animal traditions, in contrast, can only ever be rudimentary in nature because the "simple" learning mechanisms that underwrite them are unable to facilitate the persistence of cumulative or complex traits. Many advocates of this type of view go on to argue that humans are unique in having culture and in undergoing any form of culturally mediated evolution (Laland and Galef 2009).

To illustrate, Michael Tomasello (2014, 2009) (a prominent player in these debates) argues that only humans are capable of cumulative culture, as it is reliant on a unique human capacity for joint attention (the ability to share attention on an object with another individual by, for example, pointing). Without joint attention, he claims, humans would be unable to engage in the type of imitative and linguistically based learning that is required for the cumulative, complex culture we only see in our own species. Entailed by this account of human culture is the assumption that nonhuman animals (lacking in joint attention, and thus imitation and linguistic social learning) are incapable of cumulative, complex cultures. Bennett Galef (2012, 2009) expresses a similar view, arguing that imitation and teaching are far more developed in humans than any other species (and it is only this more developed sort of social learning that can support what we would call culture).

This orthodoxy has some intuitive pull. As I have outlined above, we have good reason to be cautious about the long-term stability and evolutionary potential of animal traditions. There is, however, some evidence that the intuitive orthodoxy is mistaken. Specifically, there are examples of what appear to be relatively complex behaviors being transferred via "simple" forms of social learning. To illustrate, black rats in the pine forests of Jerusalem learn from their parents via local enhancement to extract the seeds from pine cones (Zohar and Terkel 1991; Aisner and Terkel 1985, 1992). Unlike in the case of the milk-bottle-opening behavior, which involves the transmission of a relatively simple and imprecise extractive foraging technique (the milk bottles are relatively easy to peck open and do not need to be pecked open in a very precise manner – simply pecking with determination will do), accessing the pine cone seeds requires that rat pups execute a precise sequence of behaviors. Specifically, the scales of the cones of Jerusalem pine are very tightly packed and can only be removed (and the seeds inside them thus obtained) by being stripped from the shaft sequentially from one particular end. To be able to successfully learn the adult technique, the naïve pups must learn a number of pieces of information: that pine cones are a food source; how to access the seeds from within pine cone scales; and that to get the scales off the cone, they must be stripped from the correct end. Naïve rat pups learn this by being exposed to partially stripped pine cones and scales by their parents as well as observing their behavior. In a two-stage process involving local enhancement similar to that already described in blue tits, the rat pups are drawn to the pine cones via social learning, and, once there, asocially innovate. In this manner, a relatively complex extractive foraging behavior is transmitted by a "simple" mechanism of social learning over multiple generations.

There is evidence of similar mechanisms being involved in other cases of much more complex animal traditions, such as the transmission of the manufacture and design of stick tools and their use in the New Caledonian crow (Hunt and Gray 2003; Kenward et al. 2006; Holzhaider et al. 2010a, 2010b). New Caledonian crows manufacture and use stick- and leaf-based tools, which they use to "fish" insect larvae out of holes. Both the manufacture of the tools and their use requires a reasonably precise set of actions (for example, for stick tools, the sticks must be broken in just the right places to fashion a "hook", and the right "hooked" end of the tool must be inserted in the hole to successfully obtain food). As with the black rat pine-cone-stripping, the activity of adult crows scaffolds the learning of juvenile crows in important ways. The juvenile crows learn to use tools by interacting with the discarded tools of adult crows. They are interested in them and pick them up and carry them about. Coupled with local enhancement, this facilitates asocial learning in juvenile crows regarding both how to appropriately use tools, *and* the types of features of good tools. Once again, *contra* the intuitive orthodoxy, a relatively simple form of social learning is playing a central role in the maintenance of a behavior in a population over multiple generations. These types of examples undermine the view that cumulative behavioral evolution driven by social learning is a purely human trait (though I do not deny that the prodigious human capacity for cumulative cultural evolution suggests something importantly different is happening in the human case – human culture doesn't seem to just be an aggregation of a lot of animal traditions).

Are animal traditions too sensitive to environmental change to be of long-term significance?

A second common concern regarding the significance of animal traditions (closely related to the first) is that, even if cases like that of the black rat and New Caledonian crow suggest that quite simple forms of social learning could *in principle* facilitate the veridical, multigenerational transmission of relatively complex traits within populations, the persistence of such traits remains too sensitive to context to be of any significance on longer (evolutionary) timescales. In short, even if the game of telephone described above is overcome, a relatively small environmental change is all that is needed for these behavioral traits to be lost from populations forever. In the case of the blue tit milk-bottle-opening, for example, when the delivery of milk bottles ceased, unsurprisingly so too did the milk-bottle-opening behavior (McCarthy 2003). The behavior simply died with those birds that carried it, as its transmission to naïve individuals was reliant on the presence of milk bottles. Similarly, the pine-cone-opening of the black rats of the Jerusalem pine forests would likely be lost to the population were there no longer pine cones to open. In the evolutionary context, this issue is particularly worrisome, and is made stark when we compare the transmission of traits via social learning to that via genetic means.

Genetic traits are transmitted across generations regardless of whether they are expressed. The classic recessive gene cases we all learned at school, such as blue eyes, cystic fibrosis, and Huntington's disease, are all examples of traits that can be transmitted from parent to offspring without expression in the parent. In contrast, no such "silent" transmission is possible for animal traditions. Being transmitted via social learning, they must be present in each generation, making them sensitive to a slew of environmental effects that genetic inheritance is not troubled by (Laland and Janik 2006). While this sensitivity to environmental change does pose an issue for the significance of animal traditions to those interested in cognitive and behavioral evolution, a similar thing can be said for any traits transmitted via social learning, human cultural traits included.

In response to the worries above, one might suggest that the challenge of fragility is only of issue if we expect large-scale and persistent environmental changes to be frequent, because social learning itself offers some robustness to the traits it fosters in populations. By facilitating the propagation of traditions and cultural traits within populations, social learning makes the persistence of those traits less sensitive to small-scale, chancy events, such as predation and localized or temporally restricted environmental change. One bad season where a particular foodstuff is scarce is not enough to lose the specific extractive foraging tradition relevant to that food, so long as some individuals live to see multiple seasons. Only a few individuals with the behavior need survive long enough to see the return of the previous environmental conditions to "reseed" the subsequent naïve generation and for the behavior to carry on.

While both the sensitivity to environmental change and the limited fidelity of transfer of the simple forms of social learning involved in animal traditions present challenges to the general view I am advocating here, they are not insurmountable. The human cultural case gives us some good pointers for the types of things that can mitigate the issues which we might expect to see in animal populations with traditions.

Drawing on the human case to better understand animal traditions

Humans intentionally and unintentionally modify their environments to make them more amenable to the transmission of cultural information from one generation to the next. For example, we provide children with toys, games, and situations that mimic those they will face in adult life (e.g. consider the ubiquity of dolls, play kitchens, doll houses, and dress-ups in the lives of our children). By provisioning our offspring with situations in which they can have cultural information presented and modeled to them, and where they can test what they have learned, we increase the likelihood that our accumulated cultural knowledge will be passed on to them (Sterelny 2012). This type of "epistemic engineering" or "downstream epistemic niche construction" also features in the lives of animals with traditions. As already mentioned, naïve black rats in the Jerusalem pine forests and the New Caledonian crows learn specific extractive foraging techniques from their parents by interacting with discarded bits of an adult "kit". In leaving their half-stripped pine cones and tools about, they are epistemically engineering the learning environment of their offspring, increasing the likelihood that their particular extractive foraging traditions will be passed on. Other forms of epistemic engineering in animals are as simple as older individuals exhibiting an increased tolerance for the presence of juveniles when hunting, mating, food processing, and so forth, thereby enabling them to learn social information about those practices. Of course, this type of engineering is very simple and far removed from that seen in humans, but this is not unexpected given the great differences between human and nonhuman cultures.

The human case offers us a further pointer regarding how animal traditions might have a lasting impact on populations, despite the challenges of fragility and fidelity in genetic assimilation. Print reading is a human cultural trait for which there are no specialized neurocognitive mechanisms, having arisen only five to six million years ago. Rather, print-reading capacities are the product of careful tuition and effortful social learning (Heyes and Frith 2014). What we do see, however, are perceptual and attentional biases that dispose human children to develop print reading (without these, learning to read can be very difficult, such as in dyslexia (Parachini et al. 2007)). While working out the evolutionary history of these biases is difficult (did they come before or after print reading, and in what form?), it is not unreasonable to think that they have been strengthened by selection for reading capacity. Specifically, following cultural innovations for reading, those individuals with perceptual and attentional biases that make them more capable of learning to read or capable of learning to read faster would plausibly have had fitness advantages over those without them (or with more rudimentary forms of them). This would have resulted for selection for such biases and a further strengthening of them in the human population over time. We expect that such processes of "genetic assimilation" are reasonably common in human populations (indeed, much of gene culture–co-evolution literature is predicated on such an assumption). Importantly for my purposes here, the process of genetic assimilation suggests that *even if* it turns out that animal traditions are only ephemeral (fleeting, lasting for only relatively brief evolutionary timescales and not particularly stable), they would still be of evolutionary importance.

In particular, just as human cultures can influence genetic evolution, so could animal traditions. When fitness-enhancing behavioral innovations arise in populations and are maintained via social learning, there is competition within individuals to gain the behavior, and gain it faster and more reliably than others. This plausibly results in selection for genetic adaptations that make the inheritance of the trait more reliable (Tebbich et al. 2016). We see this playing out in the case of the finches of the Galapagos.

Evolutionary biologists have long been impressed by the diversity of beak morphologies and foraging techniques seen in the numerous finch species found on the Galapagos Islands (often known as Darwin's finches). This diversity is even more impressive given that it has its origins in a relatively small founding flock of finches blown from Central or South America (Sato et al. 2001; Vincek et al. 1997). It is also curious, as other similar bird species endemic to the Galapagos have not undergone the same level of diversification. Recent work (Tebbich et al. 2010) suggests that the differences in diversification are likely the consequence of an increased disposition to foraging innovation in the finches. Capacities for social and asocial learning allowed ancestral finch populations to take advantage of novel food resources that other birds did not utilize. This occurred over multiple generations, altering the selective regime that these ancestral populations were under, and ultimately "driving" finch populations to further adaptation to the novel foraging niches and diversification. The sharp-beaked ground finch serves to illustrate this well. This species of finch makes use of the abundance of sea birds on the Galapagos. Sometimes called "vampire finches," they peck out the feathers of sea birds and drink blood from the wound they create. They also make use of the sea birds' eggs by kicking or pushing the large, heavy eggs over ledges or onto rocks and breaking them open to access the nutritious yolk inside. Both of these foraging behaviors are enhanced by a series of morphological adaptations seen only in the sharp-beak ground finch. In particular, they have pointier and stronger beaks and stronger legs than other finches of the Galapagos (Schluter and Grant 1984). The unique morphological adaptations of the vampire finch appear to have arisen only after the unique foraging behavior (or some rudimentary form of it) had evolved. This is because, before the behavioral foraging innovation occurred and its spread in finch populations, there would have been no selective advantage to the morphological adaptations in question, and they are costly to maintain. Given this, it has been claimed (Tebbich et al. 2010) that the innovative foraging behavior arose first, most likely by accident or learning-based exploration, and was then reinforced by further success. The novel behavior then proliferated through the population, most likely through a combination of social and asocial learning (Tebbich et al. 2016). Only once this had occurred was there sufficient selective pressure in place for morphological adaptation to occur. In this way, a behavioral tradition can be said to have "driven" the evolution of the beak morphology of the sharp-beaked ground finch via genetic assimilation.

Conclusion

In this short chapter, I have offered a number of examples of the multigenerational transmission of traits in nonhuman animals via so-called "simple" forms of social learning, such as stimulus enhancement (also known as "animal traditions"). Although there are questions surrounding the evolutionary significance of animal traditions relating to their long-term robustness, I have a variety of reasons to think that they may be important in explaining aspects of both the behaviors and morphologies of many animal populations.

Notes

1 As the daily delivery of fresh milk has dwindled, so too has the milk-bottle-opening behavior, and in areas where milk bottle delivery has subsequently recommenced, the milk-bottle-opening trait has not resurfaced (McCarthy 2003). This is not unsurprising if social transmission (rather than genetic inheritance) was playing a central role in the maintenance of the behavior in tit populations.

2 There is also some recent evidence (Aplin et al. 2013) that cultural conformity plays a role in the transmission of behaviors in blue tit populations. Although this has not been shown for the milk-bottle-opening behavior, it is reasonable to believe that it was in play in that case also.

3 The distinction between so-called "simple" and "complex" forms of social learning in comparative psychology is a fraught one (see Meketa 2014, and Mikhalevich (nee. Meketa) Chapter 41 in this volume, for a useful discussion of the challenges to a single objective index for assessing the "simplicity" of cognitive structures, processes, or mechanisms). Here it is intended to delineate between explicit teaching or "true" imitation and other mechanisms; whether there is a "real" difference between them is, however, not particularly important to the claims being made.

4 This is not unsurprising given that blue tits are attracted to shiny objects. As foil milk-bottle lids are shiny, and were very commonly in the blue tit's environment during this period, the eventual interaction between a blue tit and a milk-bottle lid was reasonably likely.

5 It is, of course, also reliant on asocial learning, both with respect to the original innovation, and in the transmission of the milk-bottle-opening behavior. Naïve individuals ultimately use *asocial* learning to acquire the milk-bottle-opening technique, but only after having been drawn to the bottles *via social learning*.

6 See Hoppitt and Laland (2013: 63–4) for definitions of the various forms of social learning. As noted by Ramsey and Goodrich (Chapters 32 and 33, respectively, in this volume), whether all these forms of social learning are importantly different, mechanistically, from asocial learning is unclear, but for my purposes here this distinction is not important.

7 The term "traditions" has been employed in various ways in the literature on the transmission of traits via social learning in nonhuman animals (see Laland and Janik (2006), Ramsey (Chapter 32 in this volume), and Goodrich (Chapter 33 in this volume)). Here, I am using a very broad definition of the term to refer to "distinctive behavior patterns, pieces of information or knowledge that are shared by two or more individuals in a social unit, which persist over time and that new practitioners acquire in part through socially aided learning" (Hoppitt and Laland 2013: 4).

8 As already mentioned above, cultural conformity plays a role in the transmission of behaviors in blue tit populations. This could offer a further reason for observing homogeneity in the socially transmitted behaviors in this instance.

Further reading

There are two key anthologies and a monograph discussing animal traditions that further develop many of the ideas here: *The Question of Animal Culture* (edited by Kevin Laland and Bennett Galef), *The Biology of Traditions* (edited by Dorothy Fragaszy and Susan Perry), and *Animal Traditions* (by Eytan Avital and Eva Jablonka). Those interested in social learning in animals will find *Social Learning* by Kevin Laland and William Hoppitt a very useful resource. For a detailed discussion of genetic assimilation, social learning, and innovation in nonhuman animals, see Tebbich et al. (2016).

References

Alem, S., Perry, C. J., Zhu, X., Loukola, O. J., Ingraham, T., Sovik, E., and Chittka, L., 2016. "Learning and cultural transmission of string pulling in an insect". *PLoS Biology*, 14(10), p. e1002564.

Aisner, R., and Terkel, J., 1985. "Habitat exploitation through cultural transmission: Pine cone feeding behaviour in black rats (*Rattus rattus*)". *Proceedings of the 19th Inter-National Ethological Conference*. Toulouse: France.

Aisner, R., and Terkel, J., 1992. Ontogeny of pine cone opening behaviour in the black rat, Rattus rattus. *Animal Behaviour*, 44, pp. 327–336.

Aplin, L. M., Sheldon, B. C., and Morand-Ferron, J., 2013. Milk bottles revisited: Social learning and individual variation in the blue tit, Cyanistes caeruleus. *Animal Behaviour*, 85(6), pp. 1225–1232.

Avital, E., and Jablonka, E., 2000. *Animal traditions: Behavioural traditions in evolution*, Cambridge: Cambridge University Press.

Brown, C., and Laland, K. N., 2003. Social learning in fishes: A review. *Fish and Fisheries*, 4(3), pp. 280–288.

Fisher, J., and Hinde, R. A., 1949. The opening of milk bottles by birds. *British Birds*, 42, pp. 347–357.

Fragaszy, D. M., and Perry, S., 2003. *The Biology of Traditions*, New York: Cambridge University Press.

Galef, B. G., Jr., 2009. Culture in Animals? In K. N. Laland and B. G. Galef Jr., eds. *The Question of Animal Culture*. Cambridge, MA: Harvard University Press, pp. 222–246.

Galef, B. G., 2012. Social learning and traditions in animals: Evidence, definitions, and relationship to human culture. *WIREs Cognitive Science*, 3, pp. 581–592.

Griffiths, P. E., and Sterelny, K., 1999. *Sex and Death: An Introduction to Philosophy of Biology*. Chicago: The University of Chicago Press.

Heyes, C. M., and Frith, C. D., 2014. The cultural evolution of mind reading. *Science*, 344(6190), pp. 1243091–1243091.

Holzhaider, J. C., Hunt, G. R., and Gray, R. D., 2010a. Social learning in new Caledonian crows. *Learning & Behavior*, 38(3), pp. 206–219.

Holzhaider, J. C., Hunt, G. R., and Gray, R. D., 2010b. The development of pandanus tool manufacture in wild New Caledonian crows. *Behaviour*, 147(5/6), pp. 553–586.

Hoppitt, W., and Laland, K. N., 2013. *Social Learning*, Princeton, NJ: Princeton University Press.

Hunt, G. R., and Gray, R. D., 2003. Diversification and cumulative evolution in New Caledonian crow tool manufacture. *Proceedings: Biological Sciences*, 270(1517), pp. 867–874.

Kenward, B., Rutz, C., Weir, A. A. S., & Kacelnick, A., 2006. Development of tool use in New Caledonian crows: Inherited action patterns and social influences. *Animal Behavior*, 72, pp. 1329–43.

Krebs, J. R., and Kroodsma, D. E., 1980. Repertoires and geographical variation in bird song. *Advances in the Study of Behavior*, 11, pp. 143–177.

Laland, K. N., Brown, C., and Krause, J., 2003. Learning in fishes: From three-second memory to culture. *Fish and Fisheries*, 4(3), pp. 199–202.

Laland, K. N., and Galef, B. G., 2009. *The Question of Animal Culture*, Cambridge, MA: Harvard University Press.

Laland, K. N., and Hoppitt, W., 2003. Do animals have culture? *Evolutionary Anthropology: Issues, News, and Reviews*, 12(3), pp. 150–159.

Laland, K. N., and Janik, V., 2006. The animal cultures debate. *Trends in Ecology & Evolution*, 21(10), pp. 542–547.

Lefebvre, L., 1995. The opening of milk bottles by birds: Evidence for accelerating learning rates, but against the wave-of-advance model of cultural transmission. *Behavioural Processes*, 34(1), pp. 43–53.

McCarthy, M., 2003. Blue tits lose their bottle as milk thieves. *The Independent*. Available at: www.independent.co.uk/environment/blue-tits-lose-their-bottle-as-milk-thieves-84526.html.

Meketa, I., 2014. A critique of the principle of cognitive simplicity in comparative cognition. *Biology & Philosophy*, 29(5), pp. 731–745.

Paracchini, S., Scerri, T., and Monaco, A. P., 2007. The genetic lexicon of dyslexia. *Annual Review of Genomics and Human Genetics*, 8(1), pp. 57–79.

Sato, A., Tichy, H., O'Huigin, C., Grant, P., Grant, R. B., and Klein, J., 2001. On the origin of Darwin's finches. *Molecular Biology and Evolution*, 18(3), pp. 299–311.

Schluter, D., and Grant, P. R., 1984. Ecological correlates of morphological evolution in a Darwin's finch, *Geospiza difficilis*. *Evolution*, 38(4), p. 856.

Sherry, D. F., and Galef, B. G., Jr, 1984. Cultural transmission without imitation: Milk bottle opening by birds. *Animal Behaviour*, 32(3), pp. 937–938.

Sherry, D. F., and Galef, B. G., Jr, 1990. Social learning without imitation: More about milk bottle opening by birds. *Animal Behaviour*, 40(5), pp. 987–989.

Sterelny, K., 2012. *The Evolved Apprentice*, Cambridge, MA: The MIT Press.

Tebbich, S., Griffin, A. S., Peschl, M. F., and Sterelny, K., 2016. From mechanisms to function: An integrated framework of animal innovation. *Philosophical Transactions of the Royal Society B: Biological Sciences*, 371(1690), p. 20150195.

Tebbich, S., Sterelny, K., and Teschke, I., 2010. The tale of the finch: Adaptive radiation and behavioural flexibility. *Philosophical Transactions of the Royal Society B: Biological Sciences*, 365(1543), pp. 1099–1109.

Thorpe, W. H., 1963. *Learning and Instinct in Animals*, New York: Taylor & Francis.

Tomasello, M., 2009. *The Cultural Origins of Human Cognition*, Cambridge, MA: Harvard University Press.

Tomasello, M., 2014. *A Natural History of Human Thinking*, Cambridge, MA: Harvard University Press.

Vincek, V., O'Huigin, C., Satta, Y., Takahata, Y., Boag, P. T., Grant, P. R., Grant, B. R., and Klein, J., 1997. How large was the founding population of Darwin's finches? *Proceedings of the Royal Society B*, 264(1378), pp. 111–118.

Zohar, O., and Terkel, J., 1991. Acquisition of pine cone stripping behaviour in black rats. *International Journal of Comparative Psychology*, 5(1), pp. 1–6.

35

PRIMATES ARE TOUCHED BY YOUR CONCERN

Touch, emotion, and social cognition in chimpanzees

Maria Botero

Introduction

Allow me to begin with an anecdote. Flirt was one of the chimpanzees who I observed during my study of chimpanzees at Gombe National Park. During this time, Flirt had the habit of sneaking up behind me and another researcher, and very quietly trying to grab our hands. She was successful only once; completely surprising me, she managed to grab my hand. I knew this was wrong and let her hand go. As part of the protocol at Gombe, humans must always maintain a distance of at least 10 meters from the chimps and never physically interact with them, for health and safety reasons. However, I really enjoyed that stolen moment of holding Flirt's hand.

This episode has remained in my memory for all these years, but it is only now that I am starting to understand its significance. There is something important about the way human primates use touch in social encounters; for example, consider greetings in airports (hugs vs. handshakes) and the way children push each other in a playground (a quick push to warn, a really hard one when it is serious!). Human primates use touch as a way of conveying a wide range of social information. In this chapter, I will argue that one of the best ways of understanding social cognition in nonhuman primates is through touch. Moreover, I will argue that if we would like to describe the evolutionary history of social cognition, touch is *one* of the ideal modes to operationalize social interaction across different kinds of primates. Flirt wanted to hold my hand and I understood perfectly well what that meant, because touch is the social language spoken among primates.

The eyes as window of the social

In their seminal paper, Scaife and Bruner (1975) designed an experiment examining mother-infant face-to-face social interactions in which the parent attempted to elicit gaze-following by turning her head. Because infants between 2–14 months old did follow their parents' gaze, the authors interpreted their results as evidence that infants are capable of joint attention. Since then, joint-attention studies have focused on triadic interactions between two individuals who alternate their attention between an object in the environment that the partner is also looking at, and their partner. The way this triadic interaction takes place has been interpreted in different ways; however, one common element in the interpretations is that joint *visual* attention provides a context in which infants can acquire information about objects and about their social partners (MacPherson and Moore 2007). Researchers also use gaze-following as a way to operationalize joint attention in testing whether chimpanzees are capable of joint attention (see Tomasello, Carpenter, and Hobson 2005, for example).

Gaze-following has also been used to operationalize experiments in theory of mind. From the beginning, theory of mind has been defined as the ability to attribute mental states such as beliefs, intent and desires (among other mental states) to oneself and to others, and as the capacity to understand that others may have mental states and perspectives different from your own (Premack and Woodruff 1978). In chimpanzees, the majority of the research has focused on theory of mind in terms of vision; these experimental protocols test whether chimpanzees know what others have seen (or not), and whether this is an indication that they have some form of theory of mind (see Rosati, Santos, and Hare 2010 for a review).

Moreover, gaze-following has been used to understand certain disorders that limit the interactional capabilities of individuals, such as autism. For example, in his highly influential book *Mindblindness*, Baron-Cohen writes: "When I step back from the model of the mind reading system that I have proposed, EDD (Eye Direction-Detector) seems to stand out" (1995: 97).

The prevalence of using visual modes in the study of social cognition is also present in the study of emotions in primates. Most of the authors who adopt a basic approach to emotions argue for the existence of a basic set of discrete emotions or of families of emotions that is the product of evolution, and present in both human and nonhuman primates (see Tracy and Randles 2011 for a review). One of the most influential ways in which basic emotions have been studied is through the Facial Action Coding System (FACS) (Ekman and Friesen 1978); in this system, facial expressions are divided into segments, and specific configurations of these facial segments are identified with each basic emotion. This scoring system has been successfully applied to nonhuman primates. For example, in humans, great apes and monkeys, researchers have applied FACS to study the relationship between facial expression and taste (Steiner, Glaser, Hawilo, and Berridge 2001 in humans, chimpanzees, orangutans, gorillas, New World monkeys and Old World monkeys; Ueno, Ueno, and Tomonaga 2004 in macaques and chimpanzees). Preuschoft and van Hooff (1995) used FACS to study homology between the chimpanzee bared-teeth display and the human smile. Parr and colleagues (Vick et.al. 2007) created the Chimpanzee Facial Action Coding System (ChimpFACS), based on Ekman's FACS, and have used it to validate the existing categories of facial expressions of chimpanzees (Waller et al. 2007). Caeiro and colleagues (2013) designed OrangFACS to study facial expressions in orangutans.

We see that the visual mode of interaction has been prevalent and highly successful as a way of operationalizing social cognition. The adoption of the visual mode has allowed us to understand many aspects of social cognition in primates; however, I believe that it is necessary to take a further step, recognize the limitations of the visual mode in understanding social cognition, and include other modes, such as touch.

The limits of vision

It is problematic to use gaze-following as a paradigm of social cognition because using the visual mode to operationalize interaction limits our understanding to a single modality. For example, it would be impossible to even consider joint attention among blind individuals using this model. In the past, it was thought that blind children had severe deficits similar to those children in the Autism Spectrum Disorder (ASD). According to Bigelow (2003), research in these infants demonstrates that vision is not necessary for joint attention. Clearly these infants experience challenges in their development, such as understanding the spatial properties of objects, and as a result they experience delays when compared to other infants. However, throughout alternative modes of interaction (i.e. tactile and auditory) with their caregivers, these infants develop the same cognitive abilities as infants with vision, in particular joint attention (see Perez-Pereira and Conti-Ramsden 2013 for review). This example shows that if we are willing to shift modes of interaction, it is possible to understand how children who do not achieve milestones in the traditional way can achieve similar cognitive skills (in particular social referring) when compared to infants who follow a more traditional developmental path.

A second example can be found in studies of Theory of Mind in non-human primates. Researchers of social cognition in apes debate whether the experimental evidence on the knowledge that animals have about what others have seen (or not seen) shows that animals posses theory of mind (see Martin and Santos 2016 for a summary of this debate; and Lurz and Halina, Chapters 21 and 22, respectively, in this volume). Gaze also plays an important role in the debate about whether apes posses joint attention. For example, Carpenter and Call (2013) suggest that apes lack joint attention, and they criticize the way that intention behind an ape's gaze-following behavior has been interpreted in other joint-attention studies (Gomez 2010). I think that this lack of agreement stems from the limitations of what we can learn from vision in apes. Researchers are setting themselves to fail if they look for social cognition in a modality in which the species doesn't demonstrate social cognition, in the same way researchers were set to failure when looking for social cognition in visually impaired children using visual paradigms.

Why think that vision isn't the modality that best demonstrates social cognitive capacities in great apes? Consider how wild apes live. While it is true that in the wild, mother and infant chimpanzees will gaze at each other (van Lawick-Goodall 1967), they rarely use prolonged gaze as a form of interaction (personal observation; for a similar finding in monkeys, see Perry and Manson 2008). Shortly after giving birth, chimpanzee mothers pay little visual attention to their babies except when they are grooming and cleaning them (Plooij 1984). Later in development, mothers are observed to "caress" their infants, by either gently stroking their fur or making grooming movements while gazing upon their babies. However, there are no reports of prolonged mutual gaze between mother and infant (van Lawick-Goodall 1967). The infants don't appear to be interested in the mother's face until around nine weeks of age (Plooij 1984), and it isn't until the infant is four months old that the infant starts focusing on the mother's face in communicative situations, such as begging for food. Before four months, chimpanzee infants typically take food from their mothers without looking at them (Plooij 1984).

These reports on wild populations seem to contradict observations of populations in captivity (Tomonaga et al. 2004). I would join others (Russell, Bard, and Adamson 1997) in arguing that the interactions between the human caregiver and the infant ape can modify the emergence of abilities in the social cognition of the ape, resulting in an inadequate model for understanding species-typical behavior in wild populations; mothers in the wild do not engage in the same kinds of behaviors as mothers in captivity, so the zone of proximal development is different in wild and captive apes. Moreover, the ecological conditions of captivity also influence the way mother and infant pairs interact. For example, Tomonaga and colleagues (2004)[1] report that, during the first two months in the lives of the infants, three mother-infant pairs were observed increasing their engagement in mutual gaze, and that this increase in mutual gaze corresponded to a decrease in cradling behavior by the mothers. Tomonaga and colleagues conclude that the frequency of mutual gaze is negatively correlated with the frequency of physical contact between mother and infant. In contrast to mothers in the safe environment offered by captivity, it has been reported that mothers in the wild carry infants constantly from shortly after birth until the infants are three months old (van Lawick-Goodall 1967; Plooij 1984). According to

Goodall (van Lawick-Goodall 1967), during the first months of life, the infant is protected from almost all contact with other individuals. This behavior is the mother's response to the environmental conditions to which mothers and infants are exposed during the first months of the infant's life; at this stage, the infant has to remain in constant physical contact with the mother because s/he is at constant risk of being killed by males during aggressive displays, by predators, and by attacks from other females. Thus, we should exercise caution when attempting to extrapolate observations done in captivity to general claims about the behavior of a species in the wild.

Finally, focusing on gaze as the modality through which researchers understand social cognition has similar consequences in the study of basic emotions in apes. One of the main problems when applying FACS to understand basic emotions in chimpanzees is that, even though chimpanzees and humans share much of the same facial musculature (Waller et. al. 2007), chimpanzees do not share some of the facial features that allow humans to easily detect facial expressions: because of skin pigmentation, reduced outer lip vermillion, and eye morphology, the chimpanzee face, unlike the human face, does not offer a salient contrast that facilitates the detection of facial movement (Vick et al. 2007). Thus, given the behavioral and morphological characteristics of apes, when researchers focus on vision to study theory of mind, joint attention and basic emotions, they are limiting what they can learn about social cognition.

Touch and social cognition

There is growing evidence that touch plays an important role in human social cognition. It has been shown that touch, in the form of grooming, has effects in social interactions and social bonds (see, for example, Dunbar 1996; de Waal 1990). However, touch can be used in more complex ways in the development of social cognition in infant primates. The interaction that the human and nonhuman primate infant experiences from birth is one of the earliest modes of interaction that allows the infant to start understanding the kinds of interaction involved in social cognition.

To understand how touch is fundamental for the development of social cognition, it is necessary to understand that there are two different kinds of neurophysiological processes behind touch in humans: emotional (affective) and discriminative (sensory), depending on the site of the touch (Olausson et al. 2010). Hairy skin, such as on the arm, contains C-tactile (CT) afferents, which are fundamental for affective touch; CT afferents give rise to the pleasurable feelings experienced in interpersonal touch. Meanwhile, glabrous skin, such as in the palm of the hand, does not contain CT afferents and is linked to discriminative touch; glabrous skin is responsible for detecting, discriminating and identifying external stimuli that will serve as a guide for behavior. As a result, depending on the site, touch is experienced in different ways by humans. Moreover, these neurophysiological characteristics are shared among different species. Human CT afferents and animal C-fiber low-threshold mechanoreceptors (CLTMs) are both afferent types and are only found in hairy skin, in mice, cats and non-human primates (Nordin 1990; Vrontou et al. 2013).

To fully understand the role played by touch in social cognition, it is helpful to focus on affective touch perceived through CT afferents. Several authors (McGlone et al. 2007; Loken et al. 2009) have argued that CT afferents play an important role in the affective processing of interpersonal touch. Olausson and colleagues (2010) have developed the "affect touch hypothesis," which predicts that the role of the CT system is to provide pleasurable feelings and increase the disposition to seek close contact with others. The function of this kind of touch is to serve as the foundation of affiliative behavior, provide a mechanism for the formation and maintenance of social bonds, and become a nonverbal means of communication of emotions (Morrison et al. 2011).

As evident in the ineffectuality of attempting to give oneself a hug, it is important to notice that this affective aspect of touch is mostly manifested in interpersonal touch. Ackerley et al. (2014) found that the touch of *another* is given higher positive emotional rating than *self-touch*. Furthermore, Gentsch and colleagues (2015) found that active stroking elicits more pleasure when this kind of touch is given to another than when it is given to one's own skin. Participants in this experiment also judged the skin of another softer than their own. This "social softness illusion" appeared when the neurophysiological system for touch (i.e. CT afferents) was activated in the receiver. Given this evidence, the researchers suggest that touch is a mechanism for social bonding and affiliation.

In summary, these studies indicate that touch, specifically touch experienced through CT afferents, is a characteristic among different species that allows organisms to perceive that there are "others" who are different from them and to become affectively bonded to those others. Thus, the neurophysiology of touch suggests that, when infants experience touch from a young age, they can understand that there are others, social partners, different from themselves – and they can learn that it is pleasant to engage with these others. As a result, the infant has, through the mode of touch, the first motivation to engage with others in social interactions.

An example of this kind of interaction through touch in human primates is the pattern of communication found in breast feeding. Kaye (1982) describes how newborn infants stop sucking, even when they are not full or when the milk has not stopped flowing, and how human mothers across cultures respond by jiggling their infants after they have stopped sucking the mother's breast or a bottle. This is the first instance of turn-taking that functions as a "conversation"; the infant "brings in" the mother when they pause, and the mother responds by jiggling in ways that adopt to the patterns of the individual infant.

Even though, to my knowledge, there are no equivalent studies of this kind of pattern in chimpanzees in wild populations, Goodall's (1967) observations of mother-infant interaction suggest a similar pattern of mother-infant communication based on touch. According to Goodall, from the moment of birth through the infant's first days of life, the mother's hands and thighs support the infant almost continually. When the mother walks, she constantly keeps one hand under her baby's back and shoulders, rounding her own back. After these initial days, during the first few weeks, the mother gradually supports her infant less frequently. The infant will continue to ride on the mother's chest for the first 6–9 months, gripping her hair with flexed fingers and toes. Because of this, Goodall argues that in the first few months of a chimpanzee infant's life, tactile signals play a major role in mother-infant coordination. The pressure of the infant's body against the body of the mother and the intensity of "hair pull," where the infant grasps the mother's hair with their hands and feet, together with changes of intensity in either of these stimulations, function as signals. At the same time, the infant can perceive through touch (for example, through piloerection (when the hair stands on end) and elevated heartbeat the mother's responses to the infant and the world.

Implications for the study of social cognition

The interaction that takes place between caregivers and young infants through the mode of touch opens the door for the infant's development of social cognition in several ways: it can serve to communicate to young infants that there is an other, and that this other has a perspective that is different from the infant's (a basic trait of joint attention and theory of mind); and it is a method for learning how to self-regulate one's own emotions.

First, touch can convey that the perspective of a caregiver is different from the perspective of the infant. Hertenstein (2002) argues that tactile communication takes place when "there are systematic changes in another's perceptions, thoughts, feelings, and/or behavior as a function of another's touch in relation to the context in which it occurs" (2002: 72). He argues that touch may transmit the caregiver's perceptions, thoughts and feelings to the infant (in a conscious or unconscious way), and that it is possible that the caregiver's experience is transmitted to the infant without being generated in the infant. For example, Hertenstein asks us to imagine what is unconsciously transmitted through touch by a parent who had a stressful day, changing an infant's diaper. Moreover, it is possible that the infant may perceive this stress but does not become stressed herself. Thus, through touch, primate infants can start understanding that there are others and that these others have a different perspective, two basic traits of joint attention and theory of mind (see Botero 2016 for how touch can be used to investigate joint attention in primates).

It may be argued that this kind of interaction can be characterized as the caregiver eliciting an emotion in the infant, but no actual information is transmitted through touch. However, according to Tronick (1995), tactile communication can transmit specific information to the infant, information such as the presence or absence of a caregiver and the identity of the person who touches the infant, through different types of touch; and according to Hertenstein and colleagues (2009), through touch, individuals can communicate eight distinct emotions (i.e. anger, fear, disgust, love, gratitude, sympathy, happiness and sadness).

Second, I believe that touch as a mode of interaction should be included in the study of social cognition because touch allows primates to learn how to regulate their emotions, and this regulation allows infants to be calm enough to pay attention to the world around them, including their social partners. Touch has a soothing effect that is so powerful that it may be used to overcome psychologically or physically stressful conditions in nonhuman primates. For example, in Harlow's early studies, it was clear that primates, and in particular infants, had a preference for "touch" in the form of a "cloth–mother" (Harlow and Zimmerman 1959). Mason and Berkson (1962) showed that chimpanzee infants who received electric shocks emitted fewer stress vocalizations when held by humans than when left by themselves on a table, and exhibited higher thresholds before vocalizing than when held by a human than when left alone on a table. It has been shown that among wild chimpanzees, the absence of the mother, who provides most of the touch to the infant, has profound effects on the infant's social behavior and levels of anxiety (Botero et al. 2013).

Studies have shown that the touch provided by the caregiver to human primate infants has an effect on an infant's levels of comfort, learning, exploration and attachment, and on the amount of crying or fussing (for a review on the effects of touch for well-being, see Field 2011). Moreover, human infants also use touch as a way to regulate their emotions in various contexts, such as maternal unavailability and exploration of new environments (Stack 2011). The interaction through the mode of touch allows infants to be calm enough and to engage in social exchanges.

These findings suggest that focusing on touch as a mode of interaction has two advantages in the study of social cognition in primates. First, non–glabrous touch is a mode that does not require use of the mode of vision or of highly visible and distinctive facial features, which means that touch is a mode that can be used easily by nonhuman primates. Second, touch is a mode that is used in affective exchanges where, given its pleasurable nature, it provides the organism with the motivation to engage with others. Third, a focus on touch allows us to study the development of social cognition in very young infants; that is, observing the caregiver-infant interaction through the mode of touch allows us to observe one of the first ways in which the infant is introduced to social cognition. In recent years, several measurements have been designed to capture the qualitative and quantitative aspects of touch in human primates (for an overview, see Brown et al. 2011). I hypothesize that these measurements could be adapted to the study of these forms of social cognition across nonhuman primates (see Botero 2014 for a discussion).

Conclusion

Most of the current research on social cognition in human and nonhuman primates has focused on vision as a way of operationalizing social cognition. I argue that to study social cognition across different kinds of primates, we should include touch as a mode of interaction. This mode will allow us to understand cognition in younger infant primates and will allow us to operationalize social cognition in nonhuman primates. Moreover, through touch, we can learn how nonhuman primates form and maintain social bonds in ways that correspond to their morphological and behavioral characteristics. In short, by focusing on touch, we can learn how social cognition emerges in nonhuman primates.

Note

1   I would like to note that among various research projects on ape development, one of the most interesting methodological designs is the one developed by Tomonaga and colleagues at the Primate Research Institute (PRI) of Kyoto University, where researchers engage in longitudinal studies, attempting to emulate as closely as possible naturalistic conditions in order to follow the development of three infant chimpanzees born at PRI. For example, as opposed to other research sites, each of the mothers at PRI successfully held her baby and did not have to be separated from her baby (for the baby's protection), as is common in captive settings. However, despite these advances, the difference between wild populations and captive population must be kept in mind.

Further reading

Field, T. M. (1995). *Touch in early development*. Hoboken: Taylor and Francis, provides a multidisciplinary approach to the role played by touch in the development of human and nonhuman primates. Hertenstein, M.J., and Weiss, S. J. (2011). *The Handbook of touch: Neuroscience, behavioral, and health perspectives*. New York: Springer, is a good introduction to the variety of approaches and methodologies currently used in the study of touch. Flom, R., Lee, K., and Muir, D. (2007). *Gaze-following: Its development and significance*. Mahwah, NJ: Lawrence Erlbaum Associates, provides an insightful overview of the role that gaze has played in the study of social cognition. Finally, Tomasello, M. (2014). *A natural history of human thinking*. Cambridge, MA: Harvard University Press, presents a carefully and comprehensive account of the evolution of social cognition that emphasizes the differences between apes and humans.

References

Ackerley, R., Saar, K., McGlone, F., and Wasling, H. (2014) "Quantifying the Sensory and Emotional Perception of Touch: Differences Between Glabrous and Hairy Skin," *Frontiers in Behavioral Neuroscience*, 8: 1–12.

Baron-Cohen, S. (1995) *Mindblindness: An Essay on Autism and Theory of Mind*. Cambridge, MA: MIT Press.

Bigelow, A. E. (2003) "The Development of Joint Attention in Blind Infants," *Development and Psychopathology*, 15(2): 259–275.

Botero, M. (2014) "How Primate Mothers and Infants Communicate, Characterizing Interaction in Mother-Infant Studies Across Species," in M. Pina and N. Gontier (eds.), *The Evolution of Social Communication in Primates: A Multidisciplinary Approach*. Heidelberg, New York, Dordetch, London: Springer.

Botero, M. (2016) "Tactless Scientists, Ignoring Touch in the Study of Joint Attention," *Philosophical Psychology* 29: 1200–1214.

Botero, M., MacDonald, S., and Miller, R. (2013) "Anxiety-Related Behavior of Orphan Chimpanzees (*Pan troglodytes schweinfurthii*) at Gombe National Park, Tanzania," *Primates* 54: 21–26.

Brown, C., Filion, D., and Weiss, S. (2011) "Measurement of Tactile Response and Tactile Perception," in M. J Hertenstein and S. J. Weiss (eds.), *The Handbook of Touch: Neuroscience, Behavioral, and Health Perspectives*. New York: Springer.

Caeiro, C., Waller, B. M., Zimmermann, E., Burrows, A. M., Davila-Ross, M. (2013) "OrangFACS: a muscle-based facial movement coding system for orangutans (Pongo spp.)," *International Journal of Primatology*, 34(1): 115–129.

Carpenter, M., and Call, J. (2013) "How Joint Is the Joint Attention of Apes and Human Infants?" in J. Metcalfe and H. S. Terrace (eds.), *Agency and Joint Attention*. New York: Oxford University Press.

de Waal, F. B. (1990) *Peacemaking Among Primates*. Cambridge, MA: Harvard University Press.

Dunbar, R. I. (1996) *Grooming, Gossip, and The Evolution of Language*. Cambridge, MA: Harvard University Press.

Ekman, P., and Friesen, W.V. (1978) *Facial Action Coding System*. Palo Alto, CA: Consulting Psychology Press.

Field, T. (2011) "Touch for Socioemotional and Physical Well-Being: A Review," *Developmental Review*, 30: 367–383.

Gentsch, A., Panagiotopoulou, E., and Fotopoulou, A. (2015) "Active Interpersonal Touch Gives Rise to the Social Softness Illusion," *Current Biology*, 25(18): 2392–2397.

Gomez, J. (2010). "The Ontogeny of Triadic Cooperative Interactions With Humans in an Infant Gorilla," *Interaction Studies*, 11(3): 353–379.

Harlow, H. F., and Zimmermann, R. R. (1959) "Affectional Responses in the Infant Monkey," *Science*, 130(3373): 421–432.

Hertenstein, M. (2002) "Touch: Its Communicative Functions in Infancy," *Human Development*, 45: 70–94.

Hertenstein, M., Holmes, R., Mccullough, M., and Keltner, D. (2009) "The Communication of Emotion via Touch," *Emotion*, 9(4): 566–573.

Kaye, K. (1982) *The Mental and Social Life of Babies: How Parents Create Persons*. Chicago: University of Chicago Press.

Löken, L. S., Wessberg, J., Morrison, I., Mcglone, F., and Olausson, H. (2009) "Coding of Pleasant Touch by Unmyelinated Afferents in Humans," *Nature Neuroscience*, 12(5): 547–548.

Mcglone, F., Vallbo, A., Olausson, H., Loken, L., and Wessberg, J. (2007) "Discriminative Touch and Emotional Touch," *Canadian Journal of Experimental Psychology*, 61(3): 173–183.

MacPherson, A., and Moore, C. (2007) "Attentional Control by Gaze Cues in Infancy," in R. Flom, K. Lee, and D. Muir (eds.), *Gaze-Following: Its Development and Significance*. Mahwah, NJ: Lawrence Erlbaum Associates Publishers.

Martin, A., and Santos, L. R. (2016) "Review: What Cognitive Representations Support Primate Theory of Mind?" *Trends in Cognitive Sciences*, 20: 375–382.

Mason, W. A., and Berkson, G. (1962) "Conditions Influencing Vocal Responsiveness of Infant Chimpanzees," *Science*, 137 (3524): 127–128.

Morrison, I., Löken, L. S., Minde, J., Wessberg, J., Perini, I., Nennesmo, I., and Olausson, H. (2011) "Reduced C-Afferent Fibre Density Affects Perceived Pleasantness and Empathy for Touch," *Brain: A Journal of Neurology*, 134: 1116–1126.

Nordin, M. (1990) "Low-Threshold Mechanorecepetive and Nociceptive Units With Unmyelinated C Fibres in the Human Supraorbital Nerve," *Journal of Physiology*, 426: 229–240.

Olausson, H., Wessberg, J., Morrison, I., McGlone, F., and Vallbo, A. (2010) "The Neurophysiology of Unmyelinated Tactile Afferents," *Neuroscience & Biobehavioral Reviews*, 34: 185–191.

Pérez-Pereira, M., and Conti-Ramsden, G. (2013) *Language Development and Social Interaction in Blind Children*. Hove, Sussex: Psychology Press Ltd.

Perry, S., and Manson, J. (2008) *Manipulative Monkeys: The Capuchins of Lomas Barbudal*. Cambridge, MA: Harvard University Press.

Plooij, F. (1984) *The Behavioural Development of Free Living Chimpanzee Babies and Infants*. Norwood, NJ: Ablex Publishing Corporation.

Premack, D., and Woodruff, G. (1978) "Does the Chimpanzee Have a Theory of Mind?" *Behavioral and Brain Sciences*, 1(4): 515.

Preuschoft, S., and van Hooff, J. (1995) "Homologizing Primate Facial Displays: A Critical Review of Methods," *Folia Primatologica*, 65: 121–137.

Rosati, A. G., Santos, L. R., and Hare, B. (2010) "Primate Social Cognition: Thirty Years After Premack and Woodruff," in A. Ghazanfar and M. Platt (eds.), *Primate Neuroethology*. Oxford: Oxford University Press.

Russell, C. L., Bard, K. A., and Adamson, L. B. (1997) "Social Referencing By Young Chimpanzees (*Pan troglodytes*)," *Journal of Comparative Psychology*, *111*(2): 185–193.

Scaife, M., and Bruner, J. S. (1975) "The Capacity for Joint Visual Attention in the Infant," *Nature*, *253*: 265–266.

Stack, D. M. (2011) "Communication via Touch," in M. J Hertenstein and S. J. Weiss (eds.), *The Handbook of Touch: Neuroscience, Behavioral, and Health Perspectives*. New York: Springer.

Steiner, J. E., Glaser, D., Hawilo, M. E., and Berridge, K. C. (2001) "Comparative Expression of Hedonic Impact: Affective Reactions to Taste by Human Infants and Other Primates," *Neuroscience and Biobehavioural Reviews*, 25: 53–74.

Tomasello, M., Carpenter, M., and Hobson, R. P. (2005) "The Emergence of Social Cognition in Three Young Chimpanzees," *Monographs of the Society for Research in Child Development*, 1: I.

Tomonaga, M., Tanaka, M., Matsuzawa, T., Myowa-Yamakoshi, M., Kosugi, D., Mizuno, Y., . . . Bard, K. A. (2004) "Development of Social Cognition in Infant Chimpanzees (*Pan Troglodytes*): Face Recognition, Smiling, Gaze, and the Lack of Triadic Interactions," *Japanese Psychological Research*, *46*(3): 227–235.

Tracy, J., and Randles, D. (2011) "Four Models of Basic Emotions: A Review of Ekman and Cordaro, Izard, Levenson, and Panksepp and Watt," *Emotion Review*, *3*(4): 397–405.

Tronick, E. (1995) "Touch in Mother-Infant Interaction," in T. F. Field (ed.), *Touch in Early Development*. Mahwah, NJ: Lawrence Erlbaum Associates.

Ueno, A., Ueno, Y., and Tomonaga, M. (2004) "Facial Responses to Four Basic Tastes in Newborn Rhesus Macaques (*Macaca Mulatta*) and Chimpanzees (*Pan troglodytes*)," *Behavioural Brain Research*, 154: 261–271.

van Lawick-Goodall, J. (1967) "Mother-Offspring Relationships in Chimpanzees," in D. Morris (ed.), *Primate Ethology*. Chicago: Aldine Publishing Company.

Vick, S-J, Waller, B., Parr, L., Smith Pasqualini, M., and Bard, K. A. (2007) "A Cross Species Comparison of Facial Morphology and Movement in Humans and Chimpanzees Using FACS," *Journal of Nonverbal Behavior*, *31*: 1–20.

Vrontou, S., Wong, A., Rau, K., Koerber, H., and Anderson, D. (2013) "Genetic Identification of C Fibres That Detect Massage-Like Stroking of Hairy Skin in Vivo," *Nature*, *493*(7434): 669.

Waller, B., Bard, K. A., Vick, S-J., and Smith-Pasqualini, M. (2007) "Perceived Differences Between Chimpanzee (*Pan troglodytes*) and Human (*Homo Sapiens*) Facial Expressions Are Related to Emotional Interpretation," *Journal of Comparative Psychology*, 121: 398–404.

36

DO CHIMPANZEES CONFORM TO SOCIAL NORMS?

Laura Schlingloff and Richard Moore

Introduction

Brandom, following Kant and Wittgenstein, distinguishes between acting according to a rule and acting according to a conception of a rule. In the first case, there are regularities that describe one's behavior, but one need not be aware of them. In the second case, one's behavior may be described by a rule precisely because one aspires to adhere to it. In the latter case, an agent's conception of the rule constrains her behavior, constituting a reason for her to act in one way and not another. This is the idea of a norm. A norm is a rule that agents feel, in some sense, obliged to follow.

Norms are philosophically interesting because they make room for a distinction between how one acts and how one thinks one should act. This distinction is central to many forms of behavior, including ethical behavior, and the formation of group identities. While norms can be both social and non-social, here we discuss only norms whose function is to constrain our interactions with others.

Social norms prohibit or encourage the performance of certain behaviors within a community. They guide both how we present ourselves to others, and how we assess others' actions. Awareness of social norms emerges early in ontogeny (Schmidt, Rakoczy and Tomasello 2011) and seems to be a universal feature of human societies. The emergence of normatively governed social behavior was likely therefore a crucial stage in the development of distinctively human forms of living, and one that contributed to our development in many ways. For example, Boyd and Richerson (2005) have argued that social norms stabilize within-group homogeneity and drive between-group differentiation (Boyd and Richerson 2005). Such behaviors likely played an important role in reinforcing group bonds, enabling norm-following communities of early humans to outcompete neighboring groups in competitive ecological niches. Zawidzki (2013) has argued that the emergence of social norms played an important role in the development of human social cognition by making human minds more easily interpretable. Finally, Kitcher (2011), Korsgaard (2010), and Tomasello (2016) – among others – have argued that the emergence of norms was necessary for the emergence of morality.

Given the importance of normative behavior to human forms of living, it is natural to ask whether our closest living relatives understand and follow norms. While some have argued that there is evidence of normative behavior in chimpanzees and monkeys (e.g., Andrews 2009), we argue against this conclusion. We start by considering a recent (and representative) example of a group-specific, socially transmitted behavior pattern in chimpanzees and argue that necessary preconditions for attributing normativity are not met here. We then spell out some alternative, non-normative explanations of group-specific behaviors in chimpanzees, and discuss which kinds of evidence would be needed to support claims of normativity. We finish by setting out recent evidence on majority influences in chimpanzees ('conformity'), and considering potential cases of morally normative behavior in chimpanzees.

Do primates conform to social norms?

One common feature of social norms – particularly where they relate to the establishment of group identities – is that they are arbitrary. This means the members of a group conform to the normative behavior only because their peers do.[1] Such behaviors likely vary between communities – and may be consciously varied by the members of rival communities, to differentiate themselves from one another. The following characterization of social norms borrows from Bicchieri (2006):

A behavior R is a norm in a community P if and only if:

(1) The members of P know that some rule R exists and holds in context C
(2) Members of P perform R in C, and expect other members of P to do the same
(3) Members of P perform R in C on condition that

  (i) Other members of P perform R in C
  (ii) Other members of P expect them to perform R in C
  (iii) Failure to perform R in C may be met with sanctions

(4) It is common knowledge among the members of P that (1)–(3) hold

Here, clause (1) captures the idea that normative behavior requires acting according to a conception of a rule, and not merely in accordance with it. Clause (2) captures the idea that members of P expect others to conform; and clause (3) specifies the conditions under which they will conform. Where R is arbitrary, commitment to it will likely be contingent upon commitment by others. Nonetheless, the members of P may still see fit to punish non-conformity. Where members desire to preserve group norms, transgressions may give rise to 'moral' emotions – from indignation and upset to anger; and to even more robust forms of norm enforcement, like gossip, censure, ostracism, or dishonor.

It is now well established that some behaviors vary arbitrarily between neighboring groups of chimpanzees (e.g., Whiten et al., 1999). The following discussion focuses on the community-specific tool preferences of chimpanzees in the Taï National Park (Luncz, Mundry and Boesch 2012). Since the behavior can be explained neither by genetic variation nor ecological differences between populations, it must be socially learned (see Moore 2013b; van Leeuwen et al. 2015 for discussion). Since variance between neighboring groups might also be interpreted as statements of group identity – "This is how we do things around here!" – this behavior has been interpreted as potentially normative (van Schaik 2012).

Luncz et al: nut-cracking

Luncz, Munddry and Boesch (2012) studied the *coula edulis* nut-cracking behavior of three neighboring chimpanzee groups in the Taï forest. Coula nuts dry out and become easier to crack as the nut season progresses. If apes use the most efficient tools, then all communities should use stone hammers (which are harder to find, but better for opening fresh nuts) early in the season, and wooden hammers (which are more common and good enough to open dried nuts) later. Luncz and colleagues found that while this happened in two groups, the third ('South') group continued to use mostly stone hammers. Additionally, there were between-group differences in the size of wooden hammers selected. Since the three communities live in the same forest, and sexually mature females migrate between the groups, both ecological and genetic explanations of these differences can be ruled out.

Further research (Luncz and Boesch 2014) showed that despite the migration of adult females, group practices remained constant over 25 years; and analysis of one migrating female's behavior showed that she adopted the practices of her new group. A study of the archaeological record (Luncz, Wittig and Boesch 2015) confirmed that chimpanzees migrating from a population south of the South group cracked nuts with wooden tools prior to migrating, but adopted the new group's preference for stone tools when they relocated. Since life for new females in a group can be difficult – it takes a year for them to be accepted by other females in the group – Luncz and colleagues suggest that females may adopt the practices of their new group as a way of smoothing their integration.

These socially learned and group-specific patterns of behavior are good candidates for social norms. We can assess whether they are genuinely normative by asking whether or not they satisfy the criteria for social norms adopted above.

Chimpanzee norms?

The nut-cracking behavior of the South group at Taï can be described by the rule *When possible, always use stone hammers*. Furthermore, the finding that migrating females adopt the practice of their new group is evidence that they act in accordance with this rule only because others do too. However, there is no reason to suppose that chimpanzees are aware of the rules that describe their behavior, nor to think that they expect others to conform to them. Thus, there is no reason to think that Taï chimpanzees satisfy clauses (1) and (2) of the criteria identified above. Moreover, while it is possible that failure to conform to the group rule would exacerbate the bullying of migrating females – and so constitute a form of sanction for non-conformity, fulfilling criterion (3)(iii) – there is currently no evidence of the sanctioning behavior that would support this conclusion.

In fact, the social modulation of tool preferences does not entail they are normative. Different preferences between groups can all be explained by low-level phenomena, like the relative salience of alternative tool types. Consequently, individuals in the group need not even be aware of the rules that describe their behavior – let alone aspire to conform to them. So there is currently no evidence that different between-group tool preferences are brought about by social norms.

The behavior of the North and East chimpanzee groups at Taï observed by Luncz and colleagues can be explained on the assumption that chimpanzees adopt the most rational techniques. Some individuals in those groups may have discovered that, as the season progresses, they can use the more readily available wooden tools. In turn, this would make these tools more salient to their peers, who might then start to use them more often. This explanation does not require that the apes are even aware of the changes in their search behavior. Since chimpanzees are known to copy the behavior of influential group members (Biro et al. 2003; Horner et al. 2010; Boesch 2012; Kendal et al. 2015), practices adopted by influential individuals might spread rapidly within groups.

Both the behavior of the South group, and the different sizes of wooden hammer used by all groups, can be similarly explained. In the South group, perhaps no ape ever learned that tools can be changed during the nut-cracking season. Alternatively, it may be that one or two high-ranking individuals preferred to use stone tools regardless of the time of year – perhaps because they had grown up surrounded only by others who used stone tools. If the preferences of these individuals served to advertise the use of stone tools to others in the group, then those search-ing for hammers may have been disposed to search for stone tools through low-level processes of association. Such a pattern could have spread in the group at one point and then stabilized itself over time. Although using stone tools instead of sticks may sometimes be less efficient than using wooden tools, the differences need not be so great as to radically disadvantage groups who prefer stones.

In the above cases, tool-choice preferences might be similar to regional accents. While indi-viduals can deliberately adopt a local accent to help them fit into a group, and while group accents are sometimes normative, individuals can also acquire accents without being aware of doing so. Subconscious copying causes within-group similarity and between-group differences, but these differences need not indicate the presence of norms.[2]

Chimpanzee conformity?

Many studies on social influences on human behavior – including the famous Asch conformity experiments (1951) – show that we change our behavior to fit in with the crowd. Although the findings described above do not show that chimpanzees change their behavior for normative or affiliative reasons, experimental paradigms have been used to investigate this possibility.

Some studies (e. g. Whiten, Horner and de Waal 2005; Hopper et al. 2011) have tested for chimpanzee conformity by watching the spread of behaviors within groups. Whiten, Horner and de Waal (2005) trained two high-ranking chimpanzees from different groups with differ-ent but equally efficient techniques to extract food from a specially designed apparatus.[3] These individuals were then used to demonstrate the same technique to members of their respective groups. Observing apes learned the technique that they had seen demonstrated, so that different behavioral traditions emerged between the groups.

Whiten and colleagues (Whiten, Horner and de Waal 2005) interpret this data as reflecting conformist tendencies in chimpanzees, which they conceptualize as "adoption of the group's norm despite being able to use both methods" (p. 738). However, their finding is consistent with the possibility that apes just reproduce salient behaviors more often than less-salient alternatives (where salience is determined by prior experience). A stronger test would be needed to establish that the apes were copying for affiliative reasons, or because the performed behavior was a social norm.

To investigate whether chimpanzees copy for affiliative reasons, van Leeuwen and colleagues tested whether they abandon individually learned information in favor of a majority strategy. They found that chimpanzees do not change a first-learned strategy to conform to a majority, although they will do so to gain higher rewards (van Leeuwen et al. 2013; see also Hrubesch, Preuschoft and van Schaik 2009; and van Leeuwen and Haun 2013). This suggests that chimpan-zees are not motivated to "do what the others do" merely to fit in (Leeuwen and Haun 2013).

In humans, individuals reduce social stress by imitating those around them – for instance, when they face exclusion or ostracism (Williams, Cheung and Choi 2000; Lakin, Chartrand and Arkin 2008). While such affiliative conformity has also been found in five-year-old children (Over and Carpenter 2009), there is no direct evidence of it in apes.[4] Nonetheless, there are documented cases of idiosyncratic and possibly affiliative behaviors appearing in chimpanzee communities. For example, van Leeuwen and colleagues describe a case in which chimpanzees at Chimfunshi copied a high-ranking female's behavior of sticking a piece of grass in her ear (van Leeuwen, Cronin and Haun 2014); and Hobaiter and Byrne describe chimpanzees at Budongo as copying the unusual movements of a physically disabled peer (Hobaiter and Byrne 2010). However, non-affiliative explanations of these behaviors cannot be ruled out. It may be, for example, that chimpanzees who first saw and then tried the grass-in-ear behavior found it pleasurable, and so repeated it; or simply that they copied a salient behavior.

Three possible behaviors would provide better evidence of affiliative or normative copying. First, instances of costly affiliation, in which adopting a prevalent behavioral variant proved disadvantageous for the conformist, would support the claim that copying behavior is affiliative. Second, if apes copied conspecifics' behavior significantly more frequently when faced with ostracism and social stress, as children do (Over and Carpenter 2009), the case for affiliative conformity would also be strengthened. Third, one could look at whether chimpanzees copy target behavior more often when candidates for affiliation are present than when observed individuals are alone. For example, if immigrant chimpanzees at Taï reverted to older tool-use patterns when alone, then this would suggest an affiliative function when matching occurred. While this evidence could be collected, there are grounds to doubt that it will be forthcoming: existing evidence seems to suggest that chimpanzees are insensitive to others' evaluations of them, since they do not attempt to manage their reputation around peers (Engelmann, Herrmann and Tomasello 2012).

Even if affiliative conformist tendencies were found in chimpanzees, these would not constitute evidence of fully normative behaviors. In human communities, not only do individuals prefer to conform, they also uphold the principles of their group – for example, by punishing those who do not conform. In humans, third-party enforcement of arbitrary conventional norms emerges in children as young as three years (Schmidt, Rakoczy and Tomasello 2012). Humans are also willing to suffer costs in order to sanction norm violations, even if they themselves were not harmed by the violation (Fehr and Fischbacher 2004). Currently, there is no evidence that chimpanzees enforce social norms. While they punish those who harm them directly (Jensen, Call and Tomasello 2007), this is consistent with them punishing out of revenge, and not because they think group norms should be upheld. They do not seem to engage in 'third-party punishment'. For example, Riedl and colleagues (2012) found that chimpanzees would not retaliate against a conspecific when a third-party's food was stolen.

A weaker view of norms?

The Bicchieri-influenced account of normativity adopted here is both cognitively and motivationally demanding. If behavioral evidence suggested that chimpanzees do conform to social norms, issues of the cognition required for normativity may need to be reconsidered. However, in the absence of behavioral evidence of normativity, these questions can be deferred.

Andrews (2009, 2012) has defended a simpler conception of norms, on the basis of which she is happy to grant understanding of such norms to several nonhuman species. On Andrews's account, norms are taken to be just familiar patterns of behavior. Norm violations occur when individuals act in ways that are an exception to a regularly performed behavior. She argues that such norm violations are philosophically interesting because they lead us to search for deeper explanations of an agent's behavior. They might therefore play a foundational role in our reasongiving practices.

Andrews may be right about the role of violations in the development of folk psychology. However, the types of norms that she is seeking to characterize are not the same as those described by Brandom and Bicchieri. On one common use of the word, a norm is what is normal – that is, a statistical regularity, deviations from which might be easily detected by many different kinds of species and systems. In a second sense that we have described here, a norm is what an individual or a society deems acceptable or appropriate. These meanings are importantly different, because construing an agent's actions as unusual does not imply any understanding that they are inappropriate. Andrews sometimes slides between these different uses of 'norm', from making a claim about statistical regularities to claims about what one ought to do. For example, she writes that:

> [N]onhuman primates … have the ability to develop variations in their behavioral repertoire that involve creating, following, and violating social norms having to do with trust, harm, and cooperation. These primates appear to have societal norms, and individuals appear to have at least an implicit understanding of the relevant normative rules.
>
> (Andrews 2009: 444)

However, there is currently no good evidence that chimpanzees understand norms in the second sense.

Andrews (2009) illustrates her case with different examples from the ape literature: in particular, when groups of chimpanzees patrol their territory borders, which Andrews interprets as reflecting norms of property; and group hunting with designated hunting roles and meat distribution according to these roles, which she interprets as showing norms of cooperation and fairness. However, the evidence to which she appeals is highly controversial. For example, there is no reliable evidence that chimpanzees do follow coordinated hunting strategies (Bullinger et al. 2011); and properly controlled studies suggest that chimpanzees do not act in light of considerations of fairness (Bräuer, Call and Tomasello 2006). Furthermore, border patrols likely reflect not an understanding of property rights, but an adaptive drive to protect scarce resources.

Moral norms in chimpanzees?

Unlike conventional norms, which emerge arbitrarily and show a great variety among human cultures, moral norms may be grounded in species-general empathic and prosocial tendencies.[5] Chimpanzees may possess moral norms or precursors to them, even if they lack conventional norms. Some (e.g., Rudolf von Rohr et al. 2010, 2012, 2015) argue that a protean form of morality may be present in chimpanzees. Candidates for moral behaviors include reconciliation and consolation behavior (de Waal and van Roosmalen 1979), instrumental helping (Warneken and Tomasello 2006), and the especially gentle treatment of infants (Rudolf von Rohr et al. 2010).

Rudolf von Rohr et al. (2010) argue that evolutionary precursors of moral norms may be present in chimpanzees, as they possess certain preconditions for morality (sophisticated sociocognitive skills, and some degree of empathy) and show behaviors derived from expectations about how others should be treated. The same authors (2012) report observations of 'policing' behavior, in which uninvolved chimpanzees intervene in others' conflicts. These interventions may reflect "community concern" for the need to maintain order, which "can be seen as the very foundation of human morality and indeed social norms" (Rudolf von Rohr et al. 2012: 7). In a comparison of policing interventions across four groups, high-ranking individuals of both sexes were found to police, and to do so more often in times of social instability (but see Riedl et al. 2012). Moreover, self-interested explanations of the policing behavior were ruled out.

Nonetheless, it would be premature to interpret policing behavior as evidence of norm-enforcement – since policing individuals may simply prefer not to live in unstable, conflict-ridden groups. If so, then anyone whose interventions could calm a tense group may be motivated to intervene. No group norms need be assumed.

It has been reported that when chimpanzees witness aggression against even unrelated infants, they react strongly – for example, by screaming, and intervening defensively. Rudolf von Rohr et al. (2015) showed chimpanzees videos of conspecific infanticide to see if this would elicit responses suggestive of an understanding of moral norms. Apes looked longer at videos of unfamiliar individuals committing infanticidal attacks than at control videos (e.g., of chimpanzees behaving aggressively towards adults). However – with the exception of one individual who performed threat displays towards the video screen – watching infanticide did not elicit negative emotional arousal. The authors interpret the findings as showing that while chimpanzees may recognize norm violations, these violations elicit strong emotional responses only when they affect group members.

Again, this conclusion is premature. The looking-time measure employed by the authors is standardly interpreted as showing that subjects were surprised by or interested in what they saw. However, while this suggests that chimpanzees have expectations regarding the treatment of infants, this seems to support a claim only about what chimpanzees take to be predictable. This is a norm sense of the word used by Andrews, but not the sort of norm that is relevant to moral evaluation. Although the authors claim to provide "evidence that chimpanzees . . . are sensitive to the appropriateness of behaviors that do not affect themselves" (p. 157), it is unclear that a longer looking time is evidence of this. The lack of emotional arousal in most apes also suggests that they did not care strongly about what they saw (consistent with the absence of a norm); and the negative reactions of one individual is consistent with her simply disliking what she saw.

Given the ambiguity of these data, it is clear that future work should focus on eliciting unambiguous criteria for the attribution of normative behavior. The best evidence for this would be third-party interventions in cases where the intervening individual did not stand to gain from entering the dispute. However, unambiguous cases may be difficult to identify. In the meantime, it is premature to conclude that chimpanzees understand and follow norms. They seem not to distinguish between what individuals do, and what they should do.

Further reading

For empirical studies of chimpanzee normativity, see Rudolf von Rohr, Burkart, and van Schaik (2011) on the possibility of moral norms in chimpanzees; and on the question of whether there are group-specific cultural norms, see Luncz, Mundry, and Boesch (2012) (along with van Schaik's commentary (2012)), and van Leeuwen et al. (2015). For the most explicit philosophical development of the claim that primate behavior is normative, see Andrews (2009), and the forthcoming Bayertz and Roughley (eds.).

Acknowledgements

For discussions and valuable feedback on the contents of this chapter, we thank Kristin Andrews, Lydia Luncz, and Edwin van Leeuwen.

Notes

1   Not all social norms are arbitrary. For example, incest is a universally adopted social norm with a clear biological justification. Although the content of a given norm may be grounded in principles conferring survival advantages to those who act in accordance with them, what matters for the purposes of

this discussion is that followers of norms are intrinsically motivated to conform. For relevant discussion of arbitrary norms, see Moore (2013a).

2 Similarly low-level explanations of behavior transmission could be used to explain other group traditions in apes – including, for example, group-specific grooming handclasp techniques (van Leeuwen et al. 2012).

3 Chimpanzees are known to copy preferentially from high-ranking individuals (Horner et al. 2010). However, this need not reflect any understanding of the normative nature of group behaviors. It could simply be an attentional bias that reflects apes' knowledge of likely sources of expertise.

4 Although, see also Paukner et al. (2009) for a relevant finding in capuchin monkeys.

5 If moral norms are not arbitrary, the characterizations of social norms offered above would need to be adjusted to ground an account of moral norms. In particular, clause (3) would need to be reformulated to show that conformity to moral norms can be independent of others' conformity, and instead be driven by a sense of what is morally right.

References

Andrews, K. (2009) "Understanding norms without a theory of mind," *Inquiry* 52(5), 433–448.

Asch, S. (1951) "Effects of group pressure upon the modification and distortion of judgments," in: Guetzkow, H. (ed.) *Groups, Leadership and Men; Research in Human Relations*, Oxford: Carnegie Press.

Bayertz, K., and Roughley, N. (eds.) (forthcoming) *The Normative Animal? On the Anthropological Significance of Social, Moral and Linguistic Norms*, Oxford: Oxford University Press.

Bicchieri, C. (2006) *The Grammar of Society: The Nature and Dynamics of Social Norms*, New York: Cambridge University Press.

Biro, D., Inoue-Nakamura, N., Tonooka, R., Yamakoshi, G., Sousa, C., and Matsuzawa, T. (2003) "Cultural innovation and transmission of tool use in wild chimpanzees: Evidence from field experiments," *Animal Cognition* 6, 213–223.

Boesch, C. (2012) *Wild Cultures: A Comparison Between Chimpanzee and Human Cultures*, Cambridge: Cambridge University Press.

Boyd, R., and Richerson, P. (2005) *The Origin and Evolution of Cultures*, New York: Oxford University Press.

Brandom, R. (1994) *Making It Explicit: Reasoning, Representing, and Discursive Commitment*, Cambridge, MA: Harvard University Press.

Bräuer, J., Call, J., and Tomasello, M. (2006) "Are apes really inequity averse?" *Proceedings of the Royal Society B* 273, 3123–3128.

Bullinger, A., Wyman, E., Melis, A., and Tomasello, M. (2011) "Coordination of chimpanzees (Pan troglodytes) in a stag hunt game," *International Journal of Primatology* 32, 1296–1310.

de Waal, F., and van Roosmalen, A. (1979) "Reconciliation and Consolation among Chimpanzees," *Behavioral Ecology and Sociobiology* 5, 55–66.

Engelmann, J., Herrmann, E., and Tomasello, M. (2012) "Five-year olds, but not chimpanzees, attempt to manage their reputations," *PLoS ONE* 7(10), e48433.

Fehr, E., and Fischbacher, U. (2004) "Third-party punishment and social norms," *Evolution & Human Behavior* 25, 63–87.

Hobaiter, C., and Byrne, R. W. (2010) "Able-bodied wild chimpanzees imitate a motor procedure used by a disabled individual to overcome handicap," *PLoS One* 5(8), e11959.

Horner, V., Proctor, D., Bonnie, K. E., Whiten, A., and de Waal, F.B.M. (2010) "Prestige affects cultural learning in chimpanzees," *PLoS ONE* 5(5), e10625.

Hrubesch, C., Preuschoft, S., and van Schaik, C. (2009) "Skill mastery inhibits adoption of observed alternative solutions among chimpanzees (Pan troglodytes)," *Animal Cognition* 12(2), 209–216.

Jensen, K., Call, J., and Tomasello, M. (2007) "Chimpanzees are vengeful but not spiteful," *PNAS* 104(32), 13046–13050.

Kelly, D., Stich, S., Haley, K., Eng, S., and Fessler, D. (2007) "Harm, affect, and the moral/conventional distinction," *Mind & Language* 22, 117–131.

Kendal, R., Hopper, L., Whiten, A., Brosnan, S., Lambeth, S., Schapiro, S., and Hoppitt, W. (2015) "Chimpanzees copy dominant and knowledgeable individuals: Implications for cultural diversity," *Evolution & Human Behavior* 36, 65–72.

Kitcher, P. (2011) *The Ethical Project*, Cambridge, MA: Harvard University Press.

Korsgaard, C. (2010) "Reflections on the evolution of morality," *The Amherst Lecture in Philosophy* 5, 1–29.

Lakin, J. L., Chartrand, T. L., and Arkin, R. M. (2008) "I am too just like you: Nonconscious mimicry as an automatic behavioral response to social exclusion," *Psychological Science* 19(8), 816–822.

Luncz, L., and Boesch, C. (2014) "Tradition over trend: Neighboring chimpanzee communities maintain differences in cultural behavior despite frequent immigration of adult females," *American Journal of Primatology* 76(7), 649–657.

Luncz, L., Mundry, R., and Boesch, C. (2012) "Evidence for cultural differences between neighboring chimpanzee communities," *Current Biology* 22(10), 922–926.

Luncz, L., Wittig, R., and Boesch, C. (2015) "Primate archaeology reveals cultural transmission in wild chimpanzees (Pan troglodytes verus)," *Philosophical Transactions of the Royal Society B* 370(1682), 20140348.

Moore, R. (2013a) "Imitation and conventional communication," *Biology and Philosophy* 28(3): 481–500.

Moore, R. (2013b) "Social learning and teaching in chimpanzees," *Biology and Philosophy* 28, 879–901.

Nucci, L., and Turiel, E. (1978) "Social interactions and the development of social concepts in preschool children," *Child Development* 49, 400–407.

Over, H., and Carpenter, M. (2009) "Eighteen-month-old infants show increased helping following priming with affiliation," *Psychological Science* 20, 1189–1193.

Paukner, A., Suomi, S., Visalberghi, E., and Ferrari, P. (2009) "Capuchin monkeys display affiliation towards humans who imitate them," *Science* 325(5942), 880–883.

Riedl, K., Jensen, K., Call, J., and Tomasello, M. (2012) "No third-party punishment in chimpanzees," *PNAS* 109(37), 14824–14829.

Rudolf von Rohr, C., Burkart, J., and van Schaik, C. (2011) "Evolutionary precursors of social norms in chimpanzees: A new approach," *Biology & Philosophy* 26, 1–30.

Rudolf von Rohr, C., Koski, S., Burkart, J., Caws, C., Fraser, O., Ziltener, A., and van Schaik, C. (2012) "Impartial third-party interventions in captive chimpanzees: A reflection of community concern," *PLoS ONE* 7(3), e32494.

Rudolf von Rohr, C., van Schaik, C., Kissling, A., and Burkart, J. (2015) "Chimpanzees' bystander reactions to infanticide," *Human Nature* 26(2), 143–160.

Schmidt, M., Rakoczy, H., and Tomasello, M. (2011) "Young children attribute normativity to novel actions without pedagogy or normative language," *Developmental Science* 14(3), 530–539.

Schmidt, M., Rakoczy, H., and Tomasello, M. (2012) "Young children enforce social norms selectively depending on the violator's group affiliation," *Cognition* 124(3), 325–333.

Tomasello, M. (2016) *A Natural History of Human Morality*, Cambridge, MA: Harvard University Press.

van Leeuwen, E., Cronin, K., and Haun, D. (2014) "A group-specific arbitrary tradition in chimpanzees (Pan troglodytes)," *Animal Cognition* 17, 1421–1425.

van Leeuwen, E., Cronin, K., Schütte, S., Call, J., and Haun, D. (2013) "Chimpanzees flexibly adjust their behaviour in order to maximize payoffs, not to conform to majorities," *PLoS One* 8(11), e80945.

van Leeuwen, E., and Haun, D. (2013) "Conformity in nonhuman primates: Fad or fact?" *Evolution and Human Behavior* 34, 1–7.

van Leeuwen, E., Kendal, R., Tennie, C., and Haun, D. (2015) "Conformity and its look-a-likes," *Animal Behaviour* 110, e1–e4.

van Schaik, C. (2012) "Animal culture: Chimpanzee conformity?" *Current Biology* 22(10), 402–404.

Warneken, F., and Tomasello, M. (2006) "Altruistic helping in human infants and young chimpanzees," *Science* 311(5765), 1301–1303.

Whiten, A., Goodall, J., McGrew, W., Nishida, T., Reynolds, V., Sugiyama, Y., Tutin, C., Wrangham, R., and Boesch, C. (1999) "Cultures in chimpanzees," *Nature* 399(6737), 682–685.

Whiten, A., Horner, V., and de Waal, F. (2005) "Conformity to cultural norms of tool use in chimpanzees," *Nature* 437(7059), 737–740.

Williams, K., Cheung, C., and Choi, W. (2000) "Cyberostracism: Effects of being ignored over the Internet," *Journal of Personality and Social Psychology* 79(5), 748–762.

Zawidzki, T. W. (2013) *Mindshaping: A New Framework for Understanding Human Social Cognition*. Cambridge, MA: MIT Press.

37

KINDS OF COLLECTIVE BEHAVIOR AND THE POSSIBILITY OF GROUP MINDS[1]

Bryce Huebner

Many species of bacteria "form complex communities, hunt prey in groups and secrete chemical trails for the directed movement of thousands of individuals" (Shapiro 1988). As they grow, divide, and multiply, they reflexively release a species-typical signaling molecule known as an autoinducer. At low levels of concentration, autoinducers rapidly diffuse; but they are reliably detected as their concentration increases. When *Alvibrio fischeri* detect their species-typical autoinducers, they express genes that evoke bioluminescence (Bassler 2010; Camilli and Bassler 2006; Rutherford and Bassler 2012). Bobtail squid have evolved to exploit the bioluminescent properties of these bacteria. They hunt at night, in clear, shallow water. By monitoring the moonlight, and adjusting the shutters on their light organ, they can cancel out their shadows and hunt in stealth mode. But each morning, they expel most of the bacteria in their light organ and bury themselves in the sand. The lights turn off. But the remaining bacteria multiply throughout the day. And as night falls, the lights come on. The squid hunts. And the cycle repeats.

Like all bacteria, *A. fischeri* are tiny adaptive machines, which have been optimized for pursuing nutrients and avoiding toxins.[2] They benefit from their mutualism with bobtail squid (which provide enough sugar and amino acids to minimize competition for nutrients). And this has put selective pressure on their capacity for collective bioluminesence. Nonetheless, their behavior can be fully explained in terms of individual mechanical capacities: each cell releases an autoinducer, each cell tracks the prevalence of that autoinducer, and each cell responds to that autoinducer as a salient feature of its environment. Nothing needs to be represented by the group, and behavioral alignment arises mechanically through the synchronized production and uptake of chemical signals. These bacteria only track autoinducers, and they only respond to locally available information. So it would be a stretch to call this a social phenomenon, even though it is a collective phenomenon.

Put bluntly, bacteria are like windowless monads. Without representing one another, they adjust their behavior in parallel. Since each organism acts in the same way, at the same time, a robust form of behavioral alignment emerges. But the resulting form of collective behavior can be fully explained by appeal to individual forms of behavioral adjustment. Each organism has been optimized to act as part of a group; but the group itself doesn't possess the capacity to adjust its behavior in light of changes in its environment. We may someday find a bacterial species that can collectively learn to track group-relevant phenomena. But for now, it is unclear what bacterial colonies could gain by moving beyond self-organized forms of Leibnizian harmony.

The main question I want to pursue in this chapter is: What more would it take for organisms to act together? And more intriguingly, what more would it take for a group of organisms to constitute a single mind? I explore these questions by examining the swarming behavior of desert locusts, the schooling behavior of golden shiner fish, and the foraging behavior of colonies of army ants. And I suggest that many organisms find reasons to act together out of contextualized self-interest.

Behavioral alignment

Desert locusts typically live as solitary animals. But when protein becomes scarce, their bodies change and they begin to move in coordinated bands. At low levels of population density, these bands display little behavioral alignment, but as density increases, "a rapid transition occurs from disordered movement of individuals within the group to highly aligned collective motion" (Buhl et al. 2006, 1403). When this happens, a million locusts can move together in unison, adjusting their behavior without external cause. This seems to suggest a centralized regulatory mechanism. But these patterns are governed by a more insidious drive.

After protein depravation, these locusts will begin to cannibalize conspecifics, as a way of obtaining salt and protein. And their cannibalistic motivations generate stable patterns of collective motion, which are driven by chasing and fleeing behavior (Bazazi et al. 2008). Each individual runs from the insects behind them and tries to cannibalize the insects in front of them; and their motions align because attacks are more common from the side than from the front or back (Bazazi et al. 2010). In these insects, the drive for self-preservation generates forward movement as well as behavioral alignment. While the social interactions between swarming locusts are more robust than the interactions between bacteria, their collective behavior is a by-product of the flow of information between conspecifics. These flows of embodied information do facilitate self-organization. Swarms can avoid obstacles, because the individuals that compose them do so; but each locust pursues its own reproductive fitness, and all forms of responsiveness flow upward through the aggregation of individual movements. These kinds of collective behavior are not cooperative; they are guided by the invisible hand of self-interest.

Of course, collective behavior is rarely governed by such severe forms of self-interest. But milder forms of self-interest often lead to robust patterns of collective behavior. Across the phylogenetic tree, forms of collective behavior arise as self-interested animals respond to the position and motion of nearby animals (Kao et al. 2014: e1003762). Like swarms of insects, schools of fish move in coordinated ways, rapidly changing speed and direction on the basis of information that only some individuals could possibly know.

Golden shiner fish, for example, prefer darker environments. And individuals will swim toward darker spaces, and slow down once inside them. They also prefer to move away from nearby fish, and toward fish that are two to four body lengths away (Katz et al. 2011). Within groups, the location of nearest-neighbors becomes a more accurate predictor of speed and direction than individual preferences (Berdahl et al. 2013). And in environments with light and dark patches, fish on the 'light' side will swim faster than fish on the 'dark' side (because of their individual preference), causing the school to curve toward darker spaces. As group size increases, the strength of attraction and repulsion are enhanced, generating stronger forms of behavioral alignment (Tunstrøm et al. 2013). And as a result, larger schools rapidly find preferable schooling locations, simply as a result of the aggregation of individual decisions.

Golden shiners also display reflexive predator avoidance behavior in response to visual, olfactory, and acoustic information (Rosenthal et al. 2015). But they are also jumpy, and they sometimes engage in similar displays though no predators are around. In schools, the effect of such false positives is dampened, as information flows through a school. And the process, here, is intriguing. These fish respond to the avoidance displays of any fish within their visual field. But they do not respond if their view is obstructed. So fish at the boundary of a school produce more avoidance signals, propagate them more frequently, and respond to most signals by others. Fish closer to the center of a school, by contrast, only respond to strong threat signals. Where many fish react in unison, the threat signal cascades through the school: each fish sees an avoidance display and reacts out of self-interest. The flow of false positives is inhibited, however, as the view of an initial reaction will be blocked for most fish, and the response will only spread as far as it can be seen. Consequently, false positives yield a local response, while predators trigger avoidance behavior that rapidly cascades through the entire school.

Since group life has a high payoff for these fish, golden shiners often face a trade-off between relying on their own preferences and favoring group cohesion. This is what makes it clear that their decisions are guided by self-interest. By schooling, these fish can rely on the information possessed by group-mates in ways that can reduce the cost of seeking new information. Suppose a school of fish contains some fish that prefer to forage in location A, and others that prefer to forage in location B. The fish at the head of a school will typically act on their own preferences; and if their decisions happen to converge, fish further back in the school will adjust their preferences in light of this new information. But if there is noise in the initial signal – for example, if some fish at the head of the school prefer location A and others prefer location B – fish further back in the school will tend to act on their own preferences. As with predator detection, each fish pays attention to the patterns they see. But where the information they receive from shoal-mates is inconsistent, personal preferences dominate decision-making. Intriguingly, if these later decisions weigh heavily in favor of location A, this can help to resolve the initial conflicts at the head of the school, as fish that initially preferred location B will revise their preference in light of the emerging consensus (Miller et al. 2013). Note, however, that this is not a school-level computation. The individual fish rely on local information to make their own decisions, and this allows them to have a greater sensitivity to conflicting preferences. And, importantly, the aggregate success of the fish in a school depends on the independence of their decisions, and the preservation of local control and local decision-making: "when individuals sense too much of the group, the result is a filtering of the local influences and an averaged (compromised) collective response" (Leonard et al. 2012: 232). And this can yield suboptimal decisions, which are worse than the decisions that individuals would have made on their own.

Social minds?

The types of collective behavior I have addressed so far are the tip of a much larger iceberg, but they help to make it clear why self-interest plays such an important role in the production and guidance of collective behavior. In most cases, thinking together would be costly, and it would offer no additional advantage beyond what can be gained by acting on self-interest. Consequently, most species of insects, fish, birds, and mammals that act together appear to act on "locally acquired cues such as the positions, motion, or change in motion, of others" (Couzin 2008: 36). As the case of the golden shiner fish suggests, locally acquired cues can be amplified or dampened in ways that impact the flow of survival-relevant information through a group: positive feedback can increase the likelihood of detecting threats, and negative feedback can diminish the effects of false positives on uninformed individuals. As a result, informed individuals can bias group behavior in ways that can guide naïve individuals toward resources and away from threats (Couzin 2008: 39). There is a great deal of variation in these effects, but in general, information appears to flow in two directions: from individual decisions to patterns of collective behavior; and from patterns of collective behavior to individual decisions. This allows the individuals in schools to better track evolutionarily salient risks and rewards by treating one another as informational resources. But it is individuals who do this tracking, not the groups themselves – and this fact is important.

Even in hierarchically organized species, such as olive baboons, decisions about where to forage are typically guided by consensus, not dominance: "baboons are most likely to follow when there are many initiators with high agreement. However, when agreement is low, having more concurrent initiators decreases the likelihood that a baboon will follow anyone" (Strandburg-Peshkin et al. 2015: 1361). And in some cases, forms of human decision-making can rely on a similarly aggregative process to yield results that are more accurate than expert opinion. The reason for this is simple:

> If you ask a large enough group of diverse, independent people to make a prediction or estimate of probability, and then average those estimates, the errors each of them makes in coming up with an answer will cancel themselves out.
>
> (Surowiecki 2004: 10)[3]

But perhaps more importantly, humans often need to capitalize on transient diversity within a group to arrive at scientific knowledge (Zollman 2010). In this respect, collective decision-making in humans may share a great deal in common with the patterns of decision-making we find in other species.

Adaptive decisions

That said, there are cases where animals act together in ways that yield more robust forms of informational integration. Some ants (*S. invicta*) form rafts to escape flooding. They adjust the structure of their rafts to maintain buoyancy, and they keep the queen and larvae at the center to prevent predation. As individuals move from the periphery to the center, they are rapidly replaced to preserve the raft's average thickness (Mlot et al. 2011). Strong selective pressures have favored this form of collective behavior. The native environment of these ants floods frequently, and raft-building colonies have been more likely to survive floods than those that do not. Since ants are highly related (each pair sharing as much genetic material as a brother or a sister), selection occurs in response to these colony-level pressures.[4] But this type of raft-building also relies on individual computations and local heuristics. Individuals track the number of ants walking on top of them, and they adjust their behavior against this locally computed value (Anderson et al. 2002; Mlot et al. 2011). As a result of these computations, colonies respond well to flooding.

This is a form of local updating, much as we saw above. But in ants, these patterns of local updating can sometimes allow colonies to function as "parallel information-processing systems capable of intricate collective decision-making during essential tasks such as foraging, moving home or constructing a nest" (Couzin 2008: 39). Where this occurs, individual behavioral adjustments resemble Hebbian processing (i.e., neurons that fire together wire together). To see what this means, consider species of army ants that link their bodies to form ladders, chains, and bridges to cross otherwise impassable landscapes.

Bridge construction typically begins at a natural diversion, and longer bridges are built to create shortcuts in the foraging trail as traffic increases (Reid et al. 2015: 15114). But continuous adjustments are made to the size and location of the bridge as ants respond to the flow of traffic across their bodies. When traffic decreases, ants abandon their position in a bridge; when traffic increases, ants are recruited to make the bridge longer. This parallels the kind of behavior that we have seen already. But bridge expansion often stops before the maximum foraging shortcut has been achieved; while no individual represents the costs and benefits to the colony, the variations in recruitment underwrite a form of parallel information processing that is sensitive to "the diminishing returns of shortening the trail to avoid the cost of locking up an increasing number of workers in the structure" (Reid et al. 2015: 15116).

These colonies function as computational networks, which analyze the costs and benefits of bridge construction, given the foraging needs of the colony. Each ant carries out a local computation based on information that is available to it; and as the information embodied in the flow of traffic is integrated with information embodied in bridge building, the colony adjusts *its* behavior in light of *its current situation*. Experiments reveal that this process reliably generates cost-benefit analyses by following an effective mechanical procedure. The movements of individuals facilitate ongoing coping with biologically relevant patterns in the environment; these patterns designate significant features of the environment (colony-level costs and benefits); and this allows colonies to represent a variety of different situations in a systematic way. Finally, there are proper and improper ways of producing and manipulating these representations – and colonies that routinely failed to process the costs and benefits of bridge construction would be less successful in foraging than their rivals. This gives us good reason to think that these colonies are carrying out distributed computations over collective representations (cf., Haugeland 1998; Huebner 2013).

Something similar happens in nest site selection. Individual ants are able to choose where to live, but doing so requires multiple visits to each location and repeated comparisons of their features. Unsurprisingly, ants rarely have the time for this; but in experimental contexts, *Temnothorax rugatulusm* can effectively compare two sites that differ in one respect (e.g., cavity volume, interior dimness, entrance size). As the number of potential nest sites increases, however, and as multiple attributes must be evaluated in parallel, individuals start to make suboptimal decisions (Sasaki and Pratt 2012). Fortunately, nests tend to be selected by consensus. Individual scouts visit one site, which they compare "to an internal scale and then decide whether to recruit nest-mates there" (Sasaki and Pratt 2013). Some succeed in recruiting nest-mates, then guide a nest-mate to the site (Shaffer et al. 2013); a comparative evaluation thus arises through 'friendly' competition over recruits. Over time, recruitment "generates positive feedback on the number of ants at each site, with the better site slightly favored by its higher acceptance rate" (Sasaki et al. 2013). As consensus on a high-grade option begins to emerge, scouts start to carry nest-mates to the preferred site, increasing the rate of recruitment by approximately three times (Pratt et al. 2002). Strikingly, where numerous potential nest sites are compared, across multiple dimensions, this form of consensus decision-making is highly accurate (Sasaki et al. 2013): colonies can choose the best nest site from eight options with approximately 90% accuracy (Sasaki and Pratt 2012).

As with bridge building, these individuals never compare the available options. Some ants recruit nest-mates; others visit advertised sites. But no ant has the information that would be required to compare these sites against one another. The collective decision arises through a winner-take-all algorithm, which is distributed across scouts and recruits.[5] As a result of the high degree of relatedness within a colony, however, individual interests converge with the interests of other ants and with the interest of the colony (Seeley 2010). So competitions for recruits remains 'friendly'. But, unfortunately, this friendly competition can go awry. The converging interests of these ants are sensitive to previous experience. And after inhabiting an environment where one factor (e.g., entrance size) has been highly salient to nest-site selection, colonies increase their sensitivity to this factor (Sasaki and Pratt 2013). Suboptimal decisions can then emerge where colonies adjust their shared preferences against their collective experience.

Because they process information as a group, these ants become more sensitive to group-relevant and local sources of distortion.

Group minds?

Natural selection tends to increase the frequency of genes associated with individual fitness, as individuals with such genes typically reproduce more frequently than those with rival alleles. When average relatedness is high, animals often find ways to cooperate; but across the phylogenetic tree, as average relatedness falls, cooperation becomes more closely tied to the immediate fitness benefits of acting together (Clutton-Brock 2009; West et al. 2011). In this chapter, I have examined some ways that contextualized self-interest can generate stable forms of collective behavior in light of these facts. And in the previous section, I suggested that under limited conditions, the pursuit of self-interest can yield a minimal form of collective mentality.

Like most other animals, individual ants act on locally available information. But because of their evolutionary history, they also play roles in the distributed computations that are carried out by the colony. This allows colonies to develop better strategies for navigating the world, and it allows them to carry out complex comparative evaluations as information is propagated between ants; but no individual carries out these evaluations, and no individual develops strategies for furthering the interests of the colony. From an evolutionary perspective, this should be no more surprising than the existence of neurons that think and act together; and the behavior of these ants does bear a striking resemblance to the computational structures we find in individual brains. Each neuron updates its state in light of the behavior of the neurons to which it is connected (e.g., modulating neurotransmitter production, extending and pruning dendritic branches, and adjusting firing patterns). And since groups of neurons constitute highly integrated, hierarchically organized, and massively parallel computational systems, these interactions often yield computational outputs that generate adaptive behavior, as well as complex comparative evaluations. But decisions are not made by particular neurons, they are made by the system as a whole.

There is good reason to treat colonies of ants (and honeybees) as unified cognitive systems, at least in some cases. But are there forms of collective mentality likely to emerge in other species? Whether it arises in groups or in individuals, mentality requires the ability to adjust behavior in ways that yield skillful coping with unpredictable environmental variation. Individuals do not need to be biologically bounded. And many individuals, including humans, are constituted by numerous smaller entities. But few animals have solved basic coordination problems in ways that would allow groups to function as unified cognitive systems. Social organisms face constant trade-offs between the benefits of independence and the benefits of group life, and while they will often rely on one another as sources of information, they rarely form integrated information-processing systems. When collective hunting and collective defense arise among hyenas, lions, wolves, and chimpanzees, "each individual simply assesses the state of the chase at each moment and decides what is best for it to do" (Tomasello et al. 2005, 11). They do not need to develop shared plans, and they do not need to process information as a group; and they never subvert their own interests to the needs of the group. Of course, complex coordination dynamics do arise in such groups, and this yields local forms of cooperative behavior that have a high payoff for group members (much as we saw in the case of golden shiners and olive baboons). But the stable forms of aggregation that would allow a group to think and act *as a group* require solving coordination problems in ways that can prevent local forms of self-interest from intruding into collective decision-making. The unification of multiple entities into multicellular organisms is one way to solve this problem; and eusocial insects have solved it by having one caste whose reproductive futures depend on the success of their colony (cf., Seeley 2010). But most animals settle for more local forms of collective decision-making. This is why I believe that collective mentality is incredibly rare outside of the eusocial insects.

I cannot address this issue here, but humans may have found a novel solution to this problem of social aggregation. We take up social roles, and we can build new ones; and we can even build computational unities by using linguistic representations to build high-bandwidth interfaces between individuals. Where this works, we can create transactive forms of cognition. We often see this in long-term partnerships, where people remember things and plan together, and highly structured groups can sometimes achieve something similar. But in general, these human forms of collective mentality will also be transient. If we wanted to create stable and persistent forms of collective mentality, this would require ongoing control and guidance by individuals, but it may be possible (see Huebner 2013).

Notes

1 I would like to thank Mattia Gallotti, Ruth Kramer, Georg Theiner, and an audience at the School of Advanced Study (London) for assistance in thinking through these issues.
2 As I learn more about bacteria, I find it harder to deny them mentality, but nothing in this chapter will turn on this issue. See Bassler (2012) and Shapiro (1988) for overviews of bacterial capacities; and see Figdor (in prep) for arguments supporting the claim that bacteria literally have minds.
3 This form of judgment aggregation only works if four conditions are satisfied: (1) each decision is made by an individual, (2) on the basis of local values and local sources of information, (3) independently of the decisions made by others, before (4) the decisions are aggregating into a collective decision. As Kristin Andrews (pers. comm.) notes, it would take a great deal of empirical effort to demonstrate that such conditions are satisfied in informal decision-making contexts; and it remains an open empirical question which forms of collective behavior in humans have this character (cf., Winsberg et al. 2014). This is one of the reasons why I remain skeptical of most discussions of collective mentality in humans (Huebner 2013).
4 In this situation, the distinction between inclusive fitness and group selection may collapse (see Marshall 2011).
5 For parallel cases in honeybees, see Seeley (2010), who argues at length that honeybee colonies are minded. For further discussion of the kinds of minds that honeybee colonies possess, see Huebner (2011).

References

Anderson, C., G. Theraulaz, and J. Deneubourg (2002). Self-assemblages in insect societies. *Insectes Sociaux*, 49 (2): 99–110.

Bassler, B. (2010). Cell to cell communication. *Proceedings of the American Philosophical Society*, 154 (3): 307–314.

Bassler, B. (2012). Microbes as menaces, mates, and marvels. *Daedalus*, 141 (3): 67–76.

Bazazi, S., J. Buhl, J. Hale, M. Anstey, G. Sword, S. Simpson, and I. Couzin (2008). Collective motion and cannibalism in locust migratory bands. *Current Biology*, 18 (10): 735–739.

Bazazi, S., C. Ioannou, S. Simpson, G. Sword, C. Torney, P. Lorch, and I. Couzin (2010). The social context of cannibalism in migratory bands of the Mormon cricket. *PloSone*, 5 (12): e15118–e15118.

Berdahl, A., C. Torney, C. Ioannou, J. Faria, and I. Couzin (2013). Emergent sensing of complex environments by mobile animal groups. *Science*, 339(6119): 574–576.

Buhl, J., D. Sumpter, I. Couzin, J. Hale, E. Despland, E. Miller, and S. Simpson (2006). From disorder to order in marching locusts. *Science*, 312 (5778): 1402–1406.

Camilli, A., and B. Bassler (2006). Bacterial small-molecule signaling pathways. *Science*, 311 (5764): 1113.

Clutton-Brock, T. (2009). Cooperation between non-kin in animal societies. *Nature*, 462: 51–57.

Couzin, I. (2008). Collective cognition in animal groups. *Trends in Cognitive Science*, 13 (1): 36–43.

Figdor, C. (forthcoming). *Pieces of mind: An essay on the proper domain of psychological predicates*. Oxford: Oxford University Press.

Haugeland, J. (1998). Representational genera. In *Having thought: Essays in the metaphysics of mind*. Cambridge, MA: Harvard University Press, 171–206.

Huebner, B. (2011). *Minimal minds: The Oxford handbook of animals*. New York: Oxford University Press, 441–468.

Huebner, B. (2013). *Macrocognition*. Oxford: Oxford University Press.

Kao, A., N. Miller, C. Torney, A. Hartnett, and I. Couzin (2014). Collective learning and optimal consensus decisions in social animal groups. *PLoS Computational Biology*, 10 (8): e1003762.

Katz, Y., K. Tunström, C. Ioannou, C. Huepe, and I. Couzin (2011). Inferring the structure and dynamics of interactions in schooling fish. *Proceedings of the National Academy of Sciences*, 108 (46): 18720–18725.

Leonard, N. E., T. Shen, B. Nabet, L. Scardovi, I. D. Couzin, and S. A. Levin. (2012). Decision versus compromise for animal groups in motion. *Proceedings of the National Academy of Sciences*, 109 (1), 227–232.

Marshall, J. (2011). Group selection and kin selection: Formally equivalent approaches. *Trends in Evolutionary Ecology*, 26 (7): 325–332.

Miller, N., S. Garnier, A. Hartnett, and I. Couzin (2013). Both information and social cohesion determine collective decisions in animal groups. *Proceedings of the National Academy of Sciences*, 110 (13), 5263–5268.

Mlot, N., C. Tovey, and D. Hu (2011). Fire ants self-assemble into waterproof rafts to survive floods. *PNAS*, 108 (19): 7669–7673.

Pratt, S. C., E. B. Mallon, D. J. Sumpter, and N. R. Franks (2002). Quorum sensing, recruitment, and collective decision-making during colony emigration by the ant Leptothorax albipennis. *Behavioral Ecology and Sociobiology*, 52(2): 117–127.

Reid, C. R., M. J. Lutz, S. Powell, A. B. Kao, I. D. Couzin, and S. Garnier (2015). Army ants dynamically adjust living bridges in response to a cost – benefit trade-off. *Proceedings of the National Academy of Sciences*, 112 (49): 15113–15118.

Rosenthal, S., C. Twomey, A. Hartnett, H. Wu, and I. Couzin (2015). Revealing the hidden networks of interaction in mobile animal groups allows prediction of complex behavioral contagion. *Proceedings of the National Academy of Sciences*, 112 (15): 4690–4695.

Rutherford, S., and B. Bassler (2012). Bacterial quorum sensing: Its role in virulence and possibilities for its control. *Cold Spring Harbor Perspectives in Medicine*, 2 (11): a012427.

Sasaki, T., B. Granovskiy, R. P. Mann, D. J. Sumpter, & S. C. Pratt (2013). Ant colonies outperform individuals when a sensory discrimination task is difficult but not when it is easy. *Proceedings of the National Academy of Sciences*, 110 (34): 13769–13773.

Sasaki, T., & Pratt, S. C. (2012). Groups have a larger cognitive capacity than individuals. *Current Biology*, 22 (19): R827–R829.

Sasaki, T., and S. C. Pratt (2013). Ants learn to rely on more informative attributes during decision-making. *Biology Letters*, 9 (6): 20130667.

Seeley, T. (2010). *Honeybee Democracy*. Princeton, NJ: Princeton University Press.

Shaffer, Z., T. Sasaki, and S. C. Pratt (2013). Linear recruitment leads to allocation and flexibility in collective foraging by ants. *Animal Behaviour*, 86 (5): 967–975.

Shapiro, J. (1988). Bacteria as multicellular organisms. *Scientific American*, 258 (6): 82–89.

Strandburg-Peshkin, A., D. R. Farine, I. D. Couzin, and M. C. Crofoot (2015). Shared decision-making drives collective movement in wild baboons. *Science*, 348 (6241): 1358–1361.

Surowiecki, J. (2004). *The Wisdom of Crowds*. Norwell, MA: Anchor Press.

Tomasello, M., M. Carpenter, J. Call, T. Behne, and H. Moll. (2005). Understanding and sharing intentions: The origins of cultural cognition. *Behavioral and Brain Sciences*, 28 (5): 675–691.

Tunström K, Y. Katz, C. Ioannou, C. Huepe, M. Lutz, and I. Couzin (2013). Collective states, multistability and transitional behavior in schooling fish. *PLoS Computational Biology*, 9 (2): e1002915.

West, S., C. Mouden, and A. Gardner (2011). Sixteen common misconceptions about the evolution of cooperation in humans. *Evolution and Human Behavior*, 32: 231–262.

Winsberg, E., R. Kukla, and B. Huebner (2014). Accountability and models in radically collaborative research. *Studies in the History and Philosophy of Science*, 46: 16–23.

Zollman, K. J. (2010). The epistemic benefit of transient diversity. *Erkenntnis*, 72 (1): 17–35.

PART VII

Association, simplicity, and modeling

38

ASSOCIATIVE LEARNING

Colin Allen

Introduction

Ever since George Romanes came under heavy criticism for his anecdotal approach to animal mind, the capacity to learn has been presented by psychologists as a deflationary alternative to the attribution of higher cognitive capacities. The capacity to learn – i.e., to alter behavior as a function of experience – is ubiquitous in the animal kingdom, leading theorists from Conwy Lloyd Morgan to Edward Thorndike to B. F. Skinner and beyond to consider learning explanations of complex behavior to be preferable to cognitive alternatives, which posit inner representational states of unknown structure and provenance.

Learning, however, comes in many forms. From simple habituation or sensitization (respectively, a decrease or increase in responsiveness to a repeated stimulus) through associative learning (whether of the classical/Pavlovian or instrumental/Skinnerian variety) to more elaborate forms of discriminative learning (Rescorla and Wagner 1972), observational learning (Galef and Laland 2005), and convention learning (Thompson-Schill et al. 2009), the cognitive demands on the learner are quite different (see, also, Chapter 34 by Rachael Brown and Chapter 39 by Cameron Buckner in this volume). Gallistel (1990) emphasizes the cognitive dimensions of even the simpler forms of animal learning, leading him to adopt an explicitly anti-associationist, cognitivist approach that emphasizes representations and computation. But, as Buckner (2011) argues, the distinction between cognition and "mere association" may, in one important sense of these terms, present a false dichotomy insofar as higher cognitive functions rely upon associative mechanisms.

Despite the enormous growth of interest in animal minds among philosophers, there remains relatively little awareness among philosophers of the complexities of animal learning theory. Partly this is a function of the area being rife with jargon (see the previous paragraph!) and correspondingly difficult to penetrate, and partly it is a function of the philosophical myth that animal learning theory hit a dead end somewhere in the late 1950s, with B. F. Skinner's work at the apotheosis and Chomsky's supposedly decisive refutation of Skinner launching cognitive science as we know it. Strict behaviorism may have been a dead end, but the learning theory that went with it is far from irrelevant to current cognitive science.

A goal of this chapter is to unpack some of the jargon and thereby familiarize the reader with some of the main concepts and developments in animal learning theory, and their application to questions about animal minds. Along the way, I will also touch upon the relevance of learning theory to human cognition. The goal, however, is not to provide a systematic or comprehensive review of the literature. (For that, see a textbook such as Domjan and Grau 2014.) Rather, my goal is to produce something akin to a *New Yorker* style map of the landscape as I see it, highlighting some of the features of learning that have guided me in my thinking about certain aspects of animal cognition. I do this in the hope that such a map will prove useful to others, but also that it will encourage them to produce alternative maps. To be clear, however, the goal here is not to converge on the one, true representation of animal learning. Just as no single flat map projection of the planet is fully adequate to its spheroid reality, even textbook treatments of animal learning selectively distort the complexities of animal learning to fit the purposes of those who write them and teach from them. While the psychologists' view of learning is definitely useful to philosophers interested in animal minds, it may not satisfy all our needs. For a similar reason, I am not starting by rehearsing a textbook definition of learning. Such definitions serve important pedagogical purposes, but do not bear the metaphysical weight that philosophers are eager to place upon them.

Delay vs. trace

To illustrate the view from where I sit, and to begin unpacking some of the jargon, let me start with a distinction between two forms of classical conditioning – delay conditioning and trace conditioning. Classical conditioning is the form of associative learning linked to Pavlov's discovery that dogs, who naturally salivate in the presence of food (the *unconditioned* stimulus, or US), would come to salivate in response to a different stimulus, such as the ring of a bell (the *conditioned* stimulus, or CS) given a certain amount of experience with the pairing of the CS and the US. This much is familiar to almost anyone with a college education, and to everyone with a basic course in psychology, although frequent repetition of "CS" and "US" may already prove challenging. Less familiar is the distinction between Pavlovian delay conditioning and Pavlovian trace conditioning. In Pavlovian training, the CS (e.g., the auditory stimulus emanating from the bell to which the dog's response is to be conditioned) is introduced just before the US (e.g., the food, to which the dog already has a prior response of salivation). In standard *delay* conditioning, the CS remains present when the US is introduced (i.e., the bell can still be heard ringing when the food arrives). This method of conditioning with CS and US co-present is effective in the sea slug *Aplysia*, using a light touch to the animal's siphon as the CS and electric shock to the tail as the US (Hawkins et al. 1983), leading to a conditioned siphon-withdrawal response. Delay conditioning is just as effective a method in humans and rabbits, using an auditory tone as the CS and a puff of air directed at the eye leading to an eye-blink response (Clark and Squire 1998). The acquisition of the delay-conditioned response is effectively 100%, whether the subjects are sea slugs, rabbits, or humans (although, of course, the conditionable responses are limited by the fact that sea slugs don't have eyes to blink, and neither rabbits nor humans have siphons to withdraw). In contrast to delay conditioning, *trace* conditioning involves terminating the CS *before* the US is delivered. For instance, a tone is heard, then silence (spanning the trace interval), then a puff of air is delivered to the eye of a subject. Under these conditions, subjects are much less likely to acquire the response (around 50% in the non-amnesiac, normal human subjects tested by Clark & Squire 1998).

Why should philosophers of animal mind and cognition care about this seemingly arcane distinction within Pavlovian learning? After all, Pavlovian classical conditioning represents the epitome of a "simple" learning mechanism, known for nearly a century, putatively involving very little cognitive capacity, capable of occurring completely without conscious awareness, and found even in organisms such as *Aplysia* with fewer than 20,000 neurons. But here is where the distinction makes a true difference. Despite a mistaken report to the contrary (Bekinschtein et al. 2011), *trace* conditioning has not been shown in *Aplysia*. Furthermore, Clark and Squire (1998) provided evidence that for their human subjects, who did not know they were in a conditioning experiment, there was *no correlation* between *delay* conditioning of the eye blink response and *awareness* of the relationship between the stimuli (the sound and the puff of air) as revealed by questioning after the procedure – all were conditioned, but only some of them could answer the questions about the relationship between the stimuli – whereas there was a *perfect correlation* between acquiring the response during *trace conditioning* and *awareness* of the relationship between the stimuli as revealed by subsequent questioning. Delay conditioning can be automatic and unconscious. Trace conditioning perhaps not. Furthermore, neuroscientists have shown that the neural mechanisms underlying delay and trace conditioning are independent and quite different. These differences, as I will go on to explain, are significant to our understanding of the cognitive architecture involved, and have implications for issues that philosophers of animal cognition care about.

Before going into more detail about the neural mechanisms, this case of trace conditioning reveals an important distinction between two important dimensions along which learning may be compared. Psychology textbooks are typically organized along a methodological dimension: whether the experimental setup involves single-stimulus learning (habituation, sensitization) or whether the setup involves an association of some kind; whether the association is between two stimuli (classical conditioning), or whether the experiment is set up to allow the animal to learn to associate its own actions with outcomes (instrumental, operant); whether or not the animal is pre-exposed to the stimuli without any associated reward (latent learning). Along this dimension, delay conditioning and trace conditioning are very similar, differing only in the offset of the CS in relation to the onset of the US. Psychologists have some practical and historical reasons for emphasizing the methodological dimension when teaching students about learning: if you can run a delay conditioning experiment, for example, it is a minor tweak of the procedure to run a trace conditioning experiment. But from a mechanistic perspective, there is no guarantee that similarity along the methodological dimension should correspond to similarity of mechanism, as investigation of the mechanisms of delay conditioning and trace conditioning has shown.

It is not my intention to provide a comprehensive review of the mechanisms – the relevant neuroscience is, after all, rapidly developing. Rather, my goal is to whet the appetite for philosophers to attend to the details. In the case of trace conditioning, an intact hippocampus is widely believed to be a key component of the system. Solomon et al. (1986) established that rabbits with hippocampal lesions were not impaired with respect to delay conditioning, but could not be conditioned with a trace conditioning procedure. Clark and Squire (1998) described a similar pattern of results with human amnesiac patients who had suffered hippocampal damage. It is tempting to speculate about the role of the hippocampus, so I will! We know from many studies that the hippocampus plays several roles in processes for which temporal and spatial sequencing is important, as well as in autobiographical memory. Trace conditioning requires a trace of the post-offset CS to be sustained long enough for the onset of the US to be associated with it. Such buffering through the trace interval must be inherently "open" insofar as the organism does not know in advance which (if any) significant events might follow, although experience may support anticipation of some of them. A sound that has just ceased may signal several different things (or signal nothing at all). But the brain cannot keep such a buffer filled with potentially relevant stimuli forever: active storage is limited, and long-range associations are perhaps less likely to be of critical importance to individual biological success (although the particular ecological application matters; see the discussion of trace conditioning in halibut, below). We have, then, in trace conditioning a manifestation of something akin to William James' (1890) conception of the stream (or waves) of consciousness constituting the "specious present." And while we cannot prove that rabbits in experiments mentioned by Clark and Squire (1998) who were successfully conditioned using the trace procedure were consciously aware of the tone preceding the puff of air in time, we can be fairly certain that they have the mechanisms which support such experiences in human beings.

That much is admittedly and deliberately speculative, but its application to questions about animal minds and consciousness is clear. Woe betide those who wade into these areas relying only on the testimony of others, however. Mistakes have happened, such as in the aforementioned paper by Bekinschtein and colleagues. Citing Clark and Squire and a number of other relevant studies, they deliberately link trace conditioning to consciousness, making connections between trace conditioning and conscious experience of events in time that are similar in sprit to those in my previous paragraph, as well as bringing in other relevant considerations about the role of attention in learning and consciousness. Their goal of using trace conditioning to answer questions about consciousness in human patients who are in a persistent vegetative state (PVS), a state of partial arousal that is above a coma but below fully functional awareness, is interesting and suggestive, especially in combination with Bekinschtein's earlier report of trace conditioning in PVS patients (Bekinschtein et al. 2009). They take a misstep, however, by regarding *Aplysia* as presenting a challenge to their view because (wrongly it turns out) they believe Glanzman (1995) to have reported trace conditioning in these sea slugs, which they presume to be unconscious. The reasons for this misstep are unclear. Glanzman's article is a review of the cellular basis of classical conditioning in *Aplysia* ("it's less simple than you think," he declares in the article's subtitle). However, nowhere in his article does Glanzman use the term "trace conditioning" (nor "delay conditioning" for that matter), and all of the studies he reviews in the literature on *Aplysia* use a standard delay conditioning approach. In places, Bekinschtein and colleagues seem to conflate classical and trace conditioning (e.g., the first sentence of the abstract begins, "Classical (trace) conditioning . . ."), although they are also very clear about the distinction between trace and delay conditioning procedures (e.g., their Figure 1 on page 1344). The point here is just that the problems of relating learning to higher cognition and consciousness is hard enough without the invention of spurious difficulties.

None of this is to say that a trace conditioning procedure might not someday be found to be effective in *Aplysia*, although here we must be careful to separate some other dimensions of comparison. By saying that rabbits and humans are capable of being conditioned by a trace conditioning procedure, we mean that these organisms can associate a wide (but not unlimited) range of CSs with a similarly wide range of USs through a trace interval (with the exact profile of that interval varying inter- and perhaps intra-specifically). Without a hippocampus, or something functionally equivalent, any capacity for trace conditioning will be much more limited. The mechanism matters to the inferences we want to make, although attention to the mechanisms must go hand-in-hand with careful analysis of the exact learning capacities. At the cutting edge of such comparisons lie questions about the capacities of various fish species. Some capacity for trace conditioning has been established in certain teleost fish (e.g., cod – Nilsson et al. 2008; trout – Nordgreen et al. 2010; halibut – Nilsson et al. 2010; see Allen 2013 for a review) and a species of shark (Guttridge and Brown 2014). Interestingly, trace conditioning in halibut was not recognized experimentally until the trace interval was extended beyond that used for cod and trout, in line with halibut feeding ecology as sit-and-wait predators, rather than being pursuit predators like trout and cod (Nilsson et al. 2010). However, the full range of trace conditioning and the corresponding neural mechanisms in fish remain unknown (Vargas et al. 2009), and are likely to remain so until scientists understand more about the functional neuroanatomy of fish brains. Trinh et al. (2016) suggest that part of the fish pallium may be functionally analogous to the mammalian hippocampus, but more investigation is needed.

Instrumental vs. operant

Trace conditioning provides but one example of how appreciation for distinctions among different forms of learning that are usually not distinguished carefully by those outside the field of animal learning can inform theories in comparative animal cognition. Another example is provided by a distinction I have also written about before (Allen et al. 2009), borrowed from Jim Grau (Grau and Joynes 2005). It is the distinction between instrumental learning and operant conditioning, a distinction which is often not made at all, even in psychology textbooks. Where it is made, it is often treated as a methodological distinction only. In either case, instrumental or operant conditioning concerns the ability of animals to learn to associate a behavioral response with an outcome. Thus, for example, Edward Thorndike pioneered the use of puzzle boxes – contraptions from which animals could escape to a food reward if they discovered the correct sequence of actions – and B. F. Skinner invented the Skinner box – a space where animals could be trained via reward or punishment to emit behaviors spontaneously or in response to specific stimuli. When instrumental and operant procedures are distinguished by psychologists, it is sometimes on the basis that Thorndike's (instrumental) procedure specifies exactly one response to obtain the reward, whereas Skinner's (operant) procedure allows the animal to emit any available response (such as pressing a lever or pecking at a key) with any frequency. Most psychologists, however, regard "instrumental" and "operant" learning as synonymous.

From their more mechanistic perspective, Grau and Joynes distinguish between instrumental response-outcome learning and more sophisticated operant response-learning. Both forms of learning satisfy methodological criteria for response-outcome conditioning, but only operant learning meets additional functional criteria concerning the relatively unconstrained nature of behavioral response and effective reinforcers, akin to what I referred to above as the "open" nature of trace conditioning. Basic instrumental learning is highly constrained with respect to which responses can be associated with which outcomes. In contrast, operant learning allows a variety of reinforcers – e.g., food, water, access to a mate, access to recreation, and even money (or tokens that can be used for exchange) – to shape a variety of behaviors. Research from Grau's lab (reviewed by Allen et al. 2009) establishes that the more constrained form of instrumental learning can be found even in the spinal cord. The more advanced form of operant learning seems to require brain circuitry whose functionality is not replicated in the mammalian spinal cord; but this is compatible with some brain circuitry being just as constrained in its ability to associate responses and outcomes.

Importantly for thinking about the relevance of learning to higher cognition, in cases of full operant conditioning, the behaviors and rewards are relatively fungible and goal-oriented. For instance, Rumbaugh and Washburn (2003) describe work by Rumbaugh and colleagues showing that monkeys trained on a computer-mediated task, using a joystick they could only reach with their feet, switched to using their hands and were more effective at the task when the equipment was re-arranged. This kind of goal-directed flexibility in operant behavior (corresponding to what Rumbaugh et al. 1996 call an "emergent") provides a useful dimension along which the capacities of different species and different individuals may be compared. It requires associative cortex or its functional equivalent (although much more would need to be said for a complete account), involving mechanisms quite different from those that are sufficient for more basic forms of instrumental learning.

Modern associationism

The associative learning phenomena described originally within the paradigm of behavioristic psychology remain highly relevant to comparative cognition, but the early models of such phenomena were too limited, in all sorts of ways. The shift to a more integrated view of associative learning and cognition has roots in early work by Tolman on latent learning and cognitive maps in rats (1948). But the challenge to early ideas about animal learning was accelerated by the discovery of various learning phenomena that were hard for strict Pavlovians and Skinnerians to explain. These phenomena include latent inhibition (the longer time taken to learn an association after pre-exposure to a stimulus; Lubow and Moore 1959), the Garcia effect (one-trial learning to avoid food after administration of an emetic (a vomiting inducer) with a long delay; Garcia et al. 1966), and blocking (the inability to learn about a predictive stimulus when it is presented in the context of a previously learned association; Kamin 1969).

In a sense, Chomsky (1959) was correct that the theories of learning espoused by Skinner were not up to the task of accounting for all behavior. But Chomsky (1967) was wrong to think that Skinner's views represented the pinnacle of associationist learning theory. The phenomena described just above have led and continue to lead modelers to develop ever more sophisticated theories, applying ideas about information processing to the elaboration of representations of the world. For example, to explain the blocking effect, Rescorla and Wagner (1972) described a model for classical conditioning based upon error correction, in which learning is proportional to the amount of "surprise" generated by an outcome. The notion of "surprise" here can be cashed out in information-theoretic terms concerning the likelihood of the outcome given previous experience. But unlike strict behaviorism, which eschews the idea of cognitive or mental representations, the Rescorla-Wagner model provides a method for discriminating and representing the most predictive cues by a process of cue competition, rather than merely associating co-occurring stimuli. The original Rescorla-Wagner model has its own limitations, and has been subsequently elaborated in various ways (e.g., Van Hamme and Wasserman 1994). Nevertheless, the naive discriminative learning capability of the basic model has promising applications, even to human language learning (Baayen et al. 2016).

The shift from categorizing learning by the methodological dimensions of training procedures used in laboratory preparations, to models of learning and description of the mechanisms required to support various kinds of behavioral flexibility, holds potential for a better understanding of the evolution of learning and cognition. Eric Kandel and colleagues (Castellucci et al. 1970; Hawkins et al. 1983) already regarded classical conditioning in *Aplysia* as an elaboration of single-stimulus sensitization. Grau and Joynes (2005, p. 4) advocate for what they call a "neuro-functional" approach, pointing out that, "a single mechanism may be called upon to solve a variety of environmental challenges" and suggesting that a single mechanism may be implicated in different cases of learning that are categorized quite differently using methodological criteria. Methodological considerations are important, but now, more than century since Thorndike (1911) invented the experimental approach to animal learning, we are in a better position than ever to recognize that detailed attention to all aspects of learning – methodology, information processing, neural mechanisms, and ecological context – provide us with the best chance of understanding how these diverse capacities came to be distributed across the animal kingdom.

Both learning theory and the comparative neuroscience of learning are currently undergoing rapid development, which makes tracking these fields from outside the field challenging. I do not pretend to know it all, but I do know that philosophers are in a privileged position: if we are willing to rise to the challenge, we are able to sample a wider range of literature than most practicing scientists, and we can connect the dots among diverse findings. These developments can be used to enrich our understanding of the diversity of learning capacities and mechanisms that make up the species of minds that have evolved on this planet.

Further reading

In addition to the textbook by Domjan and Grau cited in the main text, S. Shettleworth's textbook *Cognition, Evolution, and Behavior* (2nd edition, New York: Oxford University Press, 2009) also covers animal learning in detail. For more on the alleged contrast between cognitive and associative approaches, see contributions to S. Hurley and M. Nudds (eds.), *Rational Animals?* (Oxford: Oxford University Press, 2006), especially chapters by N. Clayton et al., Papineau & Heyes, and myself. My contribution to the volume was partly in reaction to T. R. Zentall's (2001) "The case for a cognitive approach to animal learning and behavior" (*Behavioural Processes* 54, 65–78) in which he argues that the primary benefit of cognitive approaches to animal learning is to inspire better associative accounts.

References

Allen, C. (2013) "Fish cognition and consciousness," *Journal of Agricultural and Environmental Ethics* 26 25–39.

Allen, C., Grau, J., and Meagher, M. (2009) "The lower bounds of cognition: What do spinal cords reveal?" in J. Bickle (ed.), *The Oxford Handbook of Philosophy of Neuroscience*, New York: Oxford University Press, pp. 129–142.

Baayen, R. H., Shaoul, C., Willits, J., and Ramscar, M. (2016) "Comprehension without segmentation: A proof of concept with naive discriminative learning," *Language, Cognition and Neuroscience* 31 (1) 106–128.

Bekinschtein, T. A., Peeters, M., Shalom, D., and Sigman, M. (2011) "Sea slugs, subliminal pictures, and vegetative state patients: Boundaries of consciousness in classical conditioning," *Frontiers in Psychology* 2 337.

Bekinschtein, T. A., Shalom, D. E., Forcato, C., Herrera, M., Coleman, M. R., Manes, F. F., and Sigman, M. (2009) "Classical conditioning in the vegetative and minimally conscious state," *Nature Neuroscience* 12 (10) 1343–1349.

Buckner, C. (2011) "Two approaches to the distinction between cognition and 'Mere Association'," *International Journal for Comparative Psychology* 24(1) 1–35.

Castellucci, V., Pinsker, H., Kupfermann, I., & Kandel, E. R. (1970) "Neuronal mechanisms of habituation and dishabituation of the gill-withdrawal reflex in Aplysia," *Science* 167 (3926) 1745–1748.

Chomsky, N. (1959) "A review of B. F. Skinner's *verbal behavior*," *Language* 35 (1) 26–58.

Chomsky, N. (1967) "Preface to the reprint of Chomsky 1959," in L. A. Jakobovits and M. S. Miron (eds.), *Readings in the Psychology of Language*, Princeton, NJ: Prentice-Hall, Inc., pp. 142–143.

Clark, R. E., and Squire, L. R. (1998) "Classical conditioning and brain systems: The role of awareness," *Science* 280 77–81.

Domjan, M. P., and Grau, J. (2014) *The Principles of Learning and Behavior (7th Edition)*, Belmont, CA: Wadsworth/Cengage Learning.

Galef, B. G., and Laland, K. N. (2005) "Social learning in animals: Empirical studies and theoretical models," *BioScience* 55 489–499.

Gallistel, C. R. (1990) *The Organization of Learning*, Cambridge, MA: MIT Press.

Garcia, J., Ervin, F. R., and Koelling, R. A. (1966) "Learning with prolonged delay of reinforcement," *Psychonomic Science* 5 121–122.

Glanzman, D. L. (1995) "The cellular basis of classical conditioning in *Aplysia californica* – it's less simple than you think," *Trends in Neuroscience* 18 (1) 30–6.

Grau, J. W., and Joynes, R. L. (2005) "A neural-functionalist approach to learning," *International Journal of Comparative Psychology* 18 1–22.

Guttridge, T. L., and Brown, C. (2014) "Learning and memory in the Port Jackson shark, *Heterodontus portusjacksoni*," *Animal Cognition* 17 (2) 415–425.

Hawkins, R. D., Abrams, T. W., Carew, T. J., and Kandel, E. R. (1983) "A cellular mechanism of classical conditioning in *Aplysia*: Activity-dependent amplification of presynaptic facilitation," *Science* 219 (4583) 400–405.

James, W. (1890) *The Principles of Psychology*, New York: Dover.

Kamin, L. J. (1969) "Predictability, surprise, attention and conditioning," in B. A. Campbell and R. M. Church (eds.), *Punishment and Aversive Behavior*, New York: Appleton-Century-Crofts, pp. 279–296.

Lubow, R. E., and Moore, A. U. (1959) "Latent inhibition: The effect of non-reinforced preexposure to the conditioned stimulus," *Journal of Comparative and Physiological Psychology* 52 415–419.

Nilsson, J., Kristiansen, T. S., Fosseidengen, J. E., Fernö, A., and van den Bos, R. (2008) "Learning in cod (*Gadus morhua*): Long trace interval retention," *Animal Cognition* 11 215–222.

Nilsson, J., Kristiansen, T. S., Fosseidengen, J. E., Stien, L. H., Ferno, A., and van den Bos, R. (2010) "Learning and anticipatory behaviour in a 'sit-and-wait' predator: The Atlantic halibut," *Behavioral Processes* 83 257–266.

Nordgreen, J., Janczak, A. M., Hovland, A. L., Ranheim, B., and Horsberg, T. E. (2010) "Trace classical conditioning in rainbow trout (*Oncorhynchus mykiss*): What do they learn?" *Animal Cognition* 13 303–309.

Rescorla, R. A., and Wagner, A. R. (1972) "A theory of Pavlovian conditioning: Variations in the effectiveness of reinforcement and nonreinforcement," in A. H. Black and W. F. Prokasy (eds.), *Classical Conditioning II*, New York: Appleton-Century-Crofts, pp. 64–99.

Rumbaugh, D. M., and Washburn, D. A. (2003) *Intelligence of Apes and Other Rational Beings*, New Haven: Yale University Press.

Rumbaugh, D. M., Washburn, D. A., and Hillix, W. A. (1996) "Respondents, operants, and emergents: Toward an integrated perspective on behavior," in K. Pribram and J. King (eds), *Learning as Self-Organizing Process*, Hillsdale, NJ: Erlbaum, pp. 57–73.

Solomon, P. R., Vander Schaaf, E. R., Thompson, R. F., and Weisz, D. J. (1986) "Hippocampus and trace conditioning of the rabbit's classically conditioned nictitating membrane response," *Behavioral Neuroscience* 100 729–744.

Thompson-Schill, S. L., Ramscar, M., and Chrysikou, E. G. (2009) "Cognition without control: When a little frontal lobe goes a long way," *Current Directions in Psychological Science* 18(5) 259–263.

Thorndike, E. L. (1911) *Animal Intelligence: An Experimental Study of Associative Processes in Animals*, New York: Macmillan.

Tolman, E. C. (1948) "Cognitive maps in rats and men," *Psychological Review* 55(4) 189–208.

Trinh, A-T., Harvey-Girard, E., Teixeira, F., and Maler, L. (2016) "Cryptic laminar and columnar organization in the dorsolateral pallium of a weakly electric fish," *Journal of Comparative Neurology* 524 408–428.

Van Hamme, L. J., and Wasserman, E. A. (1994) "Cue competition in causality judgements: The role of nonpresentation of compound stimulus elements," *Learning and Motivation* 25 127–151.

Vargas, J. P., López, J. C., and Portavella, M. (2009) "What are the functions of fish brain pallium?" *Brain Research Bulletin* 79 436–440.

39

UNDERSTANDING ASSOCIATIVE AND COGNITIVE EXPLANATIONS IN COMPARATIVE PSYCHOLOGY

Cameron Buckner

Introduction

In the introduction to their influential anthology on comparative cognition research, Wasserman and Zentall (2006: 4–5) summarize what I have called that discipline's 'Standard Practice':

> [Cognition is] an animal's ability to remember the past, to choose in the present, and to plan for the future.... Unequivocal distinctions between cognition and simpler Pavlovian and instrumental learning processes ... are devilishly difficult to devise.... [but] unless clear evidence is provided that a more complex process has been used, C. Lloyd Morgan's famous canon of parsimony obliges us to assume that it has not; we must then conclude that a simpler learning process can account for the learning.... The challenge then is to identify flexible behavior that cannot be accounted for by simpler learning mechanisms. Thus, a cognitive process is one that does not merely result from the repetition of a behavior or from the repeated pairing of a stimulus with reinforcement.

Several ideas can be unpacked from this short characterization of the field. First, there is a default concern for associative explanations of behavior; associative processes must be considered as a possible explanation for any experimental data. Second, there is a default preference for "simpler" associative explanations; producing a plausible associative account of some behavior is seen as a trump card which undermines a cognitive interpretation of the results. Third, these practices are only cogent if associative and cognitive explanations of behavior are mutually exclusive alternatives.

Combined, these three ideas outline a clear research agenda for the discipline: to carefully devise experimental tasks that could be solved only by the use of a cognitive strategy, and not by any plausible associative strategy. Though some form of Standard Practice has been with us at least since C. Lloyd Morgan formulated his famous Canon (Morgan 1903), this research program became dominant in the 1960s and 1970s due to the challenge fledgling cognitivists faced in justifying their approach to skeptical behaviorists. They defended their approach by arguing that animals were capable of certain feats which could not be explained in terms of the stock components of the behaviorist toolkit. Love it or hate it – and many influential theorists have recently expressed some ire – there is little doubt that most comparative cognition research still fits this mold.

Though this methodology has produced a fine body of research, without a great deal of additional conceptual work it will soon lead the discipline to disaster. We must confront two problems, the first conceptual and the second empirical. The first problem is that the terms 'associative' and 'cognitive' are equivocal in contemporary practice. The second is that it recently appears that all cognitive processes will be fruitfully describable by associative models. We consider each in turn.

Defining 'cognition' and 'association'

Over the millennia, something like a cognitive/associative distinction has manifested itself in a variety of forms, and as a result much discussion about the distinction today involves equivocation and talking-past. Vague dichotomies are notorious in their ability to absorb the hopes and fears of many incompatible perspectives, so a first step to reform is to recognize the terminological diversity in the literature and require theorists to clarify key terms, especially 'cognition' and 'association'.

Let us begin with 'cognition'. At one extreme, Shettleworth defines 'cognition' as any process "by which animals acquire, process, store, and act on information from the environment" (Shettleworth 2010: 4). As a justification for this inclusive definition, it might be noted that the term is commonly taken this way in cognitive science more broadly, where it is used to delimit the lower bounds of the subject matter studied by cognitive scientists. However, this definition would class even the most basic forms of classical and instrumental conditioning as cognitive, leaving Standard Practice obviously confused in at least two different ways. First, a label that does not discriminate does no classificatory work, so it would be strange for comparative psychologists to expend so much energy trying to determine whether a process is cognitive. Second, such an inclusive definition rules out by fiat the possibility that cognition and association could be mutually exclusive, rendering the attempt to experimentally distinguish them clearly incoherent.

Recognizing these difficulties, others have argued that Standard Practice operates instead with a more restrictive "supercognitive" (Heyes 2012) or "rational" (Dickinson 2012) notion of cognition that the simplest forms of classical and instrumental conditioning do not satisfy. Since the simplest forms of associative learning are ubiquitous in the animal kingdom, the interesting empirical questions in Standard Practice concern which nonhuman animals have which supercognitive or rational processes, and whether the category of supercognitive or rational processes is mutually exclusive with associative processing. To be clear, in the remainder of this chapter, when I use the word 'cognition', I use the term in this more restrictive sense. This interpretation still allows for the possibility that Standard Practice is confused, of course; but if so, it would be a substantive empirical discovery.

Thus, I have argued that Standard Practice holds that cognition requires the manipulation of declarative knowledge, higher-order processes, or symbolic, rule-based reasoning (Buckner 2011, 2015). Here, learning that a process is cognitive tells us something interesting about the nature of its representational structure and consequently about the flexibility of the behavioral capacities it enables. Specifically, it suggests forms of processing that are not rigidly bound to particular stimuli and perceptual similarity, enabling adaptive and flexible responding in perceptually novel circumstances. When an animal can arrive at the "rational" solution to a problem that is perceptually dissimilar from those which it has faced in the past – but similar, perhaps, in terms of its underlying logical or causal structure – it is said to display "reasoning" or "insight" that is cognitive in nature. This account leaves much to be desired in terms of empirical precision – significant leeway remains for researchers to disagree as to what counts as an empirical test for rational insight or stimulus independence, leeway we shall begin to constrain below.

Before proceeding further, though, the interpretation of 'association' must also be clarified. We might think association, by comparison, easy to define by indexing it to behaviorist theory circa 1950 – perhaps as any learning that can result from the pairing of one stimulus with another or with a behavioral response (a 'stimulus' here being any event that can be registered by the sensory organs, such as a light, sound, or odor). The difficulty here is that associative learning theory has progressed in leaps and bounds since the advent of the cognitive revolution – with prominent associationists also now going to great pains to distinguish their approach from behaviorism (Rescorla 1988). As a result, associative learning theory now covers a dizzying and highly technical array of higher-order stimulus relations, preprocessing of stimuli, cue competition, and even complex architectural ideas (see Table 39.1). An ecumenical way to delimit the scope of associative learning might be as any form of processing that can be accounted for with a fixed set of relations learned amongst representations of stimuli by observing spatiotemporal contiguities between cues and/or responses. Many authors also add the constraint that the nature of the links themselves – whether causal, temporal, or modal – not also be represented by the system. As I use the term here, an explanation is associative if it shows how an animal could produce a behavior only by tracking a fixed set of relations amongst stimuli and/or responses presented in its learning history.

Table 39.1 Sample associative learning paradigms

Learning Effect/Paradigm	Schematic
Stimulus Generalization	A+ | perceptually similar variants of A?
Higher-order Conditioning	A+ | AB | B?
(Forward) Blocking	A+ | AB+ | B?
Backward Blocking	AB+ | A+ | B?
Higher-order Backward Blocking	AC+ | CB+ | B– | A?
Overshadowing	AB+ | B?
Sensory Preconditioning	AB– | B+ | A?
Latent Inhibition	A– | A+ | A?
Reversal Learning	A+, B– | A–, B+ | A?, B?
Context-Shifting	A+ in X | A? in Y
Negative Patterning	A+, B+, AB– | A?, B?, AB?
Value Transfer	$A_{100}B_0, C_{50}D_0$ | BD?

An example of some learning paradigms considered part of associative learning theory. A, B, and C indicate stimuli (such as lights or tones); X and Y indicate contexts (such as different rooms or times of day); + indicates reward, – indicates no reward, and | indicates a break between trial blocks; subscripts indicate the percentage of time a stimulus is rewarded in training; and ? indicates the test situation where an effect is expected. To consider some examples, higher-order conditioning occurs when an animal is conditioned to respond to one stimulus, then the rewarded stimulus is repeatedly paired with a second, neutral stimulus, and the animal later responds to the previously neutral one in isolation (because it has been associated with the originally rewarded stimulus). Overshadowing is found when one stimulus is naturally more "salient" than another, and the overshadowing effect occurs when an animal is only conditioned to respond to one of two stimuli presented together with reward during training. Context-shifting occurs when an animal is trained to respond to a stimulus in one context, but does not respond to that stimulus in a different context. Negative patterning occurs when an animal can be trained to respond to two stimuli in isolation, but not to their compound (which requires the animal to create a distinct third representation for the compound stimulus). Value transfer occurs when a more highly rewarded stimulus (such as A100 or C50) has some of its value "bleed" to other cues with which it co-occurs (such as B0), which can allow preferences to emerge between stimuli with equivalent elemental reward histories (such as B0 and D0) because the other stimuli with which each has co-occurred have been differentially rewarded.

The return of association

The second and even bigger problem with Standard Practice is that, under the ecumenical interpretations of 'cognition' and 'association' just described, the mutual exclusivity assumption that drives its experimental design appears to be empirically false. Sufficiently flexible associative processes can sometimes implement cognition; or in other words, the same process might be simultaneously, correctly described by both a cognitive and an associative model. Though this important possibility has been widely appreciated in other areas of cognitive science – especially in the debate between classicists and connectionists over cognitive architecture – it comes as a shock to some Standard Practitioners. Nevertheless, I argue it is an inevitable consequence of the other principles they already endorse, discussed above.

The source of this problem is associative learning theory's surprising potential; its basic principles (discussed above) have not constrained its scope as much as cognitivists originally supposed. The number of processes that appear fruitfully describable in associative terms has dramatically expanded over the past few decades. Associative models are now live competitors as descriptions of many different cognitive capacities, including transitive inference, episodic memory, causal learning, metacognition, goal-directed behavior, imitation, early word learning, and many others. Though some theorists still insist that there is something crucial that associative models will never do, associative learning theory's continued ability to exceed all predicted limits recommends some epistemic modesty. Considering our previous failures as inductive evidence, we should prepare for the possibility that associative models will eventually be able to fruitfully describe all psychological processes – lest we fall into the same kind of wishful thinking deployed by doomsday prophets continually pushing back the date of the expected apocalypse as it repeatedly fails to materialize.

In fact, this dramatic extension of associative learning theory has been a direct result of the empirical arms race between proponents and skeptics of animal cognition in Standard Practice. A typical pattern that emerges is that a clever cognitivist will devise an experimental test that cannot be passed using current principles of associative learning theory, and, after a high-profile publication, this test comes to be widely used as a benchmark for cognition across different species. A clever associationist will then devise a modest extension of prior associative learning theory that can allow associative models to pass the cognitivist's benchmark. The cognitivist in turn devises a yet more sophisticated behavioral test for cognition that controls for this revised associative mechanism, inspiring yet another modest innovation by the associationists. For many different faculties, this back-and-forth appears capable of continuing indefinitely.

If associative models can eventually accommodate any behavioral data, then theorists face a choice point. On the one hand, if we continue to endorse the assumption that associative models and cognitive models depict mutually exclusive kinds of psychological process, then we should all admit that the hard-nosed associationists will probably win the field – and that cognition does not exist. On the other hand, if (as I recommend) we abandon Standard Practice's mutual exclusivity assumption, then we need to provide specific guidance that allows researchers to know when associative processing has become sufficiently flexible to count as implementing cognition. In short, we would need to develop principled, empirically plausible methods to distinguish (at least) two different kinds of associative processing, (at least) one of which serves as a deflationary alternative to cognition, and the other of which implements cognition.

Though we should not get bogged down in the details here, I have recommended a specific version of the latter approach (2015). The basic idea is to tie the distinction between cognitive and associative psychological processes to the distinction between multiple memory systems in the brain, with the distinctively cognitive system centered on the hippocampus and other medial temporal lobe structures in mammals and its functional homologues in other classes. The theory of multiple memory systems has been richly elaborated in the field of cognitive neuroscience and is growing in popularity in comparative psychology itself. This body of work provides strong support for the conclusion that there are dissociable memory systems in the brain that, while all fruitfully describable by associative models, differ markedly in the degrees of behavioral flexibility they support – specifically in the forms that have been traditionally assessed by comparative psychology's benchmarks for cognition. The methodology of Standard Practice can thus largely be salvaged if we reinterpret it as trying to determine which memory system controls some observed behavior.

This gross classification is only the initial stage of study, of course, but determining the memory system that controls a behavior can help guide its future investigation. I have suggested that the labels 'cognitive' and 'non-cognitive' should be seen as superordinate natural kind terms that organize a variety of more specific psychological kinds like transitive inference, cognitive mapping, theory of mind, and so on. To provide an analogy, they function in psychology like the similarly general labels 'metal'/'non-metal' do in chemistry. Learning that a sample of some unknown element is a metal tells us only highly abstract information, but it does give us a general idea what kind of other properties we should expect the sample to possess (conducts electricity, ductile and solid at room temperature, etc.). In doing so, it tells us which future tests might produce useful results as we continue our investigation into that element's distinctive characteristics.

Though many articles could be written linking these psychological and neural details, a few metaphors and examples may help explain the view and make it more accessible. Consider the contrasting pictures provided by Tolman (1948) in his classic "Cognitive Maps in Rats and Men". In that work, Tolman (p. 192) distinguished two different approaches to the study of associative learning that were present in his day. The first, the "stimulus response" school, held that

> the rat's central nervous system ... may be likened to a complicated telephone switchboard ...
> There are the incoming calls from sense-organs and there are the outgoing messages
> to muscles . . . *Learning*, according to this view, consists in the respective strengthening
> and weakening of various of these connections.

Behavior, according to this school, is generated by elemental stimulus-response links, akin to the telephone operator connecting stimulus inputs to motor outputs in a piecemeal fashion, following that linkage's individual history of reinforcement. The other school, Tolman's "field theorists", held that

> in the course of learning something like a field map of the environment gets estab-
> lished in the rat's brain ... the intervening brain processes are more complicated, more
> patterned and often, pragmatically speaking, more autonomous ... his nervous system
> is surprisingly selective as to which of these stimuli it will let in at any given time ...
> the incoming impulses are usually worked over and elaborated in the central control
> room into a tentative, cognitive-like map of the environment.
>
> (Tolman 1948: 192)

Several key points of contrast emerge: whether the animal's representation of its environment forms an integrated whole or a set of disorganized elemental links; whether the effect of any given stimulus is determined by that stimulus' informational value or each is treated indifferently; and whether behavior is determined in a centralized, coordinated manner or via independent stimulus-response links. Though Tolman intended to contrast two competing approaches to the study of associative learning, these metaphors work well if we hold that *both* approaches are right, but characterize different memory systems, with the map-like hippocampal system controlling cognitive processing. That the metaphors can be so easily repurposed may not be so surprising, given that much of the foundational work on the hippocampal system was derived from O'Keefe & Nadel's classic work on the neural mechanisms behind cognitive mapping (1978).

Looking forward: guiding principles

I close by extracting several principles from an instructive and commonplace example of a clash between different memory systems: conditioned taste aversion, also known as the Garcia Effect. Conditioned taste aversion is a specialized, rapid, and long-lasting form of associative learning that can occur in a single trial between a taste stimulus and nausea, resulting in powerful and enduring aversion to that stimulus in the future. Anyone who has ever overindulged in tequila and later cringed away from a single harmless margarita is in the grips of conditioned taste aversion. No matter how many times one rehearses the fact that one drink poses no real threat, it is not possible to revise the taste–nausea association through explicit reflection alone. This insulation of one inflexible form of associative learning against revision by another, more flexible system provides a vivid example of the kind of dissociation between memory systems that I have been discussing. From this example, we can extract several important principles which can be used to guide future research in comparative psychology.

> First Principle: Psychological kinds should be assessed by defeasible tests for property clusters, rather than definitive tests of necessary and sufficient conditions.

One obvious difficulty posed by conditioned taste aversion is that it defies one of the most typical characterizations of associative learning: that it be slow and incremental. This complication demonstrates that we must move away from the idea that psychological kinds can be distinguished by neat sets of necessary and sufficient conditions, for accurate characterization of nearly any psychological category is complex and riddled with exceptions. Such exceptions do not pose a fatal problem to the framework I proposed above, however, for conditioned taste aversion is in nearly all other relevant ways highly inflexible.

Though it is good to insist that our cognitive and associative hypotheses generate clear predictions, we must give up on the idea of critical tests that can cleanly confirm or falsify such hypotheses in isolation. This simplistic philosophy of science should have died under the lash of the Quine-Duhem thesis, but it has persisted in corners of comparative psychology to this day. Some of the savviest comparative psychologists are now beginning to look instead for correlations amongst clusters of independent behavioral properties (Cheke and Clayton 2015), which provides a better methodology for assessing the kinds of psychological categories I have been discussing here. In short, the task of assessing which memory system controls a psychological process through behavioral experiment is like trying to determine whether a car has a 4-cylinder or a 6-cylinder engine without opening the hood: both engines do many of the same things, and in some conditions the 4-cylinder may outperform the 6-cylinder, but they will reliably differ in their full performance profiles.

> Second Principle: Psychological models must be regarded as incomplete descriptions of real underlying phenomena, whose full nature is determined by the neural mechanisms those models target.

A difficulty with the move just sketched, however, is that we want to be able to distinguish principled exceptions from unprincipled exceptions. In other words, why should we not count the admission that association may sometimes be more rapid than cognition as an unforgivably ad hoc attempt to salvage an empirically impugned hypothesis? The solution is to tie the criteria for various memory systems to underlying neural mechanisms, and decide whether an exception is principled by seeing whether the two different memory systems can still be successfully empirically distinguished by the other characteristic properties. The key (but often neglected) idea here is that psychology is the study of the actual causes of behavior in humans and animals, so all models in comparative psychology must aim to describe, at some level of abstraction, real psychological processes operating in humans and animals. By contrast, they cannot – like models of ideally rational economic agents or perpetual motion machines – aim to describe some merely possible system under unrealistic assumptions.

This principle sounds obvious, but neglecting it can quickly lead to mischief. For example, consider the deflationary model of transitive inference proposed by De Lillo et al. (2001), a simple three-layer feed-forward connectionist network (Figure 39.1) that can demonstrate transitive-like choice when trained on the same sorts of stimuli as animals that have been said to demonstrate the cognitive solution to transitive inference problems. It does so by implementing the associative principle of "value transfer" (Table 39.1). Surely, the associationist might respond, such a simple model could not be thought to implement cognition, because it is incapable of any other forms of flexibility characteristic of cognition. Thus, they argue, this network shows that transitive-like choice in animals is not cognitive either.

In comparative psychology, however, it is of little consequence what a disembodied network can or cannot do in isolation. The real question is whether the brains of animals actually

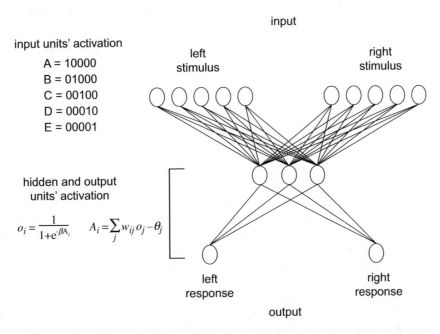

input

input units' activation

A = 10000
B = 01000
C = 00100
D = 00010
E = 00001

left
stimulus

right
stimulus

hidden and output
units' activation

$$o_i = \frac{1}{1+e^{-\beta A_i}} \qquad A_i = \sum_j w_{ij} o_j - \theta_j$$

left
response

right
response

output

Figure 39.1   De Lillo et al.'s three-layer, feed-forward model of transitive inference. The five-digit strings representing stimuli are fed to the input units. The formula describes the sigmoidal transfer function used to determine the activation of the hidden and output units in response to the input vectors.

implement value transfer without also implementing the other forms of representational flexibility characteristic of cognition. And here, the many lesion and modeling studies on transitive inference suggest that the hippocampal system is responsible for value transfer in the mammalian brain. Thus, if the De Lillo et al. model is relevant at all in comparative psychology, it must be regarded as an incomplete depiction of the much more flexible hippocampal system – and so cannot stand as a general deflationary alternative to cognitive approaches to transitive inference. (For references and a longer discussion of this example, see Buckner 2015.)

To return to conditioned taste aversion, what is known about its neurobiology supports the claim that the exception in question is principled rather than ad hoc. It is for this reason that the exception does not threaten the cognitive/non-cognitive distinction any more than the fact that mercury is a liquid at room temperature threatens the metal/non-metal distinction in chemistry. In rats, at least, conditioned taste aversion appears to be controlled primarily by a specialized and evolutionarily older circuit located in the brain stem. Following lesion and electrophysiology studies, the taste–nausea associations are believed to form at the intersection of the midbrain and pons, in the parabrachial nucleus. Given this location's neurobiology and connectivity, conditioned taste aversion exhibits a number of other surprising features; for example, the lag between the taste stimulus and nausea onset can be extremely long – up to several hours – and can be formed without modulation by higher brain structures, during general anesthesia and deep hypothermia. These associations then trigger aversion reactions via a downstream connection to the amygdalae. Because the rapidity with which conditioned taste aversion follows from distinctive neural architecture and connectivity that is inflexible in many other relevant ways, this exception does not impugn the strategy of tying the distinction to the theory of multiple memory systems.

A possibly painful corollary of the preceding discussion, however, is that comparative psychologists must give up on the idea that their discipline is independent and autonomous from neuroscience. The sorts of uncertainties of the previous paragraph will only become more common as comparative psychology continues to mature, diverse models proliferate, and the relationships between them – competition, complementation, or implementation? – become more difficult to determine. Not every researcher needs to be wholly multi-disciplinary, but it will become increasingly untenable to insist that every pressing question in psychology be answered by appeal to behavioral data alone.

> Third Principle: Associative models do vital explanatory important work, even when they are redundant with cognitive models.

I close by attempting to forestall a mistaken conclusion that might be drawn from the preceding discussion: that, because associative models can depict implementations of cognition, they are somehow second-rate explanations or uninteresting "implementation stories" for cognitive processes. This unfortunate attitude has been endorsed by some in the older debate between classicists and connectionists about cognitive architecture (e.g. Fodor and Pylyshyn 1988), but it is based on bad philosophy of science. Instead, cognitive and associative models can be independently legitimate models that depict a process with different goals and at different levels of abstraction, with overlapping and complementary explanatory virtues.

A typical difference between cognitive and associative models of the same process is that associative models usually make predictions about fine-grained adjustments in response to the next stimuli observed, whereas cognitive models usually abstract away from this detail to predict the learning outcomes that reliably emerge from diverse learning histories. Associative models would thus rank more highly on many criteria valued by philosophers of science, especially counterfactual explanatory power, the ability to answer "what if things had been different" questions. Associative models have more counterfactual power because they can make many more specific predictions about arbitrary interactions amongst low-level stimulus representations throughout the whole trajectory of learning. However, to make these predictions, they require a daunting amount of background information – researchers must usually know the full associative learning history for that experimental subject regarding the relevant stimuli, information which is unavailable in many laboratory and field contexts and which tends to be highly idiosyncratic. Associative models thus excel at telling you where a particular subject is heading in the next step, whereas cognitive models excel at telling you where the average subject will tend to end up, given a typical learning history. Both explanatory goals are important, and neither reduces to a merely second-rate understudy of the other. (See Buckner 2014 for a case study in the predictive value of the latter kind of hypothesis in theory of mind research.)

Conclusion

The Standard Practice of comparative psychology presumes that cognitive and associative causes of behavior are mutually exclusive alternatives, and attempts to distinguish them by means of cleverly controlled experiments. I have provided reasons above for thinking that this methodology is due for a serious revision, but not the wholesale rejection recommended by many recent commentators. If we reinterpret the methodology as trying to determine the memory system under which a behavior is controlled – accepting that all memory systems, even the distinctively "cognitive" ones, can fruitfully be described by associative models – then this methodology can be largely salvaged, and indeed emerge with a strengthened self-understanding. This revision requires numerous changes of perspective, and especially a willingness to cooperate with neuroscience; but if we are up to the task, comparative psychology may continue to enjoy a bright future for many years to come.

Further reading

J. Pearce, *Animal Learning and Cognition 3rd edition* (New York: Psychology Press, 2013) presents an up-to-date and accessible review of recent advances in associative learning theory. M. Gluck and C. Meyers, *Gateway to Memory: An Introduction to Neural Network Modeling of the Hippocampus and Learning* (Cambridge, MA: MIT Press, 2001); and H. Eichenbaum and N. Cohen, *From Conditioning to Conscious Recollection: Memory Systems of the Brain* (Oxford: Oxford University Press, 2004) relate this learning theory to computational and anatomical neuroscience. Finally, an excellent collection of different perspectives on these methodological issues can be found in S. Hurley and M. Nudds, *Rational Animals?* (Oxford: Oxford University Press, 2006).

References

Buckner, C. (2011) "Two Approaches to the Distinction Between Cognition and 'Mere Association,'" *International Journal of Comparative Psychology*, 24(4), 314–348.
———— (2014) "The Semantic Problem(s) With Research on Animal Mind-Reading," *Mind & Language*, 29(5), 566–589.
———— (2015) "A Property Cluster Theory of Cognition," *Philosophical Psychology*, 28(3), 307–336.
Cheke, L. G., and Clayton, N. S. (2015) "The Six Blind Men and the Elephant: Are Episodic Memory Tasks Tests of Different Things or Different Tests of the Same Thing?" *Journal of Experimental Child Psychology*, 137, 164–171.

De Lillo, C., Floreano, D., and Antinucci, F. (2001) "Transitive Choices by a Simple, Fully Connected, Back-propagation Neural Network: Implications for the Comparative Study of Transitive Inference," *Animal Cognition*, *4*(1), 61–68.

Dickinson, A. (2012) "Associative Learning and Animal Cognition," *Philosophical Transactions of the Royal Society of London B: Biological Sciences*, *367*(1603), 2733–2742.

Fodor, J. A., and Pylyshyn, Z. W. (1988) "Connectionism and Cognitive Architecture: A Critical Analysis," *Cognition*, *28*(1), 3–71.

Heyes, C. (2012) "Simple Minds: A Qualified Defence of Associative Learning," *Philosophical Transactions of the Royal Society B: Biological Sciences*, *367*(1603), 2695–2703.

Morgan, C. L. (1903) *An Introduction to Comparative Psychology*, London: Walter Scott, limited.

O'Keefe, J., and Nadel, L. (1978) *The Hippocampus as a Cognitive Map* (Vol. 3), Oxford: Clarendon Press.

Rescorla, R. A. (1988) "Pavlovian Conditioning: It's Not What You Think It Is," *American Psychologist*, *43*(3), 151.

Shettleworth, S. J. (2010) *Cognition, Evolution, and Behavior*, 2nd Edition, London: Oxford University Press.

Tolman, E. C. (1948) "Cognitive Maps in Rats and Men," *Psychological Review*, *55*(4), 189.

Wasserman, E. A., and Zentall, T. R. (2006) *Comparative Cognition: Experimental Explorations of Animal Intelligence*, Oxford: Oxford University Press.

40

A NEW VIEW OF ASSOCIATION AND ASSOCIATIVE MODELS

Mike Dacey

Introduction

Despite criticisms dating back to the 18th century, the concept of association has remained central in psychology, and the core idea has remained largely unchanged. This chapter describes a fundamental rethinking of the concept of association and of how associative models are used in psychology. While I intend my view to apply generally, associative models are most commonly used in comparative psychology, and a fundamental revision of the concept of association would lead to significant changes in the methods and practices there.

The core that has remained unchanged is the general, if not universal, assumption that association is *a kind of* psychological process, also called "associative processing." This assumption has caused problems. The alternative view I advocate solves these problems, while also opening up associative models to play a more constructive role in psychology generally. It is not my goal here to argue for the view in depth,[1] but to describe it and its motivations.

The general idea behind my view is that "association" is a generic term that refers to any causal relationship between representational states in a psychological process. As such, an association can be implemented by any number of mechanisms, not only by the specific mechanism of associative processing. Associative models, then, are highly abstract characterizations of the sequence of representational states that become active in a process as it operates.[2] In principle, they can be applied to any kind of process. This view allows for associative models to be compatible with other kinds of models, like cognitive models. In fact, the two kinds of models can work together: each can be helpful in characterizing the other in greater detail. Associative models, so conceived, are helpful when we do not understand a process well. And in psychology, this is often the case.

Problems with the current view

In the current literature, association is treated as a kind of process. Associative models are treated as denoting a member of that kind: using an associative model to describe some process implies that the process is a member of this kind. In comparative psychology, associative models, which describe members of the class of associative processing, are usually contrasted with *cognitive models* that describe members of the class of *cognitive processing*. So, for instance, an associative process could be distinguished from a process that allows an animal to simulate another's perspective (this will be my main example of a cognitive process here). The ability to simulate others' perspectives allows flexible engagement in social situations, and an ability to respond to cues that are not directly present to the simulating animal, which associative processing does not. It has been assumed that the distinction between associative and cognitive processes generalizes straightforwardly: associative processes are simple and inflexible, while cognitive processes are more complex and more flexible. But this way of distinguishing the kinds of process has become problematic. I'll discuss two arguments, one based in comparative psychology, and one in human psychology.

Buckner (2011 and Chapter 39 in this volume) has done an excellent job of developing the concerns that have arisen in comparative psychology, and bringing them to philosophical attention, so I describe them rather quickly here.[3] The basic setup comes when the dichotomy between associative and cognitive processes is paired with a widespread methodological principle known as "Morgan's Canon." In its modern interpretation, Morgan's Canon is taken to dictate that, *ceteris paribus*, models that posit simpler processes should be preferred. This means that whenever an associative model gets the behavioral predictions right, it will be the preferred model; even if a cognitive model also predicts, the associative model describes a simpler process.

Suppose, to start, that some behavior is predicted by an associative model. This, as noted, is taken to be reason to think that the process itself is associative. Research proceeds from here roughly as follows: to further test the model, the experimental task is made more complex, such that the associative model does not predict success. If the animal succeeds in this new task, the associative model is considered to be falsified, and it is replaced with a cognitive model of some kind. However, it is often the case that the associative model can be modified in a way that predicts this new behavior as well. In such a case, the process repeats. It can do so indefinitely.

For instance, research on social learning in pigeons has gone through several iterations. At each iteration, new complications are built into the task, and in turn, the associative model. In the initial experiment, pigeons acted as if they had learned that pressing a lever produced a food reward simply by watching another pigeon be rewarded for doing so. This seemed to go beyond pure associative learning, perhaps indicating an ability to simulate the perspective of the demonstrator. But then a new associative model was created to predict the effect (Zentall 1996). In a subsequent experiment, pigeons were able to differentiate between rewards that came specifically when pecking the lever or when stepping on the lever, which the modified associative model did not predict (Zentall, Sutton, and Sherburne 1996). But again, a new associative model was built to explain this behavior (Meltzoff 1996), and again, subsequently shown to be too simple by another task (Akins and Zentall 1998). This process has continued to iterate since.[4]

I'd like to point out here that this practice implicitly assumes that all of these tasks probe a single psychological capacity. This is usually not mentioned because each experiment is only a minor variant of the previous. But it should be made explicit: the assumption that there is a common capacity justifies the proposition that one experiment can falsify the associative model as a model of performance *in the previous experiments* as well as performance in the experiment where the model actually failed to predict. The evident goal is to produce a model of the process that predicts how it will respond across conditions.

We are now in position to understand how the distinction between associative and cognitive processes has become problematic. As mentioned, this distinction has traditionally been cast in terms of complexity. But this iterating, back-and-forth dynamic produces more complex associative models at each turn. As associative models become more complex, the line is blurred. Some commentators have suggested that this has undermined, or at least threatened, the distinction (e.g. Allen 2006; Penn and Povinelli 2007; Papineau and Heyes 2006). At the same time, there are concerns that the "is it associative or is it cognitive?" orientation misses the really interesting issues: what information is encoded and how the animal interprets the task itself (Smith,

Couchman, and Beran 2014). Putting these concerns together, it looks bad for the distinction between association and cognition: there are no real standards for drawing the distinction, and it is not clear what we even gain by doing so.

A parallel argument appeals to research on priming and associative learning in humans. Priming is when presentation of one stimulus facilitates some task involving a second, related stimulus. For instance, if the word "lion" is flashed, a subject will read the subsequently presented word "tiger" more quickly. While the basic phenomenon of priming looks associative, there are good reasons to believe that the *processes* responsible are too complex to reasonably be counted as associative processes. For instance, it matters what kind of list a specific prime-target pair appears in (*list context effects*; e.g. McKoon and Ratcliff 1995), and it matters what task participants are instructed to perform on the prime (*prime task effects*; e.g. Smith, Bentin, and Spalek 2001). Associative models don't predict either of these effects.

Associationists reply to evidence like this by pointing to instances in which associative models *do* predict. For instance, when Mitchell, DeHouwer, and Lovibond (2009) argue that human associative learning is propositional in a target article, the phenomenon of *affective priming* is mentioned repeatedly in this role in the commentary. In these replies, the fact that associative models predict some basic priming phenomena is taken to be evidence that the basic processes responsible for priming are associative, while complex-looking effects come from other processes running in parallel, as in dual-process theories generally.

The problem for this reply is that the evidence of complexity in human priming and associative learning is too pervasive to easily cordon off as effects of a distinct process.[5] But it also remains the case that associative models predict the behavior of these processes in some cases. I argue that both of these facts should be taken seriously. The standard view forces a dilemma: either deny that the processes are complex, or deny that associative models are properly applied. Both horns come with costs. On the first horn, one is forced to explain away evidence of complexity that is so pervasive that it suggests that, even if there are multiple processes, the simplest processes involved are not associative (or so I argue). On the other horn, one is forced to reject potentially useful associative models; we should not simply dismiss their predictive success as accidental or irrelevant due to presuppositions about what associative models do.

Moreover, because it is not clear what behavioral evidence can settle the question of how many processes are present (or how to attribute effects to specific processes if there are many), these debates tend to trade on competing appeals to parsimony (as in Mitchell, DeHouwer, and Lovibond 2009 and commentary). It is difficult to make progress in debates over clashing parsimony claims like this (Dacey 2016b). So once we find ourselves facing this dilemma, both options have real costs, and fruitful debate becomes difficult. A view that avoids this dilemma (as mine does) would be better than the current standard view, which does not.

I have presented two arguments that the standard view of association is problematic. Really, these are two sides of the same coin. It turns out that some processes look associative in some contexts, but not in others. On the standard view, these two pieces of evidence are in tension; associative models are assumed to only describe simple processes, and if they apply at all, they apply across contexts. We see two, effectively opposite, responses to this tension. Sometimes, evidence of complexity is taken to trump previous success of associative models; sometimes the previous success of associative models is taken to trump evidence of complexity. The responses given dictate how each literature has progressed. In comparative psychology, the practice of taking evidence of complexity to falsify associative models has driven the iterating back-and-forth dynamic that has blurred the distinction between association and cognition while obscuring other questions of interest. In the human literature, researchers take both sides, though both have costs, and the debate can make little progress.

The way to avoid these problems is, I hope, clear: reject the view that associative models must denote a particular kind of process. The trouble is that there is no systematic alternative in the current literature. I now describe an alternative, and the role it gives association in psychology.

A new view

The view I advocate treats "association" as a highly abstract, generic term that could be realized by many different mechanisms. An association *itself* is simply a causal relation (any causal relation) between representations that become active in a process. This view of *association* comes from a simplified interpretation of *associative models*. Associative models describe only sequences of representational states (often in terms of spreading activation) and/or the influence that variables in learning have on those sequences. Representations, in turn, are specified purely by content, so no specific kind of representation is required. This is all the models themselves say. I propose that we take this at face value. The claim that associative models denote associative processes *is not* necessitated by the most basic interpretation of the models. We can simply jettison this claim, and with it, the commitments that have caused the problems discussed above. Associative models are partial descriptions of a process; they are highly abstract, and only tell us about these specific features of the process.

So specified, an association could be underwritten by any number of neural or psychological processes: in principle, it could be produced by the application of a rule in an algorithm, the manipulation of a mental map, or a mental model (to name a couple cognitive process). Returning to the pigeon social learning example, an associative model could describe the (cognitive) process of simulating the perspective of conspecifics. It could do so in two ways: either by describing the sequences of representations that occur within the simulation, or by describing the representational states that trigger the simulation (more on this below). Similarly, any variables can be included in an associative learning model. An associative learning model that includes variables like contact, latency between events, and patterns of movement as relevant to learning might provide a precise, mathematical description of a process for learning mechanical-causal relations between objects (e.g. Spelke 1990).

Cognitive models generally include greater causal detail, so they still indicate kinds of processes (the *specific* kind depends on the specific model), while associative models do not. This is why both can be applied to the same process; they can describe the same causal structure at different levels of abstraction. Associative models and cognitive models are not differentiated by the kind of process they describe; they are differentiated by what they say about the process, and as a result, the descriptive and explanatory work they do. Whether you use an associative model or a cognitive model depends on the question you are asking and the information you have, not on the process you are describing.

In any single task, this view does not change the behavioral predictions that a specific associative model makes. The difference comes when we consider how a model applies *across* conditions. As discussed above, if we take associative models to denote associative processes, it implies that an associative model should predict behavior across conditions in which the relevant process drives behavior. Instead, I argue that we should restrict the scope of each associative model to the specific task for which it was designed. So if an associative model fails to predict behavior in a *new* task, that does not falsify it as a model of the process in previous tasks where it does predict. It still may be the case that the model accurately describes the sequence of representational states that the process follows, and the learning variables it responds to, *in those original tasks*. There may be a different associative model that predicts behavior in the new task, or several, or none.

If we take these different tasks to probe the same capacity, the goal is to integrate the associative models that predict behavior in different tasks into a model of a single mechanism that can produce them all. In principle, it is possible that multiple associative models predict behavior even in a single task. In these cases, only one of these can be the right one. The way to tell which is to find a set of associative models, one in each task, that could be a product of a single mechanism. This requires constructing a model of the mechanism, and determining which sequences it would produce and which learning variables it would respond to. Again, in principle, there may be multiple such sets. Building these mechanism models and arguing for one of them is difficult, likely involving an inference to the best explanation, including background theory. So performance on one task does bear on the evaluation of an associative model of performance in another task, but not as a direct confirmation or falsification. Instead, the question is whether two different associative models of performance on different tasks could be products of the same mechanism.

For example, we can build associative models that predict behavior in all of the experiments that we believe probe pigeons' capacity to learn socially. Some of these may include a simulation, and some not. We then compare these models, and look for a set that could be the product of a single mechanism. If the best explanation posits a mechanism that simulates the perspective of conspecifics, the resulting characterization of that mechanism would show what sequences of states are (and are not) included in the simulation, and what conditions do (and do not) trigger the simulation. Thus, we would not only have systematic evidence the capacity is present (contrasted with the current back-and-forth that emphasizes single experiments over integrating evidence), and we would have a much more detailed characterization of the capacity (contrasted with the vagueness of many current appeals to cognitive processes).

So associative models set abstract constraints on more detailed models of the mechanism. Any more detailed model must follow the sequence of representations and/or respond to the learning variables specified by the associative models. Far from excluding other kinds of models, like cognitive models, associative models become an important part of the process of developing those models. We do not need to draw a distinction between association and cognition in order to use both kinds of models.[6] This view also explains why associative models can predict the behavior of a complex process (like priming) in some conditions, but not all. So it solves both problems with associative models discussed above.

Simplicity

No discussion of associative processing can proceed without addressing the issue of simplicity (or parsimony) as a scientific virtue. This issue bears on the discussion in two ways. Firstly, one might argue that associative models must denote associative processes by applying Morgan's Canon when *interpreting* the models (not just when choosing them). Associative processes are the simplest processes that an associative model could describe, and thus, the standard view would be reinstated. However, this would require a very strong, universally applicable version of Morgan's Canon. There are good reasons to reject such a view, which I cannot canvas here (see Fitzpatrick 2008 and Chapter 42 in this volume; Dacey 2016b). Given the problems caused by the resulting view of association, along with these more general concerns about Morgan's Canon, this argument cannot justify a reinstatement of the standard view.

Secondly, on my view simplicity remains a virtue of associative models. This is not because the *process* is simple, but because the *model* is simple. The model is simple because it abstracts away from details of the way the process operates. This is valuable for three reasons. First, we often don't need those details; for instance, an associative model is often sufficient for pragmatic concerns like prediction and control. Second, because associative learning models focus on specific variables, we can characterize their influence in precise, mathematical terms (models like this are often derived from the Rescorla-Wagner model [Rescorla and Wagner 1972]). Many, probably most, psychological models lack this precision, so the precision of associative models is valuable, and not readily replicable. My view of association allows associative models to lend their mathematical rigor to other kinds of models, following the process described in the last section. Third, treating associative models as *partial* models avoids theoretical commitments about the nature of psychological processes that we may not have good evidence for. This is valuable when we do not understand processes well. This is often the case in psychology.

Historical precedent

This view is a fundamental revision of the way association is viewed in contemporary cognitive science. By way of concluding, I would like to stress that it is not, as it may seem, a break from the history of the concept; it is, in many respects, a return to a view as old as association itself. Views like the current standard view have traditionally been the most common interpretation of association (as I said above, this core of the concept has changed little), but it is only since roughly the mid-20th century that this has been the only interpretation. One can find views of association much like mine in both the empiricist associationist and behaviorist traditions.

Among the associationists, the view is made explicit by Thomas Brown (1840). Brown first published his main work on the topic in the year of his early death in 1820, and was prominent for several decades after. He occupied a unique place at the intersection of different traditions, but he was a close follower of Hume in many respects: he was an associationist and a staunch Humean about causation. At the time of his writing, the dominant view was that association was a real link between thoughts that drove them to follow a sequence. He disagreed, largely because of his Humeanism: just as there are no causal "links" between successive events in the world, there are no associative "links" between successive thoughts in the mind. Association (like causation) is just invariant sequence. The "associative link," argued Brown, is explanatorily vacuous and metaphysically dubious.

In this respect, Brown was more Humean than Hume. For his part, Hume does struggle with the obvious inconsistency between his rejection of causal links in the world and his acceptance of links in the mind in an appendix to the Treatise (Hume 1978). He never resolved this concern in print, and his writing betrays an ambiguity between a view like Brown's and the associative link view. This ambiguity was never really resolved in general, and remained, in various guises, through the associationist tradition.[7]

When behaviorism rose to prominence in the 1920s, the behaviorists retained association as the core concept of psychology, but reframed it as a relation between external, observable stimuli and responses rather than mental representations. Even then, the same ambiguity remained. In this tradition, it was a divide between those who argued that the specific physical stimuli or muscle movements were the *relata* of association, and those who argued that association had to be a relation between more abstract patterns of stimulation and response.

The distinction between two interpretations of association is made most clearly by Edwin Guthrie, Edward C. Tolman, and Edward S. Robinson. Guthrie (1959) sees his emphasis on behavior as an abstraction designed to exclude complicating factors, much like the use of constructs such as frictionless planes in physics. Thus, for Guthrie, behaviorism abstracts away from details about mental states, rather than denying their existence. He also argues that views that treat association as a "mechanism" (by which he means an invariant sequence of specific physiological/chemical changes) are much too specific to actually explain behavior. Tolman (1932; 1948) attacks the same view, characterizing it as treating the brain as a neural "switch-board" which simply connects stimulus to response. For both Tolman and Guthrie, associations are formed between abstract *patterns* of stimulation and response that can be realized (to put it in modern terms) by many different specific mechanisms. Robinson (1932) agreed, and (perhaps presciently) argued that associationism was dying out because the mistaken view dominated.

While the details vary with historical context, the spirit is the same: association is not a particular, concrete mechanism that drives sequences in thought, it is something more abstract. My view updates this insight. Association is not a kind of psychological process; it is a generic causal relation between representational states of the system. Associative models, in turn, describe the sequence of states a process moves through and the variables it responds to in learning at a very abstract level. This view of association avoids problems with the current standard view, and gives association a more productive role in psychology.

Notes

1 I do so elsewhere: Dacey 2016a; in prep.
2 I distinguish associative models from neural network models like neural circuit models and distributed connectionist models. It is common to treat these kinds of models as the same (e.g. Bechtel and Abrahamson 1991; Clark 1993), a view which I call *reductive associationism* (see Dacey 2016a, and note 3 below). There are certainly interesting similarities between these kinds of models, but they tell us different things about the target system. Associative models describe the relationships between representational states (i.e. localist associative models); neural network models describe relationships between distributed "parts" of representations, activation in neurons, or activation in neural areas. Because they tell us different things about the system, they do different work, and they should not be equated.
3 In this volume (Chapter 39), Buckner sketches his own solution to these problems as well. In effect, we have made opposite moves: he treats associative models as being *less* abstract than cognitive models, while I treat them as being *more* abstract. The way I see it, Buckner's view amounts to a version of reductive associationism (see note 2). I reject this view because I take associative models and neural network models to each do different, valuable work. And so they should be kept separate. Buckner has helpfully characterized a role for neural network models, while I characterize the role for associative models here.
4 See Dacey 2016a for more detail.
5 I develop this argument in more detail in Dacey (in prep). I discuss human psychology because the argument would be substantially more controversial if applied to any nonhuman animal. For similar arguments, see Mitchell, DeHouwer, and Lovibond (2009) and Mandelbaum (2015).
6 One should not mistake my view for eliminativism (e.g. Gallistel 1990, 2000) or instrumentalism about association. Associations are real features of psychological processing. Moreover, there may be processes that can only be described with associative models (exactly as associative processes are thought to be). But these processes are not defined by being describable by associative models, they are defined by their *failure* to be describable by cognitive models. A name that better reflects this, like "non-cognitive processing," would lead to less confusion (see also Buckner, Chapter 39 of this volume). There is a related question about whether processes cluster such that there is a distinct *kind* here. Buckner (2013) is optimistic that they do, while I am not. But we won't know until much more empirical work is done, and the view of association I advocate will help answer this question, rather than presuming that there is such a class.
7 I discuss this aspect of the associationist tradition in more detail in Dacey (2015).

References

Akins, C. K., and Zentall, T. R. (1998) "Imitation in Japanese quail: The role of reinforcement of demonstrator responding," *Psychonomic Bulletin & Review*, 5(4), 694–697.
Allen, C. (2006) "Transitive inference in animals: Reasoning or conditioned associations," in Hurley, S., and Nudds, M. (eds.) *Rational animals*, Oxford: Oxford University Press.

Bechtel, W., and Abrahamson, A. (1991) *Connectionism and the mind: An introduction to parallel processing in networks*, Cambridge, MA: Blackwell.

Brown, T. (1840) *Lectures on the philosophy of the human mind*, Hollowell: Glazier, Masters, and Smith.

Buckner, C. (2011) "Two approaches to the distinction between cognition and 'Mere Association,'" *International Journal of Comparative Psychology, 24*, 314–348.

——— (2013) "A property cluster theory of cognition." *Philosophical Psychology, 28*(3), 307–336.

Clark, A. (1993) *Associative engine: Connectionism, concepts, and representational change*. Cambridge, MA: MIT Press.

Dacey, M. (2015) "Associationism without associative links: Thomas Brown and the associationist project," *Studies in History and Philosophy of Science Part A, 54*, 31–40.

——— (2016a) "Rethinking associations in psychology," *Synthese, 193*(12), 3763–3786.

——— (2016b) "The varieties of parsimony in psychology," *Mind & Language, 31*, 414–437.

——— (in prep) "Associative models and the mechanisms of priming"

Fitzpatrick, S. (2008) "Doing away with Morgan's Canon," *Mind & Language, 23*, 224–246.

Gallistel, C. R. (1990) *The organization of learning*, Cambridge, MA: Bradford Books/MIT Press.

——— (2000) "The replacement of general-purpose learning models with adaptively specialized learning modules," in Gazzaniga, M. S. (ed.) *The cognitive neurosciences*, 2nd ed., Cambridge, MA: MIT Press.

Guthrie, E. R. (1959) "Association by contiguity," in Koch, S. (ed.) *Psychology: A study of a science Vol. 2*, New York: McGraw-Hill.

Hume, D. (1978) *A treatise of human nature*, Oxford: Clarendon Press.

McKoon, G., and Ratcliff, R. (1995) "Conceptual combinations and relational contexts in free association and in priming in lexical decision and naming," *Psychonomic Bulletin & Review, 2*(4), 527–533.

Mandelbaum, E. (2015) "Attitude, inference, association: On the propositional structure of implicit bias," *Noûs 50*(3), 629–658.

Meltzoff, A. N. (1996) "The human infant as imitative generalist: A 20-year progress report on infant imitation with implications for comparative psychology," in Heyes, C. M., and Galef, B. G. (eds.) *Social learning in animals: The roots of culture*, New York: Academic Press.

Mitchell, C. J., De Houwer, J., and Lovibond, P. F. (2009) "The propositional nature of human associative learning," *Behavioral and Brain Sciences, 32*(2), 183–198.

Papineau, D., and Heyes, C. (2006) "Rational or associative? Imitation in Japanese quail," in Hurley, S., and Nudds, M. (eds.) *Rational animals*, Oxford: Oxford University Press.

Penn, D. C., and Povinelli, D. J. (2007) "Causal cognition in human and nonhuman animals: A comparative, critical review," *Annual Review of Psychology, 58*, 97–118.

Rescorla, R. A., and Wagner, A. R. (1972) "A theory of Pavlovian conditioning: Variations in the effectiveness of reinforcement and nonreinforcement," in Black, A. H., and Prokasy, W. F. (eds.) *Classical conditioning II*, New York: Appleton-Century-Crofts.

Robinson, E. S. (1932) *Association theory to-day*, New York: The Century Co.

Smith, J. D., Couchman, J. J., and Beran, M. J. (2014) "Animal metacognition: A tale of two comparative psychologies," *Journal of Comparative Psychology, 128*(2), 115–31.

Smith, M. C., Bentin, S., and Spalek, T. M. (2001) "Attention constraints of semantic activation during visual word recognition," *Journal of Experimental Psychology: Learning, Memory, and Cognition, 27*(5), 1289–1298.

Spelke, E. S. (1990) "Principles of object perception," *Cognitive Science, 14*, 29–56.

Tolman, E. C. (1932) *Purposive behavior in animals and men*, New York: Appleton-Century-Crofts.

——— (1948) "Cognitive maps in rats and men," *Psychological Review, 55*(4), 189.

Zentall, T. R. (1996) "An analysis of imitative learning in animals," in Heyes, C. M., and Galef, B. G. (eds.) *Social learning in animals: The roots of culture*, New York: Academic Press.

Zentall, T. R., Sutton, J. E., and Sherburne, L. M. (1996) "True imitative learning in pigeons," *Psychological Science, 7*(6), 343–346.

41

SIMPLICITY AND COGNITIVE MODELS

Avoiding old mistakes in new experimental contexts

Irina Mikhalevich

Simplicity is as intuitive as it is popular.[1] Simple explanations are easier to understand, simple formulae are easier to use, and when a single equation describes radically different systems, the world appears to be united through simplification. Comparative cognition is no stranger to erring on the side of simplicity, as can be seen in the long-standing debate about chimpanzee mindreading abilities.[2] One of the most common heuristics in experimental comparative cognition advises that, all else being equal, one ought to prefer the simplest explanation of animal behavior: one that interprets observed behavior in terms of the simplest cognitive mechanism or ability. Unfortunately, the theoretical basis for this "simplicity heuristic" has not been adequately established.[3] In this chapter, I examine how the simplicity heuristic adversely affects a relatively new tool in experimental comparative cognition: cognitive models. It does so, I argue, by directing intellectual resources into the development and refinement of putatively simple cognitive models at the expense of putatively more complex ones, which in turn directs experimenters to develop tests to rule out these simple models. The result is a state of affairs wherein putatively simple models appear more successful than less simple ones not in virtue of their epistemic superiority, but, rather, because a disproportionate amount of resources have been devoted to their development and evaluation. This has, in turn, adversely affected the design and direction of behavioral experimentation aimed at describing cognitive processes in animals, shutting down alternative research programs. I conclude that moving toward a more quantitative science of animal minds is likely to improve the explanatory and predictive power of animal cognition research, but only if these models do not fall prey to existing biases such as the simplicity heuristic.

The search for simplicity

The simplicity heuristic is intuitively appealing, widely accepted, and commonly employed in the design and interpretation of experimental results (Shettleworth 2012). However, it is currently unjustified, and may be unjustifiable, on either conceptual or empirical grounds (Fitzpatrick 2009; Meketa 2014; Starzak 2016; Sober 1998; Sober 2005), for several reasons.

First, the concept of simplicity is too ambiguous to offer any substantive guidance in either constructing or interpreting experiments, as there is no such thing as simplicity *simpliciter*. Not only are there many ways to "simplify" scientific entities, but there are also many dramatically different scientific entities that may be *simplified*. We might, for instance, simplify through homogenization by reducing the number of entity types; by reduction through reducing the total number of entities; by idealization through eliminating some features but retaining critical others; and so on. Similarly, the subject of simplification may be either the *form* of our explanations (i.e., the number of variables in equations, the length of the description, how easy it is to understand) or its content (i.e., the number of token or types of entities, processes, or properties posited). In addition, the simplicity of explanations may not correspond to the simplicity of the entities it postulates. For instance, an explanation using a large number of variables may be needed to explain the mechanism of a single entity (such as a human liver), while an explanation using a single formula may explain the behavior of a complex system (such as predator-prey interactions as described by the Lotka–Volterra equations).

Second, this ambiguity is compounded by the fact that the cognitive ontology to be simplified is itself underspecified: do we prefer to simplify *mechanisms, processes*, or *structures*? Answering this question is critical, as what it means for a mechanism to be simple may not be what it means for a process to be simple, or what it means for a structure to be simple, and so on.

Third, problems remain even when simplicity is indexed to particular cognitive structures, processes, or mechanisms. One problem is that some mechanisms do not lend themselves to classification along simple-complex lines. For instance, comparative cognition researchers typically believe that representational mechanisms are more complex than associative mechanisms, and yet there is no obvious intuitive sense in which this is true. The need to craft an unintuitive explanation for why representational mechanisms are more complex than associative mechanisms suggests that something other than simplicity is likely driving the intuition.[4] A more general problem is that even if unintuitive answers are accepted, it is incumbent on the proponent of the simplicity heuristic to explain why we should prefer these simpler ontologies. That is, why should the fact that something is simpler make it a better default hypothesis? Why should the burden of proof be on the more complex hypothesis when explaining animal behavior?

If a given behavior is indeed more *likely* to be underwritten by a simple mechanism, then we would have a strong reason to place the burden of proof onto the complex explanation. Support for this probabilistic claim has typically been couched in term of the "evolvability" of complex cognition. Arguments of this form aim to identify selection pressures or constraints that would (ceteris paribus) favor the evolution of simpler cognitive mechanisms over more complex ones. For instance, one argument holds that, ceteris paribus, the high metabolic costs of complex cognition (a product of the metabolically expensive brain tissue needed to sustain it) should favor the selection of simpler and less costly cognitive mechanisms. Such evolvability arguments are numerous and, if true, would potentially shift the burden of proof as directed by the simplicity heuristic. However, to the extent that justifications of the probabilistic claim have been attempted, few have been persuasive (Sober 2009; Meketa 2014; Mikhalevich 2015). Consider the metabolic costliness argument above. First, the argument fails to take into account the trade-offs between increased metabolic cost and the benefits that accrue to clever organisms: a bigger or denser brain needed to sustain increased cognitive function may be a reasonable price to pay for the ability to, e.g., outwit prey or predators, or to maintain close social ties needed for fitness-enhancing cooperation, and so on. Second, it wrongly presupposes that all or most increases in cognitive complexity require increases in metabolic output. While brains are indeed pound-for-pound more expensive than other organs, the addition of complex cognitive functions may not require the addition of expensive new neural tissue – e.g., it may require a no-cost repurposing of existing tissue. Moreover, the precise relationship between increases in neural tissue and changes to cognitive output remains unknown, while mounting evidence from comparative neuroscience strongly suggests a far more complex relationship between cognition and neuro-anatomy than the metabolic costliness argument presupposes (Chitkka and Niven 2009; Němec 2016; Olkowicz et al. 2016). Third, the argument ignores developmental constraints that may leave more complex cognitive mechanisms as the only viable options. These objections are not exhaustive, but they illustrate that when it comes to interpreting cognitive evolution, all else is indeed far from equal. With the metabolic costliness argument, as with many similar evolvability arguments, once the "ceteris paribus" clause is unpacked, it rapidly becomes clear that the claim that evolution favors cognitive simplicity holds for only a narrow range of cases. Much more may be said about the notion that simplest mechanisms are the most likely ones to underwrite a given behavior, but in the interest of space I will proceed on the assumption that the evidence is at present equivocal.

If simplicity is such a vexed concept, one might understandably wonder how it can have any effect at all on scientific practice, much less one so significant as a shift in the burden of proof. One possibility is that the intuitive appeal of simple explanations and their promise of lightening the cognitive load encourage the practice of supposing appealing explanations to be simple, even when it is not simplicity that makes them appealing. In fact, as Elliot Sober (1998) convincingly argues, this very appeal is often due to the some (real or imagined) background epistemic virtue on which "simplicity" is parasitic (Sober 1998; Fitzpatrick 2009; Fitzpatrick 2015). In the case of comparative cognition, this apparent virtue is the careful avoidance of "over-attributing" sophisticated and, it is often thought, "human-like" cognition to nonhuman animals. This caution may be traced back to a misinterpretation of C. Lloyd Morgan's famous "canon"[5] – a single phrase that comparative cognition researchers have adopted as central to the project of comparative cognition. Yet Morgan himself notes that simplicity often favors "anthropomorphism," since it is simpler to assume that we are just like other animals than to imagine how we might be different (Thomas 2006). Thus, even on Morgan's view, far from protecting against anthropomorphism, simplicity *encourages* it.

When complexity is understood as a sign of anthropomorphism, the project of simplifying begins to take shape. Thus, in comparative cognition, certain explanations and mechanisms are commonly presumed to be simpler – as a rule of thumb, these have traditionally tended to be the mechanisms not employed by humans (although researchers are increasingly questioning the sophistication of human cognitive mechanisms as well). These include "lower-order" explanations, which postulate fewer entities or processes or representational levels than putatively more complex, "higher order" abilities such as metacognition, theory of mind, planning, and more. While it is unclear that these processes and abilities are indeed simpler, the simplicity heuristic may be, and often is, applied without such justification. For instance, comparative cognition researchers commonly assume that associative mechanisms are simpler than representational ones, such as metacognition and mindreading.[6] With these labels in place, applying the simplicity heuristic yields a clear rule: prefer associative accounts over representational accounts, barring compelling evidence to the contrary. This rule shifts the burden of proof on to putatively more complex explanations of animal behavior, resulting in a systematic "under-attribution" of complex cognition to nonhuman animals (Meketa 2014; Mikhalevich 2015).

Simplicity and model-building

Earlier critiques of the simplicity heuristic have focused on its effects on the development and interpretation of traditional experiments in comparative cognition. But the simplicity heuristic does more than shape the design of experiments and adjudicate among competing hypotheses. It also affects novel techniques in experimental comparative cognition that the earlier critiques did not discuss, such as the design and integration of cognitive models into the broader experimental approach within the study of animal minds. These models are "mathematical or logical structures . . . whose terms are specified precisely enough to make testable predictions about cognitive capacities such as perception, categorization, memory, learning, and decision making" (Allen 2014: 84). Since they are neither mere explanations nor freestanding experiments, they play a unique role in the experimental methodology of animal cognition, and they are affected by the simplicity heuristic in ways similar to but distinct from traditional experimental methodology.

The introduction of cognitive modeling has energized comparative psychologists and philosophers, who are encouraged by the possibility of converting vague qualitative hypotheses about the mind, typically couched in natural language or folk psychological terminology, into quantitative cognitive models concretized in a formal language. Colin Allen, for example, is optimistic that these novel tools promise "better experiments, better predictions, and better science" (Allen 2014: 93). Allen envisions a science of animal minds that fully utilizes the modeling techniques now common in cognitive science, wherein cognitive models and traditional (material) experiments challenge and refine one another in an iterative fashion.[7]

Allen's characterization nicely captures the goings-on in comparative cognition today and is properly optimistic. What it does not (and does not purport to) offer, however, are the conditions of productive or fruitful iteration. For instance, it does not specify what justifies the refinement of experiments in any given case in response to model-based findings: is it the model's usefulness in predicting behavior, in explaining the behavior of a wider array of organisms, or in describing – at some grain of resolution – the actual mechanisms underpinning the observed behavior?

This is where the simplicity heuristic gains some traction: it offers a clear decision-procedure for which models to develop and which experiments to pursue. It does so by directing scientists to develop and refine models of the simplest cognitive mechanisms (those operating with the fewest rules or perhaps the fewest causal factors) while at the same time directing experimenters to design experiments so as to rule out explanations based on these simple models. Because associative mechanisms are presumed to be simper than alternatives, modelers invest their time in refining these models over possible alternatives. As a result, associative models have proliferated. While associative models are not the only kinds of model favored by the simplicity heuristic, they are the most common since they serve as all-purpose alternatives to numerous putatively sophisticated explanations of behavior, such as metacognition, mindreading, planning, the existence of mental maps, and much more. In the interest of space, I will consider just one example in some detail: the case of metacognition in rats.[8]

Jonathon Crystal and Allison Foote conducted a series of experiments to test for the presence of one type of metacognitive ability among rats: the ability to monitor their own uncertainty. The "uncertainty-monitoring" paradigm tasks animals with classifying a stimulus into one of two categories, with the option to decline to answer and move on. The stimuli can be visual arrays of different densities, audio tones of different duration, and even smells of varying concentration. The test assumes that animals who preferentially decline the more difficult trials, where the stimulus is ambiguous, must do so because they are capable of monitoring their degree of certainty about the correct choice. Foote and Crystal employed this paradigm with rats, publishing the positive results first in 2007. When given the choice to decline tests, their rats consistently opted to decline the ambiguous ("harder") tests but not the unambiguous tests. Moreover, the overall accuracy improved when rats were allowed to opt out of difficult tests. Foote and Crystal (2007) concluded that the rats' behavior demonstrated awareness of their metacognitive uncertainty.

Shortly after the publication of this study, another group of researchers – Smith et al. – offered a competing associative "response-strength" model to account for the rats' behavior. This model introduces a "low level, flat threshold for the decline response," which activates whenever the response strengths for either SHORT or LONG are lower than the threshold (Foote and Crystal 2012: 188). The model maps response strengths as exponential curves declining from their thresholds, and crossing in the middle, where both strengths are low. Thus, the rats' consistent preferences for the DECLINE option during the most difficult trials is explained by the activation of both LONG and SHORT dropping below the threshold for the DECLINE option. Since DECLINE was more strongly activated than either LONG or SHORT, the model predicts that the rats will activate the button that allowed them to decline the test and move on to more tests with the possibility of future rewards – mimicking the behavior of the rats in Crystal and Foote's experiment.

In response to Smith et al.'s model, Crystal and Foote (2009) withdrew their metacognitive interpretation, reasoning that because the rat's behavior *could* be explained in terms of "simpler" associative processes relying on "primary representations," their previous *metacognitive* explanation was unwarranted (Crystal and Foote 2009). The introduction of putatively simpler models, they wrote, "necessitates the development of new, innovative methods for metacognition," something that they tried to accomplish in subsequent experiments (Foote and Crystal 2012). Having thus accepted the simplicity heuristic (on which the metacognitive or "higher-order" representational hypothesis carries the burden of proof), Foote and Crystal (2012) revised their experiments in order to accommodate the simple model.

This example illustrates how the heuristic allows associative models to shape the arc of the experimental research programs on metacognition. Without the simplicity heuristic, metacognition might have been on equal epistemic footing with alternatives, and cognitive modelers such as Smith et al. (2008) would have needed to produce a model that was in some way superior to the metacognitive explanation in terms of, e.g., predictive power. Without this ability, the model would have been unable to dislodge the metacognitive explanation, though it might rightly have slightly decreased credence in the metacognitive hypothesis.

As this example illustrates, in challenging inferences from physical experiments, these models are shaping the setup of *future* physical experiments. Smith et al. (2008) are explicit on this point, writing in their introduction that their "models and related discussion have utility for metacognition researchers and theorists broadly, because they specify the experimental operations that will best indicate a metacognitive capacity in humans or animals by eliminating alternative behavioral accounts." In this way, they indeed contribute to the iterative process of model-experiment "refinement," but this interaction is unproductive, and perhaps harmful to scientific progress, as long as the models are chosen over qualitative explanations on the grounds of their putative simplicity rather than, e.g., explanatory scope or predictive power. As long as the simplicity heuristic places the burden of proof onto the more complex model, alternative cognitive models that are not (or are perceived as not being) as simple are less likely to be developed: research is time-consuming, and when a research program is unlikely to pay off in terms of publications, funding, or other career-enhancing rewards, researchers will be rational to avoid investing their time in programs that their field deems unlikely to yield fruitful results.[9] Yet without this time and effort, the simpler models will remain unchallenged and will continue to be regarded as the theoretical defaults.

The metacognition example is not an outlier. Consider a few more examples of the heuristic at work in model-building, in which "simplicity" is attributed not only to associative models, but also to models that postulate few variables, rules, or causes. Each of these is expressly non-representational and regarded as simple in that respect. For example, van der Vaart et al. (2012) propose a model, based on a single rule ("cache more when stressed"), to explain the observation that scrub jays re-cache more often when their initial caching had been observed by others (Dally et al. 2006). This behavior was interpreted as evidence that these corvids possess some mindreading abilities – the ability to take the visual perspective of another, or perhaps to impute to others the intention to pilfer. Proposing a similarly "simpler" model of nonhuman primate reconciliation behavior, van der Vaart and Hemelrijk (2014) reason that because "the same patterns arise as a consequence of simple rules about fighting and grooming, and their effects on spatial proximity [as developed in their model]" it follows that the behavior is "not necessarily the product of sophisticated social reasoning" (348). The implication is clear: an alternative model poses a legitimate challenge to a dominant interpretation of behavior just in case it is putatively simpler.

The presumption that such putatively complex explanations, such as "social reasoning," comes through in the common refrain that these explanations are rendered unnecessary whenever simpler models become available. Consider another example. Cruse and Wehner (2011) propose a cognitive model of ant and bee navigation, which is intended to displace explanations adverting to "cognitive maps" – representations of an animal's environment that organisms may use to navigate. On this model, information from peripheral systems acts on disparate parts of the organism to produce behavior that's only *apparently* coordinated. It thus bypasses the need for a central processor required to collate information into a single representation – a feature that the authors regard as an extravagant hypothesis. They conclude that since their model is purportedly simpler than the cognitive map model, there is "no need" for a cognitive map. Similarly, Puga-Gonzalez et al. (2009) argue that "the use of grooming [among primates] as a 'currency of exchange' is dangerously anthropomorphic according to us and others" and that "often *simple rules suffice* to cause many of the observed patterns and herewith an integrative theory," concluding that "*fewer cognitive processes* may *suffice* as shown for instance in a model for dominance style" (2; emphasis added).

But note that a claim that a putatively more complex account is not needed or that a simple one may "suffice" is a claim about the proper direction of the research program. It is a claim, guided by the simplicity heuristic, that advises against developing alternative explanations of putatively complex mechanisms – or of developing quantitative models that may account for the behavior as well as or better than the simple models. Instead, the heuristic suggests that experiments must be redesigned in order to rule out the inference from the simple model, and it repeats this request each time a "simple" model challenges the experimental finding.

As long as the simplicity heuristic directs the development of application of cognitive models, it will discourage the development of alternatives. This appears to be the situation in comparative cognition today, where models of simple mechanisms far outnumber models of putatively complex mechanisms. The result of this heuristic is cumulative: because the simplicity heuristic encourages researchers to channel their efforts into refining "simpler" and allegedly non-anthropomorphic models, these models gain an unearned competitive advantage over alternatives that are deemed "complex." As a result, these alternatives are more likely to remain qualitative, which further diminishes their apparent value in the eyes of researchers, who would be rational to view a qualitative explanation with suspicion when a quantitative explanation is on offer. Thus, without understanding the history of the models, it may appear that they have outcompeted more complex alternatives on their epistemic merit. Yet, as I suggest, their staying power may be due to having benefitted from a biasing heuristic that funneled more intellectual capital into their development while simultaneously discouraging the proliferation of viable (quantitative) alternatives.

Objections

One may object that simple models are defaults because simplicity is a virtue insofar as simple models may be more predictive as well as easier to use than complex models.[10] I grant that the predictive power of a model is a virtue that justifies the further exploration of that model. However, predictiveness does not necessarily track accuracy, and simplicity is not a virtue if the models are intended to explain animal behavior by *describing* actual cognitive processes or mechanisms. There is no reason to suppose a priori that the target mechanism described by the model is in fact simple.[11] Thus, simple models ought not to be defaults just as long as these models are intended to describe the cognitive system.

Another objection holds that simple models of animal minds are well developed not because they are favored by the simplicity heuristic, but because alternatives such as metacognition are so vague as to be impossible to model quantitatively. However, if metacognitive hypotheses appear vague, this may be because fewer attempts at quantifying these models have been made. This objection may prove true of some putatively complex cognitive explanations of animal behavior, but the best means of putting this objection to the test is by attempting to formulate alternative models of, e.g., metacognition.

Finally, one may grant both that simple models receive more investment and that they do so for a poor reason (simplicity), but nevertheless maintain that the iterative process of model-experiment development is not sensitive to initial conditions – that eventually, the models and experiment will converge on the truth. In fact, there is some reason to believe that simple associative models have become more complex by having to accommodate more experimental information and, as a result, have come to resemble cognitive models of more sophisticated cognition. However, even if this turns out to be true for association, this need not be so in other cases. The optimism must be grounded in something like the view that no matter what the starting point, scientific research programs (or the research programs of comparative cognition specifically) are virtually guaranteed to ultimately arrive at the best (most accurate, most useful, etc.) answer. Thus far, however, no adequate justification for the assumption that experimental research will asymptotically approach the best explanation has been given. In the absence of persuasive reasons to retain the simplicity heuristic, and given its epistemically undesirable consequences, there remains little reason to continue to deploy it in the study of animal minds.

If not simplicity, then what?

Suppose that we eliminate simplicity as a guide for shaping the arc of model-experiment development. Without simplicity acting as a gatekeeper, what is to prevent an influx of empirically adequate and predictive models that presuppose metaphysically suspect entities, such as chakras and spirits? Should scientists open up the borders to every conceivable model, including those that seek to explain animal behavior in terms of such entities? At least simplicity permits the modeler to claim that we do not "need" such entities in our explanations. Without simplicity, how do we discourage such promiscuous proliferation of models, and, relatedly, how do we adjudicate at all among empirically adequate models?

These are important concerns, and while space does not permit a full answer to the second query, I believe that we have reason for optimism with respect to the first. Reasons to reject these metaphysically suspect entities go beyond the desire for clean ontologies. These are the same reasons that generate the suspicion in the first place: namely, that most of these entities do not fit into a naturalistic view of the world on which science is premised. Admittedly, not all such unwelcome entities are metaphysically suspect – for instance, interventions by aliens or global government conspiracies – but the sheer improbability of these explanations is enough to guard cognitive models from their influence. We have excellent reasons to restrict model-building to the range of entities and causes in an epistemically responsible fashion, and these reasons stem from background theoretical assumptions about the kinds of entities that populate our world. These theories tell us that metacognition is real but chakras are probably not, and for this reason to permit models describing metacognition but not those describing chakras.

Simplicity, therefore, is not a unique bulwark against an anything-goes science of metaphysical extravagance. Rather, it is an occasionally useful but frequently detrimental guide that risks closing off potentially fruitful research programs. Instead of the simplicity heuristic, comparative cognition flourishes when all epistemically equal models are encouraged equally, rather than being ruled out without a fair trial or being saddled with an impossible burden of proof, in the courtroom of scientific ideas. Such model diversity would put a new and productive pressure on experimenters, encouraging them to devise experiments not to rule out "simpler" alternatives, but to identify novel means of experimentally adjudicating among competing models of animal mind.

Notes

1 I am grateful to participants of the Washington University in St. Louis Philosophy of Science Reading Group for helpful comments on an earlier version of this essay, and to Russell Powell for his thorough reading and thoughtful suggestions.

2 See Call and Tomasello (2006) and Povinelli and Vonk (2003) for examples of appeals to simplicity. For recent discussions of the chimpanzee mindreading controversy, see Chapters 22, 21, and 13 in this volume by Halina, Lurz, and Proust, respectively.

3 My "simplicity heuristic" roughly resembles what Fitzpatrick (Chapter 42 in this volume) calls the "Conservative Canon."

4 To say that the reasons are not intuitive is not to say that they are necessarily mistaken.

5 For a thorough review of the multiplicity of meanings of Morgan's Canon, see Thomas 2006. For a historical analysis, see Kimler 2000; see Burkhardt 2005 for a detailed history of the study of animal behavior which places the canon into proper context. For examples of explicit appeals to the canon, see Kennedy 1992, Wynne 2007a, and Wynne 2007b. For analyses and critiques of specific interpretations, see Fitzpatrick 2008; Meketa 2014; Allen-Hermanson 2005; and Sober 1998 and 2005. For arguments against *any* plausible interpretation of the canon, see Starzak 2016 and Fitzpatrick (Chapter 42 in this volume). See Dacey (2016) for a limited defense of some forms of the canon.

6 This assumption is problematic for two reasons. First, it is unclear that association is simpler than metacognition, since the ontology of metacognition and association are under-specified. For example, see Heyes 2012 and Gallistel 2000. Second, even if association is simpler than metacognition, it is far from clear that simplicity should play any role in adjudicating among hypotheses.

7 See Buckner 2011 for a discussion of such iterative model-experiment development.

8 This trend is mirrored in developmental psychology as well. For instance, associative explanations for language acquisition in human infants continue to be preferred despite their explanatory and predictive failures. Their staying power may be attributed not to an epistemic virtue, but to something extra-epistemic, such as theoretical simplicity. I thank Richard Moore for this point.

9 This is not to say that no research will be conducted without substantial rewards, much less to suggest that scientists are driven exclusively or predominantly by career-enhancing goals. It is, however, to acknowledge a sociological constraint on the development of intellectual tools and the cascading effects of these social dimensions of science.

10 See, for instance, Sober 2009.

11 One might argue that my objection rules out all models since all models are idealizations. However, there is a difference between simplicity and idealization. All models are idealized, including metacognitive models. Yet metacognitive models would be considered more "complex" by the simplicity heuristic because they are representational or because they contain more elements. Thus, it is not the fact that putatively simple models are more idealized that makes them ineligible as defaults, but, rather, that there is no a priori reason to prefer them over putatively more complex models.

Further reading

For additional readings on simplicity in biology, psychology, and philosophy, see Elliott Sober's *Ockham's Razors: A User's Manual*, Cambridge: Cambridge University Press, 2015.

References

Allen, C. (2014) "Models, Mechanisms, and Animal Minds," *The Southern Journal of Philosophy* 52: 75–97.

Allen-Hermanson, S. (2005) "Morgan's Canon revisited," *Philosophy of Science* 72(4): 608–631.

Buckner, C. (2011) "Two Approaches to the Distinction Between Cognition and 'Mere Association,'" *International Journal of Comparative Psychology* 24: 314–348.

Burkhardt, R. W. (2005) *Patterns of Behavior: Konrad Lorenz, Niko Tinbergen, and the Founding of Ethology.* Chicago: University of Chicago Press.

Chitkka, L., and Niven, J. (2009) "Are Bigger Brains Better?" *Current Biology* 19: R995–R1008.

Cruse, H., and Wehner, R. (2011) "No Need for a Cognitive Map: Decentralized Memory for Insect Navigation," *PLoS Computational Biology* 7: e1002009.

Crystal, J. D., and Foote, A. L. (2009) "Metacognition in Animals," *Comparative Cognition & Behavior Reviews* 4: 1–16.

Dacey, M. (2016) "The Varieties of Parsimony in Psychology," *Mind & Language* 31: 414–437.

Dally, J. M., Emery, N. J., and Clayton, N. S. (2006) "Food-Caching Western Scrub-Jays Keep Track of Who Was Watching When," *Science* 312: 1662–1665.

Fitzpatrick, S. (2008) "Doing away with Morgan's Canon," *Mind & Language* 23(2): 224–246.

——— (2009) "The Primate Mindreading Controversy: A Case Study in Simplicity and Methodology in Animal Psychology," in R. Lurz (ed.) *The Philosophy of Animal Minds*, New York: Cambridge University Press.

——— (2015) "Nativism, Empiricism, and Ockham's Razor," *Erkenntnis* 80: 895–922.

Foote, A. L., and Crystal, J. D. (2007) "Metacognition in the Rat," *Current Biology* 17: 551–555.

——— (2012) "'Play It Again': A New Method for Testing Metacognition in Animals," *Animal Cognition* 15: 187–199.

Gallistel, R. (2000) "The Replacement of General-Purpose Learning Models With Adaptively Specialized Learning Modules," in M. Gazzaniga (ed.) *The New Cognitive Neurosciences*, Cambridge, MA: MIT Press.

Heyes, C. (2012) "Simple minds: A qualified defence of associative learning," *Philosophical Transactions of the Royal Society of London B: Biological Sciences* 367(1603): 2695–2703.

Kennedy, J. S. (1992) *The New Anthropomorphism*, Cambridge: Cambridge University Press.

Kimler, W. C. (2000) "Reading Morgan's Canon: Reduction and Unification in the Forging of a Science of the Mind," *American Zoologist* 40: 853–861.

Meketa, I. (2014) "A Critique of the Principle of Cognitive Simplicity in Comparative Cognition," *Biology & Philosophy* 29: 731–745.

Mikhalevich, I. (2015) "Experiment and Animal Minds: Why the Choice of the Null Hypothesis Matters," *Philosophy of Science* 82: 1059–1069.

Olkowicz, S., Kocourek, M. Lučan, R. K., Porteš, M., Fitch, W. T., Herculano-Houzel, S. and Němec, P. (2016) "Birds Have Primate-Like Numbers of Neurons in the Forebrain," *PNAS* 113: 7255–7260.

Povinelli, D., and Vonk, J. (2003) "Chimpanzee Minds: Suspiciously Human?" *Trends in Cognitive Sciences* 7: 157–160.

Puga-Gonzalez, I., Hildenbrandt, H., and Hemelrijk, C. K. (2009) "Emergent Patterns of Social Affiliation in Primates: A Model," *PLoS Computational Biology* 5(12): e1000630.

Shettleworth, S. J. (2012) "Modularity, Comparative Cognition and Human Uniqueness," *Philosophical Transactions of the Royal Society B* 367: 2794–2802.

Smith, J. D., Beran, M. J. Couchman, J. J., and Coutinho, M. V. (2008) "The Comparative Study of Metacognition: Sharper Paradigms, Safer Inferences," *Psychonomic Bulletin & Review* 15: 679–691.

Sober, E. (1998) "Morgan's Canon," in C. Allen and D. Cummins (eds.) *The Evolution of Mind*, Oxford: Oxford University Press. 224–242.

―――― (2005) "Comparative Psychology Meets Evolutionary Biology: Morgan's Canon and Cladistic Parsimony," in L. Datson and G. Mitman (eds.) *Thinking With Animals: New Perspectives on Anthropomorphism*, New York: Columbia University Press, 85–99.

―――― (2009) "Parsimony and Models of Animal Minds," in R. W. Lurz (ed.) *The Philosophy of Animal Minds*, New York: Cambridge University Press, 237–257.

Thomas, R. K. (2006) "Lloyd Morgan's Canon: A History of Misrepresentation," *History & Theory of Psychology Eprint Archive*. Available at http://archive.is/kQasr and by the author at https://faculty.franklin.uga.edu/rkthomas/sites/faculty.franklin.uga.edu.rkthomas/files/MCPrintOptimal.pdf

Tomasello, M., and Call, J. (2006) "Do Chimpanzees Know What Others See – Or Only What They Are Looking At?" in S. Hurley and M. Nudds (eds.) *Rational Animals?* New York: Oxford University Press.

Starzak, T. (2016) "Interpretations Without Justification: A General Argument Against Morgan's Canon," *Synthese*: 1–21. doi: 10.1007/s11229-016-1013-4

van der Vaart, E., Verbrugge, R., and Hemelrijk, C. K. (2012) "Corvid Re-Caching Without 'Theory of Mind': A Model," *PLoS One* 7: e32904.

Wynne, C. D. (2007a) "Anthropomorphism and its Discontents," *Comparative Cognition & Behavior Reviews* 2: 151–154.

Wynne, C. D. (2007b) "What Are Animals? Why Anthropomorphism Is Still Not a Scientific Approach to Behavior," *Comparative Cognition & Behavior Reviews*, 2: 125–135.

42

AGAINST MORGAN'S CANON

Simon Fitzpatrick

Introduction

Despite a variety of critiques (e.g., de Waal 1999; Sober 1998, 2005; Fitzpatrick 2008; Andrews and Huss 2014; Meketa 2014; Starzak 2016), the principle known as *Morgan's Canon* retains a significant hold on modern scientific and philosophical discussions of nonhuman animal (henceforth, "animal") cognition and behavior. Proposed by the late-nineteenth-century British philosopher-psychologist, Conwy Lloyd Morgan – generally regarded as the "father" of modern comparative psychology – it states that:

> In no case may we interpret an action as the outcome of the exercise of a higher psychical faculty, if it can be interpreted as the outcome of the exercise of one which stands lower in the psychological scale.
>
> (Morgan 1894: 53)

Morgan saw this principle as necessary for scientifically rigorous investigation into the minds of animals. It went on to exert enormous influence on the subsequent development of comparative psychology, though not always in ways consistent with Morgan's original intent (Costall 1993; Thomas 1998; Fitzpatrick and Goodrich 2016).

My focus will be on how Morgan's Canon has been interpreted and applied by psychologists and philosophers since Morgan's day, particularly over the last few decades, and whether or not it should continue to be accepted as a fundamental guiding principle for the study of animal cognition and behavior – to which the answer will be an emphatic "no". However, one problem with discussing the place of the Canon in the contemporary literature is that it has been explicated and interpreted in several different ways. The distinctions between these different versions of the Canon have not been fully appreciated, even in the most careful discussions. I'll first distinguish between four formulations of the Canon that one can find explicitly or implicitly in the literature. I'll then argue that each of these Canons is unjustified and unnecessary. We will see that comparative psychology has absolutely no need for Morgan's Canon, on any of its current interpretations, and that the field would be better served by an alternative principle that I call *Evidentialism* (Fitzpatrick 2008).

Four canons

Morgan's Canon remains widely accepted primarily because it is seen as a bulwark against a natural bias of human beings towards explaining animal behavior in terms of sophisticated, human-like cognitive capacities, when the relevant behavior might in fact be the product of much less sophisticated causes. Morgan himself criticized the tendency of his contemporaries to reflexively attribute instances of animal learning, such as a dog learning to open a latched gate using its nose, to a sophisticated faculty of "reason" (e.g., an abstract conceptual understanding of the workings of the latch), when the behavior might be the product of a much less sophisticated process of trial and error (where the animal merely forms an association between a given action and achieving a desired outcome). Such a bias, it is argued, still afflicts modern discussions of animal intelligence, particularly in the popular media, but also in parts of the scientific literature. The Canon serves as a counterweight, ensuring that researchers don't overestimate the capacities of animals. But if this is the problem the Canon is meant to cure, exactly *what* treatment is it meant to provide?

The strongest formulation in the literature has the most tenuous relationship to Morgan's original words, but was the interpretation that became most prevalent in the decades after Morgan proposed the principle (Costall 1993; Thomas 1998). Though, as stated, Morgan's Canon admits for the possibility of accepting "higher" explanations of behavior, given appropriate evidence (see also Morgan 1903: 59), some interpreted it as banning entirely what are derisively referred to as "anthropomorphic" explanations of behavior. This is the *Prohibitive Canon*.

Here, the terms "higher" and "lower" are synonymous with "cognitive" and "non-cognitive", respectively. The idea is that cognitive explanations of behavior – ones that invoke internal mental states such as thoughts, beliefs, emotions, desires, or other representational states and processes – are to be viewed with inherent suspicion, because they are "anthropomorphic". Since anthropomorphism is to be avoided at all costs, animal behavior is always to be explained *without* reference to such things. Such was the attitude of the behaviorist movement in the early decades of the twentieth century, some of whom co-opted Morgan as their intellectual forefather and presented the Canon in this light. Here is a textbook rendition from this period:

> In Morgan's case, the principle amounted to this. Where there is a pattern of animal behavior which must be explained, both as to form and to origin, and in the simplest, but at the same time, most adequate way, the experimenter should appeal to factors observable in the situation in which the animal has been placed, in the behavior itself, and in the machinery by which the behavior is made possible. It is not incumbent on him to pass over these factors in order to appeal to a verbal construct, to a mind, or to any other kind of mental factor which lies outside of, behind, or within the behavior-situation.
>
> (Griffith 1943: 322)

As the popularity of behaviorism has receded and cognitive approaches have become widely accepted, the Prohibitive Canon is much less popular than it once was, but one can still find researchers advocating something very close to it. Clive Wynne (2007) is perhaps the most prominent contemporary defender of a categorical "anti-mentalism" (as he refers to it), though Wynne is careful to distinguish his view from the historical Morgan.

Today, the most common articulations of the Canon are not flatly prohibitive, but rather correspond to what I want to call the *Conservative Canon*. For example:

> [I]f principles of associative learning or habit formation operating on a primary representation may account for putative metacognition data, then it would be inappropriate

to explain such data based on metacognition (i.e., based on a secondary representation); the burden of proof favors primary representations, by application of Morgan's canon.

(Crystal and Foote 2009: 2)

Following the principle of parsimony, also known as Morgan's Cannon or Ockham's Razor, we should prefer the simplest explanation for pointing and the reaction to it. A reaction without insight seems to be a simpler explanation than with insight. Of course, one has to keep an open mind for data that justify more complex interpretations for pointing behavior and the reaction to it than the interpretation without insight.

(van Rooijen 2010: e8)

Here, the terms "higher" and "lower" are generally understood in terms of degrees of cognitive sophistication. For instance, purely physiological explanations of behavior – e.g., in terms of reflexes or innate releasing mechanisms – and other non-cognitive explanations – e.g., in terms of the most basic forms of associative conditioning – are to be understood as "lower" than cognitive explanations, such as those that involve some form of means-end reasoning, say. Moreover, explanations in terms of first-order cognitive processes are to be regarded as "lower" than those in terms of more sophisticated higher-order processes, such as the ability to reason about one's own mental states (metacognition) or those of others (mindreading). As the second passage above illustrates, this notion of cognitive sophistication is often dressed up in the language of simplicity, where explanations in terms of less sophisticated processes are taken to be "simpler" or more "parsimonious" than those in terms of more sophisticated ones. Crucially, this principle allows that "higher" – i.e., relatively cognitively sophisticated – explanations of behavior can potentially be accepted. However, when we have a choice between more cognitively sophisticated and less cognitively sophisticated explanations, we should adopt the least sophisticated explanation available. The Conservative Canon can thus be viewed as a *decision principle*, which tells us how to choose between competing explanations for behavior: we should always default to the least cognitively sophisticated explanation consistent with the available data.[1]

Though most explicit presentations of the Canon can be seen as instances of the Conservative Canon, many advocates don't actually follow it in practice. Instead, what they often seem to abide by is a weaker principle that I want to call the *Restraining Canon*. The distinction between these two principles coincides with a largely ignored ambiguity in Morgan's original framing of the Canon. When Morgan says that we shouldn't endorse higher explanations for behavior when lower ones are available, are we to actively *endorse* the relevant lower explanation, or are we to merely *withhold judgment* until future evidence enables us to decide between the respective higher and lower explanations? Morgan actually equivocated on this, sometimes using the Canon to defend lower accounts of behavior, sometimes urging us to merely withhold acceptance from a higher account, given the availability of a lower one (compare Morgan 1894: 248, 302, 370). In contrast to the Conservative Canon, then, the Restraining Canon doesn't say that we should automatically endorse the lower explanation when higher and lower accounts are consistent with the available behavioral data. Rather, it says that when a lower explanation is available, we must not accept a higher one. We should be especially restrained in our endorsement of higher explanations, being sure to eliminate lower explanations before accepting them. Here are some examples that seem to be consistent with this weaker formulation:

[I]t is our intention to highlight the principle enshrined in Morgan's Canon; namely that accounts of animal behavior in terms of higher-order mental functions should only be accepted when explanations in terms of simpler mechanisms are unavailable.

(Dwyer and Burgess 2011: 361)

[W]e must not abandon Morgan's canon. For example, we should not accept the idea that honey-bees have such capacities before eliminating every other possibility.

(Manning and Dawkins 1998: 297)

The final interpretation of the Canon that I want to discuss is the *Cautionary Canon*. I've not seen it stated explicitly, but it does capture a possible way of thinking about the role of the Canon in modern comparative psychology. In contrast to the three canons just discussed, this canon is not really a methodological principle at all. It doesn't give any specific methodological guidance; it is just a cautionary exhortation – the sort of thing that professors pound into the heads of their students in introductory lectures, but not a principle to be employed in actual research. It just serves to emphasize that the history of research into animal cognition has been marred by cases – the infamous case of Clever Hans, for instance – where researchers leapt too quickly to higher-level accounts of animal behavior without adequately considering the possibility of lower-level processes being at work. In this respect, the Canon is merely a pedagogical tool, reminding future researchers not to make the same mistakes as their forebears.

The Prohibitive Canon

The categorical anti-cognitivism embodied in the Prohibitive Canon has received much criticism (Allen and Bekoff 1997; Keeley 2004; Andrews 2015), so I won't rehearse all the arguments against it. The key point is that labelling cognitive explanations of nonhuman behavior "anthropomorphic," where this is understood as a conceptual or inferential mistake, just begs the question by assuming that cognitive processes are uniquely human. It is surely an empirical question whether such processes exist in other species, not something that can be resolved by methodological fiat.

Of course, anti-cognitivists usually assert that internal mental processes in other species cannot be studied scientifically, because they are intrinsically unobservable or because we cannot describe them in a way that isn't inextricably tied to human language and concepts (Blumberg and Wasserman 1995; Wynne 2007). The first claim forgets that unobservable theoretical entities are a common component of modern science generally (consider quarks and Higgs bosons), while the second ignores the fact that modern cognitivists typically assume a broadly functionalist perspective, according to which mental states and processes are defined by their characteristic functional or causal roles. Crucially, such definitions can be seen as analogous to (and no more anthropomorphic than) the causal-role definitions that physicists provide for things like Higgs bosons. Just as physicists can legitimately posit the existence of such unobservable theoretical entities in order to explain things that we do observe, so cognitivists can legitimately posit the existence of a kind of episodic memory in scrub jays, say (understood as the capacity to store and utilize information about "what" events occurred "where" and "when"), in order to explain their observable behavior (e.g., Clayton and Dickinson 1998).

In short, there is no reason whatsoever to think that cognitive states and processes cannot be attributed to animals in a scientifically legitimate manner, and hence no reason to prohibit such attributions.

The Conservative Canon

Here is a typical presentation of the Conservative Canon:

> Unless clear evidence is provided that a more complex cognitive process has been used, C. Lloyd Morgan's famous canon of parsimony obliges us to assume that it has not; we must then conclude that a simpler learning process can account for the learning.
>
> (Wasserman and Zentall 2006: 4)

Suppose we are concerned with how an animal learns to perform a particular task. We consider various types of learning process that can account for the observed behavior – e.g., basic associative learning versus a more sophisticated form of means-end reasoning – but we are unable to turn up decisive evidence that discriminates between them. Wasserman and Zentall would appear to have us "conclude" that it must therefore be the lower, associative learning process at work. But what is the status of this conclusion? Are proponents of associative learning to declare victory, and the field to move on to some new topic? That hardly seems appropriate, and I seriously doubt that most of those who espouse something like the Conservative Canon would recommend such a verdict. So, what exactly *are* we to take away from a case like this? Perhaps the conclusion that it is the lower learning process at work and the higher one is absent is just a provisional one, to be accepted pending future research into the matter? That sounds better, but notice how *unempirical* it is. We are to accept, albeit provisionally, an associative learning explanation, not because it is better supported by the data, but because the data do not discriminate between it and one that invokes a more sophisticated process.

Crucially, the usual rationale offered for Morgan's Canon – the supposed tendency to attribute sophisticated cognitive processes to animals on the basis of insufficient evidence, or without proper attention being paid to alternative, less cognitively sophisticated explanations – actually undercuts this aspect of the Conservative Canon. Why is it an appropriate response to this problem to enshrine a default bias towards lower explanations? That seems like overkill, given that one could just remain neutral if there is insufficient evidence to decide between higher and lower explanations. Moreover, if over-attribution of cognitive sophistication to animals is an error that needs to be corrected, then so is under-attribution (de Waal 1999; Sober 2005; Andrews and Huss 2014). The Conservative Canon clearly increases the chance of making the latter error: it asks us to always favor the least cognitively sophisticated explanation, even when there is no empirical reason to do so. Hence, the logic thought to motivate Morgan's Canon actually runs against the Conservative Canon.

I think this is one reason why many that express the Conservative Canon don't actually abide by it in practice. However, there clearly are researchers genuinely committed to the principle. Carruthers (2008) argues that the existing experimental results that supposedly indicate metacognitive capacities in animals can be explained in terms of purely first-order processes. Hence, "we should, at present, refuse to attribute meta-cognitive processes to animals. This inference is grounded in an application of Morgan's Canon" (2008: 59). While this might sound like an instance of the Restraining Canon, Carruthers' position isn't one of agnosticism. Though he remains open to the possibility of future work establishing the existence of metacognition in animals, the "inference" he refers to is to the (at least provisional) conclusion that such capacities are in fact absent. This is an example of what I call "armchair denialism", where the mere ability to *construct* a hypothetical lower explanation for the relevant behavioral data is enough not only to suggest that the higher explanation shouldn't be accepted – or that the relevant experiments might not show what they are claimed to show – but that the lower one should be accepted *instead*. It is worth considering, then, what justification, if any, can be given for the Conservative Canon.

As we've seen, expressions of the Conservative Canon usually also include the claim that explanations in terms of less sophisticated cognitive processes are somehow "simpler" or more "parsimonious". Hence, the alternative to justifying the Conservative Canon in terms of concerns about over-attribution is to argue that it is just a special case of *Ockham's Razor* – the general rule of scientific method that simpler explanations ought to be preferred to more complex ones, other things being equal.

This appeal to simplicity is problematic on many levels, however (see also Mikhalevich, Chapter 41 in this volume). We shouldn't just take it for granted that it *is* a legitimate rule of scientific method that simpler theories or explanations are to be preferred, other things being equal. Though many scientists do espouse principles like Ockham's Razor, it is far from clear that simplicity really does play a significant role in theory evaluation, and it is certainly not a trivial problem to explain *why* it is reasonable to choose between rival theories on such grounds. I am sympathetic to Sober's (1994, 2015) claim that when considerations of simplicity *appear* to play a legitimate role in science, it is typically some other consideration that does the real epistemic work (Fitzpatrick 2009, 2015).

In any case, why should we regard explanations in terms of less sophisticated processes as necessarily simpler? Even if one accepts that the level of cognitive sophistication attributed can be regarded as one way in which rival psychological theories might be evaluated for their comparative simplicity, there are multiple *other* ways of assessing relative simplicity, many of which conflict with the recommendations of the Conservative Canon. Morgan (1894: 54–55) himself argued that the Canon ran against a preference for simplicity because it was generally simpler to explain animal behavior in the same way as one would explain similar behavior in a human being. Similarly, as Sober (2005) and de Waal (1999) point out, considerations of evolutionary parsimony – minimizing the number of independent evolutionary changes that have to be posited – can sometimes favor attributing higher processes to animals. For instance, when trying to explain the emergence of similar behaviors in humans and a closely related primate species, such considerations might incline us to posit the evolution of a single higher cognitive mechanism in a common ancestor of both species, rather than the independent evolution of two different mechanisms. In addition, an explanation that attributes more sophisticated learning capacities to an animal might be said to be "simpler" than an associative learning explanation, if the latter requires us to make more assumptions about the animal's previous experiences with the relevant task. Hence, whatever one thinks about the legitimacy of appeals to simplicity in comparative psychology, there are *many* different ways of measuring the relative "simplicity" of behavioral explanations. Given that the Conservative Canon prioritizes *one* particular kind of simplicity – level of cognitive sophistication – over others, we need another justification, aside from a completely general appeal to simplicity, for the Conservative Canon.

Shettleworth (2012: 12–13) suggests that the Canon makes sense insofar as it leads us to prefer explaining behavior in terms of lower processes – "habituation and classical conditioning", for instance – that we already know are widely distributed in the animal kingdom, rather than in terms of more sophisticated processes that are likely to be much rarer in nature. Similarly, Carruthers (2008: 59) argues that it makes sense to default to a purely first-order explanation of the putative metacognition data, given the plausible rarity of metacognitive capacity in nature, which follows from the fact it requires that first-order reasoning is already in place and because it is "extremely cognitively demanding". The idea seems to be that, given that lower processes are more common in nature, the antecedent probability of lower explanations is greater than that for higher explanations.

However, Shettleworth's claim seems to beg the question, since it is not entirely clear what role associative learning, as she understands it, plays in explaining animal behavior (Meketa 2014). Researchers like Randy Gallistel (2000) have long been arguing that traditional models of associative learning can't even explain the results of standard classical and operant conditioning experiments, which are better accounted for by much richer information-processing models. Much the same is true in Carruthers' case. Even if he is right that metacognition is particularly cognitively demanding, research into this capacity is at such an early stage that we just have no idea how widely distributed this capacity is likely to be in the animal kingdom – it might turn out to be quite widely distributed because it confers peculiar evolutionary advantage. Moreover, Carruthers' argument loses its force when we consider primates closely related to humans, who are surely more likely to possess such a rare capacity, given their evolutionary proximity to a species known to have it.

To be clear, there are cases where relevant background information about the species in question – level of neurological complexity, type of ecological niche, information about closely related species, etc. – may legitimately lead us to elevate the antecedent probability of particular lower explanations relative to higher ones. Metacognition probably is too demanding for the tiny brains of fruit flies, for instance. However, the Conservative Canon enshrines a completely general preference for lower over higher. That it may *sometimes* be reasonable to favor lower over higher is not sufficient to justify such a blanket bias. Indeed, the fact that the antecedent probability of having particular psychological capacities *is* different for different species constitutes reason to reject the Conservative Canon, since the principle does not take that into account.

Aside from such justificatory problems, the blanket bias towards lower explanations enshrined in the Conservative Canon is also demonstrably pernicious in terms of its actual and likely effects on the conduct of research (see also Mikhalevich, Chapter 41 in this volume). Consider Gallistel's claims again. Associative learning hypotheses are often the first port of call for skeptics about sophisticated cognition in animals. Consequently, experimentalists (quite rightly) try to devise experiments capable of ruling out such hypotheses. However, one of the effects of associative learning occupying the position of being the default hypothesis is that comparative psychologists have generally adopted a distinctly uncritical attitude toward the process, assuming it to be a pervasive domain-general process, capable of explaining a very wide range of seemingly complex behaviors, but which requires little cognitive sophistication. However, if Gallistel is right, this seems to have largely just been taken for granted. That is what happens when certain types of hypothesis win by default: the nature and actual explanatory power of such hypotheses receives very little critical scrutiny.

Moreover, consider the effects of *all* researchers actually abiding by the Conservative Canon – i.e., *accepting* or at least *preferring* the lowest explanation consistent with the available data in all possible areas of inquiry. This could be potentially extremely damaging, insofar as it would discourage researchers from taking seriously the idea that particular species *may* possess cognitive capacities more sophisticated than deemed necessary by an application of the Canon to the existing data. Discoveries in science often come when scientists actively pursue bold and provocative hypotheses that can't initially be demonstrated empirically. Von Frisch's famous work on the honeybee dance language provides an important example of this (Fitzpatrick 2008). The idea that honeybees actively communicate information to each other about the location and quality of foraging sites was not something that von Frisch could empirically establish until after decades of patient investigation, and there certainly were less cognitively sophisticated explanations for bee foraging behavior that didn't involve communication available throughout this period – for instance, that bees merely follow the scent given off by returning foragers. Indeed, I suspect that this remarkable communication system might not have been discovered had von

Frisch abided by the Conservative Canon and accepted the lowest explanation that was available at the beginning of his investigations.

The Restraining Canon

Given these problems with the Conservative Canon, the Restraining Canon seems much more appropriate. This canon does not state that lower explanations automatically win when they are available. Rather, it urges that we *withhold* endorsement from a higher explanation when a lower one can be offered. Initially, this seems thoroughly reasonable, and I suspect it is what many apparent advocates of the Conservative Canon really have in mind. Nonetheless, the Restraining Canon is highly problematic.

The first problem concerns the conditions under which higher explanations *can* be accepted. The strongest version of the principle would require that it be *impossible* to explain the relevant behavior in lower terms. This is clearly too strong. Scientists are almost never in a position to conclusively rule out all alternative explanations, no matter how well a series of experiments has been designed. The most one can hope for is to render alternative hypotheses implausible relative to the candidate hypothesis. Deciding between rival explanations for empirical data – especially behavioral data – is typically a matter of determining the balance of plausibility, rather than a strict process of elimination. Nonetheless, there do seem to be some researchers that employ the Canon in such a strong fashion, demanding that advocates of higher processes produce data that cannot *possibly* be interpreted in any other way (e.g., Povinelli and Vonk 2003). Such demands are both excessive and distract from what is really at stake, which is weighing the overall balance of evidence (Fitzpatrick 2009; Andrews 2015).

There is a more fundamental problem with the Restraining Canon, however. The core idea is that higher explanations ought to face the burden of proof in order to counteract our supposed bias toward cognitively sophisticated accounts of animal behavior. According to one recent defense of the Canon:

> Adherence to the canon forces one to dig deeper when designing experiments and devising theories, and, in doing so, Morgan's canon pressures comparative psychologists to produce better science.
>
> (Karin D'Arcy 2005: 197)

But why should comparative psychologists be "pressured" in only one direction? Karin D'Arcy writes as if only higher explanations can be endorsed erroneously, focusing on the tendency to project human folk psychology onto other creatures. Yet, comparative psychologists can fall prey to all sorts of inferential biases, not all of which lead to attributions of higher processes. The history of twentieth-century comparative psychology demonstrates that researchers are just as capable of accepting lower explanations without sufficient evidence. It was once widely taken for granted that all animal behavior could be explained in terms of classical or operant conditioning, not because this enjoyed direct empirical support, but because of a compulsion, motivated by spurious concerns about "anthropomorphism", to adopt the least cognitively sophisticated account of animal behavior one could imagine. These scientists *also* needed to "dig deeper" and "produce better science".

If the problem Karin D'Arcy and other advocates of the Canon are concerned with is researchers endorsing explanations of animal behavior without due attention being paid to alternatives, we can see that the asymmetry built into the Restraining Canon is quite inappropriate as a response. This is as much a problem with respect to lower explanations as higher ones; yet, the Restraining Canon places the focus only on higher explanations. Instead, the following sort of principle, which I call *Evidentialism*, would much better serve the field:

> In no case should we endorse an explanation of animal behavior in terms of cognitive process X on the basis of the available evidence if that evidence gives us no reason to prefer it to an alternative explanation in terms of a different cognitive process Y – whether this be lower *or* higher on the 'psychological scale'.
>
> (Fitzpatrick 2008: 242)

This principle urges us to *always* be mindful of alternative explanations, be these cognitively more or less sophisticated than the one that is being advanced, and only endorse a given explanation when one is able to show that that explanation, whatever it is, is better supported by the available evidence than the alternatives – "evidence", here, needn't just be behavioral evidence, but may include any information relevant to assessing the evidential status of a given psychological hypothesis.

I don't deny that advocates of higher processes sometimes fail to pay adequate attention to lower-level alternatives when accounting for the results of particular experiments. In this respect, researchers *do* need to "dig deep" and try to design experiments that can provide differential evidence for higher processes, if they are present, but we don't need the Restraining Canon to remind them to do that. As Sober (2005: 97) has put it, the only "prophylactic" we need for the kinds of inferential errors and biases that Morgan's Canon has been thought to control for is "empiricism". Crucially, Evidentialism captures whatever genuine methodological benefits can be brought with the Restraining Canon, but it doesn't enshrine the problematic asymmetry that is built into that principle, which places the focus exclusively on higher explanations. That asymmetry is both completely unjustified by the genuine concerns highlighted by advocates of the Canon and *pernicious*, insofar as it distracts away from parallel concerns about systematically underestimating the cognitive capacities of animals.

The Cautionary Canon

This leaves us with the Cautionary Canon. On this interpretation, the Canon shouldn't be seen as offering any specific methodological advice; rather, it serves to remind students of the checkered history of animal cognition research, and urges them not to make the same mistakes as their forebears. The problems I have identified with the other canons might then be seen as a product of taking the Canon out of this pedagogical context.

This is fine, as far as it goes. To some extent, the Canon has been useful as a pedagogical instrument, and Morgan should continue to be remembered as a pivotal figure in the history of comparative psychology for pointing out the errors of much early work in the field – though the tendency of modern researchers to focus exclusively on the Canon has obscured many of his key contributions (Fitzpatrick and Goodrich 2016). However, the asymmetric focus on attributions of sophisticated cognitive capacities to animals remains problematic, and the general absence of parallel cautionary exhortations about how researchers can go astray when it comes to denying the presence of sophisticated cognitive capacities in animals has, in my view, been extremely damaging to the conduct of research in comparative psychology. Hence, the key message should really be what one finds in Evidentialism. It is this, not Morgan's Canon, that should be pounded into the heads of future generations of researchers.

Note

1   Some critics have seen the very notion of a psychological scale as problematic, particularly if it is anchored (as it was in Morgan's case) to the notion of an *evolutionary* scale, where "higher" processes are taken to represent a higher stage of evolutionary development. I will not consider such concerns here, except to say that I think that modern interpretations of the Canon can be separated from an evolutionary scale, and that the notion of cognitive sophistication I have described is best understood in functional terms (Fitzpatrick 2008).

Further reading

Morgan's key statement of the Canon can be found in C. L. Morgan, *An Introduction to Comparative Psychology* (London: Walter Scott, 1894), which is widely cited but rarely read. It provides a fascinating insight into the philosophical and methodological problems facing early comparative psychologists. R. Boakes, *From Darwin to Behaviorism* (Cambridge: Cambridge University Press, 1984), and G. Radick, *The Simian Tongue* (Chicago: University of Chicago Press, 2007), are useful guides to Morgan's life and work and the historical context from which Morgan's Canon emerged. S. Shettleworth, *Fundamentals of Comparative Cognition* (Oxford: Oxford University Press, 2012), and K. Andrews, *The Animal Mind* (New York: Routledge, 2015), provide accessible introductions to current debates over the methodological problems of comparative psychology and the role accorded to Morgan's Canon in dealing with them.

References

Allen, C., and Bekoff, M. (1997) *Species of Mind: The Philosophy and Biology of Cognitive Ethology*, Cambridge, MA: MIT Press.

Andrews, K. (2015) *The Animal Mind: An Introduction to the Philosophy of Animal Cognition*, New York: Routledge.

Andrews, K., and Huss, B. (2014) "Anthropomorphism, anthropectomy, and the null hypothesis," *Biology and Philosophy* 29: 711–729.

Blumberg, M., and Wasserman, E. (1995) "Animal mind and the argument from design," *American Psychologist* 50: 133–144.

Carruthers, P. (2008) "Meta-cognition in animals: A skeptical look," *Mind & Language* 23: 58–89.

Clayton, N., and Dickinson, A. (1998) "Episodic-like memory during cache recovery by scrub jays," *Nature* 395: 272–274.

Costall, A. (1993) "How Lloyd Morgan's Canon backfired," *Journal of the History of the Behavioral Sciences* 29: 113–122.

Crystal, J. D., and Foote, A. L. (2009) "Metacognition in animals," *Comparative Cognition and Behavior Reviews* 4: 1–16.

de Waal, F. (1999) "Anthropomorphism and anthropodenial: Consistency in our thinking about humans and other animals," *Philosophical Topics* 27: 255–280.

Dwyer, D. M., and Burgess, K. (2011) "Rational account of animal behavior? Lessons from C. Lloyd Morgan's Canon," *International Journal of Comparative Psychology* 24: 349–364.

Fitzpatrick, S. (2008) "Doing away with Morgan's Canon," *Mind & Language* 23: 224–246.

———— (2009) "The primate mindreading controversy: A case study in simplicity and methodology in animal psychology," in R. Lurz (ed.) *The Philosophy of Animal Minds*, New York: Cambridge University Press.

———— (2015) "Nativism, empiricism, and Ockham's Razor," *Erkenntnis* 80: 895–922.

Fitzpatrick, S., and Goodrich, G. (2016) "Building a science of animal minds: Lloyd Morgan, experimentation, and Morgan's Canon," *Journal of the History of Biology*. doi: 10.1007/s10739-016-9451-x

Gallistel, R. (2000) "The replacement of general-purpose learning models with adaptively specialized learning modules," in M. Gazzaniga (ed.) *The New Cognitive Neurosciences*, Cambridge, MA: MIT Press.

Griffith, C. R. (1943) *Principles of Systematic Psychology*, Urbana, IL: University of Illinois Press.

Karin-D'Arcy, M. R. (2005) "The modern role of Morgan's Canon in comparative psychology," *International Journal of Comparative Psychology* 18: 179–201.

Keeley, B. (2004) "Anthropomorphism, primatomorphism, mammalomorphism: Understanding cross-species comparisons," *Biology and Philosophy* 19: 521–540.

Manning, A., and Dawkins, M. S. (1998) *An Introduction to Animal Behavior* (5th Edition), Cambridge: Cambridge University Press.

Meketa, I. (2014) "A critique of the principle of cognitive simplicity in comparative cognition," *Biology and Philosophy* 29: 731–745.

Morgan, C. L. (1894) *An Introduction to Comparative Psychology*, London: Walter Scott.

——— (1903) *An Introduction to Comparative Psychology* (2nd Edition), London: Walter Scott.

Povinelli, D., and Vonk, J. (2003) "Chimpanzee minds: Suspiciously human?" *Trends in Cognitive Sciences* 7: 157–160.

Shettleworth, S. (2012) *Fundamentals of Comparative Cognition*, Oxford: Oxford University Press.

Sober, E. (1994) "Let's razor Ockham's Razor," in E. Sober (ed.) *From a Biological Point of View*, Cambridge: Cambridge University Press.

——— (1998) "Morgan's Cannon," in D. Cummins and C. Allen (eds.) *The Evolution of Mind*, Oxford: Oxford University Press.

——— (2005) "Comparative psychology meets evolutionary biology: Morgan's Canon and cladistic parsimony," in L. Daston and G. Mitman (eds.) *Thinking With Animals: New Perspectives on Anthropomorphism*, New York: Columbia University Press.

——— (2015) *Ockham's Razors: A Users Manual*, Cambridge: Cambridge University Press.

Starzak, T. (2016) "Interpretations without justification: A general argument against Morgan's Canon," *Synthese*. doi: 10.1007/s11229-016-1013-4

Thomas, R. K. (1998) "Lloyd Morgan's Canon," in G. Greenberg and M. Haraway (eds.) *Comparative Psychology: A Handbook*, New York: Garland.

van Rooijen, J. (2010) "Do dogs and bees possess a 'theory of mind'?" *Animal Behaviour* 79: e9–e8.

Wasserman, E., and Zentall, T. R. (2006) "Comparative cognition: A natural science approach to the study of animal intelligence," in E. Wasserman and T. R. Zentall (eds.) *Comparative Cognition*, New York: Oxford University Press.

Wynne, C. (2007) "What are animals? Why anthropomorphism is still not a scientific approach to behavior," *Comparative Cognition and Behavior Reviews* 2: 125–135.

43

A BRIDGE TOO FAR? INFERENCE AND EXTRAPOLATION FROM MODEL ORGANISMS IN NEUROSCIENCE

David Michael Kaplan

1 Introduction

Like many other biological sciences, research in modern experimental neuroscience is heavily reliant on a range of model organisms, including but not limited to rats, mice, monkeys, birds, fish, and insects. The model organism approach is extremely well established in contemporary neuroscience as a means to investigate the nature of mind and brain. According to one recent estimate, studies involving nonhuman animals account for more than half of all the research undertaken (Manger et al. 2008). Even more strikingly, approximately 40% of all studies focus on just two model organisms that are quite evolutionarily distant from humans – the rat and the mouse (primarily the species *Rattus norvegicus* and *Mus musculus*) (Manger et al. 2008; Keifer and Summers 2016). Given that two central goals of neuroscience are arguably to: understand the distinctive structure and function of the *human* brain; and develop therapies for *human* brain diseases such as Alzheimer's, Huntington's, and amyotrophic lateral sclerosis, among others, a fundamental question naturally arises concerning what can be learned indirectly about humans by studying the brains and nervous systems of nonhuman animals.

Neuroscientists frequently make inferences about the human brain indirectly by studying the nervous systems of nonhuman species (Schaffner 2001; Preuss 1995). In each case, empirical findings about some causal process or mechanism in the model organism are used to draw conclusions about that same process or mechanism in another species (typically humans) or set of species. This kind of inference is often called *extrapolation* (Steel 2008). Although the label is not intended in the strict mathematical sense – of estimating the value (or set of values) of a variable beyond its observed range – both involve a degree of inferential uncertainty. But why is extrapolation inherently risky? As others have noted (Burian 1993; Steel 2008), extrapolation would be trivial if the model organism and target species were perfectly similar. Yet it is inevitable that there will be some differences between different species, especially when separated by millions of years of evolution. Therefore, the challenge is to articulate how it is possible to extrapolate reliably from model to target even when differences are known to be present (Steel 2008).

In this chapter, I address the widespread use and justification of model organisms in neuroscience with a focus on the problem of extrapolation. The model organism approach promises to provide specific insights into the workings of the human brain and reveal general principles of neural organization and function. Yet the ability to deliver on these promises depends on the extent to which the model organisms studied are representative of humans and other species or taxa beyond themselves. If model organisms are carefully selected and the assumption of representativeness holds, the approach provides a suitable platform for generalizing or extrapolating findings to humans and other organisms. In other words, there is a real but bridgeable inferential gap. As will be discussed in detail in this chapter, the criteria by which neuroscientists select model organisms are not typically optimized for representativeness, and instead reflect biases of convenience and convention. Consequently, many studies do not automatically provide a strong basis for extrapolation to humans or other organisms – it is an inferential bridge too far. After highlighting the main features and limitations of the model organism approach in contemporary neuroscience, I describe a different approach – an evolutionary-comparative approach – which, although less widespread, does provide a sound basis for extrapolating research findings from model organisms.

2 What is a model organism?

A model organism may be defined as any species primarily investigated to yield specific insights into the workings of another species or general mechanisms common to many or all living things (Ankeny and Leonelli 2011). Importantly, for model organisms to play their intended role, they must be representative of other species beyond themselves. This is what makes them appropriate and effective experimental surrogates or proxies for the target species (or target set of species). The fact that model organisms serve in this kind of stand-in role is also what justifies the label "model", since theoretical models in science are commonly understood to do precisely that (Ankeny and Leonelli 2011; Frigg and Hartmann 2017; Weisberg 2013). But this is a matter of ongoing debate, as others reject this identification (e.g., Levy and Currie 2014).

Model organisms can vary along two dimensions (Ankeny and Leonelli 2011). First, model organisms can vary in terms of the specific phenomenon they are used to investigate (the "representational target"). For example, the squid was used as a model organism to study the phenomenon of action potential generation (Hodgkin and Huxley 1952), and the rabbit was selected to study long-term potentiation (Lømo 2003). The second dimension characterizes how widely the research findings derived from a given model organism can be projected or extrapolated to a wider group of organisms (the "representational scope"). The ability to generalize findings to other organisms is the ultimate motivation behind work with model organisms, and representational scope captures the extent to which model organisms are, in fact, representative of other taxa. At one end of the spectrum, representational scope can be maximally narrow such that findings extend only to a single species, such as humans (e.g., rat models of human neurodegenerative diseases, such as Parkinson's). At the other end of the spectrum, representational scope can be maximally wide, so that findings from the model organism extend to all biological organisms. Although it is difficult to identify examples that are known to be perfectly universal, there are many that approximate this limit. For example, the bacterium *Streptomyces lividans* was used to investigate the structure of the potassium channel underlying selective potassium conduction (Doyle et al. 1998). In a parallel study, the same potassium channel was shown to be structurally conserved across prokaryote and eukaryote domains, demonstrating its wide representational scope (MacKinnon et al. 1998). Finally, scope can be intermediate such that findings cover some but not all living things, such as all and only mammals or all and only vertebrates.

Although Ankeny and Leonelli (2011) do not highlight the point, these two dimensions are interdependent. Specifically, one's choice of representational target automatically constrains representational scope. For example, if the representational target for a study is an evolutionarily "late" phenomenon such as vocal learning, this restricts how widely any subsequent findings will generalize from the model organism, because many species will simply lack the behavioral capacity in question. By contrast, if the representational target is a phenomenon such as ionic selectivity in potassium channels, which appears to be highly conserved across organisms, then representational scope will be relatively wide.

3 Why study model organisms in neuroscience?

Model organisms are studied for two main reasons. First, many of the central experimental methods in neuroscience involve highly invasive or terminal procedures and therefore cannot ethically be employed on humans. Indeed, some have argued that this makes them equally impermissible when used in nonhuman animals (Levy 2012; LaFollette and Shanks 1997). But this is a highly controversial debate that is outside the scope of the present discussion. Second, many model organisms have simpler nervous systems that are more experimentally tractable than the human brain (Marder 2002; Olsen and Wilson 2008; Haberkern and Jayaraman 2016). The human brain presents serious scientific and technical challenges due to the sheer number of neurons (~86 billion) and synaptic connections involved (~100 trillion). In light of this daunting complexity, researchers often retreat to the study of simpler nervous systems, such as those of invertebrates with far more tractable and stereotyped circuitry, in the hopes that these investigations will yield highly general principles of neural organization and function – which can then be applied to more complex nervous systems, including those of humans.

4 Model organism selection in biology: some initial lessons

It is illuminating to consider first how model organisms are selected in other more established areas of biology, such as genetics and developmental biology. In these fields, model organisms are often chosen based on convenience, cost, experimental tractability, or some combination of these. For example, Thomas Morgan Hunt and other founders of modern genetics selected the fruit fly (*Drosophila melanogaster*) primarily because it is cheap to raise in the lab and has short generation times (Allen 1975). It was also desirable to early geneticists because of its experimental tractability, since it possesses relatively few chromosomes (four pairs), and observable mutations could easily be induced with the methods available at the time (Kohler 1994). Importantly, the degree to which a given organism is experimentally tractable reflects the methods and state of theoretical knowledge available at a given time. For example, what counts as a model organism with experimentally tractable genetics has changed considerably with the genomic revolution and the emergence of sequencing and other tools.

Similar considerations drove the selection of the roundworm (*Caenorhabditis elegans*) as the model organism of choice in molecular and developmental biology. Nobel Prize-winning molecular biologist Sydney Brenner recounts searching through zoology textbooks to identify candidate model organisms satisfying a checklist of explicit criteria, including having a rapid life cycle; a tractable reproductive cycle and genome; and a small body size so that structures of interest would fit under an electron microscope objective (Ankeny 2001). Analogous considerations underlie the introduction of inbred mouse lines in genetics (Rader 2004).

This basic pattern of selecting model organisms based on their convenience and experimental tractability has been elevated into something of a guiding principle in experimental biology (Krebs 1975). Named after August Krogh, the Nobel-winning physiologist who expressed the idea in a lecture many decades ago, Krogh's principle states that "for a large number of problems there will be some animal of choice, or a few such animals, on which it can be most conveniently studied" (Krogh 1929: 202). Importantly, as the principle implies, precisely which organisms will turn out to be "most convenient" depends both on the specific research question being asked or phenomenon being investigated (the representational target), and the experimental methods available to carry out the study (Burian 1993). As the above examples indicate, this principle codifies a basic working assumption in contemporary experimental biology.

5 Model organism selection in neuroscience

Unsurprisingly, the adoption of particular species as model organisms in experimental neuroscience also reflects similar considerations. For example, the squid (*Loligo forbese*) was selected as an ideal experimental preparation to investigate action potential generation and propagation (Hodgkin and Huxley 1952). Tissue from *Loligo* axons remains physiologically responsive for many hours, making it highly convenient for extensive experimentation. But the main reason the squid axon was chosen was because of its size, which is among the largest known in the animal kingdom (Hodgkin 1976). This made it tractable to perform critical intracellular recordings of the membrane potential without damaging the cell. Given the state of intracellular recording techniques available at the time, this goal would have been out of reach in smaller experimental systems.

For similar reasons, early groundbreaking work on neural excitation and inhibition was carried out in the lobster and crayfish, and the choice of organisms was firmly grounded in considerations of experimental tractability. In the introduction to an early paper, Kuffler writes: "[t]he greatest advantage of the present preparation lies in its accessibility, since all cellular components can be isolated and visually observed" (Eyzaguirre and Kuffler 1955: 87). Kuffler chose the invertebrate preparation because it was well suited to investigate the experimental questions about neural signalling he was addressing. Many other studies involving different invertebrates have yielded major insights in neuroscience largely because these organisms have tractable nervous systems that are readily functionally and structurally dissected (Marder 2002).

Although vertebrates and especially mammals are generally less convenient to work with than invertebrates – having longer generation times, more demanding housing requirements, higher costs to maintain, increased ethical concerns, etc. – sometimes the phenomena neuroscientists seek to understand are simply absent or difficult to discern in lower-order taxa. As described above, there is no invertebrate model for vocalization learning. Therefore, vertebrates and especially other mammals with more broadly similar nervous systems to humans and similar behavioral and cognitive capacities are necessary for many of the research questions neuroscientists are trying to answer (e.g., what is the neural basis of language, semantic memory, etc.).

As a general rule, for any given phenomenon, neuroscientists will try to study it in the simplest organism known to exhibit that phenomenon. Indeed, this is likely why most neuroscience research involving mammals uses the mouse or rat model whenever possible (Manger et al. 2008), and only rarely involves nonhuman primates. Indeed, this is demonstrated by the current trend towards using mice and rats to study complex phenomena traditionally investigated in primates, primarily because they have smaller, more experimentally tractable nervous systems. In addition, powerful new methods, including optogenetics, are currently available in rodents, but these methods (at least so far) have proven less reliable in primates (Diester et al. 2011).

6 Assessing the prospects for extrapolation

Given this haphazard manner in which model organisms are typically selected in neuroscience, what are the prospects for extrapolating findings to other organisms, including humans? One worrisome fact is that major failures of extrapolation routinely occur (e.g., Schnabel 2008). Yet many researchers working with model organisms have failed to take notice, leaving a broad consensus about the representativeness of model organisms largely unshaken. Neuroscientists frequently assume that research involving model organisms can reveal highly general, even universal, insights into the structure and function of all nervous systems. For example, neurobiologist Eve Marder claims that invertebrates such as crustaceans "provide ideal platforms for the study of fundamental problems in neuroscience . . . [and] to uncover principles that are general to all nervous systems" (2002: 318). Surprisingly, she provides no evidence in support of this claim, but instead seems to assume a degree of similarity between the model organism and the intended target of the extrapolation that ensures the extrapolation will go through and general principles can be revealed. These assumptions appear to be widely embraced (e.g., Churchland and Lisberger 2015; Ahrens and Engert 2015; Nussbaum and Beenhakker 2002). For instance, many researchers studying mammalian model organisms (e.g., rodents or nonhuman primates) often simply assume that all mammalian brains are highly similar, and that the cerebral cortex in particular is essentially invariant in its internal organization across species (Rockel et al. 1980; Preuss 1995, 2000, 2010). This assumption that brain evolution was highly conservative across mammals justifies the liberal investigation of any particular mammalian species as broadly representative of the class, including humans. Indeed, Logan (2002: 358) argues that the presumption "that nature might not be so diverse after all" combined with an "a priori expectation of generality" are hallmark commitments of the model organism approach in biology more generally. So it should come as little surprise that neuroscientists also frequently accept these assumptions.

Importantly, this way of thinking was not always prevalent. For example, even though the use of *Drosophila* soon came to dominate research, early investigations of the mechanisms of inheritance in classical genetics involved a large variety of organisms (Davis 2004). And it was only in virtue of appreciating how the rules of inheritance were observed across many organisms that the generality of the findings from any particular experimental organism were established (Davis 2004). Accordingly, generality is an empirical conclusion to be reached by examining data from many species, and the appropriateness of a given model organism for extrapolation is an empirical hypothesis that must be supported by evidence (Logan 2002; Steel 2008). According to this strategy, a causal relationship or mechanism found in a given model organism is inferred to hold approximately in the target system in proportion to the available empirical evidence (Steel 2008).

In treating the representational scope of model organisms as a default or a priori assumption rather than an empirically supported conclusion, these researchers adopt what Steel (2008) refers to as the strategy of "simple induction": infer that a causal relationship or mechanism found in the model organism holds more or less approximately in other related systems unless there is some reason to suppose otherwise. Simple induction is problematic because it can frequently lead to mistaken extrapolations and provides no guidance when there is reason to suspect the extrapolation might be incorrect (Steel 2008). But why think this is inferentially precarious in neuroscience? The general worry lies in the diversifying nature of evolutionary change, which poses a challenge for freely extrapolating findings from one species to the next. This concern is well expressed by Burian (1993):

> Evolution is a branching process in which each organism (each lineage, each species) has distinct characters, differing in some ways at least from the organisms (lineages, species) from which it stemmed . . . At (virtually?) all levels of the biological world – including the biochemical – it is an open question how general the findings produced by the use of a particular organism are.
>
> (Burian 1993: 365)

In light of considerations of this sort, a growing number of scientists and philosophers have started to emphasize the importance of evolutionary considerations when choosing model organisms and extrapolating from them.

7 Towards an evolutionary-comparative approach in neuroscience

Given evolution's proximity to other areas of biology, the lack of a role for information about evolution in shaping model organism choice in neuroscience is puzzling. If the goal of studying model organisms is to provide a platform for generalizing to other organisms, including humans, then surely information about the phylogenetic relationship between the model organism and the target species must guide selection (Preuss 1995, 2000, 2009, 2010; Hedges 2002). Strikingly, neuroscience is not alone in this regard; evolution is also neglected in many areas of biology (Bolker 1995, 2012). Discussing the situation in developmental biology, Bolker argues that "[p]hylogeny is rarely or never a factor in the choice of model systems" (1995: 453), and she highlights how biologists will sometimes even actively avoid species known to occupy critical branch points or nodes in the phylogenetic tree if they are difficult to work with experimentally (Bolker 1995: 453).

Adopting an evolutionary-comparative approach offers a unifying framework in which to understand the similarities and differences among organisms. Information about interspecies similarities reflecting the phylogenetic relationship between model organism and target species (i.e., homologies) can help to empirically ground extrapolation. Similarities are required because if the two species differed in every respect, nothing could be learned about one by studying the other. And common evolutionary descent is a major source of similarities between species that can underwrite the reliability of extrapolation. As Marcel Weber puts it:

> The usefulness of model organisms crucially depends on the extent to which the mechanisms in question are *phylogenetically conserved*. Any extrapolations from model organisms are only reliable to the extent that the mechanisms under study have the same evolutionary origin in the model organism and in humans.

> (Weber 2004: 181, author's emphasis)

Consequently, information about its evolutionary history and phylogenetic relationship to other species can provide crucial guidance to help ensure the representativeness of a model organism.

The evolutionary-comparative approach also offers a useful perspective on, and appreciation of, interspecies differences. Whereas the model organism approach presumes similarities between the brains of different species (and minimizes differences), the evolutionary-comparative approach embraces the diversity among species produced through evolutionary change. Specifically, the nervous system of every potential model organism is understood as reflecting its own unique evolutionary history, which makes it likely to vary in important respects from the human brain.

From this perspective, is neuroscience investigating the right model organisms? First, let us reconsider the widespread rodent model. As indicated above, the last common ancestor between rats and mice and humans was approximately 90 million years ago (Figure 43.1). This is a considerable amount of time for independent brain evolution to occur. Given that the structural (molecular, cellular, and regional) organization of mammalian brains provides a rich platform of variation on which natural selection can operate, it is probable that changes in brain

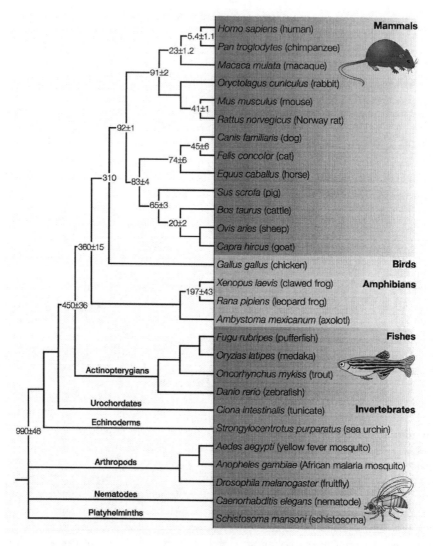

Figure 43.1 Phylogeny of animals based on genomic data. Relationships and divergence times (millions of years ago (MYA) ± one standard error) for a selection of model organisms are shown.

Source: Hedges 2002

organization have independently accumulated in human and rodent lineages. Although there are many known similarities in brain organization (including cortical organization) between rats and mice and other mammals, including humans, many important differences are also known (Preuss 2000). This presents an obvious challenge for extrapolation and raises important questions about whether the heavy focus on the rat and mouse is justified. It also elicits more general concerns about whether the model organism approach in neuroscience offers a promising way to gain insights into the workings of the human brain and discover general principles of nervous system structure and function.

Next, consider the use of nonhuman primates as model organisms. Humans and macaques (the dominant primate species studied in neuroscience) diverged over 20 million years ago, and therefore have about 40 million years of cumulative independent evolution between them (Figure 43.1). The standard view in neuroscience is that findings derived from the macaques readily transfer to humans since their brains are largely the same and share the same general design. But the macaque brain cannot simply be viewed as a scaled-down, ancestral version of the human brain (Herculano-Houzel 2012; Rilling 2006), since both humans and macaques have evolved in response to different selective environments in the time since they shared a common ancestor. This implies that caution should be exercised in extrapolating from monkeys to humans. Similar cautionary notes can be sounded for many other model organisms widely used in neuroscience today.

The evolutionary-comparative approach does more than raise critical challenges for many standard model organisms; it also helps refine the selection of model organisms. This is best illustrated by example. As mentioned earlier, long-term potentiation (LTP) and its role in memory was initially discovered in rabbits and then extensively studied in rodents (Lømo 2003). Of course, the ultimate goal of these studies was to infer something about the role of LTP in human memory. Yet these model organisms were selected for study largely because of their convenience and availability, without any detailed examination of their phylogenetic relationships to humans, and any conclusions drawn about humans were based on the presumed similarity between rabbit, rodent, and human brains (Section 6). But if the goal is to extrapolate these findings to humans, close attention must be paid to phylogeny, and a critical gap to fill is therefore to demonstrate LTP in a closely related nonhuman primate species, such as the macaque. Eventually, such studies were carried out in the macaque hippocampus, and LTP was confirmed to be similar to what was previously reported in rodents (Urban et al. 1996).

If, by contrast, the objective is to establish LTP as a general principle of memory storage that extends beyond mammalian brains, demonstrating its evolutionarily conserved role across a wide range of animal lineages is critical (Figure 43.1). Along these lines, LTP has recently been demonstrated in invertebrates like *Aplysia* (Lin and Glanzman 1994). Generally speaking, understanding which characteristics of model organisms are common to other species, and determining exactly how widespread any particular characteristic is (e.g., whether it is shared by all mammals, all vertebrates, or all animals), requires detailed comparative evidence from a number of other carefully selected species and can never be established by investigating the model organism alone. The broader lesson here is that since neuroscientists cannot study every single species, model organism selection must be optimized by paying close attention to evolutionary history. Doing so promises to improve the representativeness of the model organisms that are chosen in neuroscience, which in turn stands to improve the reliability of extrapolating findings to humans and other species.

8 Conclusion

The model organism approach affords a potentially promising way to gain insights into the workings of the human brain and discover general principles of nervous system structure and function. Yet the power of this approach to reveal such insights and principles depends on the extent to which the selected model organisms are representative of other taxa beyond themselves. Therefore, when the goal is to generalize or extrapolate findings based on model organisms to other species, including humans, the choice of model organisms must be guided by more than mere convenience and convention. The evolutionary-comparative approach provides additional phylogenetic criteria for selecting model organisms that are optimized for representativeness. Consequently, it provides a more solid foundation for extrapolating from model organisms than the traditional convenience- and experimental tractability-based approach to model organism selection which remains widespread in neuroscience. With the increasing availability of genomic data and sophisticated tools for comparative analysis and phylogenetic reconstruction, the time is right to reconnect neuroscience with its evolutionary biological roots. One natural place to start this process is with the choice of model organisms. Careful consideration of a candidate model organism's evolutionary history – especially its phylogenetic relationships to humans and a range of other species – can improve its overall representativeness, which can in turn improve the reliability of extrapolation. Paraphrasing the famous words of the eminent biologist Theodosius Dobzhansky (1973): Nothing in neuroscience – including how findings are extrapolated from one species to another – makes sense except in the light of evolution.

References

Ahrens, M. B., and Engert, F., 2015. Large-scale imaging in small brains. *Current Opinion in Neurobiology* 32, 78–86.

Allen, G. E., 1975. The introduction of Drosophila into the study of heredity and evolution: 1900–1910. *Isis* 66, 322–333.

Ankeny, R. A., 2001. The natural history of Caenorhabditis elegans research. *Nature Reviews Genetics* 2, 474–479.

Ankeny, R. A., and Leonelli, S., 2011. What's so special about model organisms? *Studies in History and Philosophy of Science Part A* 42, 313–323.

Bolker, J. A., 1995. Model systems in developmental biology. *BioEssays* 17, 451–455.

Bolker, J., 2012. Model organisms: There's more to life than rats and flies. *Nature* 491, 31–33.

Burian, R. M., 1993. How the choice of experimental organism matters: Epistemological reflections on an aspect of biological practice. *Journal of the History of Biology* 26, 351–367.

Churchland, A., and Lisberger, S., 2015. Contributions from different model organisms to brain research: Introduction. *Neuroscience* 296, 1–2.

Davis, R. H., 2004. The age of model organisms. *Nature Reviews Genetics* 5, 69–76.

Diester, I., Kaufman, M. T., Mogri, M., Pashaie, R., Goo, W., Yizhar, O., Ramakrishnan, C., Deisseroth, K., and Shenoy, K. V., 2011. An optogenetic toolbox designed for primates. *Nature Neuroscience* 14, 387–397.

Dobzhansky, T., 1973. Nothing in biology makes sense except in the light of evolution. *The American Biology Teacher* 35, 125–129, March.

Doyle, D. A., Cabral, J. M., Pfuetzner, R. A., Kuo, A., Gulbis, J. M., Cohen, S. L., Chait, B. T., and MacKinnon, R., 1998. The structure of the potassium channel: Molecular basis of K+ conduction and selectivity. *Science* 280, 69–77.

Eyzaguirre, C., and Kuffler, S. W., 1955. Processes of excitation in the dendrites and in the soma of single isolated sensory nerve cells of the lobster and crayfish. *The Journal of General Physiology* 39, 87–119.

Frigg, R., and Hartmann, S., 2017. Models in science. In Zalta, E. N. (ed.), *The Stanford Encyclopedia of Philosophy* (Spring 2017 Edition). https://plato.stanford.edu/archives/spr2017/entries/models-science/

Haberkern, H., and Jayaraman, V., 2016. Studying small brains to understand the building blocks of cognition. *Current Opinion in Neurobiology* 37, 59–65.

Hedges, S. B., 2002. The origin and evolution of model organisms. *Nature Reviews Genetics* 3, 838–849.

Herculano-Houzel, S., 2012. The remarkable, yet not extraordinary, human brain as a scaled-up primate brain and its associated cost. *Proceedings of the National Academy of Sciences* 109, 10661–10668.

Hodgkin, A. L., 1976. Chance and design in electrophysiology: An informal account of certain experiments on nerve carried out between 1934 and 1952. *The Journal of Physiology* 263, 1.

Hodgkin, A. L., and Huxley, A. F., 1952. A quantitative description of membrane current and its application to conduction and excitation in nerve. *The Journal of Physiology* 117, 500.

Keifer, J., and Summers, C. H., 2016. Putting the "biology" back into "neurobiology": The strength of diversity in animal model systems for neuroscience research. *Frontiers in Systems Neuroscience* 10: 69. Published online Aug. 22, 2016. doi: 10.3389/fnsys.2016.00069

Kohler, R. E., 1994. *Lords of the fly: Drosophila genetics and the experimental life*. Chicago: University of Chicago Press.

Krebs, H. A., 1975. The August Krogh principle: "For many problems there is an animal on which it can be most conveniently studied." *Journal of Experimental Zoology* 194, 221–226.

Krogh, A., 1929. The progress of physiology. *Science* 70(1809), 200–204.

LaFollette, H., and Shanks, N., 1997. *Brute science: Dilemmas of animal experimentation*. London: Routledge.

Levy, A., and Currie, A., 2014. Model organisms are not (theoretical) models. *The British Journal for the Philosophy of Science* 66(2).

Levy, N., 2012. The use of animal as models: Ethical considerations. *International Journal of Stroke* 7, 440–442.

Lin, X. Y., and Glanzman, D. L., 1994. Long-term potentiation of Aplysia sensorimotor synapses in cell culture: Regulation by postsynaptic voltage. *Proceedings of the Royal Society of London B: Biological Sciences* 255, 113–118.

Logan, C. A., 2002. Before there were standards: The role of test animals in the production of empirical generality in physiology. *Journal of the History of Biology* 35, 329–363.

Lømo, T., 2003. The discovery of long-term potentiation. *Philosophical Transactions of the Royal Society of London B: Biological Sciences* 358, 617–620.

MacKinnon, R., Cohen, S. L., Kuo, A., Lee, A., and Chait, B. T., 1998. Structural conservation in prokaryotic and eukaryotic potassium channels. *Science* 280, 106–109.

Manger, P., Cort, J., Ebrahim, N., Goodman, A., Henning, J., Karolia, M., Rodrigues, S.-L., and Strkalj, G., 2008. Is 21st century neuroscience too focussed on the rat/mouse model of brain function and dysfunction? *Frontiers in Neuroanatomy* 2, 5.

Marder, E., 2002. Non-mammalian models for studying neural development and function. *Nature* 417, 318–321.

Olsen, S. R., and Wilson, R. I., 2008. Cracking neural circuits in a tiny brain: New approaches for understanding the neural circuitry of Drosophila. *Trends in Neurosciences* 31, 512–520.

Preuss, T. M., 1995. The argument from animals to humans in cognitive neuroscience. In Gazzaniga, M. S. (ed.), *The Cognitive Neurosciences* (1st edition), pp. 1227–1241. Cambridge, MA: MIT Press.

Preuss, T. M., 2000. Taking the measure of diversity: Comparative alternatives to the model-animal paradigm in cortical neuroscience. *Brain, Behavior and Evolution* 55, 287–299.

Preuss, T. M., 2009. The cognitive neuroscience of human uniqueness. In Gazzaniga, M. S. (ed.), *The Cognitive Neurosciences* (4th edition). Cambridge, MA: MIT Press, 49–64.

Preuss, T. M., 2010. Reinventing primate neuroscience for the twenty-first century. *Primate* Neuroethology (Eds. M. L. Platt and Ghazanfar, A. A.), Oxford: Oxford University Press, 422–454.

Rader, K. A., 2004. *Making mice: Standardizing animals for American biomedical research, 1900–1955*. Princeton, NJ: Princeton University Press.

Rilling, J. K., 2006. Human and nonhuman primate brains: Are they allometrically scaled versions of the same design? *Evolutionary Anthropology* 15, 65–77.

Rockel, A. J., Hiorns, R. W., and Powell, T. P., 1980. The basic uniformity in structure of the neocortex. *Brain* 103, 221–244.

Schaffner, K. F., 2001. Extrapolation from animal models. In McLaughlin, P., Machamer, P., and Grush, R. (eds.), *Theory and method in the neurosciences*, pp. 200-230. Pittsburgh: Pittsburgh University Press.

Schnabel, J., 2008. Neuroscience: Standard model. *Nature News* 454, 682–685.

Steel, D., 2008. *Across the boundaries: Extrapolation in biology and social science*. Oxford: Oxford University Press.

Urban, N. N., Henze, D. A., Lewis, D. A., and Barrionuevo, G., 1996. Properties of LTP induction in the CA3 region of the primate hippocampus. *Learning & Memory* 3, 86–95.

Weber, M., 2004. *Philosophy of experimental biology*. Cambridge: Cambridge University Press.

Weisberg, M., 2013. *Simulation and similarity: Using models to understand the world*. Oxford: Oxford University Press.

PART VIII

Ethics

44

ANIMALS AND ETHICS, AGENTS AND PATIENTS

Dale Jamieson

The topic of animals and ethics existed only around the margins of philosophical and scientific discourse until the second half of the twentieth century. Classical philosophers, such as Aristotle, and moderns such as Kant and Bentham, briefly discussed what we owe animals, but their views were consequences of their broader philosophical outlooks rather than the results of focused investigation. (For a somewhat different view, see Sorabji 1993.) Since animals were ubiquitous in daily life and central to food production and transportation in this period, it is surprising how invisible they were as independent objects of philosophical interest and moral concern.

There were exceptions to the neglect of animals. In the fourth century CE, Porphyry wrote powerfully on behalf of vegetarianism, and during the Renaissance the sixteenth-century philosopher Montaigne argued brilliantly against human exceptionalism. Animals edged further onto the stage in the writings of eighteenth-century Enlightenment philosophers such as Voltaire and Rousseau, but it was only with the publication of Charles Darwin's *Origin of Species* in 1859, and especially his *Descent of Man* in 1871, that the foundation was established for a fundamentally different way of regarding animals. Humans could now be seen as continuous with other animals in ways that much of the philosophical tradition had obscured.

In the second half of the nineteenth century, animal cruelty became a concern throughout much of Europe. In 1876, the United Kingdom became the first country to pass an animal cruelty law regulating animal experimentation. In 1892, Henry Salt published *Animals' Rights: Considered in Relation to Social Progress*, as good a defense of animal rights as has ever been published. In the second half of the twentieth century, the rise of factory farming brought questions about our treatment of animals to widespread public view. Ruth Harrison's 1964 *Animal Machines* (with a foreword by Rachel Carson) was extremely influential, and Brigid Brophy's cantankerous 1965 essay "The Rights of Animals," published in the *Sunday Times*, argued against vivisection, in favor of vegetarianism, and drew an analogy between the way we treat animals and human slavery. These strands of concern came together with a powerful philosophical perspective in Peter Singer's 1974 *Animal Liberation*, a book that dramatically changed the discussion of ethics and animals.

In the more than forty years since the publication of *Animal Liberation*, the philosophical landscape has changed appreciably. Animals are no longer invisible and the subject of "animal ethics" has been "normalized," at least to some extent. While top journals are still relatively reluctant to publish on these topics, most leading moral philosophers feel compelled to stake out some sort of position regarding animals.

The most profound shift over the last forty years has been the shrinking of the distance between normal humans and other animals with respect to agency. This shift has had consequences both for particular normative views, and also for which areas of concern are regarded as most salient.

Agents and patients

Published just eight years after *Animal Liberation*, Tom Regan's 1983 *The Case for Animal Rights* was the second landmark work on ethics and animals published in the latter half of the twentieth century. Central to Regan's theory is the distinction between moral agents and moral patients.[1] A necessary condition for being a moral agent, according to Regan, is being autonomous in the "Kantian sense." Moral agents

> are individuals who have a variety of sophisticated abilities, including . . . the ability to bring impartial moral principles to bear on the determination of what . . . morally ought to be done . . . and to freely choose . . . to act as morality . . . requires. Because moral agents have these abilities, it is fair to hold them morally accountable.
>
> (pp. 151–152)

Regan thinks that it is "highly unlikely that any animal is autonomous in the Kantian sense" (p. 84), so therefore it is highly unlikely that any animal is a moral agent. Normal adult humans are moral agents, but some humans are not (e.g., "human infants, young children, and the mentally deranged or enfeebled of all ages" p. 153). They, like "normal mammalian animals aged one year or more" are moral patients.

Moral patients are beings

> who have desires and beliefs, who perceive, remember, and can act intentionally, who have a sense of the future, including their own future (i.e., are self-aware or self-conscious), who have an emotional life, who have a psychophysical identity over time, who have a kind of autonomy (namely, preference-autonomy), and who have an experiential welfare.
>
> (p. 153)

Regan recognizes a second class of moral patients who are conscious, sentient, and possess other cognitive states such as belief and memory, but are not self-aware or self-conscious. Moral patients of whatever type

> lack the prerequisites that would enable them to control their own behavior in ways that would make them morally accountable. . . . A moral patient lacks the ability to formulate, let alone to bear, moral principles in deliberating about which one among a number of possible acts it would be right or proper to perform.
>
> (p. 152)

Regan's categorical distinction between moral agents and moral patients is in some ways intuitive, and it helps him make one of the major points of his book and also simplifies the moral landscape. At the time Regan was writing, the Kantian-inspired view that only those who can respect rights can have rights was extremely influential. Regan was eager to reject this view, and the distinction between moral agents and moral patients was part of the conceptual machinery that allowed him to do so. Some humans and animals have rights in virtue of being moral patients, even though they cannot respect the rights of others (they are not moral agents). This distinction also gave Regan the resources to block a common argument against vegetarianism, perhaps most charmingly formulated by the eighteenth-century polymath, Benjamin Franklin.

> [I]n my first voyage from Boston, being becalmed off Block Island, our people set about catching cod, and hauled up a great many. Hitherto I had stuck to my resolution of not eating animal food, and on this occasion I considered, with my master Tryon, the taking every fish as a kind of unprovoked murder, since none of them had or ever could do us any injury that might justify the slaughter. All this seemed very reasonable. But I had formerly been a great lover of fish, and when this came hot out of the frying-pan, it smelt admirably well. I balanced some time between principle and inclination, till I recollected that, when the fish were opened, I saw smaller fish taken out of their stomachs. Then thought I, "If you eat one another, I don't see why we mayn't eat you."
>
> (Franklin 1903; 2008, p. 51)

Franklin's response is no good at all, according to Regan: Franklin is a moral agent who is accountable for his actions; the cod with fish in its belly is a moral patient and not accountable for its actions. Only agents like us are accountable for what we do. The vast suffering wreaked by nature and animals is beyond the reach of moral accountability.

Despite its apparent intuitiveness, Regan's criteria for being a moral agent involve a set of very sophisticated abilities, and it is not clear what counts as evidence for having these abilities short of manifesting them in recognizable ways. Suppose that we agree, as is plausible, that there are beings with unmanifested abilities. How can we recognize them? I think it can be plausibly argued that large swaths of humanity have never actually brought (to quote Regan again) "impartial moral principles to bear on the determination of what . . . morally ought to be done." Do they have the unmanifested ability to do so? On the other hand, a being can be remarkably sophisticated but fail to have the abilities that Regan requires for being a moral agent. A being can be self-conscious and have the ability to regulate its behavior according to "partial" moral principles and yet not be a moral agent on Regan's view. This invites questions about what it is to be a moral principle and what exactly impartiality consists in. Motivating this worry is the concern that for Regan, only those with the ability to be a practicing Kantian or Direct Utilitarian count as moral agents.

Even before the publication of Regan's book, there were arguments in the literature that suggested that some animals are moral agents, or moral agents to some extent, thus suggesting that the distinction is not categorical. The same year that Regan's book was published, Lawrence Johnson (1983) argued that "moral agency does not require acting from principle" (p. 50) and that "we . . . share moral agency . . . with animals." Even earlier, S. F. Sapontzis (1980) had claimed that animals can be virtuous even though they are not "moral beings."

While the moral agent/patient distinction has continued to be used, the categorical distinction that it marked between "normal adult humans" and animals has become increasingly blurred (see, e.g., Pluhar 1988; Shapiro 2006; Sebo 2017). We have increasingly identified what appears to be agential behavior in many nonhuman animals, while at the same time we have come to see that much of the apparently agential behavior of "normal adult humans" succumbs to naturalistic (even reductionist) explanations, either through appeals to evolutionary notions such as inclusive fitness, neurological explanations, or non-conscious psychological mechanisms.[2] The gap between "normal adult humans" and other animals has shrunk as we have learned more about both. As philosophical naturalism has gained ground, an argument that Johnson made in 1983 seems prescient:

> [M]oral rules do not just fall from the sky . . . [M]oral concepts, if they are not to be empty, must be based on an awareness of and valuing of some difference . . . [T]here seems to me to be no persuasive reason to believe that an animal cannot be aware of, value, and act on those factors which give moral content to concepts and principles. . . . [S]uch an animal is displaying moral agency. . . . He, like most humans, would never do as a meta-ethicist, but he might be able to do the right thing on the basis of morally relevant factors in a given situation.
>
> (Johnson 1983, p. 55)

This perspective directs us towards what humans and animals do rather than on the principles on which they may act. It is now clear that many animals cooperate, reconcile, punish, reciprocate, and engage in altruistic behavior (see, e.g., Bekoff and Pierce 2009, but data continue to appear on an almost weekly basis). Flack and de Waal (2000) say that these are the "building blocks" of morality, Rowlands (2012) claims that this is sufficient to show that animals are "moral subjects" (they can be motivated to act by moral reasons), and Bekoff and Pierce (2009) claim that some animals have full-blown moralities. The more we learn about nonhuman animals, the more ubiquitous these marks of agency become both within and across species (see Rowlands, Chapter 45, and Schlingloff and Moore, Chapter 36, in this volume).

Thus, the following dilemma: if moral agency is expressed in behavior, then it looks like many nonhuman animals are at least to some extent moral agents; if, on the other hand, moral agency requires psychological explanations of the sort given by Descartes and Kant, then the idea of moral agency is at risk of disappearing altogether. In different ways, both horns of this dilemma narrow the gap between "normal adult humans" and other animals when it comes to moral agency.

This is the influential current backdrop for thinking about ethics and animals. While there are other topics that are worthy of attention, in what follows I will discuss three substantive areas of inquiry that have been affected by these changes of outlook.

Suffering

The distinction between suffering and pain can be viewed as tracking the distinction between agents and patients. This distinction has often been influential in discussions of ethics and animals (see Shriver, Chapter 16 in this volume). The idea is that while all conscious beings feel pain, only self-conscious creatures who are aware of their being in pain suffer. This distinction is sometimes used to explain why it's worse to cause pain to normal adult humans than to most animals (but for a contrary view, see Akhtar 2011). When normal adult humans are in pain, they can have the additional bad experience of suffering because of their awareness that they are in pain. This distinction between suffering and pain naturally tracks the distinction between agents and patients, because the capacity (self-consciousness) that allows normal adult humans to suffer by reflecting on their pain is the same capacity that allows self-regulation, and is at least an important requirement for holding beings accountable for what they do. Anything that problematizes the agent/patient distinction thus can ramify through the consciousness/self-consciousness and pain/suffering distinctions. If many more animals than we might have thought have features of agency, then many more of them may suffer (or at least be in states that are more complex than simply registering pain). If these states are worse than being in pain, then harming many animals may be even worse than we had imagined.

Convinced that animal suffering is more ubiquitous than many have thought, some philosophers have begun to look at predation in a new way (e.g., Everett 2001, Cowen 2003, McMahon 2015). The natural relations between predator and prey are a site of enormous pain and suffering, and the world would be much better (at least in hedonistic terms) if we could prevent even a fraction of that suffering and pain. The blurring of the agent/patient distinction raises the salience of this issue, both by upgrading the experience of many animals from pain to suffering, and also by suggesting that some predators may, to some extent, be accountable for some of what they do (see, e.g., Donaldson and Kymlicka 2011).

Captivity

Once animals are seen not just as moral patients capable of registering pain and pleasure, but as complex beings to whom it matters how they live their lives, then questions about captivity become even more salient.[3] For beings who display characteristics of agency, the causes of their suffering and the frustration of their desires can be many and varied. For these creatures, the traditional criteria of animal welfare (e.g., adequate water and nutrition) look lame and limited. Moreover, the recognition of rich behavioral and psychological repertoires in animals also forces the recognition that "one size fits all" is a bad approach to animal welfare. Diverse, complex creatures have diverse, complex requirements.

Tragically, the widespread recognition of the complexity of other animals has occurred simultaneously with the systematic human transformation of the planet, driven by exponential increases in population and consumption, and expressed most dramatically in climate change. This transformation makes it almost impossible for us to ensure that wild animals can live in the habitats and under the natural conditions in which they evolved and which sustained them for millions of years. Furthermore, as the human domination of nature increases, the old distinction between captivity and natural habitat breaks down. There is almost nowhere on the planet that is now beyond the reach of humanity. The parks and reserves that provide sanctuary for shrinking populations of animals are increasingly taking on the characteristics of captivity, with guarded, patrolled, and often fenced borders. Our idea of protecting these animals increasingly looks like putting them in protective custody.

Some may think that protective custody is not such a bad idea. Just as the agent/patient distinction is increasingly breaking down with respect to humans and animals, so is the idea that culture is for humans and nature is for animals. When it comes to preventable disease and the depredations of others, we don't let "nature take its course" among humans. The same case can be made with respect to animals. If humans have reason to escape the ravages of nature, so do other animals. An extreme version was discussed in the previous section (protecting predators from prey), but there are less extreme views that would require providing wild animals with vaccinations and veterinary care.

Killing

Questions about whether it is permissible to painlessly kill animals to serve our purposes after giving them happy lives have been discussed since at least the nineteenth century. Although there are disagreements about what this principle means in practice, it has been endorsed in different forms and with various qualifications by philosophers such as R. M. Hare (1999) and Peter Singer (2011). When animals are seen as loci of hedonic states, the permissibility of "painless killing with replacement" may look plausible. But when animals are seen as agential, the question of killing them painlessly to serve our purposes seems more fraught. Indeed, questions about killing agential animals begins to look a lot like questions about the permissibility of killing humans, and here our intuitions are clear, at least in broad brush. Except under the most extreme circumstances, almost no one believes that it is permissible to painlessly kill innocent, adult, normal human beings in order to serve our purposes. Greater latitude for killing is accepted when these qualifiers are weakened, but in those cases, intuitions tend to divide quickly, and many people would deny that many such killings are permissible. These considerations land us in the broader world of moral philosophy, with all of its disagreements.

In recent years, concern has grown about killing animals. This is evidenced by a growing philosophical literature on this topic (e.g., Višak and Garner 2016), and by what seems to be a growing public debate (e.g., Foer 2009). Either because many people believe that animals cannot be killed painlessly or that it is wrong to do so, there is growing interest in various meat substitutes. In some cases, these involve "real meat," grown in vitro from cell cultures, while in other cases, these substitutes are derived entirely from non-animal products. While some may object to these substitutes on various grounds, their growing popularity indicates how uncomfortable many people have become with killing animals for food. Growing awareness of the environmental consequences of animal agriculture is surely part of the explanation as well, but so is the shrinking boundary between humans and other animals.

Conclusion

If we were to trace the arc of thinking about ethics and animals over the last half century, we would see that it begins with the recognition that animals are sentient, and so we ought not to cause them gratuitous suffering. This was based on the recognition of an important commonality between humans and other animals: their ability to feel pain. It also presupposed an important difference: that normal adult humans are moral agents and accountable for what they do, while most animals are not. In response to the growing recognition of the wide range of other, even agential, features shared by humans and other animals, the arc has moved towards integrating "animal ethics" into the broader domain of ethics, with ethics as a field becoming more attuned to variability and difference, both within and across species. Here, animal ethics has joined other currents emphasizing variability and difference, such as feminist ethics, disability studies, and the philosophy of race.

The landscape of moral philosophy has changed. Sensitivity to the variegated nature of the domain it investigates may limit the power of some of the grand old theories, complexify what seemed simple, and complicate some of our responses to particular cases, but it helps us to see how vast the domain of ethics really is, and how provincial and limited our appreciation of the needs of others and the demands of morality has been through much of our history. This is a gift that thinking seriously about the ethics of animals has given to moral philosophy as a field. I also hope that this work has made our treatment of animals a little better. In any case, the story is nearer to the beginning than the end.

Acknowledgments

Thanks to Nicolas Delon and Jeff Sebo.

Notes

1 I'm not sure how far back this distinction goes, but the earliest use of it that I have been able to find is in Nicolas Fotion's *Moral Situations* (1968). Fotion introduces it as a situation–relative, role distinction (e.g., "[w]hen a husband . . . does something . . . for his wife, the former is the agent while the later is the patient" (p. 17)). He goes on to ask whether various kinds of beings could occupy the patient role: "Would men-like creatures barely able to develop a language qualify as patient-candidates? How about men-like creatures just below that level? How about seaweed?" (p. 26).

2 Changing views of agency has been a major theme in the social sciences and humanities since at least the 1980s. As the world is increasingly seen as dynamic and active, agency is identified with loci of activity rather than with beings that manifest a particular psychology. For an important early articulation of this perspective, see Callon 1986.

3 I first addressed these issues in "Against Zoos" (Jamieson 1985). An excellent early paper bearing on these issues is James Rachels (1976), "Do Animals Have a Right to Liberty?" For some recent perspectives, see Lori Gruen (ed.), *The Ethics of Captivity* (2014).

References

Akhtar, S. (2011) "Animal Pain and Welfare: Can Pain Sometimes Be Worse for Them Than for Us," in T. Beauchamp and R. Frey (eds.), *The Oxford Handbook of Animal Ethics*, New York: Oxford University Press.

Bekoff, M., and Pierce, J. (2009) *Wild Justice: The Moral Lives of Animals*, Chicago: University of Chicago Press.

Brophy, B. (1965) "The Rights of Animals," *The Sunday Times*, 10 October.

Callon, M. (1986) "Some Elements of a Sociology of Translation: Domestication of the Scallops and the Fishermen of Saint Brieuc Bay," in J. Law (ed.), *Power, Action and Belief: A New Sociology of Knowledge? Sociological Review Monograph*, London: Routledge and Kegan Paul, 196–233.

Cowen, T. (2003) "Policing Nature," *Environmental Ethics* 25 (2): 169–182.

Darwin, C. (1859) *On the Origin of Species*, London: John Murray.

——— (1871) *Descent of Man, and Selection in Relation to Sex*, London: John Murray.

Donaldson, S., and Kymlicka, W. (2011) *Zoopolis: A Political Theory of Animal Rights*, Oxford: Oxford University Press.

Everett, J. (2001) "Environmental Ethics, Animal Welfarism, and the Problem of Predation: A Bambi Lover's Respect for Nature," *Ethics and the Environment* 6 (1): 42–67.

Flack, J. C., and de Waal, F. B. M. (2000) "'Any Animal Whatever': Darwinian Building Blocks of Morality in Monkeys and Apes," *Journal of Consciousness Studies* 7 (1): 1–29.

Foer, J. F. (2009) *Eating Animals*, New York: Little, Brown and Company.

Fotion, N. (1968) *Moral Situations*, Yellow Springs, OH: The Antioch Press.

Franklin, B. (2008/1903) *The Autobiography of Benjamin Franklin*, Beford, MA: Applewood Books.

Gruen, L. (ed.) (2014) *The Ethics of Captivity*, New York: Oxford University Press.

Hare, R. M. (1999) "Why I am Only a Demi-Vegetarian," in D. Jamieson (ed.), *Singer and His Critics*, Oxford: Basil Blackwell.

Harrison, R. (1964) *Animal Machines*, London: Vincent Stuart Ltd.

Jamieson, D. (1985) "Against Zoos," in P. Singer (ed.) *In Defence of Animals*, Oxford: Basil Blackwell, 108–117.

Johnson, L. (1983) "Can Animals Be Moral Agents?" *Ethics and Animals* 4: 50–61.

McMahon, J. (2015) "The Moral Problem of Predation," in A. Chignell, T. Cuneo, and M. Halteman (eds.), *Philosophy Comes to Dinner: Arguments About the Ethics of Eating*, London: Routledge, 268–294.

Pluhar, E. B. (1988) "Moral Agents and Moral Patients," *Between the Species* 4 (1): 32–45.

Rachels, J. (1976) "Do Animals Have a Right to Liberty?," in T. Regan and P. Singer (eds.), *Animal Rights and Human Obligations*, Englewood Cliffs, NJ: Prentice-Hall, 205–223.

Regan, T. (1983) *The Case for Animal Rights*, New York: Basil Blackwell.

Rowlands, M. (2012) *Can Animals Be Moral?* New York: Oxford University Press.

Salt, H. (1892) *Animals' Rights: Considered in Relation to Social Progress*, New York: Macmillan & Co.

Sapontzis, S. F. (1980) "Are Animals Moral Beings?" *American Philosophical Quarterly* 17: 45–52.

Sebo, J. (2017) "Agency and Moral Status," *Journal of Moral Philosophy*.

Shapiro, P. (2006) "Moral Agency in Other Animals," *Theoretical Medicine and Bioethics* 27 (4): 357–373.

Singer, P. (1974) *Animal Liberation*, New York: HarperCollins.

——— (2011) *Practical Ethics*, 3rd ed. New York: Cambridge University Press.

Sorabji, R. (1993). *Animal Minds and Human Morals: The Origins of the Western Debate*, Ithaca, NY: Cornell University.

Višak, T., and Garner, R. (eds.) (2016) *The Ethics of Killing Animals*, New York: Oxford University Press.

45

MORAL SUBJECTS

Mark Rowlands

A dog has been hit by a car, and lies unconscious on a busy highway in Chile. The dog's canine companion, at enormous risk to his or her own life, weaves in and out of traffic, and eventually manages to drag the unconscious dog to the side of the road (see www.youtube.com/watch?v=-HJTG6RRN4E). A female elephant, Grace, tries to help the dying matriarch of another family of elephants, and appears distressed when she is unable to do so effectively (Douglas-Hamilton et al. 2006). A gorilla lifts the unconscious body of a small boy, who has fallen into her enclosure, and carries him to the gate where she hands him over to a keeper (Bekoff and Pierce 2009). A rhesus monkey refuses to take food, when doing so will subject another monkey to an electric shock. The monkey persists in this refusal for twelve days, nearly starving himself to death (Wechkin et al. 1964). What should we make of cases such as these? Here is one possibility: these cases form parts of a large and growing body of evidence for the claim that some nonhuman animals (henceforth 'animals') can exhibit moral behavior (see de Waal 2006 and Bekoff and Pierce 2009 for excellent surveys of the evidence). Most philosophers and scientists reject this possibility. I shall defend it.

Two issues should be distinguished. One is an *empirical* issue about the actual nature of an animal's motivation in any given case. The near blanket rejection of the possibility of moral behavior in animals, however, is not driven by an empirical examination of particular cases but by *conceptual* considerations. There is, allegedly, something about the nature of moral behavior that renders animals incapable of engaging in it. And, skeptics aver, we can establish this claim without the need for empirical examination of individual cases (Dixon 2008). The basis of this denial is always the same: whatever else is true of animals, they are not *responsible* for what they do, and being responsible for what one does is a necessary condition of acting morally. I shall argue that, on the contrary, there are no insuperable conceptual obstacles to regarding animals as capable of moral behavior. I have developed this case in much more detail elsewhere (Rowlands 2011, 2012). Here, I can merely provide an outline of that case.

If something falls within moral space at all, it is generally thought to belong to one or both of two categories: it can be a moral *patient* or a moral *agent* or both, where:

(1) X is a moral *patient* if and only if X is a legitimate object of moral concern.
(2) X is a moral *agent* if and only if X is morally responsible for, and so can be morally evaluated for, their motives and actions.

I shall argue for the existence of a third category – an additional, curiously overlooked, region of moral space:

(3) X is a moral *subject* if and only if X is, at least sometimes, motivated to act by moral considerations.

I doubt any animals are moral agents. I'm not sure humans are. But I think at least some animals are moral subjects.

The category of the moral subject has languished unrecognized because it is almost universally thought to collapse into that of moral agent. The reason for this stems from Kant's dictum: *'ought' implies 'can'*. Imagine someone – for entirely obvious reasons, we can call him Sigmund – whose motivations are always hidden from him. The motivational component of his mind is akin to a black box: replete with states that successfully guide Sigmund's behavior, but to which he has no first-person access. Sigmund, it seems, would be 'at the mercy' of his motivations: having no idea what motivates him and, therefore, having no control over those motivations. Sigmund just finds himself doing things on the basis of motivations he neither recognizes nor understands. Sigmund, therefore, cannot be a moral subject. Having no control over his motivations, he can neither embrace nor resist them. But if he *can* neither embrace nor resist his motivations, it makes no sense to say that he *should* embrace or resist them. Sigmund's motivations, in this sense, make no *normative claim* on him. However, moral motivations are precisely things that make normative claims on their subjects. Good motivations *should* be embraced, and evil ones *should* be resisted. Therefore, it seems Sigmund's motivations cannot be moral ones. Generalizing: without control, there can be no moral motivation. Therefore, the category of the moral subject collapses into that of the moral agent.

In the Kantian tradition, also, we find a specific conception of control: control over one's motivations derives from the ability to *critically scrutinize* them. Thus, Korsgaard writes:

> Once you are aware that you are being moved in a certain way, you have a certain reflective distance from the motive, and you are in a position to ask yourself, "but should I be moved in that way?' Wanting that end inclines me to do that act, but does it really give me a reason to do that act? You are now in a position to raise a normative question about what you *ought* to do.
>
> (2006, p. 113)

We might call this the *Scrutiny-Control-Normativity-Morality* (S–C–N–M) nexus. The ability to critically scrutinize one's motivations gives one control over them. This control permits these motivations to make a normative claim on their subject, and so makes them the sort of motivations that might be moral. Thus: animals cannot have moral motivations because they have no control over their motivations. And they have no control over their motivations because they lack the ability to critically scrutinize them.

This argument is only as strong as the claim that 'ought' implies 'can'. And while it has the status of dogma, I think it is untenable. To see why, consider two arguments.

Evil children

Three-year-old Jamie Bulger was abducted, tortured, and murdered by two boys, Robert Thompson and Jon Venables. At the time of the murder, both Venables and Thompson were ten years old, and became the youngest convicted murderers in English history. They kicked Bulger, threw bricks at him, and hit him with an iron bar. Bulger suffered ten skull fractures, and so many injuries that none could be definitively identified as the mortal one. Following the murder, Venables and Thompson placed Bulger's body on railway tracks in the hope that a train would make his death appear an accident. Under questioning, they revealed that they had planned to abduct and murder a child that day (and also that their initial intention was to take him to a busy road and push him into oncoming traffic – that aspect of the plan later changed).

Suppose one decides – as many theories of moral development suggest – that Venables and Thompson were below the age at which they could be regarded as morally responsible. One deems them to lack the control over their motivations necessary for responsibility. Even *if* this were true, would we really want to deny that their motivations were morally bad ones? Even *if* we wished to rescind from attributions of moral responsibility to Venables and Thompson, would we really want to say that, therefore, their motivations carry no moral weight? That claim, if one is not in the grip of a peculiarly warped moral psychology, is as counterintuitive as a claim can get.

Rescinding from moral evaluation of *individuals* is one thing; rescinding from moral evaluation of their *motivations* is quite another. However, if 'ought' implies 'can', the former rescindment entails the latter. A subject's lack of control over a given motivation would entail that the motivation makes no normative claim on the subject: it would not be the sort of thing he *should* resist because it is not the sort of thing he *can* resist. Therefore, the motivation could not be a moral one (it would be amoral). If they were not responsible, Venables and Thompson's motivations would not be morally bad. To avoid this conclusion, we need to reject the idea that 'ought' implies 'can'.

Determinism world

In determinism world – which may or may not be the actual world – hard determinism is true, and no one is, therefore, ever responsible for what they do. Would we really want to say that, in this world, there is no such thing as moral motivation? When Hitler (or the worldly equivalent thereof) starts a World War and attempts to exterminate various races, would we want to say that his motivations do not count as morally evil? We might, in such a world, justifiably rescind from evaluation of Hitler, the person: we might, that is, refuse to blame or hold him responsible for what he does. But refusing to classify his motivations as even falling into the category of the moral is highly counterintuitive. The principle that 'ought' implies 'can' commits us to this. If Hitler cannot control his motivations, no sense can be made of the idea that he should resist them. His motivations make no normative claim, and therefore cannot qualify as moral. To avoid this, we must reject the idea that 'ought' implies 'can'.

The category of the moral subject is, therefore, a desirable one. But the desirability of a category is one thing; its actual existence is quite another. We can bolster these considerations by attacking the S-C-N-M nexus. Two links in the chain are particularly vulnerable: (i) scrutiny-control, and (ii) control-normativity.

Generally speaking, the idea of critical scrutiny of motivations comprises three distinguishable elements: *recognition, interrogation,* and *judgment*: a subject *recognizes* that she has certain motivations, and on the basis of this recognition can *ask* herself questions such as 'Is this motivation one I should embrace or resist?' Moreover, she also understands how she should attempt to answer this question by *judging* the motivation in the light of moral principles or propositions that she antecedently holds.

The idea that the ability to engage in critical scrutiny of her motivations gives a subject control over those motivations does, admittedly, have intuitive appeal. In the absence of this ability, she is, it seems, at the 'mercy' of her motivations. She has them, she acts on them, and that is pretty much that. The ability to critically scrutinize her motivations would, seemingly, transform her. She could, now, sit above the motivational fray: observing, judging, and evaluating her motivations, coolly deciding the extent to which she will allow them to determine her decisions and actions. This gives her a control over her motivations that she would otherwise lack.

Intuitively appealing or not, this account has familiar problems (Friedman 1986, Thalberg 1989, Noggle 2005, Rowlands 2012). There is a recalcitrant property – the property of being under the control of the subject – that first-order states (motivations) lack. We, therefore, introduce higher-order states – recognitions, interrogations, and judgments of those motivations – to supply this control. But the same issue of control will, logically, arise at this higher order too. Do we have control over our higher-order recognitions, interrogations, and judgments of our motivations? If so, then we have not explained the notion of control, but simply assumed it. But if not, then it is difficult to see how these higher-order interrogations and assessments could supply us with control over our motivations. The ability to critically scrutinize our first-order motivations was supposed to lift us above the motivational fray, allowing us to dispassionately pass judgment on our motivations, and thus providing us with control over them. But it, in fact, does no such thing: *either* because the higher-order states and processes are themselves part of that fray *or* because the appeal presupposes what it is supposed to explain – a subject's control over her mental life.

This problem is reasonably familiar, and there is an equally familiar response: additional specification of the conditions under which this critical scrutiny is to take place. For example, it must take place under conditions free of distorting factors, or must reflect an adequate causal history, and so on (Christman 1991, Mele 1995). For our purposes, this kind of response is irrelevant: whether or not the scrutiny takes place under conditions free of distorting factors or reflects an adequate causal history is not something that is, generally, under the subject's control. The response seeks – in effect, by stipulation – to divorce the idea of control from what is often called *autonomy*. The response attempts to preserve a viable notion of the latter in the absence of the former. Our question, however, is whether we can explain control over motivations by appeal to higher-order states such as recognitions, interrogations, and judgments – for it is the lack of *these* that is what is thought to deny animals the possibility of controlling their motivations. It is, therefore, simply irrelevant to point out that there is another conception of autonomy that does not require control over motivations.

The control-normativity link is also vulnerable: it is clear that normativity, in general, does not require control. After all, other cases of 'ought' do not seem to imply 'can'. Consider, for example, the prudential ought. An alcoholic ought – prudentially speaking – to give up drinking. Whether he is capable of doing so is irrelevant to the truth of this claim. He ought to give up drinking – to resist this motivation to drink – even if he, in fact, can't. Why *must* the moral 'ought' require 'can' when at least some other versions of 'ought' do not?

There is, in fact, a conception of the moral 'ought' under which it does not imply 'can'. This is an *externalist, consequentialist* one. The type of externalism in question is *evaluational* and the type of consequentialism is *objective* (Driver 2000). Such an account will assume a reasonably robust sense of ethical objectivity: situations contain features that make them good or bad independently of the subjective states of the agent. The evaluation of a motivation will then be a function of whether it systematically (as opposed to accidentally) promotes good- or bad-making features of situations. The normative status of a motivation is, therefore, explained in terms of relations it bears to certain external factors, rather than the subject's control over it.

With this general model in mind, consider the case of the dog described earlier. His companion lies unconscious on a busy road. This is, let us suppose, a bad-making feature of the situation. The first requirement is that the would-be rescuer is sensitive to this bad-making feature. Such sensitivity does not require that the dog is able to think thoughts such as 'This is bad!' The appropriate sensitivity can, in fact, be purchased by other means. Most obviously, suppose the dog possesses a mirror neuron system. When he sees another animal in distress, he is caused to feel distress too. The other's distress is not merely a cause of the dog's distress. Rather, the other's distress is an intentional object of the dog's distress: he is distressed *that* the other is distressed. (Or, if one has qualms about attributing mindreading abilities to the dog, one can reframe his distress in terms of behavior reading: the dog is distressed *at* the other's distress behavior. See Monso, 2015.) The distress experienced by the dog will cause him to attempt to ameliorate the distress of the other.

Nowhere in this general picture is there any suggestion that the dog has control over his sentiments, still less that he is able to critically scrutinize them. Rather, the dog has an emotional sensitivity to at least some of the good- and bad-making feature of the environment. This sensitivity is fragmentary. There is no suggestion that the dog is sensitive to *all* the good- and bad-making features of situations. Rather, the claim is simply that he can recognize some of them and, moreover, when he does so, he can be correct (or incorrect) in this recognition. This possibility is a consequence of the robust sense of ethical objectivity advertised above. If it is indeed true that the condition of his companion is a bad-making feature of the environment, then in his experienced distress and resulting attempt to help, the dog is responding to this bad-making feature in a morally appropriate way.

Is the dog morally motivated – motivated to act by way of a moral motivation? One way to address this question is by way of considerations of *parity*. Suppose there were a human who exhibited the same kind of profile as the dog. He is sensitive to some (but not all) of the (morally) good- and bad-making features of situations. This sensitivity is *reliable* and takes an *emotional* form: with respect to the good- and bad-making features to which this human is sensitive, he reliably experiences distress at the bad-making features and joy at the good-making features.

Is such a human a moral subject? A dyed-in-the-wool Kantian would deny that he is. I have raised some objections to the Kantian model, and attacked some of its crucial elements – the connection between scrutiny and control, and between control and normativity. But experience suggests that if someone really wants to be a Kantian, then that is precisely what he/she is going to be. But other accounts of morality are far more hospitable to the idea that our imagined human is a moral subject. A sentimentalist account will have to take seriously the idea that this imagined human is a moral subject. And if the human is a moral subject, then the sentimentalist will have to take seriously the idea that some animals are too. The *blanket* dismissal of the possibility of moral behavior in animals has no justification. Can animals be moral? On at least some, prominent and respectable, accounts of morality, yes they can.

References

Bekoff, Marc, and Pierce, Jessica (2009) *The Moral Lives of Animals* (Chicago: University of Chicago Press).

Christman, John (1991) 'Autonomy and personal history', *Canadian Journal of Philosophy* 21, 1–24.

de Waal, Frans (2006) *Primates and Philosophers: How Morality Evolved* (Cambridge: Harvard University Press).

Dixon, Beth (2008) *Animals, Emotions, and Morality* (New York: Prometheus Books).

Douglas-Hamilton, Iain, Bhalla, Shivani, Wittemyer, George, and Vollrath, Fritz (2006) 'Behavioural reactions of elephants towards a dying and deceased matriarch,' *Applied Animal Behaviour Science* 100, 67–102.

Driver, Julia (2000) *Uneasy Virtue* (New York: Cambridge University Press).

Friedman, Marilyn (1986) 'Autonomy and the split-level self', *Southern Journal of Philosophy* 24, 19–35.

Korsgaard, Christine (2006) 'Morality and the distinctiveness of human action', in Frans de Waal, *Primates and Philosophers: How Morality Evolved* (Princeton, NJ: Princeton University Press), pp. 98–119.

Mele, Alfred (1995) *Autonomous Agents: From Self Control to Autonomy* (New York: Oxford University Press).

Monso, Susana (2015) 'Empathy and morality in behavior readers', *Biology and Philosophy* 30(5), 671–690.

Noggle, Robert (2005) 'Autonomy and the paradox of self-creation: Infinite regresses, finite selves, and the limits of authenticity', in J. Taylor ed., *Personal Autonomy* (Cambridge: Cambridge University Press), pp. 87–108.

Rowlands, Mark (2011) 'Animals that act for moral reasons', in T. Beauchamp and R. Frey eds., *Oxford Handbook of Animal Ethics* (New York: Oxford University Press), pp. 519–546.

Rowlands, Mark (2012) *Can Animals Be Moral?* (New York: Oxford University Press).

Thalberg, Irving (1989) 'Hierarchical analyses of unfree action', in John Christman ed., *The Inner Citadel* (New York: Oxford University Press), pp. 123–136.

Wechkin, Stanley, Masserman, Jules H., and Terris, William (1964) 'Shock to a conspecific as an aversive stimulus', *Psychonomic Science* 1, 17–18.

46

DECISIONAL AUTHORITY AND ANIMAL RESEARCH SUBJECTS

Andrew Fenton

Introduction

My position is simply stated. Animal research ethics should take the question of the decisional authority of other intensely social cognitive animals very seriously. But for a few exceptions I will introduce later, we should not include, or continue to use, an intensely social cognitive animal who expresses sustained dissent in the course of research (Fenton 2014).

Three terms require a brief explanation (I will leave "dissent" until later). An individual has decisional authority over a course of action just in case their decision on the matter holds or is respected. Cognitive animals possess various capacities to acquire and store information about themselves or their environment, use it to order their future behavior, and correct it in light of negative feedback arising from its use (Allen and Bekoff 1997; Fenton 2012a; Gould 2004). Intensely social animals require a stable social environment in order to develop typically and are vulnerable to the development of behavioral disorders when it is not (Bloomsmith et al. 2006).

Various behavioral and cognitive studies of other intensely social cognitive animals, from chimpanzees to rats, are revealing preferences of treatment expressed inside and outside of laboratory settings (e.g., Bloomsmith et al. 2006; Olsson and Westlund 2007). Dissent can signal such preferences. I am very aware of the dangers of anthropomorphism lurking in the background of talk about animal preferences, but I do not think I am guilty of this error of ascription. Several empirical claims, useful for defending my position, are not in serious doubt within the relevant behavioral and cognitive sciences. First, sociality did not first emerge with the appearance of our species, or even earlier hominins. Second, we are not the first animals to have developed various perceptual, affective (e.g., emotional) and cognitive capacities with which to engage our physical and social worlds. Third, it is not even the case that, among social cognitive animals, plastic social hierarchies first emerged with our species (De Waal and Tyack 2003). Taken together, these widely accepted empirical claims should soften resistance to the view that other intensely social cognitive animals form preferences of treatment. What may clinch it are the lengths taken by some animals to secure better treatment from conspecifics (or even heterospecifics like us), the frustration sometimes expressed if they fail, and retaliations when attacked or unsupported by allies during conflict (e.g., Thierry 2011; de Waal 1998).

One species that will come up in this chapter and make these claims more concrete is the chimpanzee. This is not because these animals are one of the few where we can find some or most of the capacities and behavior I have introduced above. I could have focused on canids like wolves (Cordoni and Palagi 2008), Cetacea like dolphins (Connor 2007), or corvids like ravens (Braun and Bugnyar 2012), but my work to date has focused on chimpanzees, and so again here (see Fenton 2012b, 2014). In what follows, I will both situate and defend my position (I also discuss some of these ideas in Fenton and Shriver, forthcoming).

A sense that it's time

The timeliness of re-envisioning the role of other animals' agential capacities when deciding to use them in research is captured in several observations about emergent attitudes or practices in laboratories (or captive settings explicitly created to study other animals) and the continuing strength of some philosophical criticisms of the status quo in animal research. As I briefly present them, it should become clear that they call out for a repositioning of animal research ethics in a way that better (and more strongly) resembles what has become standard fare in human bioethics.

"Good science is humane science" is a sentiment that resonates through much of the literature touching on the "3 R's,"[1] laboratory enrichment, and animal research ethics (e.g., Orlans 2002; Poole 1997). Admittedly, this can confuse largely descriptive with normative claims about animal research – after all, good science need not be humane science – but there are strong correlations between stressed animal subjects and confounders that undermine the clarity, quality, or reliability of experimental data (Coleman 2010). Though the elimination of stressors in the environment can help alleviate confounders, two other efforts are often recommended: (a) enriching the captive conditions in which animal research subjects live, and (b) where possible, training the subjects through positive reinforcement (henceforth, PRT) to cooperate during routine husbandry, research, or veterinary procedures (Bloomsmith et al. 2006).

Both (a) and (b) are relevant to situating my position. Where intensely social cognitive animal research subjects are group housed (a form of social enrichment), a social hierarchy emerges that facilitates the satisfaction of, as well as reflects, preferences of treatment (not unlike what we observe in free-living counterparts). These expressed preferences of treatment remind us that how these other animals are treated matters to them, a point that we will return to later. The importance of PRT for my purposes lies in the effort to secure the cooperation of animal research subjects. Such training not only reduces the stress of the research animals, it also reduces the stress of those handling them, and permits a respectful treatment that can better cohere with the concern that many laboratory personnel have for the research subjects in their care (Coleman 2010). PRT encourages the animal research subjects to build expectations about daily procedures and imminent events (e.g., a blood draw or moving to another cage) and allows the possibility of cooperation, or refusal to cooperate, in contexts where the animals have some understanding of what is about to happen (Walker 2006). This point will be useful when we discuss consent.

Adding to these developments, some conscientious animal researchers have drawn attention to the ethical space in which they use other animals in research (and the moral commitments they make in using them). They emphasize that their research subjects are beings who are due respect and will sometimes express this in terms of valuing their subjects' cooperation (e.g., see Berns et al. 2012). Matsuzawa writes:

> The chimpanzees in the KUPRI [Kyoto University Primate Research Institute] laboratory are free: it is completely up to each subject whether he or she will come to the booth to participate in a cognitive task or not. If they prefer not to participate, they

may stay outside. It must be noted that choosing to participate in an experiment does not affect the total amount of food given to a chimpanzee per day. . . . Suppose that a chimpanzee does decide to come to the booth. Again, it is up to them whether to start the first trial of the test session or not. . . . This means that nothing happens before the subject touches the key [on the monitor] of his or her own will. . . . [T]he response-contingent delivery of the food has a special value for the chimpanzee. Based on their free will, they work on a cognitively challenging task and as a result they are rewarded.

(Matsuzawa 2006: 20)

Such emergent practices or changing attitudes in laboratory (or captive) contexts demonstrate that the cooperation of other animals is enjoying greater significance to some of those working in animal research. As I shift to more theoretical considerations, the need to re-envision the moral weight of this cooperation, and by implication lack of cooperation, will take on considerable force.

Typically, one of two background value systems frame the use of other animals in research: (1) anthropocentric speciesism, and (2) human exceptionalism. Either value system permits the use of other animals in research that is prohibited on (at least some) humans. Though some may view (1) and (2) as different terms for the same thing, they can be distinguished. Anthropocentric speciesism is the differential moral regard of individuals on no other grounds than that they belong, or do not belong, to the species *Homo sapiens*. Human exceptionalism, on the other hand, concedes that not all humans (or their interests) will enjoy moral preeminence over all other animals (or their interests). For human exceptionalism, it is enough that some (perhaps many) humans (or their interests) will consistently enjoy it (Dunayer 2013). An example of this position is privileging the interests of persons over the interests of nonpersons, at least as long as personhood is restricted to *Homines sapientes*. Such a use of personhood typically includes human juveniles and adults and, more controversially, infants.

Two examples where one or the other of these value systems is probably at work may be illustrative. Consider toxicological research. Toxicology research involves both the study of typically functioning cells, tissues, and biological processes, and what happens when they are exposed to various chemical agents at different dose levels. To get a sufficient understanding of the potential toxicity of an agent, it is often important to see how it is absorbed and distributed within a complex living system (e.g., a mouse or rat) (Society of Toxicology 2006). Such *in vivo* research can cause physical damage, considerable pain, and even death. The use of other animals is supposed to reduce such risks to humans (Beauchamp et al. 2008; Rowan 2011). Though pharmaceutical phase 1 trials provide an example of using humans to test product safety, dominant ethical frameworks restrict intentionally harming or endangering research subjects to nonhumans. This effectively implies differential moral treatment based on species identity and so reflects anthropocentric speciesism. Human exceptionalism is more readily seen in differential ethical constraints as we cross from human to nonhuman biomedical or behavioral research. As I will discuss in a little more detail below, it is now standard to seek the consent of research subjects, or their surrogates, in research using humans. It is widely held to be immoral to fail to do so. The fundamental basis of this constraint is a respect for persons (Meslin and Dickens 2008). To date, this constraint is widely absent in nonhuman animal research. This is particularly evident when the nonhuman animals who fail to cooperate during routine or research-related laboratory procedures are physically restrained or immobilized. Though I have previously noted that an increasing number of researchers reject these practices, they are commonly regarded as ethically justified (Carbone 2004).

There is an extensive literature critical of anthropocentric speciesism with no need to rehearse it in detail here. One of the more illuminating moves is DeGrazia's argument involving other, now extinct, hominins (DeGrazia 2007). Making some slight adjustments to his argument, suppose for the moment that *Homo sapiens* is not the only extant species of our genus. Imagine, rather, that members of the species *Homo neanderthalensis* and *Homo floresiensis* still walk the Earth. How should we regard their interests in, say, liberty or freedom from intentional harm (assuming, not unreasonably, that they have them)? Could we imagine that our own interests in expanding our biological knowledge or product safety rightly trump them? For DeGrazia, it would be arbitrary to think that our interest in expanding our knowledge enjoys a higher moral status than a *Homo floresiensis'* interest to not be intentionally harmed, when we would not similarly intentionally harm a fellow *Homo sapiens*. After all, what could possibly be the difference that would justify such an ethical stance? Restating their respective species' identities is not an adequate answer to that question (it merely restates the point at issue). To make any progress here, we must turn our gaze to the presence or absence of capacities enjoying moral significance (e.g., capacities to suffer, enter into reciprocal relationships, or form preferences of treatment). Once this is recognized, it challenges credibility to think that there are moral significant capacities possessed by every *Homo sapiens* that are absent in every *Homo floresiensis* and justify the differential moral regard in dispute. This "capacities turn" is the keystone to rejecting anthropocentric speciesism, and of course quickly moves us beyond our genus or even tribe (*Hominini*) (DeGrazia 2007).

The second value system – human exceptionalism – is much more entrenched and more difficult to abandon. As I mentioned earlier, a standard ground for the differential moral treatment of, and regard for, humans and nonhuman animals is the personhood of the relevant humans (along with restricting the notion of "person" to some or many members of our species). On the face of it, human exceptionalism appears to lack the arbitrariness of anthropocentric speciesism. After all, on a common construal of the term, "person" picks out individuals with particular capacities rather than simply all members of the taxon *Homo sapiens*. Though the exact number is in dispute, these capacities often include emotionality, linguistic or communicative capacity, rationality, self-awareness, and sentience (Warren 2014; see also DeGrazia 2007). Arbitrariness is often revealed, however, when the conditions of, or candidates for, personhood are interrogated. Consider that much effort can be spent protecting under-developed humans (think of late-term fetuses or newborns) while avoiding comparable efforts on behalf of other animals. Where these humans do not possess interests or vulnerabilities relevantly different from those of at least some other animals, the arbitrariness is revealed. The recurrent use of arguments concerning so-called marginal others (e.g., fetuses, infants, or neurologically atypical humans), despite understandable criticisms about their implicit ableism (e.g., Kittay 2009), are best understood as a response to human exceptionalism. If some humans were not placed at the "center" of the moral universe (where their interests enjoy preeminence over the interests of all others), there would be no margins to concern us. Those politically opposed to the use of arguments concerning so-called marginal others would do well to oppose human exceptionalism (some similar points are made in Donaldson and Kymlicka, Forthcoming). Arguably, their reasonable concerns about our social views of (and duties to) the differently abled – particularly those who do not qualify as persons in any straightforward (non-arbitrary) way – provides a powerful reason for doing so.

Though I am not alone in my wariness of the use of personhood in applied ethics (Beauchamp 1999), its pervasive presence might incline some to regard my stance as absurd, or at least implausible. After all, ethicists associate appeals to personhood with core commitments in human research ethics: respect for autonomy and preferences of treatment as well as obligations not to treat subjects merely as means to the ends of greater scientific or biomedical knowledge

(Luna and Macklin 2009). As these commitments are not under serious dispute, it might appear as if personhood should not be either. Two considerations should cause pause here: (1) the lack of decisive conditions of personhood, and (2) the lack of progress in certain areas of bioethics because of intractable disputes over the nature and scope of personhood. As I have already mentioned, it is something of a received tradition to restrict the ascription of personhood to individuals possessing a to-be-specified number of psychological or behavioral capacities (see those listed above). This tradition faces challenges from those who do not share its conviction about the favored capacities or their relevance (think of those who would defend the personhood – and not just the potential personhood – of properly developing human fetuses). Philosophers can be quick to talk of different senses of "personhood" to try and protect the traditional (metaphysical) use of the term – perhaps fetal advocates are using a legal sense of personhood, which makes an individual visible to law as a possessor of certain rights or obligations, or a moral sense that simply picks out individuals who should enjoy certain strong protections from harm or exploitation (for an example of this breakdown, see Kind 2015). But dissenters are not obviously doing anything untoward if they refuse to re-see their view of personhood as different from, or used in a different sense than, the one favored by such philosophers. Even if their position is underpinned by an appeal to a conception of the human soul or to the belief that humans are created in the image of divinity – appeals commonly rejected in at least contemporary analytic philosophy – their position does not then become obviously wrong. Where, in moments of non-sectarian reflection, we can concede this legitimate plurality of views of personhood, we can see that it can do little to resolve issues surrounding our treatment of other animals. What's more, as we can now readily observe stalemates in bioethical disputes at the beginning or end of human lives (e.g., the permissibility of human embryonic experimentation/enhancement or our obligations to individuals with advanced dementia), we should be reticent to appeal to personhood in animal research ethics. There is little reason (except, perhaps, species prejudice) to think such appeals will be any more decisive when the focus is a chimpanzee or domestic dog rather than a human (Fenton 2012b).

Where, then, have my comments or contentions taken us? With the collapse of anthropocentric speciesism and strong reasons to reject human exceptionalism, we must face the following possibility: if another animal, say a chimpanzee, dissents from participation in a harmful study – imagine that she refuses to extend her arm for a blood draw or present her body for a biopsy – this may be sufficient reason to exclude her from the study. Without an appeal to anthropocentric speciesism or human exceptionalism ready at hand, this chimpanzee's preference of treatment would appear to enjoy relevantly similar moral weight to a relevantly similar preference of treatment expressed by a member of our own species. Diekema and Wendler have independently defended the view that sustained dissent, even of very young children, in a research setting is a good prima facie reason to exclude them from the relevant study (Diekema 2006; Wendler 2006). Though I will have more to say about their positon in the next section, such a progressive stance could be extended to other animals and, in a framework devoid of anthropocentric speciesism and strong human exceptionalism, probably should be. Alternatively, if we are to weight a chimpanzee's preferences differently than we would a young child expressing sustained dissent, we will need something other than anthropocentric speciesism or human exceptionalism to justify it, and I know of no alternatives.

As I am committed to avoiding anthropomorphic errors in talking of the agential capacities of other animals, I now need to say more about how my sense of dissent can be applied to other animals. I also need to say more about repositioning animal research ethics in a way that better (and more strongly) resembles what has become standard fare in human bioethics. It is to these two concerns that I now turn, though in reverse order.

On decisional authority in a progressive animal research ethics

The decisional authority of research subjects is not in doubt when they are competent humans. Since the emergence of the Nuremberg Code in the aftermath of the Second World War, the consent of competent human research subjects has enjoyed ever increasing prominence in research ethics (see *The Belmont Report* or the latest version of the *Declaration of Helsinki*). Such research atrocities as the Tuskegee Syphilis Studies have served to underline its significance, even though the Willowbrook Hepatitis Studies remind us that consent is not a panacea to protect vulnerable human subjects from exploitation and harm (Diekema 2006; Luna and Macklin 2009). The importance of consent lies in respecting the decisional authority of human agents. A number of normative ethical theories, be they utilitarian, deontological, or virtue theories, can justify this respectful treatment, so its importance is over-determined in applied ethics. What is interesting for my purposes is that some progressive bioethics has taken a turn to consider the decisional authority of non-competent human agents such as children.

Talk of competence, at least as it is used in contemporary bioethics, is a way of acknowledging the decisional authority of typically functioning, autonomous agents (the exemplar is a typically functioning, autonomous human adult) to make decisions that (positively or negatively) impinge upon their well-being or welfare. Respecting this authority in research settings requires providing these agents with information needed to make an informed decision relative to their values or preferences (Beauchamp and Childress 2012). Children, particularly under the age of 14, are customarily held to be incompetent. But this does not preclude them from decisions to participate in research. Seeking assent from juvenile humans is taken to be required where it is an expression of respect for the kind of being they are (Diekema 2006). Typically, assent requires that the relevant children understand something of the nature of the research (and that it is research, not therapy) as well as the risks involved. It will also require their express willingness to participate (Diekema 2006). Such understanding is beyond the ken of some very young children (or children who can neither consent nor assent), but, as I mentioned earlier, progressive bioethics does not preclude them from decisions to participate in research. Where a procedure or research setting is distressing to a very young child (or a child who can neither consent nor assent), and they express "sustained dissent" (Wendler 2006: 233), they should be precluded from participating – or so some have powerfully argued (see Diekema 2006; Wendler 2006).

I agree with this progressive bioethics but do not think that some of these commitments concern only humans (Fenton 2014). Instead, I take the view that both an understanding of consent and dissent is relevant to animal research ethics. We have already seen why the preferences of treatment of other intensely social cognitive animals should not be ignored. I have also noted the rising use of PRT to secure the cooperation of cognitive research subjects in routine husbandry, research, or veterinary procedures. PRT connects quite quickly to consent, when seen in a certain way. During PRT, animals learn to associate certain cues with the imminent occurrence of what, without the relevant training, can be a (significant) stressor (think of the presentation of a needle or even the appearance of a particular laboratory technician who regularly takes blood samples or genital swabs) (Laule et al. 2003). It can reasonably be said that, over time, these cognitive animals come to understand something of what is about to transpire, and this understanding offers them a to-be-specified degree of resilience against stress. What's more, their continued cooperative behavior despite the relevant cues can be reasonably interpreted as consent to the imminent procedure (for some similar points, see Walker 2006). Though such consent is not consent to research (as the relevant cognitive animals cannot think in terms of research versus, say, therapy), it can qualify as consent to procedures.

Dissent, in contrast to either consent or assent, does not require a deep understanding of stressors or the imminent occurrence of stressors. After all, this is how it can be used in progressive pediatric research ethics to deal with young children. In my previous work, I have suggested three conditions for dissent capacity that fall out of its use in that area of human research ethics: a dissenter must have a "capacity (1) for distress, pain, or stress; (2) to anticipate the future occurrence of distress, pain, or stress; and (3) to 'ask' that it stop or to express that the relevant distress, pain, or stress is unwanted" (Fenton 2014: 134). For young children, this can be expressed in their inconsolable distress when presented with relevant stimuli, their refusal to extend their arm or turn their head, or their refusal to sit still (Diekema 2006).

Typically functioning chimpanzees are examples of nonhuman animals who possess these capacities of dissent. Conditions (1) and (2) are acknowledged in the scientific literature that advocates training chimpanzees to cooperate when presented with stressors or where they discuss the use of analgesics, anesthesia, anxiolytics, and tranquilizer darts (e.g., Laule et al. 2003; Lopresti-Goodman et al. 2015). Condition (3) is in evidence where control of uncooperative chimpanzees is achieved through the use of immobilizing devices, such as squeeze cages or even restraints (e.g., Perlman et al. 2012). Among non-laboratory chimpanzees, aggression, retaliations, and tantrums have been connected with anger at being socially snubbed, unsupported by allies at times when they are under threat from conspecifics, or frustrated after failing to manipulate the behavior of a conspecific (e.g., de Waal 1998). In each of these cases, preferences of treatment can play a crucial role in explaining the relevant chimpanzee's behavior. That such animals can form preferences of treatment connects us again with condition (3) above.

To summarize, PRT can be understood as a way of seeking an animal research subject's consent to research procedures. The sustained dissent of chimpanzee research subjects – expressed, say, in an unwillingness to present their arm or hindquarters or move into an adjacent cage – should be respected, all things being equal. To do anything less is to introduce a differential regard for the decisional authority of research subjects that, to remain consistent, threatens advances in progressive pediatric research ethics.

Okay, now what?

The central implication of my position seems clear: chimpanzees (and other intensely social cognitive animals with dissent capacity) should not be forced to participate in research. Their dissent should be respected, all other things being equal. But why use the phrase "all other things being equal"? Discussions in pediatric research ethics have highlighted two areas where the research can at least sometimes proceed even when the child is not cooperating or actively resisting participation: (1) where the research offers some to-be-specified hope of therapeutic benefit (that cannot be obtained outside of a research setting), and (2) where the research promises to yield substantial knowledge relevant to the (typically, patient) population of which the child is a part. Risk to child subjects is an important restriction on pediatric research and, with regards to (2), permits their inclusion where the risks only slightly exceed what is regarded as minimal. This appeal to minimal risk will take into account the harm from ignoring their distress, and so cannot serve to override their sustained distress if we have good reason to think that they will be significantly harmed by our doing so (Diekema 2006; Wendler 2006). This, then, can be extended to research involving other intensely social cognitive animals. Where research either promises therapeutic benefit or substantial knowledge relevant to a population of which a chimpanzee is a part, we might be able to proceed with research even in the face of dissent (for similar points, see DeGrazia 2007). The relevant sense of minimal risk would need to be specified, but it could be captured by risks ordinarily faced by chimpanzees either in captive settings, where they are respectfully treated, or where, in free-living populations, they are not facing anthropogenic risks to life or limb (Ferdowsian and Fuentes 2014). This sense of minimal risk approximates a sense prevalent in US pediatric research ethics. There, something presents minimal risk

> where the probability and magnitude of harm or discomfort anticipated in the proposed research are not greater, in and of themselves, than those ordinarily encountered in daily life or during the performance of routine physical or psychological examinations or tests.
>
> (Diekema 2006: S7)

There is another implication of my approach. We cannot commit to respecting the dissent capacity of other intensely social cognitive animals if we place them in circumstances or settings that serve to erode or destroy that capacity or preclude its acquisition. This will constrain how these animals are raised, housed, and treated in research settings. It is common knowledge that some laboratory environments have had catastrophic impact on the psychological well-being of captive chimpanzees (see Brüne et al 2006). Where this impact negatively affects a chimpanzee's ability to deal with future stressors, including interactions with laboratory technicians or conspecifics (perhaps they become overly aggressive at the presentation of a needle or in response to a conflict with a conspecific in group housing), or where this impact adversely affects their ability or willingness to express dissent (e.g., they express a learned helplessness), they should be removed from, or excluded from participation in, research. Their future inclusion in research should be predicated on their ability to dissent (or to express uncooperative behavior) in a way that is not indicative of a behavioral problem. Where the research might itself impact their capacity to dissent, it is ethically out of bounds.

Conclusions

I have both explained and defended my view that intensely social cognitive animals should not be forced to participate in research. When, say, a chimpanzee refuses to cooperate with researchers or attending personnel, their sustained refusal should be respected – all other things being equal. If their sustained dissent threatens their place in a study, and cannot be overcome with non-coercive measures (e.g., rewards), the chimpanzee should be excluded from the research – again, all other things being equal. What's more, the research setting in which intensely social cognitive animal research subjects are housed and used should not destroy or preclude the acquisition of their dissent capacity. Where it has, they should be removed from the relevant studies until they recover. If there are research settings that inevitably destroy or preclude the acquisition of such an animal's dissent capacity, they are ethically proscribed.

Note

1   The 3 R's are refinement, reduction, and replacement. Together, they are supposed to work to reduce the distress, pain, or stress of animals used in science. Refinement prescribes the reduction or elimination of scientifically unnecessary pain or suffering (distress). Reduction prescribes the use of the least number of animals that are scientifically necessary to conduct a study. Replacement prescribes the use of less sentient animals or non-animal systems where the use of more sentient animals is scientifically unnecessary (Flecknell 2002).

Further reading

L. Carbone, *What Animals Want: Expertise and Advocacy in Laboratory Animal Welfare Policy* (New York: Oxford University Press, 2004). D. DeGrazia, "Human-Animal Chimeras: Human Dignity, Moral Status, and Species Prejudice," *Metaphilosophy* 38(2–3) (2007): 309–29. A. Fenton, "Can a Chimp Say "No"? Reenvisioning Chimpanzee Dissent in Harmful Research," *Cambridge Quarterly of Healthcare Ethics* 23 (2014): 130–9. H. Ferdowsian and A. Fuentes, "Harms and Deprivation of Benefits for Nonhuman Primates in Research," *Theoretical Medicine and Bioethics* 35 (2014): 143–56. H. Kantin and D. Wendler, "Is There a Role for Assent and Dissent in Animal Research?" *Cambridge Quarterly of Healthcare Ethics* 24(4) (2015): 459–72. R. Walker, "Human and Animal Subjects of Research: The Moral Significance of Respect Versus Welfare," *Theoretical Medicine and Bioethics* 27 (2006): 305–31.

References

Allen, C., and Bekoff, M. (1997) *Species of Mind: The Philosophy and Biology of Cognitive Ethology*, Cambridge, MA: The MIT Press.

Beauchamp, T. L. (1999) "The Failure of Theories of Personhood," *Kennedy Institute of Ethics Journal* 9(4): 309–24.

Beauchamp, T. L., and Childress, J. F. (2012) *Principles of Biomedical Ethics*, Seventh Edition, New York: Oxford University Press.

Beauchamp, T. L., Orlans, F. B., Dresser, R., Morton, D. B., and Gluck, J. P. (2008) *The Human Use of Animals: Case Studies in Ethical Choice*, Second Edition, New York: Oxford University Press.

Berns, G. S., Brooks, A. M., and Spivak, M. (2012) "Functional MRI in Awake Unrestrained Dogs," *PloS One* 7(5): 1–7.

Bloomsmith, M. A., Schapiro, S. J., and Strobert, E. A. (2006) "Preparing Chimpanzees for Laboratory Research," *ILAR Journal* 47(4): 316–25.

Braun, A., and Bugnyar, T. (2012) "Social Bonds and Rank Acquisition in Raven Nonbreeder Aggregations," *Animal Behaviour* 84: 1507–15.

Brüne, M., Brüne-Cohrs, U., McGrew, W., and Preuschoft, S. (2006) "Psychopathology in Great Apes: Concepts, Treatment Options and Possible Homologies to Human Psychiatric Disorders," *Neuroscience and Biobehavioral Reviews* 30: 1246–59.

Carbone, L. (2004) *What Animals Want: Expertise and Advocacy in Laboratory Animal Welfare Policy*, New York: Oxford University Press.

Coleman, K. (2010) "Caring for Nonhuman Primates in Biomedical Research Facilities: Scientific, Moral and Emotional Considerations," *American Journal of Primatology* 71: 1–6.

Connor, R. C. (2007) "Dolphin Social Intelligence: Complex Alliance Relationships in Bottlenose Dolphins and a Consideration of Selective Environments for Extreme Brain Size Evolution in Mammals," *Philosophical Transactions of the Royal Society B* 362: 587–602.

Cordoni, G., and Palagi, E. (2008) "Reconciliation in Wolves (*Canis lupus*): New Evidence for a Comparative Perspective," *Ethology* 114: 298–308.

DeGrazia, D. (2007) "Human-Animal Chimeras: Human Dignity, Moral Status, and Species Prejudice," *Metaphilosophy* 38(2–3): 309–29.

de Waal, F. B. M. (1998) *Chimpanzee Politics: Power and Sex Among Apes*, Revised Edition, Baltimore, MD: The Johns Hopkins University Press.

de Waal, F. B. M., and Tyack, P. L. (2003) *Animal Social Complexity: Intelligence, Culture, and Individualized Societies*, Cambridge, MA: Harvard University Press.

Diekema, D. S. (2006) "Conducting Ethical Research in Pediatrics: A Brief Historical Overview and Review of Pediatric Regulations," *The Journal of Pediatrics* 149: S3–S11.

Donaldson, S., and Kymlicka, W. (Forthcoming) "Rethinking Membership and Participation in an Inclusive Democracy: Cognitive Disability, Children, and Animals," in B. Arneil and N. Hirschmann (eds.) *Disability and Political Theory*, New York: Cambridge University Press.

Dunayer, J. (2013) "The Rights of Sentient Beings: Moving Beyond Old and New Speciesism," in R. Corbey and A. Lanjouw (eds.) *The Politics of Species: Reshaping Our Relationships with Other Animals*, New York: Cambridge University Press, pp. 27–39.

Fenton, A. (2012a) "Neuroscience and the Problem of Other Animal Minds: Why It May Not Matter So Much for Neuroethics," *The Monist* 95(3): 463–85.

———— (2012b) "On the Need to Redress an Inadequacy in Animal Welfare Science: Toward an Internally Coherent Framework," *Biology and Philosophy* 27: 73–93.

———— (2014) "Can a Chimp Say "No"? Reenvisioning Chimpanzee Dissent in Harmful Research," *Cambridge Quarterly of Healthcare Ethics* 23: 130–39.

Fenton, A., and Shriver, A. (forthcoming) "Animal Minds: The Neuroethics of Nonhuman Dissent," in L. Syd, M. Johnson, and Karen S. Rommelfanger (eds.) *Routledge Handbook of Neuroethics*, New York: Routledge.

Ferdowsian, H., and Fuentes, A. (2014) "Harms and Deprivation of Benefits for Nonhuman Primates in Research," *Theoretical Medicine and Bioethics* 35: 143–56.

Flecknell, P. (2002) "Replacement, Reduction and Refinement," *ALTEX* 19: 73–8.

Gould, J. L. (2004) "Animal Cognition," *Current Biology* 14(10): R372–75.

Kind, A. (2015) *Persons and Personal Identity*, Cambridge: Polity.

Kittay, E. F. (2009) "Ideal Theory Bioethics and the Exclusion of People With Severe Cognitive Disabilities," in H. Lindemann, M. Verkerk, and M. U. Walker (eds.) *Naturalized Bioethics: Toward Responsible Knowing and Practice*, New York: Cambridge University Press, pp. 218–37.

Laule, G. E., Bloomsmith, M. A., and Schapiro, S. J. (2003) "The Use of Positive Reinforcement Training Techniques to Enhance the Care, Management, and Welfare of Primates in the Laboratory," *Journal of Applied Animal Welfare Science* 6(3): 163–73.

Lopresti-Goodman, S. M., Bezner, J., and Ritter, C. (2015) "Psychological Distress in Chimpanzees Rescued From Laboratories," *Journal of Trauma and Dissociation* 16: 349–66.

Luna, F., and Macklin, R. (2009) "Research Involving Human Beings," in H. Kuhse and P. Singer (eds.) *A Companion to Bioethics*, Second Edition, Malden, MA: Wiley Blackwell, pp. 457–68.

Matsuzawa, T. (2006) "Sociocognitive Development in Chimpanzees: A Synthesis of Laboratory Work and Fieldwork," in T. Matsuzawa, M. Tomonaga, and M. Tanaka (eds.) *Cognitive Development in Chimpanzees*, Tokyo: Springer-Verlag Tokyo, pp. 3–33.

Meslin, E. M., and Dickens, B. M. (2008) "Research Ethics," in P. A. Singer and A. M. Viens (eds.) *The Cambridge Textbook of Bioethics*, New York: Cambridge University Press, pp. 187–93.

Olsson, I. A. S., and Westlund, K. (2007) "More Than Numbers Matter: The Effect of Social Factors on Behaviour and Welfare of Laboratory Rodents and Non-Human Primates," *Applied Animal Behaviour Science* 103: 229–54.

Orlans, F. B. (2002) "Ethical Themes of National Regulations Governing Animal Experiments: An International Perspective," in J. P. Gluck, T. DiPasquale, and F. B. Orlans (eds.) *Applied Ethics in Animal Research: Philosophy, Regulation, and Laboratory Applications*, West Lafayette: Purdue University Press, pp. 131–47.

Perlman, J. E., Bloomsmith, M. A., Whittaker, M. A., McMillan, J. L., Minier, D. E., and McCowan, B. (2012) "Implementing Positive Reinforcement Animal Training Programs at Primate Laboratories," *Applied Animal Behaviour Science* 137: 114–26.

Poole, T. (1997) "Happy Animals Make Good Science," *Laboratory Animals* 31: 116–24.

Rowan, A. N. (2011) "The Use of Animals in Toxicological Research," in T. L. Beauchamp and R. G. Frey (eds.) *The Oxford Handbook of Animal Ethics*, New York: Oxford University Press, pp. 906–18.

Society of Toxicology (2006) "Animals in Research: The Importance of Animals in the Science of Toxicology," www.toxicology.org/pubs/docs/air/AIR_Final.pdf, accessed September 3rd, 2016.

Thierry, B. (2011) "The Macaques: A Double-Layered Social Organization," in C. J. Campbell, A. Fuentes, K. C. MacKinnon, S. K. Bearder, and R. M. Stumpf (eds.) *Primates in Perspective*, Second Edition, New York: Oxford University Press, pp. 229–41.

Walker, R. (2006) "Human and Animal Subjects of Research: The Moral Significance of Respect Versus Welfare," *Theoretical Medicine and Bioethics* 27: 305–31.

Warren, M. A. (2014) "On the Moral and Legal Status of Abortion," in H. LaFollette (ed.) *Ethics in Practice: An Anthology*, Fourth Edition, Malden, MA: Wiley Blackwell, pp. 132–40.

Wendler, D. S. (2006) "Assent in Pediatric Research: Theoretical and Practical Considerations," *Journal of Medical Ethics* 32: 229–34.

47

EMPATHY IN MIND

Lori Gruen

In everyday discussions as well as in psychological research, "empathy" has many different meanings. It has been described as an epistemic state – knowing what another individual is feeling, or as an affective state – feeling what another individual is feeling. Some see empathy as a discrete act – coming to experience the world as you imagine someone else does. Some see it as a process that blends attunement, judgment, and action.

There are also different kinds of empathy. Here we can briefly distinguish five: emotional contagion, emotional empathy, fellow feeling empathy, cognitive empathy, and a blend I call entangled empathy. One type of empathy seen in both humans and other animals is *emotional transfer/contagion*, sometimes also referred to as affective resonance. This is a spontaneous response to the feelings of another. Anyone who has lived with dogs will be familiar with this phenomenon. Dogs are emotional sponges – they often become stressed when their person is stressed, sad when their person is sad, joyful when their person is joyful. Other animals, as well as human infants and small children, also seem to experience these spontaneous reactions. Emotional contagion is a kind of mirroring that is relatively automatic.

There are less automatic, slightly more developed, versions of *emotional empathy* described in the literature. Karsten Stueber presents this type of empathy as "a pre-theoretical, quasi-perceptual capacity that enables you to recognize that someone is experiencing this or that emotion or that someone intends to accomplish such-and-such a goal" (2010, 21). This capacity, too, is something that humans share with other animals. Most helping behaviors, toward conspecifics or even other species, can best be described as a type of emotional empathy. I'll mention specific helping actions below.

While we share emotional empathy with animals, that doesn't mean that animals share with us the capacity to distinguish between the feelings of the person empathizing and the feelings or mental states of another, nor does it mean that animals project themselves into the emotional lives of others. In many social animals, for example, when an individual expresses alarm or fear, and sometimes even glee, that emotion can spread through a group and is often strongest among those who are close to the individual initially expressing the emotion. I've had the delightful experience of watching two chimpanzees in a tickle game, and as the chimpanzee who is being tickled laughs, others start laughing too, and come to join in on the fun. This *fellow feeling* sense of empathy is yet another variety, and some theorists, particularly those critical of the value of empathy in ethics or epistemology, have limited their understanding of empathy to just these sorts of experiences and reject its importance for ethics (Bloom 2016). When empathy is understood exclusively to involve an experience in which the agent loses herself in the emotions of another, might project her own feelings onto the other, or is unable to reflect upon the experience or engage in a cognitive perspective-taking process, then it seems reasonable to wonder what role, if any, empathy should play in an account of mature, reflective ethical engagement.

But for many working on empathy, empathic experiences are not thought to be simple emotional responses, but rather are reflective response from individuals who are able to differentiate themselves from others, who can knowingly simulate or take the perspective of another, and who can at least make rudimentary causal inferences. This is a type of *cognitive empathy*, and the primary difference between emotional empathy and cognitive empathy is that in the latter, the empathizer is not merely mimicking, reacting, or projecting onto the emotions of the other, but is engaged in a reflective act of imagination that allows her to gain understanding of another's frame of mind. And, as with any attempt to understand another, one might do this well or not so well, and thus there is room for revising or correcting one's empathy.

To illustrate how empathy can get things right, or sometimes wrong, consider the much-cited case of cognitive empathy discussed by Frans DeWaal:

> Kuni, a female bonobo at the Twycross Zoo in England, once captured a starling. She took the bird outside and set it onto its feet, the right way up, where it stayed shaking. When the bird didn't move, Kuni threw it a little, but it just fluttered. Kuni then picked up the starling, climbed to the highest point on the highest tree, and carefully unfolded the bird's wings, one wing in each hand, before throwing it into the air.
>
> (Preston and de Waal 2002: 19)

If Kuni is empathetically responding to the starling, her response does not seem to be emotional empathy, as she is not described as sharing the starling's fearful emotion. Rather, she appears to be attentive to the needs or interests of the starling, and may even believe that the starling would be better off flying away. And her response does not illustrate fellow feeling empathy; Kuni seems to distinguish herself from the starling, apparently recognizing that the starling flies on wings and she does not. Kuni doesn't jump with the bird off the highest branch. Yet, if this is a form of cognitive empathy, Kuni appears to have made some basic errors in her empathetic engagement. Throwing a bird who cannot fly off the highest branch of the highest tree is not a particularly sophisticated act of empathy! In the case of more apt cognitive empathy, the empathizer would seek to better understand the situation of the object of empathy. Empathy of this sort enables the empathizer to not only grasp the object's state of mind or interests, but also the features of the situation that affect her and information about what led to someone in need of empathy being in that situation in the first place.

While the Kuni anecdote is an example of cognitive empathy coupled with a mistake in understanding, recent experimental work with rats suggests that perhaps they engage in more apt forms of empathy. In one set of experiments, a rat was placed in a small plastic tube that they could escape from only if another rat who was not in the tube was able to open it. The "free" rats quickly figured out how to open the tube to release the trapped rat. In these experiments, releasing the rats did not accompany any reward other than the company of the other rat.

In another set of experiments, the "free" rat was presented with two tubes, one that contained chocolate treats, and the other that contained a trapped rat. The free rat would open both tubes, often releasing the trapped rat first so that they both could enjoy a treat (Ben-Ami et al. 2011). The free rat's behavior looks like an effective form of cognitive empathy, because they were able to understand that the trapped rat didn't like being trapped, and that a good way to resolve the trapped rat's situation would be to open the tube.

In these experiments, the free rat certainly is engaged in successful helping behavior, but perhaps they are not displaying empathy for the trapped rat but rather are just interested in satisfying their own desires for companionship (of course, both empathy and a desire for company can be operating simultaneously). To control for this possibility, however, in a set of experiments conducted in Japan, the motivation for companionship was experimentally held at bay in order to determine whether the rat would respond empathetically. In these experiments, two rats were in separate translucent boxes joined together. One of the boxes starts to fill with water, and the rat in that enclosure becomes distressed. The rat in the dry area releases the rat who is distressed getting wet, even though they will not be together upon release. As it turns out, rats who themselves have experienced being soaked act more quickly to release the trapped rat. Importantly, the rats will also release the distressed, soaked rats when they have the option of opening a door with chocolate instead. The researchers report that the rat will free the soaked rat first, 50–80% of the time (Sato et al. 2015). Given that the rats who had previously experienced their enclosure filling with water were quicker to free another in a similar situation, this experiment also demonstrates how increased empathetic aptness is a function of knowledge – not simply an automatic emotional response.

Rats are highly social and sensitive animals, and it is not surprising to observe that they respond to alleviate the distress of others. Are rats then more empathetic than chimpanzees? Of course, it may be easier for the rat to empathize with another rat as opposed to a chimpanzee empathizing with a bird, but before we jump to conclusions based on one case of Kuni's unsophisticated empathy, let's explore some other experiments with chimpanzees designed to learn about various components of cognitive empathy. These experiments sought to determine whether chimpanzees can understand that others have mental states distinct from their own; can understand the distinct interests, desires, or goals of the other; and can successfully engage in helpful behavior that facilitates the other in satisfying those interests or reaching those goals. The initial work of this kind was done by David Premack and Guy Woodruff with Sarah the chimpanzee.

In Premack and Woodruff's experiments, they videotaped humans trying to solve problems, like how to acquire a banana that is too high to reach, or how to turn a light on when there is no bulb, or how to open a can of soup. They made videotapes of a human actor in a cage trying to accomplish some task. In addition to the videos, still photographs were taken of the actor engaged in a behavior that solves the problems. Sarah was shown each video, until the last five seconds, at which point the video was put on hold. Sarah was then shown two photographs, only one of which represented a solution to the problem. For example, in the video in which the actor was trying to open a can of soup, Sarah was presented with a picture of a can opener and a picture of a hammer. The experimenter left the room, and Sarah selected one of the two photographs by placing her selection in a designated location. Sarah made the correct selection in 21 of 24 trials. So, it looked as though Sarah understood that the human actor was attempting to achieve a particular goal, understood that he faced a problem that he wanted to overcome, and was able to determine what would allow the actor to overcome the problem to reach his goal. To be able to do that, Sarah would have to attribute "at least two states of mind to the human actor, namely, intention or purpose on the one hand, and knowledge or belief on the other" (Premack and Woodruff 1978, 515).

Premack and Woodruff's work with Sarah was to try to determine whether chimpanzees had theory of mind (see the chapters in Part IV: Mindreading). One very odd criticism of this early work was that maybe Sarah was simply "empathizing" with the subject. Apparently, the concern was that empathy would somehow undermine theory of mind. Although they didn't spell it out, presumably the thought was that empathy wouldn't require any cognitive processes that built upon a distinction between one's own state of mind and that of another. Premack and Woodruff tried to control for empathy by testing different actors using a former acquaintance of Sarah's, to whom she showed no affection, and, alternatively, Sarah's favorite caregiver. Sarah selected the right responses to solve the problem for the actor she liked and selected the wrong responses, failing to solve the problem for the actor she didn't care for, at a highly significant rate. Premack and Woodruff suggested that this meant that she wasn't putting herself into the position of the human but, instead, could recognize distinct humans, solving the problem for the human she liked and not solving the problem for the human she didn't.

I have known Sarah for over a decade (although not when she was performing these particular tests) and have a sense of her distinct personality, and it seems to me that she is usually eager to help someone she likes and not help someone she doesn't like. But what does this have to do with empathy? I find that the worry that she was empathizing as a deflationary account of her attribution of cognitive states to others to be misplaced, because attributing cognitive states to others is precisely what cognitive empathy requires. Indeed, what Premack and Woodruff were suggesting is that Sarah can engage in a complex act of imagination, in which she understands the position of the other who is facing a problem that is not one that she faces (a very human problem, no less, but one that she was familiar enough with given that she was raised among humans from a very early age). And she can determine what it would take to solve the problem. In addition, she might decide she doesn't want to help someone she doesn't like. We might say that she could empathize, but chooses not to complete her empathetic imagination process with action to solve the problem. Despite her refusal to help someone she doesn't like, it is hard to deny that this is a fairly sophisticated cognitive process.

It appears that some chimpanzees, like the rats, are able to recognize when others are in need of help. In work done decades after the experiments with Sarah, young chimpanzees were asked to identify a human's goal, and reliably and spontaneously helped a friendly human achieve his goal. While engaged in what appeared to be informal social interactions with the experimenter, the young chimpanzees were tested on their ability to respond to a nonverbal request for help. For example, when the experimenter was using a sponge to clean a table and dropped the sponge onto the floor, the chimpanzee he was interacting with responded to his gestural request to retrieve the sponge by picking it up and handing it to him (Warneken and Tomasello 2006). In Sarah's case, she decided when and whether to help, but presumably, like the younger chimpanzees in the Warneken studies, was able to recognize that help was needed.

While there are a number of other studies showing that chimpanzees understand quite a bit about others' mental states and are able to respond appropriately to others' goals, intentions, and emotions, all of which makes sense given the complexity of the social relationships they have to navigate, there is still some skepticism about whether other animals are empathetic in anything like the way that humans can be. Yet when we look at the rat empathy experiments, it makes sense to describe the free rats as caring about the state that the distressed rats are in. They may or may not feel that distress, but they recognize the conditions that are the cause of distress, they understand what it might take to alleviate that distress, and they act to do so. Sarah, too, may or may not experience, affectively, the frustration the actor is exhibiting, but she understands that the actor has a problem to solve and she recognizes how to solve it, and when she is so inclined, she may help solve the problem.

Empathy that isn't merely emotional empathy involves understanding the state of mind of the other, others' physical or social situation, and their differing goals. I have argued that it also involves engaging in some action to help the other (Gruen 2015). The relationships that the empathizer is in also will play some role. This is what I call *entangled empathy*. Entangled empathy is an experiential process involving a blend of emotion and cognition in which we recognize we are in relationships with others, and are called upon to be responsive and responsible in these relationships by attending to another's needs, interests, desires, vulnerabilities, hopes, and sensitivities. Relationships between interacting individuals are absolutely crucial to gaining insight into what other humans and other animals might be thinking (Andrews and Gruen 2014). We know that chimpanzees recognize relationships between individuals. Group members know the relationships between mother and infant, and relationships between males who form a coalition. They can identify familiar individuals, individuals from rival groups, and unknown individuals. They have a very keen sense of the quite distinct personalities of others in their social groups. They can even make determinations about whether to take seriously the vocalizations and displays of others. In experimental setups, they make choices based on individual differences; chimpanzees prefer to cooperate with partners who share rewards more equitably (Melis et al. 2009), and they know which partners will best help them to achieve certain tasks (Melis et al. 2006).

People who live with dogs usually understand the complexities of these relationships well. We know that dogs form different sorts of relationships with particular dogs, and this will impact a whole range of behaviors – for example, how they communicate intentions, how they read signals (in play, for example), and even who they show concern towards. (See, e.g., Horowitz 2010 or Hare and Woods 2013.)

By ignoring relationships, investigators assume it is possible to step outside of the social or to detach from the experiences of our particular embodiments and deny that we are entangled with others. It is indeed odd that most of the studies on empathy don't mention the particular relationships, when it seems so important given that the ability to empathize functions as a key resource in social navigation. It is an especially important skill in the absence of language. Being able to empathize with others in one's group allows one to learn what is expected and what is prohibited, and the safest way to interact with others. Empathy is important for understanding group norms. This is true of most social beings, like chimpanzees and dogs and rats.

Other animals may not have the exact kinds of empathy that humans are capable of, but sadly, humans continually fail to engage their empathy. We're too often like Kuni, lifting up someone's broken wing and thinking they should be able to fly, or ignoring those who are suffering altogether. Many people just don't want to think too far beyond their living rooms, workplaces, and neighborhoods. When people *do* care, that care is often limited to those closest to them or most like them but not beyond, so whatever empathy they have is truncated. Empathy is also something we are taught to "get over" or grow out of. We learn to quash our caring reactions for others, and our busy lives and immediate preoccupations provide excuses for not honing our empathetic skills. Yet not recognizing that we are in complex relationships that require entangled empathetic responses, towards other humans as well as animals, is a mistake. It minimizes our agency, weakens our imagination, and undermines compassion. To correct it, perhaps we could learn a thing or two from empathetic rats.

Further reading

Lori Gruen. 2015. *Entangled Empathy: An Alternative Ethic for Our Relationship With Animals*. New York: Lantern Books.
Heidi Maimbom (ed.). 2014. *Empathy and Morality*. Oxford: Oxford University Press.
Carl Safina. 2016. *Beyond Words: What Animals Think and Feel*. New York: Henry Holt.

References

Andrews, Kristin, and Lori Gruen. 2014. "Empathy in Other Apes" in H. Maimbom (ed.) *Empathy and Morality*. Oxford: Oxford University Press, 193–209.

Ben-Ami, Inbal, Jean Decety, and Peggy Mason. 2011. "Empathy and Pro-Social Behavior in Rats". *Science*, 334(6061): 1427–1430.

Bloom, Paul. 2016. *Against Empathy*. New York: Ecco Press.

Gruen, Lori. 2015. *Entangled Empathy*. New York: Lantern Press.

Hare, Brian, and Vanessa Woods. 2013. *The Genius of Dogs*. New York: Plume.

Horowitz, Alexandra. 2010. *Inside of a Dog*. New York: Scribner.

Melis, Alicia P., Josep Call, and Michael Tomasello. 2006. "Chimpanzees Conceal Visual and Auditory Information From Others". *Journal of Comparative Psychology*, 120: 154–162.

Melis, Alicia P., Brian Hare, and Michael Tomasello. 2009. "Chimpanzees Coordinate in a Negotiation Game". *Evolution and Human Behavior*, 30: 381–392.

Premack, David, and Guy Woodruff. 1978. "Does the Chimpanzee Have a Theory of Mind?". *Behavioral and Brain Sciences*, 1(4): 515–526.

Preston, Stephanie D., and Frans de Waal. 2002. "Empathy: Its Ultimate and Proximate Bases". *Behavioral and Brain Sciences*, 25(1): 1–20.

Sato, Nobuya, Ling Tan, Kazushi Tate, and Maya Okada. 2015. "Rats Demonstrate Helping Behavior Toward a Soaked Conspecific". *Animal Cognition*, 18(5): 1039–1047.

Stueber, Karsten. 2010. *Rediscovering Empathy*. Cambridge, MA: MIT Press.

Warneken, Felix, and Michael Tomasello. 2006. "Altruistic Helping in Infants and Young Chimpanzees". *Science*, 311(5765): 1301–1303.

48

USING, OWNING AND EXPLOITING ANIMALS

Alasdair Cochrane

A key feature of many debates in animal ethics is the distinction between 'animal welfare' and 'animal rights'. According to prevailing thought, most theories of animal ethics can be assigned to one of two schools. Theories of animal welfare accept that sentient nonhuman animals have moral status; that is, that individuals with the capacity for consciousness and sensation are worthy of moral consideration in their own right. As a result of this status, these theories are claimed to argue that humans' use of animals ought to be reformed, most commonly by restricting or eliminating the infliction of pain on the animals involved. Theories of animal rights, on the other hand, are argued to be much more radical. For what is said to distinguish animal rights positions is that they do not seek to *regulate* the use of animals in zoos, agriculture, laboratories, pet-keeping and so on; rather, they seek to *abolish* all such uses. According to this perspective, animal rights theories are those which call for the end of the human use, ownership and exploitation of animals (Francione 1996, 2000, 2008; Sztybel 1998). We can see, then, how this understanding of animal rights considers them to be analogous to human rights. For human rights do not demand that we regulate slavery, torture or human trafficking to make those practices more humane; instead, they demand that such forms of exploitation be abolished.

In this chapter, I want to challenge this understanding of animal rights – and in so doing, to challenge the strict dichotomy between animal welfarism and animal rights which has come to dominate so much ethical thinking about animals. For the idea that sentient nonhuman animals possess rights does not, in itself, tell us anything about *which* rights that they have. To understand which rights animals possess, we need to have an underlying theory which we can use to justify the ascription of particular rights to them. In the next section, I will briefly outline the most popular and plausible such theory, the interest-based approach, which assigns rights to the important interests of individuals. In the following sections, I will then argue that when we have a proper understanding of the interests of nonhuman animals, it becomes clear that the majority of them have no intrinsic interest in not being used, owned or exploited; and because they lack those interests, they also lack the equivalent rights. In sum, then, I will argue that contrary to the prevailing view, under the best understanding of animal rights, animals have no rights not to be used, owned or exploited by human beings, when such use, ownership or exploitation does not cause them suffering or other forms of harm.

Animal interests and animal rights

To reiterate, in order to understand just what kinds of rights (if any) animals have, we need to have a robust understanding of the kinds of things that rights are and how they can be justified. In other words, then, we need a theory of rights. In the philosophical literature on rights, there are two main rival theories: the 'will theory' and the 'interest theory'. For the will theory (some-times also known as the choice theory) of rights, the essential feature of a right is the presence of choice in the right-holder. To be more specific, it is claimed under this theory that when an individual has a right to something, then that individual is able to demand or waive enforcement of the relevant duty (Hart 1967; Sumner 1987; Simmonds 1998; Steiner 1998). To clarify, let us take the example of a loan: I have lent you some money, and you have agreed to pay me back. It is clear that in this situation, you have a duty to repay me. Moreover, it is perfectly legitimate for me to demand repayment from you, or, if I so choose, I can waive your duty to repay, thereby cancelling the debt.

One of the important problems with this understanding of rights is that it means that indi-viduals without the power of choice – such as young babies and the severely mentally disa-bled – lack rights. This implication is hard to reconcile with the powerful conviction many of us share which takes it as obvious that vulnerable individuals such as these possess rights. After all, it seems to clash violently with our ordinary understanding of rights to claim that young babies and the severely mentally disabled lack the right not to be tortured, for example. And that conviction is unmoved by the simple fact that such individuals lack the power of choice. Many of us would argue that these individuals have such a right for the simple reason that they have a powerful interest in not being caused the excruciating pain which torture entails. For this and other reasons, then, many philosophers have adopted a theory of rights which is grounded in *interests*. For interest theories of rights, the essential feature of rights is the *benefit* afforded to the right-holder (MacCormick 1977; Raz 1988; Kramer 1998). On this view, rights are essentially those interests that are sufficiently important to ground duties on the part of others (Raz 1988). Because babies have an interest in not being tortured which is weighty enough to ground a duty in others, they have a right not to be tortured; and because I have an interest in being repaid which grounds a duty on your part, I have a right to the repayment of the money I leant you.

Of course, the adoption of the interest theory of rights also has another important impli-cation. It means that any individual who has interests is also a putative possessor of rights. Since interests are usually attributed to those individuals who can experience the world and themselves in it, this means that sentient nonhuman animals are possible rights bearers (Fein-berg 1974). And indeed, the interest theory has been adopted by many philosophers who have sought to justify the extension of rights to animals (Feinberg 1974; Rachels 1990; Rollin 2004; Cochrane 2012). Less attention, however, has been given to using the theory to outline the *con-tent* of animal rights. This is unfortunate, because the simple fact that animals can possess rights on the basis of their interests does not, by itself, determine which rights they have. It certainly does not mean that they have the same rights as humans, or each other, for they are unlikely to possess the same set of interests, or interests of the same weight. The important question for any theory of animal rights, then, is which animal interests (if any) are sufficiently important to ground duties in other individuals.

I believe that sentient animals have many interests which are important enough to ground duties on the part of others. Indeed, elsewhere I have argued (Cochrane 2012) that their inter-ests in *not being made to suffer* and in *continued life* are sufficiently important to generate rights to such goods. And quite obviously, the recognition of just these two rights has radical implica-tions for a huge range of human practices, including agriculture, medical research, sport and far more. There is not the space here to provide a full defence of this claim. Instead, the aim of this chapter is to concentrate on a range of other rights that are alleged to flow logically from an animal rights position: the rights of animals not to be used, owned or exploited by human beings. In the following sections, I will argue that the vast majority of animals do not have sufficiently important interests in not being used, owned or exploited by human beings to ground equivalent rights. This is not to say that animals are not and cannot be harmed by their use, ownership and exploitation by humans. Clearly, the use of animals frequently inflicts all sorts of harms upon them, including suffering and death – and those forms of use should be condemned on the basis of the harms they cause. But my concern is with whether use, ownership and exploitation *per se* cause harm to sentient animals. And I will argue that for the vast majority of animals, they do not.

Using animals

As outlined above, for many proponents of animal rights, all human uses of animals must be abolished. But do animals have an interest in not being used by humans? Moreover, do they have an interest in not being used by humans, even when such use causes them no suffering or other forms of hardship? One way in which it might be argued that they do is to point to a more general interest that animals possess in being treated 'respectfully'. To explain, one of the most famous proponents of animals rights, Tom Regan (2004), has argued that animals have one basic moral right: the right to respectful treatment. Regan claims that sentient animals possess this right on the grounds that they are individuals whose value cannot be reduced to their usefulness to others. In other words, sentient animals possess 'inherent value'. Regan (243) argues that they have such value because they are 'subjects-of-a-life': beings with beliefs, desires, a sense of themselves over time, interests in their own fate, and so on. For Regan, subjects-of-a-life possess a value all of their own, a value which is independent of how they are valued by others. In turn, this means that they have a right to respectful treatment: a right never to be treated solely as a means to securing the best overall consequences (249, 277). For Gary Francione, Regan's theory logically entails the abolition of *all* human use of animals: "The use of animals for food, sport, entertainment, or research involves treating animals merely as means to ends, and this constitutes a violation of the respect principle" (Francione 1996: 18).

The first issue that arises from this analysis is whether animals do indeed have an interest in always being treated as beings with inherent value, and thus in never being treated solely as a means to securing the best overall consequences. Attributing such an interest to animals certainly seems plausible. After all, treating an individual in a way which is *solely* designed to secure the best overall consequences fails to recognise that individual as having any worth at all. And surely if animals have any interests at all, they must have an interest that they and their interests count for something. But just because animals possess this interest, it does not follow, as Francione thinks, that all human uses of animals are thereby impermissible. For quite simply, not all human uses of animals – or indeed other humans – do or must treat those individuals *solely* as a means to secure the best overall consequences, and thus as if they have no inherent value. In fact, it is actually quite hard to think of examples of uses of animals which grant absolutely no value at all to animals, and which are aimed squarely at the best overall consequences. Take industrial animal farming, which entails extracting as much protein at as little cost as possible, usually resulting in severe suffering and death for the animals involved. Even in this context, most jurisdictions place *some* limits on such practices for animal welfare concerns. We may justifiably regard those limits as woefully inadequate, but they are limits nonetheless. As such, even the use of animals in industrial animal agriculture treats animals as if they have *some* value of their own. More importantly, we can all think of many other uses of animals – whether it be the use of cats as companions, of backyard chickens to produce eggs, of dogs to provide assistance to those with disabilities – where the animals involved are obviously and uncontroversially treated as possessing value of their own. Many such animals lead flourishing lives that are of value to them, in spite of the fact that they are used by humans.

At this point it may be objected that even these animals are harmed by their use by humans. For while many companion cats, for example, seem to enjoy their lives, the truth is that they are pursuing ends that they have had no choice in setting. Humans control every aspect of cats' existence, including their features, characteristics and opportunities. In effect, it can be argued that these animals are 'slaves' who lack meaningful control over their own lives, and are thus harmed as a result (Francione 2012; Bryant 1990: 9). The problem with this view, however, is that it is unclear that the majority of animals do have an interest in having control over their own lives in this way. To explain, the reason why we believe that most adult humans possess an interest in pursuing ends that they have chosen for themselves comes down to the fact that they are *persons*: individuals with the ability to frame, revise and pursue their own conceptions of the good (Rawls 1993: 72). This means that for most humans, being in control of fundamental choices regarding family, employment, religious belief and so on are central to living well. The requirements of a decent life for most animals, however, are quite different in this regard. The majority of nonhuman animals lack the ability to frame, revise and pursue their own concep-tions of the good.[1] They thus also lack that intrinsic interest in having ultimate control over their own lives (Cochrane 2009). As such, while controlling humans through coercing them into particular forms of use is necessarily harmful, no such harm is entailed by using most ani-mals in such a way.

There thus seems to be little reason to believe that most animals have an intrinsic interest in not being used by humans. As such, we cannot claim that all sentient animals have a right not to be used by humans when such use does not entail suffering, death or other forms of harm.

Owning animals

What then of owning animals? You will recall that another purported implication of animal rights is that it means that they ought never to be the property of human (or other) beings. But do animals have an interest in not being owned? Many proponents of animal rights take it for granted that they do have such an interest. In so doing, they have largely followed the claims of Gary Francione (2008), who has argued that animals have a basic interest in not being owned, because of a strict dichotomy in the law between 'things' and 'persons'. He argues that if an entity has the status of 'property', then that individual is classified as a 'thing' whose interests will necessarily be subordinated to those of property-owning 'persons'.

But there are two problems with this analysis. First of all, it is not at all evident that the property status of animals means that all of their interests are necessarily subordinated to those of their human owners. The right of ownership is not an absolute right to do as one pleases with one's property; it is instead a much more qualified concept entailing a bundle of rights and entitlements (Honoré 1961). Crucially, the content and stringency of that bundle of rights will vary upon context. This means that animals may well be property under the law, but that the law can still place restrictions on what an owner can do with her property. Importantly, the law can place restrictions which prioritise the interests of the owned animal above the human property-owner. And we can see that the law does precisely that in many jurisdictions. For example, in the EU, it is illegal to chain calves in veal crates. As such, human property-owners are denied the freedom to pursue their business and culinary interests as they might desire; and such a restriction is in place for the sake of the welfare of animals. Put simply, ownership does not necessarily entail that the interests of the owner must be prioritised over those of the property (Sunstein 2004, 11; Garner 2006; Cochrane 2009).

Nonetheless, it still might be claimed that animals have an interest in not being owned quite simply because it officially confers upon them an inferior and 'second-class' status. But if being owned does not necessarily mean that their interests will be undermined or subordinated to those of others, it is unclear why having such a status would be of concern to animals. After all, animals have no conception of what property is, nor do most of them have the kinds of capacities for self-respect which might be undermined if they were aware of their second-class status. Furthermore, it is also worth challenging the oft-repeated claim that there is and must be a strict and hierarchical dichotomy in the law between things and persons. To reiterate, owner-ship signifies the presence of a bundle of rights: to use, to possess, to transfer and so on. But the particular bundle of rights and the stringency of those rights will vary with different examples of ownership. In this light, there is no strict dividing line between owners and the owned, but instead a far more fragmented picture where the vast majority of us are both the subjects and objects of various incidents of ownership. By way of example, just consider the incidents of ownership that parents have over their children, such as the right to possess; or that employers have over employees, such as the right to income; or that states have over citizens, such as the right to manage; and so on. All such incidents ought to be qualified, of course; but still, they are nonetheless incidents of ownership to which human persons are subjected.

In sum, then, we cannot say that animals have an intrinsic interest in not being owned by humans. As such, there is no reason for assigning to them a right not to be owned by humans, provided that such ownership does not cause them suffering, death or other forms of harm.

Exploiting animals

As well as ruling out the use and ownership of animals, many also claim that an animal rights position necessarily entails that animals ought not to be exploited. But do animals have an inter-est in not being exploited? This is a somewhat tricky question on the basis that the term 'exploi-tation' is used in a rather loose way, usually with negative connotations, in both the animal ethics literature and in everyday discourse. And, of course, if exploitation is simply equivalent to being caused suffering or other forms of harm, then it would be very easy to acknowledge that animals have such an interest, and one which can be said to ground duties on the part of others.

However, exploitation also has a more specific Marxist definition, and this is one that is employed by some proponents of animal rights. To explain, a number of thinkers (Noske 1997; Perlo 2002; Hribal 2003) have drawn on Marxist theory to justify animal rights. Furthermore, part of that reasoning entails showing how animals are exploited by capitalist production in much the same way as human workers. After all, both humans and animals work for the capital-ist who extracts a surplus from their labor in order to make a profit. It is this element of 'unpaid labor' which makes the relations between the capitalist and human or animal workers necessarily exploitative.

So do animals have an interest in not performing unpaid labor for human employers? If they are compensated for their labour to the extent that they may lead flourishing lives and enjoy freedom from suffering, death or other forms of hardship, then it is hard to see why they have such an interest. If chickens are kept to lay eggs for profit, or sheep are kept to produce wool for profit, so long as the animals involved are able to lead enjoyable lives free from suffering, it is very hard to identify the harm in these practices. In other words, then, it is hard to see why the animals involved have an interest in not being exploited.

But perhaps there is a deeper reason to believe that animals have an interest in not being exploited. For perhaps animals have an interest in not being *alienated* from the full product of their labour. To explain, Marx sees productive labour as the essential human activity. A truly human life necessarily entails intentionally labouring on the world, transforming the world and producing objects. Free, conscious and spontaneous productive labour is what Marx calls humanity's 'species-being'. However, when an individual is forced to labour for someone else, as they are under wage-labour capitalism, then that individual is *alienated* – which includes being alienated from the full product of her labour (Marx 1994: 58–66). Perhaps, then, animals share this interest in not being alienated from the full product of their labour – explaining why the chickens and sheep in the examples above are harmed by their exploitation.

The obvious problem with this reasoning, however, is that it is far from clear that productive labour *is* the essential activity of human beings, let alone of animals. After all, most of us readily accept that those individuals who cannot transform the world and produce objects – such as young children or those with serious disabilities – can nevertheless flourish as human beings. This seems obvious on the simple basis that such individuals can enjoy a whole host of other goods, such as love, play, intellectual stimulation and so on. In this light, transforming the world to produce objects is not of ultimate importance to humans. This makes being alienated from the full product of one's labour of questionable importance to a flourishing life. And the same reasoning surely applies to nonhuman animals. Transforming the world and producing objects is not the essential feature of any species of animal. There are a whole range of goods that are far more important to them. As a result, it is reasonable to believe that it is permissible for humans to take some of what animals produce, so long as they are not made to suffer, killed or otherwise harmed in the process.

It may, of course, be responded that under capitalism, suffering is intrinsic to the process of exploitation. After all, it can be argued that capitalist processes have an insatiable demand for profit, which entails extracting as much surplus value as possible from workers, which inevitably entails suffering for the worker. And perhaps we can see this evidenced in the ways in which animal agriculture has increasingly become more intensive in order to boost profits. But while we should not downplay the ways in which the search for profits has led to increased levels of animal suffering, that should not lead us to the conclusion that increased suffering is *inevitable* under the capitalist mode of production. And we can see this from the example of animal agriculture itself. For as methods have become more intensive, many states have legislated to outlaw some of the most egregious forms of intensive animal agriculture in order to reduce suffering. We can, of course, readily acknowledge that such measures are woefully inadequate. Nevertheless, they show that the suffering of animals within the capitalist system need not necessarily increase, and is not intrinsic to the extraction of profit itself. That is to say, if there is sufficient political will to reduce suffering, it can be done.

Conclusion

In this chapter, I have sought to challenge the prevailing view that a theory of animal rights necessarily demands that the use, ownership and exploitation of animals be abolished. I have argued that to understand what rights animals possess, we need a convincing theory of rights, and the most plausible such theory for animals is interest-based. As such, in order to discover which rights animals possess, we need to know what interests they have which are sufficiently important to ground duties in others. I have argued that animals have no intrinsic interest in not being used, owned or exploited by human beings. As such, they have no such equivalent rights. This is not to say that uses of animals which cause animals suffering, death or other harms should not be condemned; they certainly should – but on the basis that such uses cause suffering, death and other harms. Using, owing and exploiting animals are not in and of themselves harmful to the vast majority of sentient animals.

Note

1   The exceptions may be cetaceans and the great apes, who many claim do exhibit capacities for personhood. See White (2007) and Singer and Cavalieri (1993).

Further reading

The most notable example of the view that an animal rights position entails the rights not to be used, owned and exploited is to be found in Gary Francione's work. His book, *Animals, Property, and the Law* (1995) outlines his argument clearly and usefully. And further helpful elaborations can be found in his collection, *Animals as Persons: Essays on the Abolition of Animal Exploitation* (2008). Cass Sunstein and Martha Nussbaum's edited collection, *Animal Rights: Current Debates and New Directions* (2005), has a number of fantastic papers which engage with these themes. I lay out my own view that animal rights do not imply the rights not to be used, owned and exploited more fully in *Animal Rights Without Liberation* (2012). Some important critiques of that argument have emerged, including Jason Wyckoff's paper "Toward Justice for Animals" (2014).

References

Bryant, J. (1990) *Fettered Kingdoms*, revised ed., Winchester: Fox Press.

Cochrane, A. (2009) "Do Animals Have an Interest in Liberty?" *Political Studies* 57: 660–79.

––––––– (2012) *Animal Rights Without Liberation*, New York: Columbia University Press.

Feinberg, J. (1974) "The Rights of Animals and Unborn Generations" in W. T. Blackstone (ed.), *Philosophy and Environmental Crisis*, Athens, GA: University of Georgia Press, pp. 43–68.

Francione, G. L. (1995) *Animals, Property, and the Law*, Philadelphia, PA: Temple University Press.

––––––– (1996) *Rain Without Thunder: The Ideology of the Animal Rights Movement*, Philadelphia, PA: Temple University Press.

––––––– (2000) *Introduction to Animal Rights: Your Child or the Dog?* Philadelphia, PA: Temple University Press.

––––––– (2008) *Animals as Persons: Essays on the Abolition of Animal Exploitation*, New York: Columbia University Press.

––––––– (2012) "'Pets': The Inherent Problem of Domestication." July 31. www.abolitionistapproach.com/pets-the-inherent-problems-of-domestication/#.Vo0hw_mLTIU. Accessed 6 January 2016.

Garner, R. W. (2006) "Animal Welfare: A Political Defense", *Journal of Animal Law and Ethics* 1: 161–7.

Hart, H. L. A. (1967) "Are There Any Natural Rights?" in A. Quinton (ed.), *Political Philosophy*, Oxford: Oxford University Press, pp. 53–66.

Honoré, A. M. (1961) "Ownership" in A. G. Guest (ed.), *Oxford Essays in Jurisprudence*, Oxford: Oxford University Press, pp. 107–47.

Hribal, J. (2003) "Animals Are Part of the Working Class: A Challenge to Labor History", *Labor History* 44: 435–53.

Kramer, M. H. (1998) "Rights Without Trimmings" in M. H. Kramer, N. E. Simmonds and H. Steiner (eds.), *A Debate Over Rights: Philosophical Enquiries*, Oxford: Oxford University Press, pp. 7–112.

MacCormick, N. (1977) "Rights in Legislation", in P. M. S. Hacker and Joseph Raz (eds.), *Law, Morality, and Society: Essays in Honour of H. L. A. Hart*, Oxford: Clarendon Press, pp. 189–209.

Marx, K. (1994) "Economic and Philosophical Manuscripts (Selections)" in L. Simon (ed.), *Karl Marx: Selected Writings*, Indianapolis, IN: Hackett.

Noske, B. (1997) *Beyond Boundaries: Humans and Animals*, Montreal: Black Rose Books.

Perlo, K. (2002) "Marxism and the Underdog", *Society and Animals* 10: 303–18.

Rachels, J. (1990) *Created From Animals: The Moral Implications of Darwinism*, Oxford: Oxford University Press.

Rawls, J. (1993) *Political Liberalism*, New York: Columbia University Press.

Raz, J. (1988) *The Morality of Freedom*, Oxford: Clarendon Press.

Regan, T. (2004) *The Case for Animal Rights*, 2nd ed., Berkeley CA: University of California Press.

Rollin, B. (2004) *Animal Rights and Human Morality*, 3rd ed., New York: Prometheus Books.

Simmonds, N. E. (1998) "Rights at the Cutting Edge" in M. H. Kramer, N. E. Simmonds and H. Steiner (eds.), *A Debate Over Rights: Philosophical Enquiries*, Oxford: Oxford University Press, pp. 113–232.

Singer, P., and Paola Cavalieri (eds.) (1993) *The Great Ape Project: Equality Beyond Humanity*, London: Fourth Estate.

Steiner, H. (1998) "Working Rights" in M. H. Kramer, N. E. Simmonds and H. Steiner (eds.), *A Debate Over Rights: Philosophical Enquiries*, Oxford: Oxford University Press, pp. 235–300.

Sumner, L. W. (1987) *The Moral Foundation of Rights*, Oxford: Clarendon Press.

Sunstein, C. R. (2004) "Introduction: What are Animal Rights?" in C. R. Sunstein and M. C. Nussbaum (eds.), *Animal Rights: Current Debates and New Direction*, New York: Oxford University Press, pp. 3–18.

Sunstein, C. R., and M. C. Nussbaum (2005) *Animal Rights: Current Debates and New Direction*, New York: Oxford University Press.

Sztybel, D. (1998) "Distinguishing Animal Rights From Animal Welfare" in M. Bekoff (ed.), *Encyclopedia of Animal Rights and Animal Welfare*, Westport, CT: Greenwood Publishing, pp. 130–2.

White, T. I. (2007) *In Defense of Dolphins: A New Moral Frontier*, Malden, MA: Blackwell.

Wyckoff, J. (2014) "Toward Justice for Animals", *Journal of Social Philosophy* 45: 539–53.

49

ANIMAL MIND AND ANIMAL ETHICS

Bernard E. Rollin

My ingression into the philosophical questions raised by animal ethics and animal mind took place in virtue of both theoretical and practical issues pressed upon me in the mid-1970s. On the theoretical level, I had been teaching history of philosophy for many years, and was struck by how little attention philosophers paid to the moral status of animals, even as they regularly developed arcane proofs that time was unreal, motion was impossible, and the world was an unchanging Plenum; and they engaged questions of whether the Absolute was happy or not, whether the mind exists in the brain or the brain exists in the mind, and so on.

Ignoring the question of our moral obligations to animals struck me as inexplicable, given the degree to which the conduct of human daily life has rested foursquare throughout all of history on the use and consumption of animals. Although at that point in my career I knew very little about animal use in society, I did know that in the United States alone, we utilized billions of animals for food; tens of millions of animals for research and toxicity testing; and killed millions of unwanted animals in pounds and "shelters," the latter a practice for which there did not exist even a slight semblance of justification. I also came to learn, *mirabile dictu*, that in none of these uses did animals enjoy the best possible treatment even commensurate with that use!

In the history of philosophy, I found only sporadic mention of the relevance of morality to animal use. St. Thomas Aquinas, for example, stressed the point that lacking immortal souls (?), animals enjoyed *no moral status*, but that one should avoid the infliction of deliberate, sadistic, deviant acts of cruelty upon them, since people who perform such acts will inexorably move to abusing people, a position echoed by Kant later based on the fact that animals are incapable of rationality. (In the 20th century, psychological research confirmed the inevitable progression from animal cruelty to abuse of humans; see Ascione 1993; Felthous and Kellert 1987.)

One notable exception to ignoring the intrinsic rather than instrumental moral status of animals was provided by utilitarian philosopher Jeremy Bentham. As Bentham opined,

> Other animals, which, on account of their interests having been neglected by the insensibility of the ancient jurists, stand degraded into the class of things. . . . The day has been, I grieve it to say in many places it is not yet past, in which the greater part of the species, under the denomination of slaves, have been treated . . . upon the same footing as . . . animals are still. The day may come, when the rest of the animal creation may acquire those rights which never could have been withholden from them but by

the hand of tyranny. The French have already discovered that the blackness of skin is no reason why a human being should be abandoned without redress to the caprice of a tormentor. It may come one day to be recognized that the number of legs, the villosity of the skin, or the termination of the os sacrum, are reasons equally insufficient for abandoning a sensitive being to the same fate. What else is it that should trace the insuperable line? Is it the faculty of reason, or perhaps, the faculty for discourse?. . . . The question is not, Can they reason? nor, Can they talk? but, Can they suffer? Why should the law refuse its protection to any sensitive being? . . . The time will come when humanity will extend its mantle over everything which breathes.

(Bentham 1789: 310–311)

Although Bentham's arguments were revolutionary, and utilitarianism persisted into the 20th century as a basis for according moral status to animals, I do not find it adequate. For example, it is difficult to see how one gives, as Bentham suggests, a numerical score to pain. How, for example, does one weigh physical pain against psychological pain on the same scale? How does one score the pain resulting from branding a cow versus the suffering engendered by removing a calf from mother shortly after birth? Also, people can and do feel comfortable rejecting a utilitarian basis for ethics. I wanted a basis for ethics that follows from what people already believe.

On the practical level, I had been asked in the mid-1970s by faculty members of the College of Veterinary Medicine at Colorado State University (CSU) to develop the first course ever taught in the world on veterinary medical ethics – in essence, to create the field. Part of the charge was extrapolating to where the moral status of animals would go in the near future, and what effect that would have on veterinary medicine. I agreed, and propaedeutic to actually teaching the course, I immersed myself in the field of veterinary medicine. In my naïveté at the time, I took it for granted that I could find no greater champions of animal welfare than veterinarians – animal doctors – even as pediatricians in the 19th century were leaders of the social fight for child protection.

After years of preparation, I taught the veterinary ethics course for the first time in the spring semester of 1978. I found myself being educated by the students in a manner that quickly dashed my utopian attitudes toward veterinary medicine. I learned of numerous atrocious laboratory exercises that students were compelled to perform during the first two years of their education – for example, being forced to bleed out dogs in order to learn that dogs without blood died of hemorrhagic shock. Or being forced to administer cyanide to animals to learn that cyanide was toxic. Or, that in the third week of the first year in veterinary school, one anatomy professor had devised a diabolical laboratory exercise. Working in groups of four, the students were ordered to feed cream to young adolescent cats, and then, *without an iota of training in surgery or anesthesia*, the students were obliged to perform exploratory visceral surgery, ostensibly in order to watch the transport of cream through the intestinal villi. Inexplicably, the professor in question was so proud of the lab that he invited me in as an observer. Morally shaken by what I saw, I asked him to explain the true purpose of the lab. With a knowing smile, he replied that it is to "teach them that they are in veterinary school now, and, if they are 'soft,' to get the hell out early."

I was treated to even more shocking revelations as the semester progressed. The most horrific thing I learned was how surgery was taught in the second year. Each small group of students was provided with a pound dog and required to do nine successive unrelated surgeries on that animal over three weeks. Even worse, only one nurse was available to provide care for those animals post-surgically. Given that we had 140 students in a class at that time, and commensurately a significant number of animals, there was little she could do. If the students wanted to provide aftercare, they needed to cut class to do so, and these students did not cut classes. At the behest of an older student, I visited the ward in which these luckless animals were held between surgeries, and what I found was a scene worthy of Hieronymous Bosch, populated by dogs in excruciating pain, not even provided with an aspirin.

I immediately protested this outrageous state of affairs and was effective in putting a stop to it (Rollin 2011a). But not before I learned that not only did these animals never receive analgesia (i.e. post-surgical pain control), but essentially no animals did in veterinary medicine. The protocol for teaching surgery was radically changed, with the animals being euthanized on the table after the first surgery, and similarly for each lab thereafter, thereby eliminating postsurgical pain.

At the same time, I established a relationship with a new staff member hired to oversee our use of laboratory animals. He had an extensive history of managing laboratory animals in both Britain and Canada, and wanted a philosopher to help sort out the many ethical issues involved in the use of animals in research. We also enlisted a world-famous professor of veterinary surgery who had helped found the professional association for laboratory animal veterinarians. He confirmed the total lack of analgesic use, even in research surgeries generating the most extreme pain. He told the story of coming to CSU to set up a research laboratory for experimental surgery. Since many of his experiments, such as those that resulted in developing the artificial hip joint for humans, involved a fairly severe level of pain for the animals, he visited the veterinary school pharmacy in order to lay in a supply of opiate analgesics. The veterinary staff was bewildered, totally unaccustomed to any use of analgesia. "If they hurt, give them an aspirin" was their response.

Thus, by the late 1970s, I was engaged both in writing a book designed to establish a higher moral status for animals than had hitherto been socially acknowledged, which book was published in 1980 (Rollin 1981), and, in consort with the above two veterinarians, attempting to create federal legislation requiring the control of pain for animals used in research, testing, and education (Rollin 2006).

In that book, and in subsequent writings, I stressed the absence of morally relevant differences between people and at least those animals we can argue are conscious. I equally argued for morally relevant similarities, most specifically that what we do to animals *matters to them*, as they possess what Aristotle called a *telos*, a biological and psychological nature consisting of a unique set of interests – what we may call the "pigness" of a pig, the "cowness" of a cow. We determine this *telos* in a common-sense manner by sympathetic observation of the animal's life.

What is particularly useful and important about my approach to animal ethics is that it is a natural consequence of our societal consensus ethic for *humans*, where we protect fundamental features of *human nature* from encroachment by use of the concept of *rights*. This approach has intuitive appeal to ordinary people, who want to see animals protected in the law, and I have used it to good effect in achieving major change in research and agriculture. In Plato's terms, I thus depend on *reminding*, rather than *teaching*.

Surprisingly, having later done more than 1,500 lectures all over the world attempting to show the need and the rationale for a higher moral status for animals, I found that it was easier to achieve that goal than to bring pain control for animals into science. In the ensuing 10 years, it became clear to me that it was easier to elicit sympathy for animal suffering from ordinary people than from scientists. The reason for this was that, by and large, ordinary common sense never denied thought and feeling to animals; rather, it did not concern itself with animal pain and suffering. In other words, as in fact occurred in society, raising moral concern for animals was largely a matter of overcoming *apathy*. The cowboys who castrate and hot-iron brand cattle never deny that it hurts. Rather, they tend to *minimize the importance of that pain*. Scientists, on the other hand, insulated themselves from the pain they cause, as we shall see, *by denying its reality, by appealing to an ideology that denies the knowability of animal thought and feeling, including pain.*

Philosophers in the Anglo-American tradition before the 20th century did not deny the presence of consciousness and mind in animals. John Locke, for example, responding to Descartes' claim that animals were simply machines, makes patent his belief in their mental lives. After affirming that perception is indubitably in all animals, and thus that they have ideas, he asserts that if they have any ideas at all, and are not bare machines, we cannot deny that they have some reason:

> It seems as evident to me, that they do some of them in certain instances reason, as that they have sense; but it is only in particular ideas, just as they received them from their senses. They are the best of them tied up within those narrow bounds, and have not (as I think) the faculty to enlarge them by any kind of abstraction.
>
> (Locke 1689: Book II, Chapter XI, Paragraph 11ff, p. 127)

In another passage, he mocks those who would assert "that dogs or elephants do not think, when they give all the demonstration of it imaginable, except only telling us that they do so" (Locke 1689, Book II, Chapter I, Paragraph 19, p. 87).

Arguably the greatest skeptic in modern philosophy was David Hume. In his philosophical writings, he denied the reality and knowability of external reality, mind, body, God, causation, and knowledge of the past or the future. Despite this radical skepticism, Hume nonetheless extends no doubt to animal mind. In section XIV of the *Treatise of Human Nature*, "*Of the Reason of Animals*," he affirms

> next to the ridicule of denying an evident truth, is that of taking much pains to defend it; and no truth appears to me more evident, than that beasts are endowed with thought and reason as well as men. The arguments are in this case so obvious, that they never escape the most stupid and ignorant.
>
> (Hume 1739, p. 176)

As we have indicated earlier, Jeremy Bentham not only attributed mind to animals, but also drew moral consequences from the indubitably of animal mentation, as did his radical empiricist successor, John Stuart Mill (Mill 1848).

On the other hand, Continental philosophy was endowed with skepticism regarding animal mind, originating with Descartes. (The snide remark at the end of the Hume statement on animal reason is presumably directed at Descartes.) For Descartes, animals were simply machines of the sort contrived by clever watchmakers at the period he was writing. Lacking language, unlike other humans, animals could not be said to be capable of thought, feeling, or any of the subjective experiences we take for granted in human mentation. With this assertion, Descartes believed he had assured the special place for humans stipulated in Catholic theology, while at the same time paving the way for scientific experimentation on animals regardless of how much putative pain it engendered. (Seventeenth-century reports documenting in lurid detail the "vivisection" occurring at the Port Royal Abbey evidence the extent to which Descartes' followers put his theories into practice.) Skepticism regarding animal mind continued in Europe, culminating in the atrocious animal experimentation evidenced in the 19th century by the work of Pasteur and Claude Bernard. In fact, it was the testimony of a European physiologist, Emmanuel Klein, before a Royal Commission investigating the use of animals in research that probably forced the passage of the British Act of 1876, the first national law protecting research animals. In accord with the Cartesian tradition, Klein made the following extraordinary assertion:

> Just as little as a sportsman or cook goes inquiring into the detail of the whole business while the sportsman is hunting or the cook putting a lobster into boiling water, just as little as one may expect these persons to go inquiring into the detail of the feeling of the animal, just as little can the physiologist or the investigator be expected to devote time and thought to inquiring what this animal will feel while he is doing the experiment. His whole attention is only directed to the making [of] the experiment, how to do it quickly, and to learn the most they can from it.
>
> (Emmanuel Klein 1875, quoted in R. D. French 1975, p. 104)

The philosophical acceptance of animal consciousness continued to dominate English philosophy through the 19th century. Most notable, of course, was the work of Charles Darwin. Throughout his life and works, Darwin made it clear and unequivocal that if physiological and morphological traits were phylogenetically continuous across humans and animals, so too were psychological traits. In addition, Darwin was very much concerned about the welfare of animals, and was very much personally affected by seeing animals in pain or fear. Although he tended to avoid involvement in political controversies, he was actively involved in drafting and supporting what became the British landmark act of 1876, imposing strict regulation upon animal research. Although Darwin supported animal experimentation as a way of making medical progress, he both believed and helped express in law the notion that animals should not suffer in the course of research, and insisted on liberal use of anesthesia for all procedures that might cause pain or discomfort.

In *The Descent of Man* (1871), Darwin specifically affirmed that "there is no fundamental difference between man and the higher animals in their mental facilities," and that "the lower animals, like man manifestly feel pleasure and pain, happiness, and misery" (Darwin 1871). In the same work, Darwin attributed the entire range of subjective experiences to animals, taking it for granted that one can gather data relevant to our knowledge of such experiences. Evolutionary theory demands that psychology, like anatomy, be comparative, for life is incremental, and mind did not arise *de novo* in man, fully formed like Athena from the head of Zeus.

In the course of his research, Darwin collected a great deal of material pertaining to animal consciousness, which material was entrusted to his colleague and friend, George John Romanes. Carefully editing this material, and equally carefully justifying the use of anecdotes, Romanes published two extensive volumes, *Animal Intelligence* (1882) and *Mental Evolution in Animals* (1883). These books remain a virtual treasure trove of common-sense understanding of animal thought and feeling.

In addition to the careful observations he made, Darwin also pursued a variety of experiments on animal mentation, including a largely forgotten series of studies on the intelligence of earthworms! Discussion of these experiments occupy some 35 pages of Darwin's *The Formation of Vegetable Mould Through the Action of Worms with Observations on their Habits* (Darwin 1886). The question Darwin asked was whether the behavior of worms in plugging up their burrows with leaves in the rainy season could be explained by instinct alone or by "inherited impulse" or chance, or whether something like intelligence was required. In a series of tests, Darwin supplied his worms with a variety of leaves, some indigenous to the country where the worms were found, others from plants growing thousands of miles away, as well as parts of leaves and triangles of paper, and observed how they proceeded to plug their burrows, whether using the narrow or the wide end of the object first. After quantitative evaluation of the results of these tests, Darwin concluded that worms possess rudimentary intelligence, in that they showed plasticity in their behavior, some basic "notion" of shape, and the ability to learn from experience.

As enlightened as Darwin was, and even given that there were some sporadic voices arguing for a higher moral status for animals, deducing that status from evolutionary continuity, there are many other signs far less hopeful. Despite the fact that general anesthesia was first demonstrated by dentist William Morton in 1846, its use for animals was extremely limited in science and veterinary medicine. For that matter, its use in human medicine was also not systematic. Historian Martin Pernick has demonstrated that the use of anesthesia was greatly constrained by questionable ideological pronouncements. For example, it was widely pronounced that educated, wealthy people needed more anesthesia than immigrants or country people. Women got more anesthesia than men, except in the case of childbirth, both because the pain of childbirth was believed to be punishment on women for Eve's transgression and because it was believed that women would not bond with babies in the absence of pain (Pernick 1985).

In the case of animals, anesthesia was very rarely used, primarily because animals were not highly valued except for their economic worth. (This remains very much the case today for agricultural animals, unfortunately.) This was *not* due to a Cartesian denial of consciousness and pain in animals. Rather, it represented a *totally cavalier disregard for the importance of animal suffering.* Merillat's 1906 textbook of veterinary surgery summed up the situation that obtained throughout the 19th century and well into the 20th. As Merillat put it,

> In veterinary surgery, anesthesia has no history. It is used in a kind of desultory fashion that reflects no great credit to the present generation of veterinarians. . . . Many veterinarians of rather wide experience have never in a whole lifetime administered a general anesthetic. It reflects greatly to the credit of the canine specialist, however, that he alone has adopted anesthesia to any considerable extent. . . . Anesthesia in veterinary surgery today is a means of restraint and not an expedient to relieve pain. So long as an operation can be performed by forcible restraint . . . the thought of anesthesia does not enter into the proposition.
>
> (Merillat 1906)

As Darwin's work quickly became the regnant paradigm in biology and psychology, one would expect that the science of animal mentation would have steadily evolved during the subsequent century and a half as a subset of evolutionary biology. Strangely enough, this is not the case. Despite Darwin's influence, animal mentation disappeared as a legitimate object of study, not only in a Europe influenced by Cartesianism, but in the Anglo-American world as well. This occurred not because of a further social dis-valuing of the moral status of animals, but by the ingression into science and veterinary medicine of an ideology, based in Positivism and Behaviorism at least as destructive to the recognition of thought and pain in animals, and to ethical issues in science. Ironically, by the end of the 20th century, this ideology had essentially thoroughly dominated science, even as societal concern for animal treatment continued to grow.

In the early 1980s, I began to wonder why, if Darwinian evolution represented the firm basis for biology and psychology, animal mind as an object of study all but disappeared in the 20th century (Rollin 1989). It was dogma in philosophy that theoretical changes in science occur in only two ways: either solid experimental evidence disproves some consequence of the theory, or else some conceptual or logical flaw is unearthed in the foundations of the theory. I knew of no empirical data that disproved the notion that animals were conscious. Nor did I know of anyone who had shown that the belief that animals have thoughts and feelings was in some way logically flawed. I thus undertook the ambitious project of reviewing the history of biology, and particularly the history of psychology, to determine what had in fact "refuted" the solidly evolutionarily-based theory of the continuity of mentation across the phylogenetic scale.

Much to my surprise, I found nothing. Indeed, it dawned on me that I could not conceive of any empirical evidence that would refute the existence of mind in animals or of any way that hypothesis could be logically flawed. In particular, I looked at standard accounts in histories of psychology of why the thesis that animals have thoughts and feelings was overturned. These books cited an allegedly irrefutable succession of thinkers whose work inexorably led to the denial of animal consciousness instantiated definitively in modern psychology.

It eventually dawned on me to be suspicious of the account provided in the histories of psychology. After all, as we all know, history is written by the "winners." Had the British defeated the colonists during the Revolutionary War, the account of the rebellion would be markedly different than what we find in US history books. I thus went back to the original texts of those who were credited with overthrowing the standard views of animal mentation – Conway Lloyd Morgan, Jacques Loeb, and H. S. Jennings. I was astonished to discover that none of these thinkers ever denied the reality of consciousness in animals. Lloyd Morgan proclaimed his "Canon," namely that one should never accept an explanation of behavior in terms of a higher mental faculty if one could explain it equally well in reference to a lower mental faculty. This Canon already presupposed *consciousness* if it was to make any sense at all! Precisely the same point was true of the writings of Loeb and Jennings. In fact, Morgan was a *panpsychist* who assumed that all of nature was conscious! In the hands of J. B. Watson, Morgan's Canon, as historian Daniel Robinson (1977) has wittily articulated, became a cannon. Furthermore, Watson argued extensively and persuasively that if psychology would just dispense with consciousness, and adopt learned behavior as its core concept, behavior could be manipulated and shaped to create a utopia, as Watson's most successful successor, B. F. Skinner, argued later in the 20th century (Watson 1913).

Thus, I argued that the hypothesis of thought and feeling in animals was in no measure disproved; it was rather *disapproved*. Science changed not in the way orthodoxy dictates, but rather resulted from a change in *values*. Watson's extravagant promises regarding psychology as Behaviorism perfectly played into what I have elsewhere called *Scientific Ideology* or the *Common Sense of Science*, which I discussed at length in my 2006 book *Science and Ethics* (Rollin 2006b).

Ideologies are strongly held, virtually unshakable beliefs that determine how those who believe in the ideology look at the world. Common examples are religious ideology, racist ideology, Marxist ideology, Nazi ideology, etc. Think for a moment of how difficult it is to dislodge the belief that "all black people are stupid" from a thoroughgoing racist, or the congruent belief that "all Jews are evil" from a Nazi. Adherence to such a belief explains how Nazis could easily murder small children, or how American racists could lynch African-American men for simply looking at a white woman, or how Catholics could slaughter Protestants (or vice versa) in the name of doing God's will.

Ideologies operate in many different areas – religious, political, sociological, economic, ethnic. Thus, it is not surprising that an ideology would emerge with regard to modern science, which has been, after all, the dominant way of knowing about the world in Western societies since the Renaissance. One dominant theme in this ideology was expressed in the ancient atomist's claim that "by convention is sweet and sour, hot and cold . . . in reality are only atoms and void" (Kirk and Raven 1957, p. 422). While this reductionistic approach to knowledge and reality was vigorously opposed by Aristotle in favor of the metaphysics treating the world of qualitatively different experiences as ultimately real, the Aristotelian world view was then discredited by the likes of Descartes and Newton, who postulated that *scientific reality* was only mathematically describable matter. Most important for our purposes is the denial of ethics as being relevant to science or even knowable, and the parallel denial of consciousness in humans or animals as knowable. (We will not here discuss the incoherences in this ideology.)

This denial of the scientific reality and knowability of ethics and consciousness was emphatically expressed in 20th-century Logical Positivism and Behaviorism. Wittgenstein, a major influence on Positivism, once remarked that if one takes an inventory of all the facts in the universe, one does not find in it a fact that killing is wrong (Wittgenstein 1965). And J. B. Watson, the father of Behaviorism, came perilously close to proclaiming that we don't have thoughts; we only think we do. Ethical judgments such as "killing is wrong" were explained away as emotive expressions, parallel to "killing yuck!" and thus not subject to rational discussion. And statements about animal mind and consciousness, or even animal pain, were dismissed as scientifically meaningless.

An excellent example of this phenomenon occurred in 1982, when I was lecturing at the University of London. As it happened, there was a conference being held at the university on pain. The featured speaker was a renowned Scottish expert on animal pain who affirmed, to my amazement, that animals did not experience pain in any sense we could understand since the pain experience was processed through the cerebral cortex, and the electrochemical activity in an animal cerebral cortex was significantly different from that of a human. Though I was allotted 20 minutes to respond to him by the organizers, and I am usually quite verbose, I informed the audience that I would need only five minutes. "Dr. X," I began, "you are a very eminent pain researcher." "Thank you very much," he replied. "If I am not mistaken," I continued, "you do your research on dogs." "That is correct," he responded. "And then you extrapolate your results to people," I affirmed. "Yes," he replied, "that is the purpose of my research." "If that is the case," I continued, "either your speech this afternoon is false or your life's work is." In other words, if what he had affirmed in his speech were correct, i.e. that animal pain was thoroughly dissimilar to human pain, he could not extrapolate the animal results to humans! To be sure, he could doubtless learn about the physiological basis of pain (what is called *nociception* in physiology), even if he denied consciousness in animals. But his work dealt with the *experience of pain*, not merely nociception.

In 1982, I appeared before a congressional committee to defend the 1985 amendments to the Animal Welfare Act. When asked why such legislation was necessary, I told the Congressman that there was virtually no use of analgesia for animals in research. He protested that the research community told him it was liberally used (an outrageous lie), and it was up to me to prove that it was not. I accomplished this by soliciting the help of a librarian friend at the National Agricultural Library. I asked him to search for research papers dealing with analgesia for laboratory animals. He found none. When I broadened the search to "analgesia for animals," he found two papers, one of which affirmed that there should be papers, and the other one affirmed that virtually nothing was known. This convinced the Congressman that the legislation was needed. I repeated the search a few years ago, this time on my personal computer, and found close to 13,000 papers. This represents major progress.

The Positivistic denial of the ethical relevance of animal pain briefly meshed well with the societal lack of moral concern for animal pain, though the latter, as we mentioned, never denied the reality of animal pain. However, in the mid-20th century, as society began to express ever-increasing concern for the moral status of animals, as well as to demand control of animal pain and suffering, scientific ideology clashed with emerging societal ethics for animals, an ethic I have explicated elsewhere (Rollin 2011b).

The rise of this new ethic was potentiated by five factors I have delineated in other writings. These factors include the fact that the former paradigm for animals in the social mind, farm and working animals, has been replaced by the companion animal as a member of the family;

the writings of a variety of philosophers and scientists, like Jane Goodall, have persuasively argued for a higher moral status for animals and an acknowledgment of animal mind; the fact that many leaders in social reform have turned their attention to animal exploitation; the fact that the media has discovered, as one reporter put it to me, that "animals sell papers"; and the fact that the traditional fair contract with animals instantiated in an agriculture based in good husbandry has, in the 20th century, been supplanted by totally exploitative industrial agriculture (Rollin 2011b).

Society has increasingly demanded the codification of moral concern for animals in law, i.e. in the societal consensus ethic. The laboratory animal laws demanding pain control for animals used in research was an early and paradigmatic example of such demand. In addition, in a society where focus on animal mind is a major theme in our culture, scientists' ideological denial of thought and feeling in animals is not sustainable.

In veterinary medicine, as companion animals have assumed center stage, control of pain has become a prominent (and lucrative) focus in veterinary research and practice. There is every reason to believe that social concern for animal well-being will move well beyond concern for physical pain alone, but will instead encompass all sorts of unhappiness we impose on the animals we use, ranging from solitary housing of social animals, paradigmatically evident in zoos as prisons, and gestation crates for sows; keeping killer whales, who, in nature, range over thousands of miles, in tiny pools; keeping nocturnal animals in 24-hour light; etc. All of the above atrocities have been abolished or rectified in the recent past. It also seems inevitable that society will expand its focus on animal welfare to the conditions that make animals happy (Rollin 2015).

Further reading

Donald Griffin, *The Question of Animal Awareness*. 1981. New York: William Kaufmann Inc.

Bernard E. Rollin, *Animal Rights and Human Morality*. Third Edition. 2006. Buffalo: Prometheus Books.

Bernard E. Rollin, *Putting the Horse Before Descartes: My Life's Work On Behalf of Animals*. 2011. Philadelphia, PA: Temple University Press.

Bernard E. Rollin, *Science and Ethics*. 2006. New York: Cambridge University Press.

Bernard E. Rollin, *The Unheeded Cry: Animal Consciousness, Animal Pain and Science*. 1989. Oxford: Oxford University Press.

References

Ascione, Frank R. 1993. Children Who Are Cruel to Animals: A Review of Research and Implications for Developmental Psychopathology. *Anthrozoos* 6, 226–247.

Bentham, Jeremy. 1789. *An Introduction to the Principles of Morals and Legislation* (New York: Hafner Press, 1948) Chapter XVII, Sec. 1, Subsection IV, pp. 310–311.

Darwin, Charles. 1871. *The Descent of Man and Selection in Relation to Sex* (reprinted New York: Modern Library).

Darwin, Charles. 1886. *The Formation of Vegetable Mould Through the Action of Worms, With Observations on Their Behaviour* (New York: D. Appleton).

Felthous, A. R., and Kellert, S. P. 1987. Childhood Cruelty to Animals and Later Aggression Against People: A Review. *American Journal of Psychiatry* 144:6, 710–716.

French, R. D. 1975. *Antivivisection and Medical Science in Victorian Society* (Princeton: Princeton University Press).

Hume, David. 1739. *A Treatise of Human Nature* (Oxford: Oxford University Press, 1968), pp. 176ff.

Kirk, G. S. and Raven, J. E. 1957. *The Presocratic Philosophers: A Critical History with a Selection of Texts*, Chapter XVII, n589. Cambridge: Cambridge University Press.

Klein, Emmanuel. 1875. Quoted in Richard French, *Antivivisection and Medical Science in Victorian Society* (Princeton, NJ: Princeton University Press, 1975), p. 104.

Locke, John. 1689. *An Essay Concerning Human Understanding*. Book II, Chapter IX, ¶12, P117; Book II, Chapter XI, ¶11ff, P 127.; Book II, Chapter I, ¶19, P 87 (New York: Dutton, 1871).

Merillat, L. A. 1906. *Principles of Veterinary Surgery* (Chicago: Alexander Eger, 1906), p. 69.

Mill, John Stuart. 1848. *Principles of Political Economy*, 3rd edition (London: John W. Parker and Son, 1852), Volume 2, p. 546.

Pernick, Martin. 1985. *A Calculus of Suffering: Pain, Professionalism and Anesthesia in 19th Century America* (New York: Columbia University Press).

Robinson, D. 1977. Preface to Volume II of *Significant Contributions to the History of Psychology 1750-1920 series D, Comparative Psychology,* C. L. Morgan (Washington, DC: University Publications of America).

Rollin, Bernard E. 1981. *Animal Rights and Human Morality*, First edition (Buffalo, New York: Prometheus Books).

Rollin, Bernard E. 1989. *The Unheeded Cry: Animal Consciousness, Animal Pain and Science* (Oxford: Oxford University Press).

Rollin, Bernard E. 2006a. The Regulation of Animal Research and the Emergence of Animal Ethics: A Conceptual History. *Theoretical Medicine and Bioethics* 27:4, 285–304.

Rollin, Bernard E. 2006b. *Science and Ethics* (New York: Cambridge University Press).

Rollin, Bernard E. 2011a. *Putting the Horse Before Descartes: My Life's Work on Behalf of Animals* (Philadelphia, PA: Temple University Press).

Rollin, Bernard E. 2011b. Animal Rights as a Mainstream Phenomenon. *Animals* 1, 102–115.

Rollin, Bernard E. 2015. "Beyond Pain." Keynote speech delivered December 10, 2015 at Johns Hopkins University Bloomberg School of Public Health.

Romanes, George. 1882. *Animal Intelligence* (London: Kegan Paul, Trench, Trubner and Co.).

Romanes, George. 1883. *Mental Evolution in Animals* (New York: Appleton).

Watson, J. B. 1913. Psychology as the behaviorist views it. *Psychological Review* 20, 158.

Wittgenstein, Ludwig. 1965. Lecture on Ethics. *Philosophical Review* 74:1, 3–12.

INDEX

Note: Entries refer to non-human animals unless otherwise specified.